The Industrial History of Dean

By the same author:
Royal Forest
The Commoners of Dean
The Free Miners of the Forest of Dean
Archaeology in Dean
The Verderers and Forest Laws of Dean
Practical Forestry for the Agent and Surveyor
etc

The Industrial History of Dean

With an introduction to its industrial archaeology

Cyril Hart

Senior Verderer

David & Charles : Newton Abbot

To
JOHN H. WATTS
of Lydney . . . a friend and benefactor
to Dean and its neighbourhood—and
one of the great pioneers of passenger
road transport in Britain.

ISBN 0 7153 5288 1

Set in 11 on 13 pt Times
and printed in Great Britain
by Clarke Doble & Brendon Limited
for David & Charles (Publishers)
Limited
South Devon House
Newton Abbot Devon

Contents

Page

List of Illustrations

List of Plates

List of Figures

Principal Abbreviations used in References
at the end of each Chapter

(The source is the Public Record Office where not stated otherwise)

BGAS	Bristol & Gloucestershire Archaeological Society
BM	British Museum
C	Chancery Papers
Cal	Calendar
CNFC	The Cotteswold Naturalists' Field Club
E	Exchequer Papers
F	Forestry Commission Records
GRO	Gloucestershire Records Office
HMC	Historical Manuscripts Commission
HMG	Historical Metallurgy Group
HRO	Herefordshire Record Office
SP	State Papers Domestic
S&W	Severn & Wye Railway
WNFC	The Woolhope Naturalists' Field Club

Preface

Picture thirty thousand acres of undulating oak and beech woodland between the rivers Severn and Wye in West Gloucestershire; grow, harvest and utilise during two thousand years some fifteen successive crops of mature trees and many of undergrowth; extract from underground some 200 million tons of coal, 10 million of iron ore, several million of stone, clay and sand, and half a billion tons of waste soil and rock; intersect the region with roads, tramroads and railways, and scatter among them both planned and unplanned villages, towns, churches, schools, factories and places of recreation; rehabilitate the woodland with tens of millions of broadleaves and conifers . . . and thereby the observer has created in the mind's eye a moving microcosm of much of the industrial history of Dean—now restored to its sylvan glory.

The Forest of Dean had little industry before 'the Roman came to Rye or out to Severn strode', but thereafter became increasingly outstanding as of national economic importance chiefly because of its mineral wealth and timber resources. Because iron ore was worked in Dean for a very long period, many of its inhabitants other than the miners and colliers have earned their livelihood as woodcutters, charcoal burners, and smelters and forgemen. The Forest, reserved at and after the Conquest by the King wherein to hunt his 'beasts of the forest', gradually—and specifically from the seventeenth century—became increasingly used for the production of timber for the Navy. Much of its history is that of conflict between on the one hand mining and smelting of iron ore, and on the other hand hunting and timber conservation; and then again between these and commoning. In later centuries, mining and its associated industries were in the forefront. Now these industries have virtually ended.

The histories of Dean's silviculture, commoners and Free Miners have been related in three of my other volumes. The present book is devoted to its industrial history, and with the closure of the Forest's last large colliery in 1965, the timing of this work is perhaps appropriate. The chief reason for writing it was that while most large industrial regions have abundant records of this aspect of their history,

Dean's published records comprise little more than the above mentioned volumes and two modern treatises on tramroads and railways.

A second reason for writing the book, in accord with the sub-title, was the intention for it to serve as an introduction to Dean's industrial archaeology, about which some largely unpublished research has already been accomplished. Indeed, much of the layout was planned bearing in mind the need for additional research into this broadly based subject which invites the expertise and enthusiasm of surveyors, engineers, chemists, metallurgists, architects, transport men, archaeologists, historians, draughtsmen and photographers. Each can learn something from the others, and equally each has his own contribution to offer. The industrial archaeology of a region consists of its industrial 'monuments'—the relics of phases of industrialisation which are now obsolete or becoming obsolete—and one of the aims of the industrial archaeologist is to record and interpret these relics, in order to show their significance in the developing pattern of social and technological history. Dean has experienced continuous industrial activity over a long period, during which a large number of processes have been carried on. Remnants still survive, but the wastage rate amongst them has been and is high under the forces of modernisation. Many industrial buildings, mills, tollhouses, railways, stations, and plant have disappeared in recent years—losses which make a systematic analysis of the subject a matter of urgency. Without a published record of Dean's industrial history, its industrial archaeology would not be comprehensible: they are complementary. Therefore this volume will serve as a necessary framework on which to base and co-ordinate field projects; and my references to what remains, and the illustrations and maps herein, will invite further research and offer some guidance to the investigations which enthusiasts may wish to pursue. The district maps in the Appendix (p. 439) should be particularly helpful.

This book does not claim to provide a definitive industrial history: in a short survey of each of many complex industries and technologies extending over many centuries, it is inevitable that a few items have been omitted, and others condensed. Furthermore, it has not been possible to chronicle every interchange of the proprietors of Dean's enterprises, nor to record the name, extent, and working-life of more than a few of the many hundreds of small and large mines, collieries, quarries and mills; to have done so would have required extended research, while many volumes might have been necessary to record the information. Attention has been given to the buildings, plant and processes, but the descriptions of some of the latter should be accepted as typical. Mention has been made of many proprietors, lessees, and workmen, with (occasionally) their successes and failures—often reminding us that the life force behind the now cold ruins and spoil heaps were men of flesh and blood: industrial heroes and 'little' men, lucky men and unlucky men, visionaries, and so on.

The student of social history will find herein some pointers to his special interests—the kind of houses in which Dean's workmen lived; what they wore; how they earned their livelihoods; their rates of pay; and a few examples of relationships between worker and master, and how they expressed themselves in their letters.

As far as possible I have purposely dispensed with detailed background information available in my earlier treatises, particularly those on Dean's Free Miners and trees. The same has been done in regard to two books, previously noted, on tramroads and railways. Similarly I have kept to a minimum an account of the present day thriving industries attracted to the district (chiefly following the run down of the iron and coal industries)—all invaluable for the wellbeing of Dean's inhabitants.

It is to be hoped that many of those who are fortunate enough to reside in Dean, and the untold numbers who visit the Forest annually—indeed, the many millions who traverse and enjoy the nearby Wye Valley—will have the inclination and find the time to learn about the region's past and present industries. Thereby they will appreciate how Dean, through its vicissitudes from prehistoric times till today, has achieved considerable importance—renowned in the past for its royal hunting, ship-timber, iron and coal, and now for its modern industries, its trees, its amenity and its facilities for recreation. Henceforth it remains with each one of us to ensure that Dean's industries and the growing of timber, both necessary for the local and national economy, do not conflict with the Forest's other functions—a refuge for wild life and a haven of recreation. In the not too distant future the importance as a Forest Park (particularly for recreation) may exceed that as a commercial forest, though the two functions are complementary.

I wish to record my thanks to H. W. Paar, who has given much help in my researches, and to other people who have provided information—two local engineers, F. B. Watkins and A. W. Trotter; two industrial chemists, N. P. Bridgewater and A. H. Churchouse; A. K. Pope, a transport enthusiast; Tom Bright (chairman of the Wyedean Tourist Board); A. E. Howell of the Gaveller's Office, H. L. Edlin,

MBE, G. R. Morton, G. Hammersley, R. F. Tylecote, W. E. Oakey, Jack James, R. A. J. Bell, and H. Roberts. Furthermore, the book owes a great deal to the courtesy and consideration shown to me by the staffs of the Public Record Office, the British Museum, the Gloucestershire Records Office, and of the libraries at Gloucester, Cheltenham, and Coleford. To all of them, and to many friends who have helped in various ways, I extend my gratitude. Finally it has been my good fortune to have publishers who combine with their efficiency the pleasantest of relationships with their authors, a co-operation which I have much appreciated.

C.H.

Chenies,
Coleford,
Forest of Dean,
Gloucestershire, GL16 8DT.

1 *January* 1971.

Introduction

The triple division of Gloucestershire into wold, vale, and forest (in particular the Forest of Dean) is a physical feature of which the effects are still somewhat discernible in the character and prejudices of the inhabitants, and which has given to the county the prominent place it has occupied in the past. Each, by its special facilities and resources, has had its particular industries; each at times has aided the others. The Severn, and to a lesser extent the Wye, were the earliest gateways to and from the outer world possessed by the western part of a county almost enclosed by woods; and the provision by the Severn of many natural small harbours (known locally as 'pills'), helped to place early Gloucestershire amongst the foremost in the race for commercial prosperity. Bristol and Gloucester set an industrial example to the other parts of the shire; the towns were assisted by the wolds with the fine growth of wool fostered on their pastures; and the merchants of the towns in their turn assisted the wolds when the wool industry migrated thither.

The Forest of Dean in West Gloucestershire, with its iron, coal, stone and timber, helped both town and wold. The region, lying within a triangle between the rivers Severn and Wye, now in extent represents only a third of woodlands which in early times stretched over some 100,000 acres. The northern limits extended to Gloucester, Newent and Ross-on-Wye, whence the western boundary was the river Wye via Monmouth, Tintern and Chepstow to Beachley; the eastern boundary followed the Severn from Gloucester southwards via Newnham-on-Severn and Lydney to Beachley, where the two rivers join to form the Bristol Channel and where stands the impressive Severn road bridge connecting England with Wales. The region is one of bold relief which slopes down gradually towards the tidal estuary of the Severn on the south and east, and runs westwards and northwards towards the Wye with its spectacular gorge and renowned valley, recently designated an area of outstanding natural beauty.

The central geographical structure is in the form of a synclinal basin wherein coal measures (no fewer than 14 seams, each one a dynasty of trees), rest on older rocks, and which extends from Mitcheldean in the north to Lydney in the south (10 miles), and from Cinderford in the east to Coleford in the west (6 miles). Under and around the coalfield lie deposits (now abandoned) of iron ore. Hence the structure of the coal and iron ore fields is in a saucer-shaped depression, the edge of which is well defined by an outcrop of Millstone Grit or Limestone which forms notable features and viewpoints ranging in elevation from about 550 to 900ft.

The centre of Dean is dominated by an uneven plateau, more precisely a block of many low hills and plains divided from north-west to south-west by three valleys: the Lydbrook-Cannop-Newerne valley, the Drybrook-Cinderford-Ruspidge-Soudley valley and another running from Mitcheldean via Abenhall and Littledean to beyond Soudley. A fourth valley runs eastwards via Mitcheldean to Longhope where it forks left to the Lea-Huntley road and right towards Blaisdon and Flaxley. Depressions run down the plateau on the east, west and north; these with the four main valleys and the two rivers have been of the greatest importance in populating and developing Dean, and have fashioned the landscape we know today. Other distinctive physiographical features of the region are the high ground in the south-west at St Briavels, in the north-west around the Buckstone and the Kymin, and in the north at Ruardean, Penyard and May Hill—all parts of ancient Dean. Today the wooded areas chiefly lie on the central plateau and in its valleys, roughly contiguous to the (now run down) coalfield. There are besides many small outlying woods, some in private ownership.

For nearly one thousand years the region has been known first as 'the Forest' (*vide Domesday*), and second as Dene or Dean (after O.E. *denu*, valley—that east of Littledean where stands the remnant of the Norman 'Castle of Dene'—Plate 1a). Comprising chiefly an extensive woodland (in part overlying mineral fields) surviving from primeval times, the region has been economically and socially of particular interest on account of three closely related features: (*a*) its 'beasts of the forest', particularly deer, (*b*) its (now bygone) wealth of iron ore and coal, and (*c*) its trees, and the timber, amenity and recreational facilities which they provide.

Iron ore was mined from early times, and smelted by the heat of charcoal. Cold-mining developed more slowly. The industries led to co-operation between and interdependence upon on the one hand several dozen generations of miners, and on the other hand woodcutters, charcoal burners, smelters, forgemen and smiths. Only the miners became privileged, and eventually attained the status of Free

Miners (a right which they retain to this day). Privileges enjoyed by some of the inhabitants (and which are still claimed) were those of commoning of animals and pannage of pigs.

By Roman times the local pockets of population were partly engaged in a shifting arable cultivation with stock-raising, and partly with the small scale trades connected with iron. The invading overlords developed the iron industry, organised the winning of a little outcrop coal for domestic purposes, and built villas, farmsteads, and roads—necessitating the quarrying of stone and sand. The woods gradually diminished in extent, and the quality of their uncared for remnant deteriorated; grazing and browsing by domestic animals and deer, wind and storm, and fires (purposeful and accidental), continued to take their toll of the trees and undergrowth.

These enterprises and processes continued after the departure of the Romans, through the Saxon era, and until the advent of the Normans, by which time two industries still governed the local economy and thereby the livelihood of the inhabitants: those not engaged in the iron industry (unrestricted mining, charcoal-burning, smelting and forging) were chiefly engaged in arable-farming, grazing of sheep, and fattening of swine particularly on the mast of oak, beech and chestnut. The woods continued to suffer: small trees were liberally taken for charcoal; large trees were felled for building and other uses; and grazing lands and rights of pannage were virtually free to all. But soon the taking of venison (the 'beasts of the forest'—deer and boars) and vert (trees and undergrowth) was prohibited except to the King and his grantees. Poaching was rife, but severely penalised; and forest law was enforced by forest officers and courts. The ancient administrative centre for forest law in medieval times was at Kensley, in the heart of the Forest. Overall control was exercised by the constable of St Briavels Castle, built c1130 (now a Youth Hostel).

Settlements and manors arose, and several levels of society became established throughout the region. Men exercised their skills in diverse local trades, including tanning, cooperage, brewing, and baking. Streams were harnessed by dams and embankments, and thereby turned water-wheels to power fulling and corn mills. Fishing proceeded in river, stream and pool. In the woods, men felled and squared trees, stripped oak bark, and corded wood and burned it into charcoal. The miners worked hard and often dangerously; and the smelters and forgemen kept pace with them.

Early mining of iron ore and coal was chiefly from the outcrops around the periphery of the Forest. Bloomeries and forges—they were not dependent upon water power—were set up almost everywhere. This pattern continued into the early seventeenth century, when seven main streams which hitherto had turned water-wheels to power small mills, were the chief factor which decided the location of charcoal iron blast furnaces (with some technicians from Sussex), forges, and (later) paper mills. The Severn and Wye into which the streams flowed were the chief channels of import and export; some produce went over ill-kept roads to Gloucester, Monmouth, and Hereford. From the 1630s the small harbours, particularly those on the Severn, provided facilities for the building of boats and ships; and the woods furnished abundant timber for the Navy and for constructional, fuelling and heating purposes.

Exploitation of the timber resources to fuel the voracious blast furnaces was at its peak during the seventeenth century; the consequent depredation of the woodlands was accentuated by extensive grazing of sheep and other animals and by opposition to enclosure emanating from commoners, landowners and ironmasters. Coal-mining became a major industry from the eighteenth century, particularly after coke replaced charcoal in the ironworks. Thereafter, the two rivers carried an increasing traffic of coal, ore, stone and timber, particularly when Dean's lack of internal transport was from c1810 progressively remedied by the provision of tramroads and the contemporary, albeit belated improving of roads. Subsequently there arose wireworks and tinplate works, and deeper mines were sunk to reach the more inaccessible deposits of ore and coal. Nevertheless, the region had not fully expanded upon the firm foundation of technical innovation in the eighteenth century.

The first rumblings of the Industrial Revolution were late in reaching Dean, where the ironworks remained dispersed in or around small centres of population. Internal roads were difficult; often they lay rutted and potholed so that in inclement weather they were almost impassable. Most of the countryside was undrained, and much was scrub and wasteland; only parts of the woodlands were productive. The workman underground, or in ironworks or field was poor indeed, and the rich owner held all the power. The worker—perhaps not the independent Free Miner—still accepted without question that he was less than dust under the feet of the industrialist or the squire. The local tradesmen sought the latters' patronage as assiduously as if he were the King himself.

The abundance of natural resources kept Dean's industry moving, although the Forest remained isolated from the main stream of industrial change. Railways, from 1854, and expansion of tinplate works, helped the economy. When change did arrive, it came late, and comparatively suddenly. Iron-making lost its significance at the end of the nineteenth century. However, from 1904, coal-mining was resuscitated by the sinking of deep shafts for six new collieries—the first attempt at a unification of the coalfield.

Two world wars helped to keep Dean's iron and coal-mining in being, and the second of these wars brought three new industries (plywood, film equipment, and fruit juices). Ore mining ended in 1945, and the Forest's collieries, becoming increasingly uneconomic, were abandoned by the end of 1965—a year which also saw the departure of a large cable manufactory. The consequent unemployment was countered chiefly by the efforts of the local Development Association, the expansion of existing factories, a new industry (corrugated cases etc) at Lydbrook, and the outstanding progress of Rank Xerox Ltd at Mitcheldean. These and other enterprises transformed the anxious situation in Dean, and have since sustained the inhabitants.

From early in the nineteenth century, the Commissioners of Woods administered the silviculture and estate management of the Crown lands in Dean, and most industrial activity in the Forest was carried out under their licences. In 1919 the management was taken over by the Forestry Commission. The rights of free mining are administered from the Gaveller's office in Coleford; but the privileges of commoning and pannage are now almost unregulated. The four verderers, charged to guard the vert and the venison, still hold their court—at the Speech House, built in 1676.

The Forest's population settlement pattern—three towns in a matrix of dozens of villages, hamlets and farms, and hundreds of (now legalised) encroachments, all enmeshed in extensive renowned woodlands—poses many problems for the planners and for the students of land use. Cinderford on the east, Coleford on the west, and Lydney in the south are three identifiable centres, where the current County Development Plan is to encourage the establishment of more industries, particularly at Lydney. The Severn road bridge and the M4 and M5 have provided routes by which numerous people annually visit and enjoy the Forest and the nearby Wye Valley. Already, with most of the industrial scars healed by Nature or clothed with trees by the Forestry Commission, Dean is among the foremost forests which practice multiple-use forestry—the complementary provision of timber, amenity, wild life and recreation.

The Forest's survival from prehistoric times as an extensive area of predominantly wooded terrain—of which not more than 11,000 acres may remain enclosed at any time—in an otherwise intensively developed countryside, is due to a combination of physiographical, geographical, and economic factors. Man during two thousand years has transformed Dean, in ways which were discussed in *Royal Forest* (OUP 1966) and which are enlarged upon and developed herein.

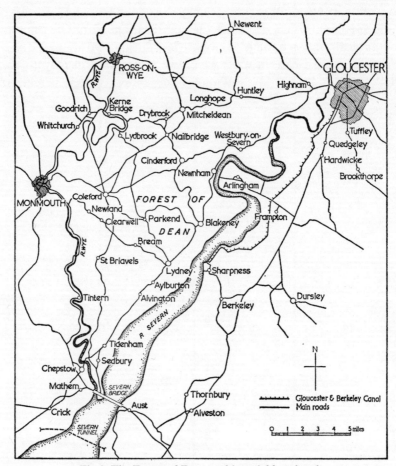

Fig 1. The Forest of Dean and its neighbourhood.

One
The Charcoal Iron Industry to 1679

The Bloomery Period (to 1611)

Iron is the result of exposing iron ores to a certain chemical environment at elevated temperatures. The easiest ores for early man to smelt were those which, after roasting, had a fair degree of porosity and a high iron content. Although the methods were wasteful they were capable of producing good-quality wrought iron in the so-called 'direct' process, necessitating two operations—smelting and then hammering the resultant bloom (with re-heating).

The knowledge of iron metallurgy reached Britain about 500 BC through the westward movement of Celtic tribes from Central Europe.[1] There is little evidence, however, that iron was much used during the next century, bronze being still the predominating material. Iron working on any noticeable scale did not begin in Britain until about 200 BC. After the arrival of the Romans, output increased considerably, initially for military exploitation, and later due to the expanding economy of both town and country. Though in Roman times iron working was widespread throughout Britain, the Weald of Kent and Sussex was a major production area, which was superseded in the late second century by the Forest of Dean.

Evidence of Roman iron working in Dean includes two adits discovered in Lydney Park. Many of the ancient surface workings, some known locally as 'scowles', may also be of the Roman period, but what proportion of the immense quantities of bloomery slag (commonly termed cinders) later found in and around Dean can be so dated is difficult to determine, though coins and other objects of the period have been discovered in close association with the workings.

Roman incursions in Dean were chiefly to reach the deposits of iron ore, the working of which by the subjugated inhabitants, with the

1

making of charcoal for smelting, the mining of a little outcrop coal, and the quarrying of stone, were encouraged.[2] The chief mining areas in Dean were those of Wigpool and Edgehill, which probably supplied ore to *Ariconium* in south Herefordshire; and those of Bream and south of Staunton which supplied Monmouth *(Blestium)*. There was also considerable iron mining activity between Bream and Lydney. Beyond the Wye, the Doward supplied ore to Whitchurch in Herefordshire.

The two main methods of smelting during this period, both using charcoal, were the bowl furnace and the shaft furnace (bloomery), the latter probably having been introduced by the Romans. Roasting of the ore in kilns or in hearths was an essential preliminary, and whereas crushing and some form of screening would have been used, it is doubtful if the gangue was removed by washing. The bloom was probably an agglomeration of reduced metal, slag and charcoal. The bloom would have been finally consolidated by heating to red heat, and hammering to shape. Evidence for roasting is suggested by the excavations at Popes Hill,[3] where the widespread scattering of bloomery slag clearly indicates a smelting site. Apart from those excavations, and the noting of typical bloomery sites (with much slag) at Staunton and Ruardean, nothing has been done to investigate Dean's Romano-British smelting sites. There were hundreds of such sites as evidenced by the thousands of tons of cinders of high iron content which were scattered over a wide area in Gloucestershire, Herefordshire and Monmouthshire, and which were re-smelted in later times. The removal of these cinders has obliterated many sites.

Ariconium, noted above, can best be described as a Roman villa estate with a posting station, situated on the XIII Iter, and surrounded by an extensive industrial belt, the whole probably occupying some 250 acres. This large area of furnace and smithing sites was not in operation all at one time, because the furnaces would have been rapidly expendable. Many of the fields in the area, when ploughed, show black soil containing iron slag, burnt clay and Romano-British pottery. The main source of ore was probably Wigpool: an excavation revealed a road metalled with iron slag, leading in this direction through the Wigg Meadow.[4] Excavations at *Ariconium* to bedrock level of a sample area yielded remains of six furnaces with associated slag heaps and many working hollows.[5] These furnaces were proved to have been working in the second half of the second century.

The whole organisation and economic basis of Dean's large iron

industry in the Roman period is somewhat obscure, and several important points need investigation. Was the ore roasted, or otherwise prepared, at the mines or scowles before despatch to the smelting sites?
Why was so much ore taken out of the Forest to be smelted in south
Herefordshire? What proportion of the iron produced was despatched
to other districts as blooms or as fabricated articles? It may be con-
jectured that the concentrated smelting activity around the fringe of
Dean, stretching from *Ariconium* to Monmouth, arose from the location of the XIII Iter as a major trade route.

How far an iron industry in Dean continued throughout the Dark
Ages and was followed by the Anglo-Saxons, cannot yet be answered.
Probably only local needs were met, though there is some suggestion
of slightly increased activity by early in the eleventh century.[6] Certainly with the advent of the Normans the industry developed apace,
yet Domesday made no assessment of the mineral wealth of Dean,
and it seems not to have troubled the Normans what persons at that
time had rights to win or use ore. Not until the thirteenth century
are there many records of the local industry.

From 1247[7] we hear of receipts to the King from the sale of
bloomery slag *(cineribus)*. It cannot be proved that those cinders were
used for re-smelting, but they would have served to provide a higher
temperature or to protect the lining of the bloomery. Perhaps improved
methods of smelting in bloomeries had been attained. There is a school
of thought that it was technically possible for cinders to be used in the
later medieval bloomeries. R. F. Tylecote has commented: [8]

Although I have no personal acquaintance with this practice in Dean,
I am sure that earlier slags were used in later bloomeries in the north
of England. There are several possible reasons. It is almost certain
that a good deal of the slag volume comes from the slagging of the
furnace lining with iron from the ore. As the refractoriness of the
clays increased, not as much of the iron would be lost in this way and
the yields would be greater. It would then be found that some of the
iron in the very high iron-containing Roman slags could in fact be
recovered. Also, we believe that the slag acted as a lubricant which
allowed the bloom to fall in the furnace as it increased in size. As the
yields increased due to improved refractories, less slag would be
formed, and then the need for additional slag would be appreciated.
We have one recent record of this practice from an African source.
Another reason may be that the dripping slag acted as a heat transfer
agent which decreased the temperature gradient in the bottom of the
furnace.

Evidence of corn and fulling mills in Dean suggests that water power was already in use, and although there is no record of such power being used to drive the bellows of bloomeries and forges, this innovation had already been in operation in Europe.[9] The immense quantities of bloomery slag (cinders) which remained in the seventeenth to nineteenth centuries show that early methods did not extract all the metal.

By c1244[10] permission to win ore was regulated by the Crown, and thereafter we have abundant records of such rights and privileges, and of small furnaces and forges which were set up in places near the iron ore deposits, or where the least labour was required in transporting wood or charcoal. In the numerous records available,[11] no clear distinction is made of the various types of plant used in the industry. We frequently read of *fabricae, forgiae arrantes*, and *blissahis*, but we cannot be sure which indicate forges, or smithies, or bloomeries. Often 'the King's great forge' is mentioned, and there are references to itinerant plants (though it may be the business, or the operators thereof, rather than the works, which was moved due to wood and ore in the immediate vicinity being exhausted), and to more permanent structures. There is no evidence of roasting or crushing before smelting, but the personal name of *le stampere* is recorded.

Though the King had three forges at work in the Forest at least as early as the beginning of Henry II's reign, there is no record of the receipts from them before the reign of Henry III. In 1228 the constable-warden was ordered not to permit the three forges to move about any longer in the Forest. Nine years later the King changed his policy, when John of Monmouth, constable-warden, with the foresters-of-fee and verderers, were to enquire in what places his eight movable forges can with least damage to the Forest be set up to use maple, thorn, hazel and dead wood; oaks, beeches, ash and chestnuts were not to be used. These forges ceased to work in 1240, but four others were set up in lieu of them in 1255. On 1 March 1255 the King ordered an enquiry 'as he has heard that the forges are harmful to the Forest because the destruction of it exceeds the issue of [the rent from] the forges'. And then allusion to them ceases; either their profits became the perquisite of the warden or they ceased to be worked.

Distinct from other forges was 'the forge belonging to the castle' of St Briavels or 'the great forge of the King'. Jurors in estimating its maximum value at £50 a year declared that the wood used to sustain it was worth considerably more than the forge brought in. The forge

1 (above) The Norman 'Old Castle of Dene' which, with the nearby 'Valley of Dene' (in Littledean), gave the Forest its name; *(below)* the How (or Hough) Brook, site of one of the seventeenth-century furnaces in Upper Lydbrook. In the nineteenth century a corn mill with a water-wheel stood to the left of the photograph

2 Part of the stonework of the Upper Soudley charcoal iron blast furnace establishment built c1612. Note the 250-year-old beech tree above the stonework. Behind the tree is a huge deposit of furnace slag

was separately accounted for in 1246–7 and 1255 and was expressly excluded from the issues of the Forest granted to Robert Walerand in the latter year. Its existence was noted each year in the Exchequer till 1281, but its profits, if any, were never put on record. It too may have passed after this date into the warden's hands.

In the first half of the thirteenth century the King wavered between willingness to avail himself of rents from private ironworks, together with iron to supplement the nation's supply, and unwillingness to sacrifice the large numbers of trees consumed and to tolerate the dis-

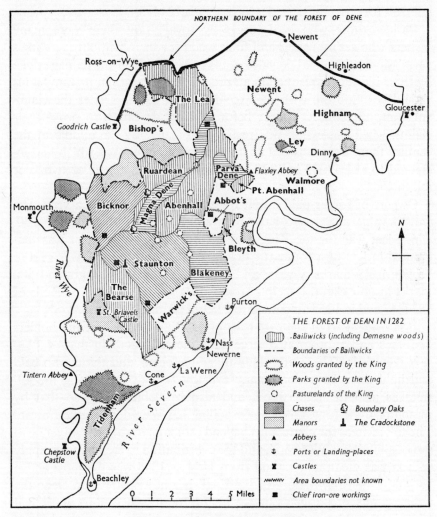

Fig 2. The Forest of Dean in 1282.

c

turbance of beasts of the forest. Yet the King was well aware of the need to permit the inhabitants to obtain a livelihood within the iron industry. Forges in private hands had been in use as early as Henry II's reign, often by licence specifically given by the King; such a grant was that to the Abbot of Flaxley at the beginning of the reign. Occasionally the grant was supplemented by the gift of wood to sustain the forge; the same abbot was entitled to two oaks a week from the middle of the thirteenth century till in 1258 he received instead the wood now named Abbotswood. John de Malemort who, with one or more of his family, spent a great part of his life at St Briavels making quarrels for cross-bows, had a forge there c1244–8.

Besides those who held forges by royal grant there were many owners who set up forges and took wood for them without the King's permission or in actual defiance of his orders. In 1217 the damage done by these illegalities resulted in an order that all forges in private hands should be removed, with six exceptions. Three years later the claimants were directed to appear before Hubert de Burgh to prove their claims, when possession was restored to many. By the middle of the century there were between 25 and 30 forges, a number which had increased to at least 43 in 1270 and 60 in 1282, but a year or two later fell to 45.[12]

Owners of forges paid a rent for each forge, usually 7s a year. The annual value appears to have been anything from 10 marks to £50, which last was for the King's great forge. The former sum was that granted in lieu of a forge at Etloe in 1249. Another forge was said to be worth 48 marks a year, and in 1276 its owner was granted 500 marks in quit claim. Receipts from forges found on the Pipe Rolls of 1237–47 and in 1255 amounted to £389 12s 0½d.

It is evident from the eyre-rolls of 1270 and 1282 that the holders of forges had appropriated large quantities of wood. In that of 1270 it is recorded: 'There are many itinerant forges, and those who held and hold them have done many evil things both concerning the tall trees as also the underwood, and also by debranching, so that by reason of these forges a great despoiling has been done in the Forest.' The toll of trees for charcoal is beyond estimate; it was certainly a good use of abundant underwood, and the contribution to the nation's supply of iron was great. The period from 1154 to 1348 was the most active period in the early history of the English iron industry.[13] In Dean the industry was probably as active in the fourteenth century as it had been in the thirteenth, and a medieval smelting site at Ruardean[14] is indicative of this activity. Documents of 1325, 1326, 1326–7, and 1333 show that charcoal-burning, hence smelting, was a regular occupation.[15] In 1341 the value, to the Warden of the Forest, of the dues on ore and forges was £34 a year. Early in Edward III's reign, the dues collected for the use of some of the large forges and of some smaller ones totalled £26 19s 3d, but all these forges had since been 'thrown down and annihilated to avoid destruction of the Forest'.[16]

By 1435, dues were still being collected from miners and transporters of iron ore and coal, and from those taking cinders.[17] Forges were permitted under an annual payment of 7s a forge; there were 33 working in 1436: 14 in Great Dean bailiwick, 2 in Little Dean, 2 in Ruardean, 10 for a full year and one for half a year in Newland, one for half a year at Lydney, and three elsewhere.

In 1519–20[18] in a dispute between inhabitants of the east of Dean and of the west of Dean, the large number of 'smyth holders' who signed an acceptance of an arbitration award seems to indicate that the dispute arose from the iron industry. No technical information relating to the industry can be derived from Dean documents, but an account in 1531 of a forge worked by Henry VIII at Llantrisant, Glamorgan, by men from Dean probably represented the local practice.[19] Five men 'kept the fire to melt the ore, having 12d a day each after the manner of the Forest of Dean'; four others, 'worked at the bellows, whereof three blow at a time and one of them stands void to refresh the others for he bloweth 6 or 7 hours at every gadde that is melting, and thus they make two gaddes a day each weighing 1cwt'. Each blower received $7\frac{1}{2}$d a day, and 12d more was paid to the four. One man 'hewed timber to stay the mine', at 6d a day; and three charcoal-burners were likewise paid that wage. Production was small: it took nine men working 12 to 14 hours to make 2cwt of iron a day, sent off in the form of gads or lumps of 1cwt; 21cwt had already been sent to Bristol. There were two gads remaining, and above ground lay 20cwt of ore, of which it was said 3cwt should make a gad of 1cwt or more. Already there were restrictive practices: the rules of the organised smiths of Coventry (dating from 1540) ordered that 'no smith shall shoe a horse with Forest-shoes or Forest-nails'.[20]

In 1540, Leland[21] recorded of Dean that 'the ground is fruitful of iron mines, and divers forges be there to make iron'. Some curtailment of wood for charcoal took place early in Elizabeth's reign, with the effect in Dean of restricting supplies to that obtained from coppices, underwood, and by debranching of 'timber-trees'. Sales were arranged to the 'ore-smiths'.[22] Iron wire 'drawn by strength of hand' is said to have been made at Soudley as early as 1565,[23] and in 1566 William Humfrey, upon information from German miners, addressed Sir William Cecil 'about the plenty of good iron' in the Forest.[24]

All iron so far had been made by the direct (bloomery) process, in which a lump of pasty malleable iron was reduced direct from the ore and wrought into the form of bar and rod. The process was intermittent in character and the cycle occupied about 8–12 hours, during which period about 1cwt of bar iron was produced, and the yield was only about $12\frac{1}{2}$ per cent from ore to bar. Thus power requirements in terms of water were low, and because the only other requirements were charcoal and ore, the industry was well established throughout the Forest when the sixteenth century drew to a close. But water power was soon to become of paramount importance.

The first Blast Furnace Period (1612-79)

INTRODUCTION The introduction of the voracious blast furnace to Britain in the sixteenth century began a new period in the history of ironmaking. By virtue of the furnace's continuous operation over a period of 6–9 months, it required a maintained water supply to drive the water-wheel, thereby to provide blast from a pair of leathern bellows. This power requirement caused the industry in Dean to shift to powerful streams. In the blast furnace a highly carburised pig iron was first produced and tapped from the base. The metal, an alloy of iron and carbon too brittle for the smith's hammer, had to be decarburised by oxidation, ie refined, by smelting the pig iron in a finery hearth, whereafter it was drawn out and shaped by the forge hammer. The whole became known as the indirect process. At what period of history limestone was added to the charge of ore and charcoal is unknown; certainly the bloomeries did not create a sufficiently high temperature for it to be used.

Three blast furnaces were set up near Dean's woods in the late sixteenth century. By 1575 Gilbert, Earl of Shrewsbury had a furnace at the west end of Whitchurch (near 'Bridge House'). From the early 1590s Robert Devereux the second Earl of Essex had two furnaces at Bishopswood and a forge at Lydbrook—a test was made there in about 1591–4 of *osmond* iron produced from the 'raw iron'.[25]

The lintels, beams and other ironwork for some furnaces of the time were made by Francis Watkins, iron-founder of Lydney; for instance, in c1597 he made in his foundry the ironwork for furnaces at Monkswood, Pontypool, and Abercarn—all for Richard Hanbury,[26] and he possibly supplied the ironwork for the furnace which Sir Edward Winter, son of Vice-Admiral Sir William Winter, owned by 1604 near his White Cross House in Lydney. Sir Edward had married a sister of the Marquis of Worcester (the author of *The Century of Inventions*), and in 1604 he obtained from the Crown licence to fell trees for charcoal on his estates in the parish of Lydney and in the Whitecroft area of the old extent of the parish of Newland, 'for the making and working of iron'.[27] Two years later his ironworks at Lydney comprised a furnace and a forge, with another forge, later a slitting mill, up the Newerne stream from Lydney.[28]

The iron industry in the Weald of Kent and elsewhere had been revolutionised by the advent of blast furnaces. In Dean, adherence for a while to the old processes is partly explained by the privileged position of the free miners and their associated smiths, which ensured to them a local corporate monopoly, and partly by the Crown's desire to conserve and replenish the oaks and beeches for shipbuilding: the comparatively small consumption of the old bloomeries lessened the danger of depleting the woods. The early blast furnaces at Whitchurch and at Bishopswood, already noted, and others at Tintern and White-brook, did not as yet depend much on Dean for cordwood, though its charcoal probably helped to sustain some of them. Several skilled workmen from Sussex had already migrated to Dean to assist in the erection of furnaces. However, entrepreneurs were anxious to obtain Dean's raw materials and facilities. In a letter 26 April 1609,[29] George Moore, steward of Goodrich Castle, informed his master, Gilbert, Earl of Shrewsbury, of plans projected for the erection of ironworks in Dean: there were 'divers good rivers and mine of iron-stone in all parts of the same, and the woods were so stately and such planted, as will continue six furnaces and as many forges at least 20 or 30 years'; more correctly the water-courses were streams, the ore lay in certain places only, and the woods, were natural, not planted.

The plans were tentative, and were contemporary with a project to erect ironworks on English 'plantations' in Ireland, yet in 1610 an ironmaster stated that the Irish ore was 'not as yieldable as the English iron ore', hence King James I should erect four furnaces in Dean where he had 'great stores of woods'.[30] The large capital required, induced the King and his advisers to leave the financial burden to men wealthy enough to bear it.

Up to 1610, the chief demand for Dean's coppices came from the Winters' Lydney furnace. By 1611 many other ironmasters, particularly those connected with the Company of the Mineral and Battery Works at Tintern, were pressing for two concessions in the Forest: firstly, wood, ore and bloomery slag (cinders), and secondly, a lease of ironworks to be erected in the King's name, he donating the building-timber and stone. Much ore could still be easily won, as well as immense quantities of cinders, some untouched since the Roman period, some partly resmelted, and much added during and after Norman times. These concessions were obtained in February 1612 by assigns of William Herbert, second Earl of Pembroke, who had vast possessions in South Wales and Monmouthshire, and was constable of St Briavels castle. Pembroke and his assigns at the Tintern works erected in Dean, on sites to be described later, four blast furnaces and three forges, which came to be known as the King's Ironworks,[31] and which necessitated a major reconstruction of the local industry. The furnaces were larger than those of the previous century, and were capable of producing about 700 tons of iron a year. The blast was provided by two pairs of leathern bellows, usually 15–20ft long and 5ft wide at the back end, tapering to 2ft 6in at the front, and driven by a single water-wheel. The blast was fed into a single tuyere, built into the tuyere arch and sealed with refractory fire-clay. At the forge, decarburisation of the brittle 'pig' took place in a finery hearth, and reheating was done in the chafery fire, followed by forging to 'bar', and possibly slitting in to the form of rod.[32] Each of these latter processes required individual water-wheels for depressing the bellows which in turn produced the blast for the hearths, and also for the 'great hammers'. Thus the water requirements were very much greater than for the blast furnace, which in consequence was usually sited upstream where there was a relatively low water supply, whilst the forges were usually further down stream where much more water could be obtained.

The necessity for streams with a good and regular supply of water, and sites suitable for damming to provide ponds and pools, had become in Dean the prime locational factors. For the first time its ironworks were sited more in relation to water power than to deposits of ore and cinders. Wood for charcoal was abundant almost everywhere, and there was royal licence to obtain sandstone for the furnace bosh, hearth, and general construction, for marl for bricks for the internal structure of the furnace stack, and for timber, turf, clay and stone for dams, races, troughs and sluices.

The characteristics of pools for furnace and forge were usually controlled by the nature of the process and the quantity of the water required to satisfy the needs of the water-wheels. Thus since the blast furnace required charging with charcoal and ore at a high point, some 20ft above the casting floor, furnaces were usually built adjacent to the sloping side of a hill, sometimes in a shallow watered valley which was readily dammed to provide a furnace pool of reasonable depth and of small surface area. In contrast, all work in the forge was performed at floor level which meant that the high level requirement was removed; and pools of much larger area, holding greater quantities of water, were established.[33]

The foregoing characteristics applied generally to the King's Ironworks erected in 1612–13, and Pembroke's lease included 'all water and water-courses', with permission to make 'stancks, ponds, pond-heads, wastes, water-courses, trenches, floodgates, and passages for water'. The lessee and his sub-lessees took advantage of three of the best streams in Dean—the Cannop (or Newerne) flowing south, the Lyd and How (or Hough) flowing north, and the Cinderford-Soudley flowing south-east. A private furnace already stood on the Lyd, at Lower Lydbrook. For later private ironworks other streams were used— namely the Valley (Newland-Redbrook), Cone, Hope, Westbury, Blackpool, Dry Brook and Bishop's Brook (Lodge Grove Brook).

The King's Ironworks comprised: on the northern boundary of the Forest at Lydbrook, a furnace powered by the Lyd (the furnace possibly stood where the Lyd was joined by the How brook, and the forge, 'The Middle', was down stream between the Upper and Lower Forges) and another forge still lower down; near the centre at Cannop, a furnace (just north of Cannop Bridge where the Howlers Slade stream joins the Cannop-Newerne); also near the centre of Dean, at Parkend, a furnace (where the Newerne is joined by the Brockways or Brookways Ditches [modern Brookhall Ditches] stream below where York Lodge now stands) and a forge down stream; and towards the eastern boundary at Upper Soudley, a furnace (alongside the present sewerage works on the Cinderford-Soudley brook) and a forge down stream (possibly where now stands Camp Mill). All the ironworks are described in later pages. Some of the 'campaigns'[34] of the furnaces, and the processes in the forges, have been commented upon by Schubert.[35]

In the industry the activity was great (in 1612–13 some 1,400 tons of ore were sent to Ireland alone),[36] but the actions of the ironmasters brought grave disputes between them and the miners; these disputes, and also the illegal taking of trees, led the Crown in 1613 to suspend the ironworks. Not till 31 May 1615 were they relet, the two furnaces and two forges at Parkend and Soudley for 15 years to Sir Basil Brooke of Madeley, Shropshire, partner with Richard Chaldecott of London; and the two furnaces and one forge at Lydbrook and Cannop for 15 years to Richard Tomlins and George Moore, steward of Goodrich Castle. The lease permitted 6,000 cords to be taken annually, paid for in iron, 320 tons a year; the iron was valued at £12 10s a ton, and the lessees thus paid the equivalent of 6s 8d a cord.[37] In 1617 and 1618 many accusations were proved against the ironmasters, chiefly of illegal felling, and in consequence ironmaking was suspended by order of the King.

On 6 April 1621 the King's Ironworks were leased for seven years to Richard Challoner and Philip Harris, and 'timber-oaks' were assigned for their repair. The Crown appointed 'overseers of ironworks', chiefly to regulate the taking of cordwood. For a few years the iron industry again flourished, but in 1625 the lessees were accused of misappropriation of trees. At Parkend they were working a furnace and a double forge (this, at the 'Park', was a forge with two hammers), and a furnace and forge at Lydbrook (besides another forge there rented from George Vaughan of nearby Courtfield). All were in regular use, but the furnace at Cannop, and the furnace and forge at Soudley were not.[38] The Crown decided to allow the lease, due to end in 1628, to run its course, but in 1627 a struggle ensued for the concessions.

The applicants were Sir Sackville Crowe of Laughern in Carmarthenshire, late treasurer of the Navy, Sir John Kirle, ironmaster in Herefordshire, and Brooke with George Mynne and Thomas Hackett of the wireworks at Tintern and Whitebrook of the Company of the Mineral and Battery Works. Pembroke, one of the governors of the Company, and by then lord steward, obtained the concessions 4 December 1627 for 21 years, and sublet at a profit to Brooke, Mynne and Hackett.[39] In 1628–9 they erected on private land a double forge at Whitecroft on the Newerne stream, and another at Bradley on the Soudley brook. The lease ran a normal course till 1633, but by that year the Crown was being urged to run its ironworks itself, and to suppress the others, particularly because of their disastrous effect on the woodland cover.

In January of the following year, Crowe submitted a list of ironworks in or near Dean: [40]

The King's:	1 Furnace at Lydbrook.
	1 Furnace at Cannop.
	1 Furnace at Soudley.
	1 Furnace at Park [end].
	1 Forge (single) at Lydbrook.
	2 Forges (one single, one double) at Soudley. [the double was that at Bradley].
	2 Forges (double) at Park [one stood at Whitecroft].
Sir John Winter:	1 Furnace at Lydney.
	1 Furnace at Rodmore.
	1 Furnace at Guns Mill.
	2 Forges (one single, one double) at Lydney.
Benedict Hall:	2 Furnaces at Newland.
	1 Forge (single) at Lydbrook [Lower Forge].
Sir John Kirle:	1 Forge at Lydbrook [Upper (Hangerbury) Forge].
	1 Furnace at Furnace Pool [probably at Bishopswood].
Sir Richard Cachemay:	1 Furnace at 'Brockweir' [presumably Coed Ithel].
Mr Typper:	2 Forges (single) at Flaxley.
Total:	11 Furnaces
	11 Forges (seven single, four double)

The Crown therefore owned 4 furnaces and 5 forges, and private entrepreneurs 7 furnaces and 6 forges. In addition there was Lydbrook Middle Forge, owned by Vaughan, also a small forge in Coleford owned by Anthony Hamon.[41] Winter's furnace at Rodmore on the upper Cone stream had been established in 1629 by John Powell of Preston, Herefordshire, for his daughter Eleanor, the widow of Edward James. Kyrle's furnace was probably that at Bishopswood, built by about 1628.[42] The two forges in the name of Typper were probably owned by Sir John Winter.

The holding of an important forest court for Dean in 1634 both halted the negotiations and the sub-lease to Brooke and Mynne, under which Sir John Winter also drew supplies of cordwood. The ambitious Winter, in favour at Court, was trying to get into his hands all the concessions in Dean. Sir Baynham Throckmorton of Clearwell also had strong but less far-reaching ambitions. The court put the leases in abeyance, and dealt with some 800 offences; 420 concerned misappropriation of trees, and ten related to unauthorised building of iron-works.[43] Among the chief offenders were Brooke and Mynne who had worked four furnaces and two single and three double forges. Another major offender was Winter who, with others, was eventually leniently dealt with. The lease of the King's Ironworks to Brooke and Mynne still held; indeed Mynne sold his share to Winter shortly before the court. The chief justice of the Forest south of Trent had suspended supplies of fuel to the ironworks, but Brooke and Winter still retained a virtual monopoly of wood to make iron. With a view to a new lease, an inventory of the King's works and their implements was taken in September 1635 by the surveyor general and other commissioners.[44] The inventory, included in this chapter under the individual works, disclosed that extensive building and rebuilding had taken place during 1631–4, but that all the ironworks, including the newly erected forges, needed repair:

	Approximate cost to repair		
	£	s	d
Park-End Furnace	60	0	0
Park-End Forge (double)	25	0	0
Cannop Furnace	7	13	4
Lydbrook (Howbrook) Furnace	50	0	0
Lydbrook Forge (single), below Howbrook Furnace	40	0	0
Soudley Furnace	130	0	0
Soudley Forge (single)	60	0	0
Whitecroft Forge (double)*	30	0	0
Bradley Forge (double)*	100	0	0

* 'Not fixed to the freehold, and erected [1628–9] by the late farmers, Sir Basil Brooke and Mr Mynne, of whom the new farmers are to buy all the movable implements and furniture of the same as they shall be appraised and valued indifferently between them.'

The Crown invited tenders for the new concessions. Brooke, who was actively concerned in producing steel by the cementation process (qv, Chapter 4), estimated that he had spent £14,000 in building and repairing the King's works; he offered the Crown financial inducements, and complained that he would be ruined if they were not accepted. Crowe pressed a scheme to be allowed to found guns in the Forest, either as manager on behalf of the Crown, or as its tenant,[45] and offered to make and deliver to the Severn 1,000 to 1,200 tons of iron ordnance annually at £9 a ton, to resign his fee of 20s a ton on all ordnance made under £11 a ton, and to pay 6s 8d a cord (he to fell) for 12,000 cords a year. Throckmorton offered 7s 2d a cord. The King's ministers considered all the proposals as well as an opposing resolution by the Treasury to demolish all the ironworks, to reserve Dean for perpetual revenue by enclosing, and to conserve its timber-trees for the Navy. The successful applicants were Throckmorton and Crowe, in partnership with John Taylor and John Gonning, junior, merchants of Bristol. On 12 July 1636 they obtained a lease for 21 years, paying £6,600 for the first 13 years and £6,000 thereafter. The £6,600 represented 12,000 cords annually at 11s.[46]

The deputy surveyor, John Broughton, who in March 1637 had an 'improved bloomery wherein was made in $2\frac{1}{2}$ hours a bar of iron of 55lb weight from one sack of charcoal and a quantity of cinders and ore',[47] tried unsuccessfully to oust the ironmasters. Their works flourished, and consumed as charcoal huge quantities of cordwood, but workers within the industry were coerced and forced to endure the 'truck' system of payment; and accusations were widespread of misappropriation of trees. For at least the previous 12 years Dean's woods had sustained about eleven blast furnaces and eleven forges, as well as contributing supplies to works further afield. A concentration of such large ironworks was probably at this time unique in England. But Dean was to be affected by intrigue at Court. Winter, pardoned for the offences brought to light at the forest court in 1634, and in favour as Queen Henrietta Maria's private secretary, was granted 21 March 1640 'all His Majesty's lands, waste, soil, minerals, trees, and underwood in Dean comprising 17 to 18,000 acres', in consideration of £10,000 to be paid in the Exchequer before the grant passed the Great Seal, £16,000 per annum for six years to begin 1 April 1640, and a fee-farm rent of £1,950 12s 8d payable to the Crown for ever.[48] It was virtually a sale for £106,000 plus the fee-farm rent, of some 18,000 acres of the Forest, to include the King's Ironworks, and the ore, cinders, and coal in that acreage and within 4,000 acres allotted to the commoners. Excluded were the Lea Bailey, the Chestnut Wood leased to Richard Brayne, and the woods of Snead and Kidnalls near Lydney leased to Tristram Flower; also excluded were 15,000 tons of ship-timber. Winter for six years had to permit Throckmorton and his partners to use the furnaces at Parkend and Soudley, and the forges at Whitecroft, Parkend, Soudley and Bradley, and to take 13,500 cords yearly. He probably retained the furnace and forge at Lydbrook and the furnace at Cannop (presumably derelict). Because he owned the furnaces and forges at Lydney,

Rodmore and Guns Mill he with his subtenants of the King's Ironworks had control of almost the whole iron production in west Gloucestershire.

Winter felled great numbers of trees and much underwood, and soon
enclosed 4,000 acres for regrowth. The local inhabitants, opposed to
the grant, threw open his enclosures, and in June 1640 petitioned the
Crown that their rights and privileges should be respected; protracted
litigation ensued between them, the ironmasters, and the Crown. Winter
fully enjoyed his grant for only about eighteen months: there was too
much opposition for him to continue; but he held persistently to his
grant until the House of Commons, 21 March 1642, voted its termination.[49] In part payment of his debts, and for the maintenance of his
wife and children, he leased his ironworks to Thomas Morgan and
others.

Commissioners for the King sold some of the timber which Winter
had felled, and were authorised to sell the remainder to John Browne,
gun-founder,[50] 'at such rates and prices as they think best for His
Majesty's benefit, the same to be taken by Browne in part payment
of moneys due to him from the King and assigned by tally upon the
rent of £16,000 due from Winter's grant'. Thereupon Browne was
allotted 5,604 tons at 10s a ton, to be cut into cordwood, together with
the logs, stubs, and roots where they lay, 'at reasonable rates'. He was
also assigned Cannop furnace, and Lydbrook furnace and forge, for
two years and three months from 1 July 1642, with permission to take
ore and cinders and 'to cut and use fern, or any other thing necessary for charcoaling'. He was to have timber to repair the ironworks
with their houses and buildings. Browne, who had works at Brenchley,
Kent, did no ironmaking in Dean, but assigned the works at Cannop
and Lydbrook to William Dunning of nearby Purton, in partnership
with his son Thomas, and Mr Mandit of London, together with half
of the timber and wood; the other half he assigned to Richard Skinner
of nearby Woolaston. Dunning and his partners ran the Lydbrook
works, but it is not certain that Cannop furnace was worked.[51] Meanwhile, 29 April 1642, Throckmorton, Crowe, Taylor, and Gonning
were promised an allocation of 13,500 cords of 'complement' and
'offal' wood at 10s a cord plus £100 per annum. Throckmorton continued with his sub-lease 'until he was in arms for His Majesty'. In the
same year, 1642, the King's forge at Bradley, was apparently being
run by John Typper of Flaxley: at Bradley, Stonegrove, Buckhold-
more, and Pigslade, woods there had been 'lately cut and yet cutting

by Typper or six servants, being adjacent to one of His Majesty's iron-works [Bradley] and fit for coppice'.[52]

During the Civil War, administration in Dean was erratic, and its inhabitants suffered by the supporters of both parties. Iron shot was supplied to both the Royalists and the Parliamentarians.[53] From the beginning, the King had in the Forest loyal and influential supporters in Winter and Throckmorton, who made use of many of the local furnaces and forges. No less important was the Herbert family at Raglan; early in 1643 Lord Herbert, the son of the Marquis of Worces-ter, reported that there was 'very good iron from the Forest of Dean when it shall be reduced', and for this purpose he needed more work-men. The reserves of iron in the area, especially those in rebel hands, were taken in.[54] At the seige of Gloucester in August 1643 the main army was supplied with over 500 iron cannon balls from Soudley furnace alone.[55] The major part of the Forest's military production was used locally, and to devastating effect in this hard-fought campaign. Winter's 'iron mills and furnaces were the main strength of his estate and garrison'.[56] In 1644 the ironworks at Lydney, Parkend, Cannop and Whitecroft were partially destroyed.

Winter lost most of his property, and his ironworks in that year were leased by the Commons to his main opponent, Major-General Edward Massey, whose assignee was Captain John Gifford. Winter's estate was later vested in trustees, while he was imprisoned in the Tower with a degree of freedom. Gifford had Winter's furnace and two forges at Lydney (most of which had been burned) and Park furnace ('at Upper Forge he drew in 3 years 300 tons of raw iron');[57] Lieuten-ant-Colonel Robert Kyrle the Bishopswood furnace; and Captain John Braine of Littledean in partnership with Kyrle in 1645 had the furnace at Redbrook and at Rodmore, and built a forge near Rodmore at Rowlands (Rowley) Mill at a place called Atkins Mill (alias Burnt Mill).[58] In 1644, Braine seized the Cannop and Lydbrook works from Dunning, and assigned the latter works to Thomas Pury and Grifantius Phillips. By 1645 Braine was also working Winter's furnace at Guns Mill, the King's forge at Bradley, and another forge at Lydbrook which had been leased by George Vaughan to Thomas Dunning. A forge at Soudley 'might yet be going', as well as a furnace seized by Braine at Howbrook, in Lydbrook; and Winter's slitting mill at Lydney had been repaired. Lydbrook furnace made 14, 20 or 24 tons of raw iron a week; and 10 tons of charcoal were delivered each week to Pury at Middle Forge nearby.

Massey, his assignee, and other Parliamentarians, enriched themselves at the expense of Dean's trees: the quantity taken for charcoaling was immense.[59] In October 1646 Kyrle was ordered by the
Committee of Parliament to deliver up Hall's furnace at Redbrook. By
June of the following year, Massey had sold his interest in the ironworks, on which he had spent £800 in repairs, to his assignee Gifford
for £2,000 under a lease for five years. Thomas Morgan and his partners petitioned the Government for restitution of the lease which they
had obtained from Winter before the Civil War. Gifford, then of
Gloucester, tried to oppose this, but in 1650 he was relieved of his
lease by the Government, who were determined to curb waste and
abuse. A halt was called to the devastation of Dean's woods—which
for 38 years had suffered intensive, yet sometimes rational, exploitation. The incessant assaults on the cover had much reduced the number and quality of its trees and the acreage of its coppices. Few forests
had been attacked with equal intensity, but increment made good some
of the loss, and Dean's timber potential was important.[60]

At the beginning of the Commonwealth, 1649, much of the economy
of Dean was still based on the ironworks. Two furnaces and three
forges were sustained by the Forest's wood. Hundreds of the inhabitants, many mere cabiners, eked out a livelihood by cutting, cording,
charcoal-burning and carrying. Timber and cordwood lay all over the
Forest, and hundreds of charcoal 'pits' were smouldering. Timber had
been used to repair the ironworks at Lydney and Lydbrook. Forty
horses a day delivered charcoal to Lydbrook, each carrying a sack
twice, sometimes thrice, a day; it took seven days to complete the
burning of a charcoal pit, and five sacks were the proceeds of a ton of
wood.[61] The effect on the cover was so disastrous that Parliament
ordered 'Preservators' to demolish the ironworks. How far the order
was obeyed is not known, but Thomas Pury junior, and Grifantius
Phillips were later told by the Council that 'if their ironworks at Lydbrook are not within the perambulation of the Forest their remedy
is by common law against those who demolished them.' There was no
known ironmaking in Dean from 1650 to 1652, nor in most of 1653.[62]

On 27 August 1653 Major John Wade was appointed by the Council as chief administrator in Dean. This efficient officer was ordered to
manufacture iron shot and ordnance, and for the purpose to erect a
furnace at Parkend and to repair that at Lydney, lately belonging to
Winter. The new furnace at Parkend, probably of the same dimensions as that of 1612–13, stood a short distance downstream but still

east of York Lodge. Wade planned the supply of a greater volume of water 'to move the bellows', and said that his new furnace 'will be one of the best watered furnaces in this nation'.[63] He reported that the two furnaces were capable of casting 50 or 60 tons of pig-iron a week at £3 a ton, and 20 tons of shot at £4 a ton. An improvement in his manufacture was the admixture of scrap-iron to the charge; the proportion, however, was fairly small compared with the cinder added, eg 16 tons 4cwt of scrap-iron and 701 tons of cinder to make 701 tons of pig-iron in 1656–7.[64] He was given authority to erect lower down the same Newerne stream at Whitecroft a forge 'to convert the raw iron thrown in the making of shot, or it will be wasted or sold at a loss'.

By 24 January 1654 Wade had 'lit the furnaces'. For six years his works supplied much ironwork for ships built on the Severn, and immense quantities of pig-iron, shot, spikes, hoops, bars and bolts to naval stores. Details of his accounts are extant.[65] From September 1654 to March 1659 he supplied to the navy 700 tons of shot and 88 tons of wrought-iron fittings. In 1655 he informed the admiralty that if sufficient shot had been made, he wished to 'turn the furnaces so as to cast pig-iron'.[66] Between September 1657 and April 1660 he sold some 1,200 tons of pig-iron at prices ranging from £6 12s to £7 5s, about 5 tons of chimney-backs and baking-plates at £12, and between 300 and 400 tons of bar iron, usually at £17 10s. Much of the bar iron, and all the backs and plates, were sent to Bristol; the pig-iron was probably supplied to forge-masters in various parts of the country.

Wade, an able administrator, superintended the ironworks, and acted for the Government as both forest-manager and timber-merchant; he will be remembered as the person responsible in Dean for the first sowing and planting of forest trees. Great difficulties, particularly opposition from the commoners and other inhabitants, led to his resignation in April 1660,[67] about the time of the Restoration of Charles II. From 24 April Wade's work was taken over by commissioners: the accounts to 3 October 1660, of the new superintendent of the ironworks, William Carpenter, are extant.[68] He had found that $5\frac{1}{2}$ short cords of wood made a load of charcoal; and two loads or sacks of coal made a ton of sow iron.[69]

By 1660, Captain John Braine had 'three ironworks', possibly a furnace and two forges, 'on private land adjoining Woolaston Wood', at Rodmore and other neighbouring sites on the Cone.[70] Benedict Hall's furnace at Redbrook was being run for him by William Probin.[71] Meanwhile Thomas Foley (b 1616), a precursor of a long line of ironmasters, was drawing charcoal, and perhaps ore and cinders, from woods neighbouring Dean. He had married Anne, daughter of John Browne, the ironfounder. By 1661 he had interests in a furnace at Hope (Longhope), and in a furnace and forge at Bishopswood. These interests and his loaning of money to ironmasters and others, paved the way to a larger involvement in Dean and its neighbourhood. An agreement which he made with Thomas Nourse of Longhope 24 February 1661 gives information on some of his interests: [72]

First, that Mr Nourse shall have the benefit of this present blast at Hope furnace till the middle of May, but if he stop in the meantime a fortnight at the furnace then he is to have liberty to blow till the end of May. And is to acquit Mr Foley of this present year's rent of the furnace, and over and besides the rent to allow Mr Foley £40 in money and 5 tons of pigs.

Second, Mr Foley is to make up the [char] coals that have been this year sent out of Newents Wood 250 loads for which Mr Nourse is to allow Mr Foley 30s for every load in the wood, besides he is to pay for the carriage of them.

Third, Mr Nourse is to make good to Mr Foley the £950 that he has rent from Mr Foley on this year's stock and likewise what the 250 loads of coals shall amount on to being £375 which in all is £1,325, towards which said sum of £1,325 Mr Foley has had of this blast 20 tons of pigs which he is to allow £130 for, and he is also to allow Mr Nourse £100 more out of it in consideration of which last £100 and also of the £40 for the profit of this blast which is above mentioned, Mr Nourse is to free Mr Foley of all the bargains he lately made with Mr Bond except the wood in Bradleys Grove which Mr Foley is to have at the price the Countess of Kent is to have for the same. And Mr Nourse is to take effectual course, according to his agreement that Mr Bond's forge and furnace at Walford [? Bishopswood] are to be hindered from going for the future, after the forge there has spent the wood that is now already cut in Penyard, and in consideration like-wise of the £100 and the £40 above mentioned, Mr Nourse is to build up and repair the house mill and appurtenances in Hope which he took of the trustees there, and to keep the said mill constantly going so that the water belonging to the said mill shall not be any otherwise employed than to the use of the said mill. And Mr Nourse is to free and discharge Mr Foley from all rents and covenants concerning the said mill and for the remaining £1,095 Mr Nourse is to pay it out for the use of the said Mr Foley upon what stock either now has already been or shall be bought or provided for the next year's blast as fast as any occasion shall require until he has paid the said £1,095 to the

3 *(above)* Top of a roasting kiln at Ruardean; *(below)* Lydney Middle Forge on the Newerne Stream

4 Lydney Middle Forge on the Newerne Stream: *(above)* remains of the spillway from the south-west; *(below)* remains of the dam wall from the south

content and satisfaction of the said Mr Foley and that the stock that shall be bought and paid for therewith to be employed at Hope furnace to the only proper use and benefit of the said Mr Foley. And Mr Nourse is to deliver the 5 tons of pigs above mentioned to whom Mr Foley shall appoint.

Following the Restoration, much of the Forest was regranted to Winter, but the ironworks were worked for the Crown by William Carpenter, Philip Rod, and George Wyrral, whose accounts dated 30 May 1661 show a profit of £1,730 16s 7d.[73] Winter, Throckmorton and others agitated for reimbursement of their past losses, and for some share in the ironworks. A Commission reported 12 April 1662,[74] 'one excellent furnace called the Park Furnace, and one forge called White-croft Forge'. The latter was in good repair, but the furnace needed 'a roof to the colehouse, and some other repairs' which might cost about £40. If the King took the works into his own hands, the following advantages would yearly accrue:[75]

The Furnace
Four long cords of wood will make two loads of charcoal, which two loads will make one ton of sow iron:

	£	s	d
Cutting and cording 4 long cords		14	0
Charcoaling same at 3s 6d a load		7	0
Carrying charcoal to the furnace		7	0
Iron ore		5	0
Cinders		3	0
The founder or caster		2	6
	£1	18	6

Which ton of sow iron will yield, one year with another, although now debased by the late mis-vending of the stock but will be brought up again, to £6 10s.

The furnace may, with the expense of £100 to preserve and procure a greater proportion of water, cast near 30 tons a week, but to reduce it to a greater certainty we will compute at 26 tons a week, which at 48 weeks will amount to 1,248 tons per annum, which at £6 10s a ton amounts to £8,112. But the charges to be deducted at £1 18s 6d a ton amounts to £2,402 8s, deducting which out of the general profit, there remains £5,709 12s.

Other charges to be deducted and allowed out of the furnace profits:

D

	£	s	d
Stocktaker	16	0	0
Clerk	40	0	0
Carpenter	6	13	4
Other repairs of the furnace	12	0	0
Clerk's travelling expenses to sell iron	5	0	0
2 Wood clerks	20	0	0
Sacks and hurdles	20	0	0
	£119	13	4

The profit is therefore £5,589 18s 8d.

The Forge

Charges to make a ton of bar iron:

Three loads of charcoal will make a ton of bar iron whereof one load may be brazes [small charcoal], but set it at three loads, the cutting, cording, charcoaling, and carriage will amount to:

	£	s	d
	2	2	0
And 26½cwt of sow iron will make one ton of bar iron, which at £6 10s a ton amounts to	8	12	0
And to the workmen, viz raffiners and hammermen	1	0	0
	£11	14	0

The forge will make, one year with another, 150 tons which will yield generally £16 10s a ton, although now debased by the late mis-vending of the stock.

Produce 150 tons at £16 10s a ton amounts per annum to: £2,475

Less charges at £11 14s a ton as aforesaid: £1,740 [*sic*]

Remains clear: £735

Other charges to be allowed out of the yearly profits of the forge:

	£	s	d
Clerk	25	0	0
Stocktaker	16	0	0
Carpenter	6	13	4
Other repairs, and oil, grease etc	20	0	0
	£67	13	4

Deducting these charges from the general profit of £735, there remains £667 6s 8d.

The Commissioners commented:

> Care must be taken whensoever His Majesty shall take the ironworks into his own hands that all the implements the late persons entrusted with the management thereof had delivered to them by inventory or otherwise, be forthcoming, or else it will be a great prejudice to His Majesty. And we humbly advise that His Majesty would be pleased to take the works into his own hands as being not only of great yearly profit but capable to serve his Navy both with better iron and at much easier rates than now he pays for all sorts, and we conceive that iron ordnance might be cast here for the service of the Navy also at the same rates; and £500 together with the young beech-timber lately blown down in the Lea Bailey will set the works agoing.

The Crown decided not to work the Parkend furnace and Whitecroft forge, but instead to lease them from 30 June 1662 with the Howbrook (Lydbrook) furnace to Winter's nominees, Francis Finch and Robert Clayton. Winter was again put in a position to monopolise Dean's woods.[76] The cover was again felled to sustain the ironworks, and with controversies over rights of common, led the Crown in 1667 to terminate Winter's official connection with the Forest. The same year, the Dean Forest (Reafforestation) Act became law. The forge at Whitecroft leased by Clayton, then sole sub-lessee, was stopped, the two furnaces leased by him at Parkend and Howbrook were denied Dean's cordwood, and after his lease ended in 1673 the works, with a forge at Parkend, were sold at £500 the following year for demolition to Paul Foley.[77] The chief reason for the sale was to conserve the Forest's trees, particularly the 'timber-trees' and those to succeed them—the ironworks being 'conceived to be the destruction of the woods and timber'.

Thus ended the sixty-four years' story of the King's Ironworks. Since about 1612, these and other ironworks in the Forest and its neighbourhood had used immense quantities of wood. This was a rational use, but it should have been more prudently regulated by the Crown and accompanied by more frequent and effective replenishment of trees by enclosure, supplemented by care of natural or artificial regeneration. The Crown's policy had fluctuated according as anxiety for the Navy or concern for a straitened exchequer was dominant in its mind. On the whole, the substantial revenues that could be obtained from the grant of monopolist rights to projectors in the iron industry outweighed the desire for conservation. Nevertheless, the proceeds of demolition were put to good use—towards building keepers' lodges in the Forest.

From 1671 Paul Foley (with, later, his partners) had almost a monopoly of the iron industry in west Gloucestershire, Herefordshire and Monmouthshire, and there emerged a close alliance between the iron-smelting Forest and the metal-consuming Midlands. In July 1674,[78] Foley admitted his brother Philip to a one-third share in his furnaces at Longhope, Bishopswood, Redbrook and Flaxley, and in his forges— 2 at Lydbrook and 2 at Flaxley.

Much of the foregoing description of the iron industry will be amplified by G. Hammersley when the results of his many years of research into Dean's seventeenth-century iron industry are published Meanwhile, some detailed information on the individual ironworks of the period 1612–79 is given hereunder.

PARKEND   The King's furnace, at the junction of the Newerne stream and the Brockways Ditches stream, below where York Lodge now stands, was built for the Crown in 1612 by Pembroke and his lessees. It was repaired in 1631, and surveyed in 1635:[79]

> Park End furnace. The body thereof 22 foot square at the bottom, repaired by the present farmers about 4 years since, and the backer wall of the furnace and part of the wall over the bellows then built from the foundation. In the front thereof two broken sows of iron, and there has been one more which is taken thence and is lying near the door of the furnace house, and there are 2 sows of iron in the tewyron wall.
>
> The furnace body and the binding beams thereof cracked and insufficient to work.
>
> The water wheel 22 foot diameter with its shaft whereon are 7 iron hoops, 6 cambs, 2 gudgeons, and brasses, in repair.
>
> The furnace house built with stone 22 foot square and 9 foot high in the side-walls, the roof good except one little breach by the bridge and tiled, built 4 years since and now in repair.
>
> A penthouse under the furnace.
>
> The bridgehouse 42 foot long 22 foot broad, the sidewalls $8\frac{1}{2}$ foot high, covered with boards, double bottomed with plank upon strong sleepers, with fence walls, built about 4 years since and in repair.
>
> Trowes cut out of sound timber 100 feet long, covered with plank.
>
> Another water-course $2\frac{1}{2}$ foot broad, and 46 foot long, built with stone on both sides and covered with plank, in which is a cast iron grate.
>
> A water-course on the north side of the said furnace about half a

mile long with a bay at the head thereof with a small breach therein, wants scouring, otherwise good.

A water-course of about half a mile long on the south side of the furnace.

The hutch 6 foot deep, 3 foot broad, 70 foot long, whereof 56 foot built of stone and 14 foot of timber, all covered with plank and in repair, but the stream stopped below the hutch with cinders.

A house enjoyed by the founder.

A cottage adjoining thereunto.

A cabin for the bridge-server 18 foot long, 11 foot broad, built of timber and covered with boards.

A cabin adjoining to the furnace for the furnace keeper.

A fair house 3 stories high, tiled, the ends built with stone and the rest with timber, 50 foot long, 16 foot broad, with a cross building in it 16 foot square, with 2 stables of timber belonging thereunto, in repair.

A small cottage now enjoyed by William Wayte.

The mine kiln decayed in the inside, and the pigs of iron taken from the draughts thereof.

Implements of Park End furnace

The bellows open with the iron furniture belonging defective in the leathers.

buckstaves	2	wheel barrows	2
damplate	1	mine hammers	2
cinder plates	2	coal rake	1
tewyron plate	1	cinder rakes	2
dam hook or stopping hook	1	great sledge	1
iron shovels	4	ringer hammer	1
ringers	9	constable	1
coal baskets	6	tunnel plate	1
beam with scales, hooks, triangles and links with half a ton of raw iron for a weight.		grindstone	1
		new bellows boards	2
		old bellows boards	4
		colliers hurdles in the woods enough for the work	

The repair of the defects in this furnace, according to an estimate thereof made, will cost about sixty pounds.

Although the furnace was destroyed in 1644 during the Civil War, the hearth and boshes were found complete by David Mushet in c1812.[80] (It could of course have been the second furnace):

About fourteen years ago, I first saw the ruins of one of these furnaces situated below York Lodge, and surrounded by a large heap of the slag or scoria that is produced in making pig iron. As the situation of this furnace was remote from roads, and must at one time have been deemed nearly inacessible, it had all the appearance at the time of my survey of having remained in the same state for nearly two centuries: there existed no trace of any sort of machinery; which rendered it highly probable that no part of the slags had been ground (the usual practice) and carried off, but that the entire produce of the furnace in slags remained undisturbed. The quantity I computed at from 8,000 to 10,000 tons.

Mushet supplied measurements to Abraham Rees, who in 1820 drew sketches (not reproduced here) and wrote an explanatory text:[81]

(*a*) Is a section of the building, and interior of the charcoal blast furnace, about the time of its first application for the purpose of making pig-iron. The remains of a furnace similarly constructed were accidentally discovered [at Parkend], in making an excavation, some eight years ago [ie 1812], in Dean Forest [by David Mushet]. From its situation on the margin of a small stream, and the remains of the watercourse, the bellows must have been worked by means of a small water wheel. The height of this furnace, from A to B, judging by the dimensions of the hearth and boshes, which were found entire, could not have exceeded 20 feet. The height of the hearth, from A to C, 4 feet, and the height of the boshes, from C to D, 2½ feet. The length of the hearth from *e*, the back wall, to *f*, the front of the dam-stone, 4 feet.

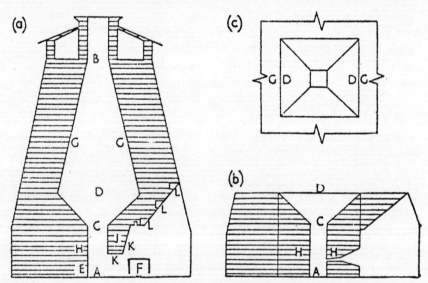

Sections through the first Parkend furnace

Fig 3. Sections through the first Parkend blast furnace (after Schubert, *The King's Ironworks*, p. 159).

G,G.—the lining, constructed of thin beds of an infusible species of sandstone. H. the hearth, composed of stronger beds of the same species of sandstone, called *land-stone*.

(*b*) Is a section sketched at right-angles of that part, comprising the space from D to A, in which the letters correspond, showing the blowing orifice called the twyre, the twyre-arch, and the three cast iron bearers called '*sows*', for supporting the same.

(*c*) Is a horizontal section of the same furnace at D, the top of the boshes, in other figures, showing the quadrangle form of the interior, which was common to charcoal furnaces at that time, and in which the letters of reference also correspond.

Schubert[82] copied (Fig 3) Rees's drawings and added comments:

Figure (*a*) is a cross-section of the stack of the furnace made through the aperture which served for tapping the molten iron. The outer casing or shell, termed the body of the furnace in the inventory, had a basement 22ft square, the outside walls of which rose almost vertically to the height where the hearth joined the boshes (C), which was 5ft from the ground. The upper part placed upon this basement resembled a truncated pyramid with a slight incline downwards. A further device to prevent the effect of moisture (not depicted in Rees's drawings) was the 'penthouse under the furnace' at Parkend; this was a chamber built underneath the bottom stone to collect ground moisture.

The body of the furnace was built of larger stones cemented together with mortar. The inner lining (GG), according to Rees, was constructed of a 'thin bed of infusable species of sandstone'. There was a space left between the lining and the outer walls which generally was filled with sand.

The hearth (H) was 'composed of stronger beds of the same species of sandstone, called land-stone'. The hearth was 4ft high (from A to C), and 4ft wide from the backwall (E) to the front of the dam stone (F). There was an aperture in the front of the furnace where the founder worked. The arch closing the top of it was strengthened by sows of cast iron (L), placed into the ceiling of the arch at intervals and frequently referred to in the inventory. The stone at the very back of the arch towards the hearth was the tymp stone (J), protected underneath and outside by the tymp plate (K)—iron tempe in the inventory. Each side of the aperture between the tymp stone and the bottom was protected by a vertical iron plate, termed a buckstave. The dam stone was covered with an iron plate, called the dam plate, with a notch on the top through which the cinder or slag ran off, upon the cinder plate. If the cinder coagulated, it was hauled out with a cinder hook. To make room for fresh cinder, the cinder plate was cleared with rakes and shovels. On one side of the dam stone there was another notch or a slit mostly closed with clay. It was opened by piercing the clay with a long iron bar (termed a ringer) whenever the molten iron was tapped. The iron ran into a furrow made in a bed of sand by a moulding ship. If it ran off too vehemently, it was held back by a stopper or dam hook, also termed a hardew. For casting small objects, such as bullets or pots and pans, the molten metal was ladled out with casting ladles and poured into moulds. Ringers were the implements most frequently used in the smelting process, which accounts for the large number. They were either hooked or pointed, the points being sharpened on grindstones. When too hot, they were cooled with water in troughs, termed boshes. The ringers also served for scraping sidewalls and corners of the hearth to break off crusts which had formed there. These, when broken off, rose to the top of the liquid mass where they melted and deposited their iron contents. The strongest and longest bar (about 8–9ft), used for cleaning the hearth, was termed a constable.

Figure (*b*) is a cross-section through the other side of the hearth, where the second or tuyere arch was situated. This arch also was supported by iron bearers, and had an opening into the hearth by which the blast entered through the tuyere. The tuyere, which was protected by the iron tuyere plate, contained the nozzles of a pair of bellows. The tuyere was fixed in clay with the help of a kind of trowel, termed a placket. A tuyere hook served for clearing the tuyere from slag which tended to adhere to it. The leather bellows, on the upper lids of which square pieces of timber, termed firkets, were laid, were pressed down alternatively by iron cams fixed on a rotating shaft or beam moved by a water wheel of 22ft diameter. The shaft turned on cast-iron gudgeons or centre-pins fixed on the two ends of the shaft and running on brasses also of cast iron. The bellows were lifted by wooden beams or poles, termed poises or counter-poises, weighted with pieces of iron on their longer ends ($3\frac{1}{2}$cwt at Cannop) and working as levers.

Figure (*c*) is a horizontal section of the furnace at the top of the boshes (D), which were $2\frac{1}{2}$ft high from C to D. It shows the quadrangular form of the interior which was common to charcoal furnaces at that time [Rees].

Modern thought and experience could find fault with some of the technicalities of Fig 3, but the information given by Mushet, Rees and Schubert is a contribution to the understanding of the early charcoal blast furnaces in Dean.

The King's Forge at Parkend was likewise built 1612–13, and by

5 Lydney Upper Forge on the Newerne Stream: *(above)* some remains from the north; *(below)* some remains from the south

6 *(left)* Flaxley charcoal iron blast furnace and forge in 1712; *(below)* Flaxley Lower Forge: remains of the dam wall and the wheel race arch from the east

7 *(above)* Guns Mill between Abenhall and Flaxley showing part of the charcoal iron blast furnace, reconstructed as a paper mill; *(right)* Lydney Furnace Cottages

8 Parkend Ironworks: *(right)* preparations for throwing the stack in 1908; *(below)* the engine house being converted to a forestry school

the same lessees as those of the furnace already described, but the site is not known—probably it was in or near the south of the village. By 1634 it was a double forge,[83] and the survey of it in 1635 reads:[84]

Park End forge consisting of two hammers, 3 fineries and 1 chaferie which were generally repaired and part new made about 2 years since.

The lower part of the bay 120 foot long, 12 foot high made of timber with sills, laces and posts, the front of the bay where the water is led to the forge, built of stone with 2 drawing gates.

A floodgate of 6 sluices in the bay 44 foot long and 22 foot broad strongly timbered, and built on each side with a stone wall 3 foot high above the apron and 3 foot thick, and aproned with plank, 160 feet below the sluices.

A storehouse for iron 24 foot long 18 foot broad and 13 foot high in sidewalls, whereof 3 foot of good stone-work, built with timber and tiled, with a convenient room over it and a pair of outside layers leading thereto.

One fair coalhouse 62 foot long, 29 foot broad, and 17 foot high in sidewalls whereof 5 foot stonework and 12 foot timber, 5 bays, covered with boards, and 2 great pair of stayers unto it, built about 3 years since. One coalyard inclosed within a wall 50 foot in circuit and 8 foot high, with a great door and hinges.

One old coalhouse adjoining.

One house built of stone for the coalkeeper 23 foot long and 17 foot broad, tiled, and contains 4 rooms.

One house built for the finer 16 foot long 15 foot broad and covered with boards.

One house for the hammerman lately repaired.

Two cottages enjoyed by the finers.

One little house adjoining to the forge for the carpenter to work in.

Implements in Park End forge

Forging hammer hoops on the hammer		boytes	2
		bray	1
beam	13	great wedges in the ham-	
gudgeons	2	mer eye	2
brasses	2	hoops on the anvil block	2
great hammer	1		
anvil	1		
hurst, and set of hurst wedges	1		

shingling hammer
    on the beam thereof 10 iron hoops and all things else as the forging hammer has.

Chaferie

plates	5	pair of chafery bellows
fixed morris plate or raw iron	1	furnished 1
morris bar of wrought iron	1	hammer bit 1
tewyron	1	hammer eye 1
plates of cast iron over the tewyron	2	pair of great tongs 1
		pair of shingling tongs 7
fixed pig of iron over the tewyron	1	ringer 1
		furgon 1
hoops on the chaferie wheel	4	handhammer 1
		clams 4
gudgeons and brasses	2	iron dish 1
brass-iron to keep down the shaft of the wheel	1	quasse 1
		loop plate of about 3cwt 1
sledge	1	cold chisels 2
shovel	1	water trowes and anvil
mandrill	1	blocks

The Upper Finerie

pair of bellows furnished	1	loop plate 1
hoops on the wheel shaft	4	tewyron 1
gudgeons and brasses	2	ringer 1
plates	5	furgons 2
chimney plate of cast		quasse 1
fixed iron	1	iron dish 1
morris bar	1	clam 1
pair of shingling tongs	1	ringer hammer 1
pair of great tongs, or maudlins	2	wheel barrow 1
iron beam scales and hooks and 2c of cast iron for a weight.		baskets and hurdles sufficient for the work

The 2 lower fineries have implements according to the upper finerie.

The chaferie wheel, the front of the bay and some earth work in the bay defective, the repair whereof, according to an estimate thereof, will cost about twenty-five pounds.

Schubert[85] wrote of such forges:

The older type of forges consisted of two fineries, one chafery, and one power hammer. In the finery the pig iron obtained from the furnace was refined, ie decarburised and freed from impurities, and in the chafery the refined iron was reheated in order to be consolidated and shaped into bars by the power hammer. To obtain a higher output, a new type of forge was introduced in England after 1600; this had three fineries, one chafery, and two power hammers. Both types are represented in the inventory of 1635 [*supra*]. The process of refining, as well as reheating, was conducted in hearths. Each hearth was surmounted by a chimney supported by a morrisbar (derived from the French *marâtre*) over the front of the aperture where the forgeman worked. Bottom and sides of the fireplace of the hearth were covered with cast-iron plates. The iron was worked with ringers or furgons which were a kind of lever used to raise the iron in order to expose new surfaces to the decarburizing blast. When the fire burnt too vehemently, it was stopped with a quass. Tongs were used for taking the lump of purified iron out of the hearth and holding it on the anvil. The great tongs, also termed maudlins, were held together with clams. Hand hammers or sledge hammers were small wooden hammers with which the refined lump (termed a loop) was beaten on a loop plate to knock off the slag covering the surface, before the loop was dragged to the power hammer. Iron dishes were vessels containing water for the cooling of implements, anvil or hammer head. A mandrill was an axe by which the half-finished product (termed a bloom) was cut into two halves which later were elongated into bars by the power hammer. The first application of the power hammer was termed shingling. Chisels of steel were used for cutting off the rough ends of the finished bar.

It will be noted that the Parkend Forge comprised the 'organisation' that Schubert mentions, ie it had 3 fineries, 1 chafery, and 2 hammers. The forge was destroyed in 1644 during the Civil War, but rebuilt and used between 1662–74 by Finch and Clayton, and demolished with the other Crown Ironworks in 1674.

A furnace was built by Wade for the Commonwealth—possibly lower down the stream than the 1612–13 furnace, but only a short distance below, because there is no possibility of a high-line lower down. In the financial accounts of the furnace, output figures are available from 28 February 1654, when the first blowing commenced, to 17 January 1660, which was the end of the last campaign referred to. The references to the two campaigns are too vague to allow safe conclusions. There is no statement indicating in which of the two campaigns the $701\frac{1}{2}$ tons of shot and bullets for the Navy were cast. More exact statements are made in the accounts of the next three campaigns, between 1657 and 1660:

Date	Duration	Total Output, Tons	Output per 24 hours
22 Apr–30 Dec 1657:	36 weeks, 1 day	725	2 tons, 17cwt 35lb
21 Sept, 1658– 6 Aug, 1659:	45 weeks, 4 days	792	2 tons, 9cwt 73¼lb
19 Aug, 1659– 17 Jan, 1660:	21 weeks, 4 days	462	3 tons, 1cwt 19½lb
Averages:	34 weeks, 3 days	659⅔	2 tons, 16cwt 5⅓lb

For the campaign of 1656–7 'broken gun metal and other scrap iron' were bought from Hawkhurst furnace, Penshurst Place.[86]

A report in 1662[87] says that £40 was needed to repair the furnace, including a roof to the 'colehouse'. It was leased to Winter's nominees, Finch and Clayton, 1662–73,[88] and sold for demolition in 1674.[89] Some accounts for 1663–4 are extant.[90] In 1692,[91] there was an intention by Wheeler and Avenant to send ore to Parkend from English Bicknor, but there is no evidence that the Parkend furnace was worked after 1674.

CANNOP   The King's Furnace stood just north of where the Howler's Slade stream joins the Cannop Brook near Cannop Bridge. The wheel might have been powered by either one or both of the streams, but the Cannop was probably the most powerful and sustained, and it had the more ample facilities for the formation of ponds. Nevertheless, the Howler's Slade stream may at the time also have been suitable— before extensive quarrying and coal-mining affected its supply—and here again there were ample facilities for ponds. 'Old Furnace Level' is shown on the Cannop Brook in Sopwith's map of 1835.

The furnace was built for the King in 1612 by Pembroke's lessees. From June 1621 until 1625 inclusive only two campaigns took place, the first continuing for about 20 weeks, with a production of 253 tons, and the second for 19 weeks, producing 247 tons. In 1626 the furnace was repaired, and in 1635 it was surveyed:[92]

Cannop furnace, now blowing, built for the most part and the rest repaired by the now farmers about four years since, 22 foot square at the bottom, in the front whereof are 4 sows of iron and 3 sows in the tewyron wall.

The wheel 22 foot diameter, on the shaft whereof are 7 iron hoops, 6 iron cambs weighing about 4cwt, 2 gudgeons and brasses, all in good repair, and new made about 3 years since.

The furnace house built of timber by the said farmers about 4 years since, in repair.

The bridge house 48 foot long 21 foot broad and 9 foot high in sidewalls, built about 2 years since, the bridge built about 4 years since, covered with boards and bottomed with plank.

A trowe leading the water to the wheel, cut out of whole timber and ledged on the top, 1 foot broad at the bottom, and $1\frac{1}{4}$ foot deep, and 225 foot long, new made about 4 years since and now in repair.

The hutch leading the water from the wheel, 5 foot square, 85 foot long.

The furnace keepers cabin built of timber by the present farmers and covered with boards.

A cottage near the said furnace built by the workmen of that furnace, now enjoyed by the filler there, and not belonging to the said works.

A house wherein the clerk of the said furnace dwells, with a little stable adjoining, built by the present farmers.

A house adjoining to the clerk's house, now inhabited by the founder.

A cabin for the mine cracker.

A mine kiln not in repair wherein are 5 pigs or iron.

Implements of Cannop furnace

The bellows furnished, defective in the leathers		buckstaves	2
water trowes	3	tewyron hook	1
grindstone	1	iron tempe	1
long ringers	10	cinder plate	1
short ringers	1	dam plate	1
constable	1	wheel barrows	1
moulding ship	1	great sledge	1
casting ladles	2	tewyron plate, cast	1
cinder hook	1	tunnel plate	1
placket	1	gage	1
cole baskets	12	A cracked wooden beam and	
mine hammers	2	scales, with triangles furn-	
mine shovels	2	ished, and a ton of iron	
coal rakes	2	pigs used for a weight.	
mine rakes	2	Colliers hurdles 8 dozen	
boshes	2	New firket	1
ladder of 14 rungs	1	$3\frac{1}{2}$cwt of raw iron upon the bellows poizes.	

The repair of the defects of this furnace will cost, according to an estimate thereof, about seven pounds thirteen shillings and four pence.

In 1642 the furnace was leased to William and Thomas Dunning through John Browne, the gunfounder. It was destroyed in 1644 during the Civil War. Late in the century cinders from it were sent to Elmbridge furnace, near Newent.[93] Subsequently part of a nearby site was in use as a chemical works (qv).

LYDBROOK   The watershed around Mirey Stock gives rise to the Lyd Brook which—supplemented by the How (Hough) Brook from the district around Brierley, and downstream by the Little How Brook from Hangerbury—flows northwards down the Lydbrook valley to the Wye. On the Lyd Brook there arose in the 1590s two private forges, and another in about 1610—respectively known as the Upper, Middle and Lower Forges. In 1612 a furnace and a forge, both given the prefix Howbrook, were built for the Crown on Forest land high up the valley where the How Brook joins the Lyd Brook (Plate 1b). It is with the three early Lydbrook forges that we are first concerned.

The Upper Forge, near the confluence of the Lyd Brook and the Little How Brook, was built in the early 1590s by Thomas Bainham, and it later came to Robert Devereaux the Earl of Essex[94] who used it with Richard Challoner.[95] In 1628–9 it was described as standing 'on Hangerbury Common, below the King's Forge'.[96] By 1633–4 Sir John Kyrle was tenant, and it was sold to Benedict Hall,[97] who was fined for it at the Justice Seat in 1634.[98] The forge had disappeared by 1668.

The Middle Forge, further down the valley, probably opposite (the modern) Beard's Bakery, was also owned by the Bainhams, and in 1590 it was tenanted by Richard Challoner and Phillip Harris.[99] In 1619 the Bainhams of Westbury compounded for it, and in the same year George Moore and Richard Tomlins paid rent to them for it.[100] In 1623 it was sold via intermediaries to George Vaughan[101] who in 1634 was fined for it at the Justice Seat.[102] By 1657 Hall had acquired it,[103] and in 1671 he leased it to Paul Foley for seven years.[104] The subsequent history of the forge (by this time termed the Upper Forge —the original Upper Forge higher up the valley having disappeared), is given in Chapter 2.

The Lower Forge stood within two hundred yards of the Wye (the present 'Forge Inn' perpetuates its name). It was built around 1610, in which year the Earl of Clanricard leased to Roger Skinner of Lydbrook, hammerman, a cottage and house newly erected by Skinner near the forges [sic] in Lydbrook.[105] The forge was in 1616

probably included in the lease (or mortgage) by Richard, Earl of Clanricard and Robert, Earl of Essex to James Hawkins of Clifford's Inn,
London, of 'two furnaces and furnace places, ruinous and in decay,
wherein iron had hitherto been made or furnaced, and all tackle, boards,
iron, timber and furniture thereto, with all domputs and watercourses
belonging'.[106]

By 1619 Thomas Smart, a smith of Ruardean, was tenant of the
forge; he was sued for 8 years' arrears of rent.[107] In 1622 he erected
a 'battering work' adjoining Gabb's grist mill in Lydbrook,[108] under
licence granted to him the previous year by the Mineral and Battery
Works who were making wire at Tintern. The battery or plating mill
was a small establishment with one water-wheel, and with hammers
and anvils of broad faces for flattening iron into plates and sheets.
Strakes for the shoeing of cart-wheels, ploughshares, and plates for
pans and for armour were among the goods produced.[109] The works
had a pond fed with water drawn through a channel out of the mill
stream of a disused cornmill. By 1627 Smart was unable to pay his
rent, and made surrender of his lease, which was taken up by his
assistant, Richard Tyler. The licence expired in 1628, but Tyler was
still tenant in 1633 under John Gardiner,[110] who sold that year to
Benedict Hall for £45.[111] Tyler was fined for the forge at the Justice
Seat of 1634.[112] Following the Civil War Hall re-acquired it by 1657,[113]
and in 1671 he leased it to Paul Foley for 7 years.[114] The subsequent
history of the forge is given in Chapter 2.

The King's Howbrook (Lydbrook) Furnace was built in 1612–13 by
assignees of the Earl of Pembroke,[115] high up the Lydbrook valley
where the How Brook joins the Lyd Brook (Plate 1b). Remnants of the
ponds and dams which served the furnace (and the later corn mill)
are to be seen up the valley which leads towards Brierley and thence
skirts it on the east. The furnace ran intermittently from 1613 to at
least 1625. During the period June 1621 to June 1625 four campaigns
took place lasting about 20, 26, 30 and 49 weeks respectively.[116] In the
first three campaigns, an average of 13 tons a week was produced,
ie 1 ton 17cwt 16lb each 24 hours. In the fourth campaign, apparently
in 1625, 720 tons were produced in about 49 weeks—approximately
2 tons 2cwt each 24 hours. The furnace was rebuilt in 1632, and surveyed in 1635:[117]

> Lydbrook furnace built about 3 years since, 23 foot square at the bottom
> and 23 foot deep, much cracked, in the front whereof is 1 sow of iron
> and 2 sows over the tewyron.

The water wheel 23 foot diameter, new made about one year since, on the shaft whereof are 6 iron hoops, 2 gudgeons and 2 brasses: in good repair.

The bellows open, with leathers, nayles, girtes, and irons.

A stone buttress 10 foot square behind the furnace to strengthen it.

The furnace house 92 foot about, the walls thereof of stone 10 foot high, roofed over and tyled.

A piece of wall to support the bridge of the furnace, 22 foot long, 11 foot high, with a half wall adjoining, to keep up the bank, 19 foot long and 6 foot high.

The bridgehouse 21 foot square, 8 foot high in sydewall, the bridge double planked, the roof uncovered, built one year since.

The fence walls thereunto 10 foot high, made of timber and wattle.

The trough leading the water to the wheel 33 foot long close, and 50 foot long underground.

A myne kiln defective, with 6 pieces of cast iron in the draught holes, of about 5c weight, built about 4 years since.

In the furnace watercourse, at the waste, a trowe 22 foot long, 2 foot square, open and borne by 2 pieces of wall, whereof one 16 foot long and two foot and half thick, the other 15 foot long and 7 foot thick.

The hutch leading the back water from the wheel, not made by these farmers, 30 feet long, 8 foot deep.

A founder's house, of timber and wattle, tyled, with a dormer and a stone chimney, floored all over, 32 foot long, 16 foot broad and ten foot in sydewall, built about 20 years since.

Three poor thatched cottages whereof one built by the present farmers.

Implements

Longe ringers	4	synder hook	1
short ringers	4	stopper	1
synder shovels	4	buckstaves	2
sledge	1	dam plate	1
cole rakes	2	wheel-barrow and baskets	
handhammer	1	enough to furnish the work.	
placket	1	colliers hurdles in the woods.	
gage	1	a set of iron cambes.	
a wooden beam with iron chains, triangles and 10c weight of raw iron.		a new pair of bellow boards, ready sawed.	

The repair of the furnace to make it fit to work, as it is estimated, will cost about fifty pounds.

9 *(right)* Whitecliff coke iron blast furnace; *(below)* Bromley Hill (Oakwood) coke iron blast furnace: general view of remains from the south east

10 (above) Darkhill Ironworks (Mushets'); (left) the barn (now demolished) in Coleford where David Mushet carried out some of his experiments

In 1636 the furnace was leased to Throckmorton, Crowe, Taylor and Gonning. It was one of the furnaces which in 1642 Sir John Winter was told to hand over to John Browne, gunfounder,[118] who that year sub-let it to William and Thomas Dunning. In 1644 during the Civil War it was seized by Captain John Braine and leased by him to Thomas Pury and Grifantius Phillips, who during the period 1644–50 made there raw iron to the amount of 14, 20 or 24 tons each week.[119]

In March 1650 the furnace was at least partly broken down by the Preservators of the Forest.[120] It was rebuilt in 1662 by Winter's nominees, Clayton and Finch,[121] and some accounts for it in 1663–4 are extant.[122] In 1674 the furnace was sold by the Crown to Paul Foley for demolition. A corn mill stood on or near the site in the late nineteenth century and early twentieth century (Plate 47).

The King's Howbrook (Lydbrook) Forge was built in 1612–13 by assignees of the Earl of Pembroke, below the King's Howbrook Furnace. In 1628 it was described as lying above the nearest forge in Lydbrook[123] (ie the Upper Forge some few hundred yards down stream). Unlike the furnace, which was powered only by the How Brook, the forge had the combined waters of that brook and of the Lyd Brook. It probably stood about opposite the (modern) Yew Tree Inn. The forge was surveyed in 1635:[124]

Lydbrook forge consisting of:
One hammer and anvil, one chaferie, and two fineries and 3 pairs of bellows furnished and working.
The house 42 foot long, 32 foot broad, covered with boards, built about 4 years since, in repair.
The great hammer beam with the wheel, with 13 iron hoops, 2 great gudgeons and brasses of about 3c of cast iron and 2 iron hoops about the anvil block.
On the 2 fynery beams, 9 hoops, 4 gudgeons and 4 brasses cast iron. On the chaferye beam, 4 hoops, 2 gudgeons and 2 brasses of cast iron.
In the chimneys, 3 chimney bars of cast iron and 3 morris bars.
One hurst, 2 boyts of cast iron, 1 bray, 1 set of hurst wedges and 2 wedges in the hammer eye of wrought iron.
One storehouse floored and tyled, built of stone 18 foot long, 13 foot wide, and 10 foot high in syde walls, with a pair of stayres to the chamber.
One colehouse 30 foot long, 24 foot wide, 11 foot high in sydewalls, covered and syded with boards, with a shut house for brayes on the side thereof 8 foot broad, leaning and defective.
A court paled about with 76 foot of paleing.

An old house on one side thereof.

The dam or bay with the waste and hammer gate and ground goyte defective.

A watercourse for the waste water 180 foot long, 4 foot square, built about 6 years since with two ranges of timber with sleepers and spreaders, and planked at the bottom, defective.

A pair of new waste gates with stems, ready framed for the fore-front and not set up.

One hammerman's house built about one year since of timber with a stone chimney, 20 foot long, 16 foot broad and 8 foot high in syde-wall.

Implements

Chaferie:

plates	5	pair of great tongs	1
tewyron	1	pair of shingling tongs	4
ringer	1	cold chisels	2
furgon	1	handhammer	1
quasse	1	sledge	1
iron dish	1		

2 fineries:

plates	10	pair of great tongs	2
ringers	2	pair of small tongs	2
furgons	2	handhammers	2
tewyrons	2	cole rake	1
quasses	2	wheel-barrow	1
iron dishes	2	shovel	1
clams	2	baskets enough for the work.	
an iron beam with scales and chains, and c weight of cast iron		a new hammer beam ready squared near at hand.	

The 2 finery wheels, the chafery wheel, the hammer beam, one of the finery beams, the waste hutch, the juttie of the bay, the trowes and penstocks, the cole house and one workman's house are in decay, and the repair thereof will cost, according to an estimate made thereof, about forty pounds.

In 1636 the forge was leased to Throckmorton, Crowe, Taylor and Gonning. It was among the iron works which in 1642 Winter was told to hand over to John Browne, gunfounder,[125] who that year sub-let it to William and Thomas Dunning. In 1644 during the Civil War it was seized by Capt John Braine and leased by him to Thomas Pury and

Grifantius Phillips.[126] In March 1650 the forge was demolished by the Preservators of the Forest,[127] and there is no evidence that it was rebuilt.

WHITECROFT   A double forge was built here on private land (ie outside the Park) alongside the Newerne stream in 1628–9 by Brooke and Mynne. It was surveyed in 1635: [128]

Whitecroft Forge: 70 feet long and 28 foot broad, consists of two hammers, one chaferie and 3 fineries, built from the ground about 6 years since, and the lower part thereof being burnt, rebuilt about three years since, in repair and working.

The bay thereof 460 foot long, 26 foot broad between the stone walls which are $5\frac{1}{2}$ foot in thickness at the tops and about $13\frac{1}{2}$ foot high about the middle and generally $8\frac{1}{2}$ foot high above the ground.

In the bay 2 sluices or hammer gates, built with stone with 2 pair of timber sluices to the same.

And one great floodgate of 6 gates 37 foot long 25 foot broad strongly built of timber, aproned with plank and double planked on the sides, with a horse bridge made over it.

One watercourse of timber 143 foot long 10 foot broad and 5 foot deep, venting the water from the forge, planked on each side with sleepers at the bottom and spreaders at the top.

One storehouse 30 foot long $16\frac{1}{2}$ foot broad 9 foot high in sidewalls, covered with boards.

One great coalhouse 58 foot long 28 foot broad 17 foot high in sidewalls whereof 5 foot from the ground built of stone, all the rest of timber, covered with tile, with 3 great doors and 2 pair of stayres on the outside thereof.

One other storehouse 15 foot square uncovered.

One house 2 stories high 34 foot long, 17 foot broad the pine ends thereof stone, the rest timber, tyled over.

One house for the clerk, built of timber 2 stories high 24 foot long and 15 foot broad, with 3 dormers, with a garden and a court paled about.

One finers house adjoining.

Three other finers houses thatched.

The implements and furniture of this forge, according to the forge at Park End.

The bay, the wheels, plummer block, hutches and some other parts thereof are defective, the repair whereof (according to an estimate thereof) will cost about thirty pounds.

Whitecroft forge was destroyed in 1644 during the Civil War. A new forge on the same stream, probably on or near the same site, was built in 1654 for the Commonwealth by Major Wade, under whom it was very active until 1660, and likewise active during 1661 for the King. According to Nicholls[129] there was an inventory dated 13 August 1656 of its tools and utensils, divided into 'all the chaffery, for the upper finery, and for the lower finery'. In 1662 the forge, not in use but in good repair,[130] was let to Winter's nominees, Finch and Clayton, and some accounts are extant for 1663–4[131] The forge was demolished in 1674, and part of the site was later used for a corn mill (qv).

SOUDLEY   The King's Furnace built high up the Soudley Valley on the Cinderford Brook 1612–13 by Pembroke's nominees, stood near the site of the present sewage works (Plate 2). Much slag remains, and an imbedded wall of a building has over part of it a dead beech of some 250 years. The furnace was extant in 1634[132] and was surveyed in 1635:[133]

Soudley furnace: The body thereof 28 foot square at the bottom and 24 foot square at the top, in the front whereof are 4 sows of iron, and 2 sows over the tewyron, and four long bars of wrought iron to keep in the corner posts, in good repair, saving one small defect in the inside of the furnace.

The water wheel 22 foot diameter, upon the shaft whereof are 7 hoops of iron, 6 cambs, 2 gudgeons, and brasses, in repair.

The furnace house and penthouses made of stone 8 foot high and 186 foot in circuit, tiled for the most part, the rest boarded.

The bridge and bridge house decayed and part of the bridge house fallen down.

A coleplace 61 foot long, 40 foot broad, whereof one side and the 2 ends are walled about with a wall 7 foot high and 4 foot thick.

A mine kiln wherein are 10 pieces of raw iron, in repair.

Five little cottages on the north side of the stream there.

The founders house built of stone 2 stories high, 20 foot long and 14 foot broad, with a penthouse adjoining covered with boards.

The trowes leading the water to the wheel 2365 foot long much decayed.

A dam about a mile above the furnace, at Cinderford, 300 foot long, 12 foot broad on the top, and 25 foot high, faced and backed with turf, with a ground goyte and a high trowe thorowe the bay, with a floodgate of three gates 36 foot long, 12 foot broad and 6 foot deep, with a little horsebridge over it, ranged with timber and aproned with plank.

Another dam about half a mile higher on the same stream 720 foot long with a sluice and a ground trowe, somewhat defective in the face thereof.

Implements of Soudley furnace

The bellows open the leathers half worn		sledge	1
		furnace shovels	8
long ringers	3	cinder plate	1
constable	1	dam plate	1
short ringers	9	tunnel plate	1
dam hook	1	tewyron plate	1
placket	1	beam scales and triangles and 1000 pounds of raw iron for a weight.	
cinder hook	1		
gage	1		

The repair of the said furnace, according to an estimate thereof made, will cost about one hundred and thirty pounds.

The incline of the Soudley furnace was the largest of the King's furnaces—indicated by the stack being 24ft square at the top and 28ft square at the bottom.

In August and September 1643 Soudley furnace supplied the following round shot to the Royalists at Oxford: [134]

Shot	Calibre of Cannon (inches)	Wt of Cannon (lb)	Wt of Shot (lb)
106 for demi-cannon	6	6,000	27–30
109 for culverin	5	4,000	15–60
202 for 12 li	?	?	12
110 for 6 li	?	?	6
527			

The furnace was probably run by a man named Skinner during 1642–4, using cordwood assigned to him by John Browne. It was taken over by Braine and Kyrle, or by Pury and Phillips, in 1644–5, and probably destroyed by the Commonwealth in 1650. Its remnants were sold for demolition in 1674. The site is now largely taken up by the Cinderford Sewage Works. The fact that the immense quantity of cinders was never crushed for bottle glass suggests that they were covered over and forgotten before this practice began. The variety of colour of the slag, and the strong flow-lines, revealing the fluid movement of centuries before, are remarkable.

The King's Forge built in 1612–13 was lower down the same brook, probably where Camp Mill (a later designation) is now situated. By 1634[135] there stood a single forge; it was surveyed in 1635: [136]

Soudley Forge.   42 foot long and 30 foot broad, consisting of one
hammer and anvil, one chafery and two fyneryes new built in the place
of a decayed forge there, about two years since. The parts and implements whereof are according to the forge at Lydbrook.

One store house adjoining to the forge 16 foot square with a room
over it built of tymber and covered with boards.

One cole house 36 foot long, 27 foot broad, 9 foot high in the side
walls, with a dormer, and covered with boards.

In the dam a new fludgate in the place of one that the fluds carryed
away, of 6 gates, 94 foot long and 10 foot broad, aproned with plank
and cheeked with stone.

The wheels, groundsills, trowes, penstocks, and some other parts
thereof defective, and the repair thereof (according to an estimate made
thereof) will cost about threescore pounds.

It was destroyed in 1644 during the Civil War, and its remains sold
for demolition in 1674.

BRADLEY   A double forge was built in 1628–9 by Sir Basil Brooke and
Mr Mynne on the lower Soudley Brook. It is stated in 1635[137] not to be
fixed to the freehold—implying it was built east of the brook (land on
the west being Crown land). It was surveyed in 1635: [138]

Bradley Forge.   70 foot long and 31 foot broad consisting of two
hammers, three fineries and one chaferie, built from the ground about
6 years since, and now working. And for the parts thereof and the
implements used therewith, is agreeable to the forge at the Park End.

The dam is 183 foot long, 20 foot broad between the stonewalls,
which are 3 foot thick on the top and 18 foot high about the middle
of the dam.

In the dam a floodgate of 4 gates, 20 foot long, 18 foot broad aproned
and covered with plank for a bridge, with a carriage for the water 76
foot long 18 foot broad walled on each side and piched with stone in
the bottom with a fall at the end thereof made of timber 36 foot long
and 18 foot broad.

The rest of the sluices and hutches, as in the forge at the Park End.

One colehouse of 6 bay, of stone building and tiled, 60 foot long 28
foot broad and 16 foot high in sidewalls, without doors, but has a court
35 foot long 26 foot broad walled about with a wall 7 foot high with
doors.

The clerks house built of stone, 3 stories high and tiled, is 56 foot
long, 20 foot broad with a cross building 19 foot square.

Four workmen's cottages thatched.

There are 2 new hammer beams ready made, lying under the wall
of the colehouse court.

The wheels, shafts, shingling hammer beam, tiling of the colehouse, hutches and plummer blocks, scales and bellows defective, the repair whereof will cost, according to an estimate thereof, about one hundred pounds.

The forge was probably worked in 1642 by John Typper of Flaxley. Though partially destroyed in 1644 during the Civil War, and repaired the following year and worked by Kyrle and Braine, it was probably derelict by 1646. The site was not used again till the mid-eighteenth century at least—by the early 1800's it had become the site of Samuel Hewlett's first forge as distinct from his later foundries.

FLAXLEY   In 1634 there were two single forges on the Flaxley Brook, run by John Typper.[139] They were probably owned by Sir John Winter, who had the woods previously belonging to Flaxley Abbey. Paul Foley owned both forges in 1674. By the same year he owned a furnace which had been built downstream[140] about 300 yards below the abbey; its history is discussed in Chapter 2.

GUNS MILL   A furnace had been erected here by 1628–9 on the Westbury Brook which lower down forms the Flaxley Brook. It was owned by Sir John Winter, who still held it in 1634.[141] In 1644, during the Civil War, it was run by Capt John Braine. It was probably destroyed by order of The Commonwealth in 1650, and was certainly in ruin by 1680[142] and not rebuilt until 1683—see Chapter 2.

LONGHOPE   An indication that a furnace powered by Hope Brook stood here by 1656 is that much iron ore was carried from the Forest to Longhope in that year.[143] By 1661 it was owned by Thomas Nourse who 15 February leased 'Hope furnace' to Thomas Foley from 24 June next for 21 years at £100 a year.[144] However, on 24 February of that year Foley agreed that Nourse should have the benefit of the 'present blast' until the middle of May 'but if he stop a fortnight in the meantime he may blow until the end of May'.[145] On 20 July 1662 Foley agreed that Nourse should have the use of the furnace for a year until Midsummer 1663.[146] Paul Foley's accounts for the furnace are extant for the period October 1671 to February 1672.[147] His brother Philip took a one-third share in it in 1674. The furnace was still standing in 1680.[148] The site has not been found, though slag has been discovered in a garden at Church Farm (SO 683197).

'BROCKWEIR' (COED ITHEL)   A document of 1634[149] states that in that year Sir Richard Catchmay owned a furnace at *Brickweare* (obviously meaning either Bigsweir or Brockweir). Extensive search has failed to discover any remains of a furnace at either Bigsweir or Brockweir—

and it appears that the furnace concerned was that later known as 'Coed Ithel' which (as its remnants show) stood halfway between the two weirs but on the opposite bank of the Wye, nearby Catchmay's Court.

Catchmay had a furnace in the 1620s. He was said to own—not to have recently built—a furnace in 1628.[150] In 1634 he was fined for setting up a furnace in the Forest, allegedly four years previously.[151] But the furnace did not stand on the Forest side of the Wye, so the fine may have related to having taken wood for charcoal from the Forest. The furnace was still operating in 1649.[152]

The interesting remnants of the Coed Ithel furnace have been excavated and reported upon.[153] A vertical section of the square shaft and the upper part of the circular bosh are visible today.

RODMORE   A furnace was erected here in 1629 on the upper Cone on land belonging to Mrs Eleanor James, by her father John Powell of Preston in Herefordshire. By 1634[154] it was being run by Sir John Winter from whom it was seized in 1645 by Robert Kyrle, governor of Monmouth, and run by him in partnership with Capt John Braine.[155] In 1647–50 the furnace was run jointly by Braine and John Gonning of Bristol, who had a quarter-share in it.[156] In 1649 it made about 15 tons a week, ie approximately 2 tons 3cwt each 24 hours. As late as 1661, Braine held 'three ironworks adjoining Woolaston Wood'— doubtless this furnace and two forges on the same stream. The Rodmore furnace was probably out of use by 1680; later it became a forge (qv), and afterwards a corn-mill (qv).

ROWLEY   In 1646 a forge was erected by Capt John Braine in partnership with Robert Kyrle 'at Atkin's Mill' or 'Burnt Mill', near Rodmore.[157] This could be Rowley Mill on the Cone, one time referred to as 'Rowlands Mill'.[158] Its subsequent history is given in Chapter 2.

LYDNEY   In c1604[159] Sir Edward Winter built a furnace a little to the north of his White Cross House, and a forge (called Pill, later Lower Forge), south-south-east of the furnace. By 1607 he also had a forge (The 'Upper'—'The Middle' of later years) on the Newerne Stream.[160] They were successively run by him and his son Sir John, who mortgaged the furnace in 1623.[161] In October 1628 Winter paid £38 for hammers and anvils to the Earl of Cork.[162] By 1634[163] the Lower Forge was a double one, and a single forge (called New, later Middle, Forge) had been erected up the Newerne Stream. Sir John in 1635 agreed to repay a £4,500 debt to Benedict Hall by supplying, over about three years, 'raw iron cast into pigs' at £6 a ton.[164] By 1640 the Upper Forge was a slitting mill.[165] In 1644, during the Civil War, all four works were partially destroyed and seized by Massey, who repaired them and leased them to Gifford. In the three years 1644-6, the forges produced 300 tons of 'raw iron out of pig iron'.[166] In 1653 the furnace and at least one of the forges were repaired by John Wade for The Commonwealth and run by him until they were restored to Winter in 1660, whose family held them for over 50 years. The four works were mortgaged by William, son of Sir John, in 1673[167] when the slitting mill was described as 'now a forge', ie the Upper Forge. The slitting mill had been used for cutting or slitting up strips and flat bars into hoopiron and rods for nail-making and other purposes. The decay of the hand-made nail trade on the one hand, and the development of the rolling mill on the other, led to the suppression of slitting mills.

BISHOPSWOOD   There were two furnaces operating in the Bishops-wood district by 1602; possibly one of them was on the Gloucestershire side of the Lodge Grove Brook, and the other on the Dry Brook within Herefordshire. One may have been built as early as 1588: it was certainly operating between 1590 and 1594. From the 1590s to about 1614, the works remained in the tenancy of J. Challoner and partners, under the Essex family. In 1617 two ruined furnaces were let to James Hawkins, with permission to build one furnace.[168] In 1633 the furnace was sold to Benedict Hall, with Sir John Kyrle as tenant.[169] Six years later the furnace was used by John Hannis as master, who employed George Williams as founder and infringed John Browne's patent for the direct casting of iron wares.[170] Benedict Hall either lost the furnace during the Civil War or sold it some time between 1634 and 1650, when the tenants were Thomas Pury and Grifantius Phillips. It was supposedly demolished by the Preservators of Dean on 30 January 1650. The furnace, or a successor, was operated there from 1674 by Paul Foley: accounts are extant as at 27 March 1675, with a statement of stock and debts.[171] Thereafter the works were within the Foley Partnership, discussed in Chapter 2.

REDBROOK   Two furnaces stood in Upper Redbrook in the seventeenth century, alongside the stream running westwards from Newland. Early documents refer to them as 'in the parish of Newland'—this excludes Lower Redbrook for which no evidence of a furnace has been found.

The furnace highest up the Redbrook-Newland valley (just above where a stream from Staunton to the north joins the stream from Newland) was built by William Hall c1604, and it is depicted by a symbol on a map of 1608.[172] It was later owned by Benedict Hall, certainly until 1634.[173] Working probably ceased around that time. The slag heap associated with it has been found a short distance WNW of the, modern, Swanpool. It contains both bloomery slag and charcoal-iron slag.

The second furnace stood some 400 yards further down the valley (its site now forms part of the little hamlet known as 'The Foundry'). It was built by Hall about the same time as the contemporary furnace, but it is not shown on the map noted above. Benedict Hall held it in 1634[174] and continued to do so until 1644 when it was seized during the Civil War and run from January 1645 by Robert Kyrle, governor of Monmouth, in partnership with Capt John Braine.[175] It was restored to Hall by The Commonwealth in 1649.

Accounts for the furnace are extant for the period 1 January 1659 to 27 April 1660, when it was managed for Hall by William Probin.[176] They show the amounts paid to wood cutters, corders, charcoal-burners and carriers, indicating the quantities and the piecework rates. For producing 3ft wood, 1s 5d a cord was paid, and for 2ft wood 1s 7d, 1s 11d or 2s 1d a cord. The wood came from such places as Usk, Bicknor, Hadnock, The Scowles and St Briavels. This shows the wide spread of suppliers, and indicates that even with the modest blast furnaces, and at this early date, finding of fuel was not purely an immediate local affair, and must have placed an unwelcome burden of transport and 'organisation' on the founder or his clerk. The ore came from Clearwell at 5s 6d a dozen, and washed cinders came from Monmouth.

Payments were made for hurdles for carrying charcoal and £18 2s was the cost of excise tickets to permit 18 tons of bar iron to be sent to Gloucester and 26 tons to Bristol. Of the furnace itself, the following items are typical:

Wages: usually 1s a day.
Keeping up the fire, 5 days: 5s.
Cleansing the kiln and ridding the bridge: £1 5s.
Breaking up and removing the hearth, and un-nailing the bellowes: £1 2s.
Supplying furnace stones and boshes: 10s.
2 bull hides to dress the bellowes: £4.
Mending the bellowes: no separate sum given.
56lb of tallow at 4½d lb.
60lb of 'chogg's licker' at 4d lb.

On 2 September 1671 Henry Hall leased the furnace (with two Lydbrook forges) to Paul Foley for seven years.[177] Around 1672 it supplied pig iron to Tintern Upper Forge for refining into *osmond* iron for wireworks; for the same purpose it sent pig iron by sea via Newport to Richard Hart's Machen Forges in Glamorgan.[178] The furnace was still in being in 1675,[179] 1676,[180] 1680[181] and 1693.[182] Its subsequent history is recorded in Chapter 2.

The foregoing surveys in 1635 of the King's Ironworks include many terms which were later explained in the eighteenth century by George Wyrral a local worthy: [183]

Sows of Iron are the long pieces of cast iron as they run into the sand immediately from the furnace; thus called from the appearance of this and the shorter pieces which are runned into smaller gutters made in the same sand, from the resemblance they have to a sow lying on her side with her pigs at her dugs. These are for working up in the forges; but it is usual to cast other sows of iron of very great size to lay in the walls of the furnaces as beams to support the great strain of the work.

Dam Plate is a large flat plate of cast iron placed on its edge against the front of the furnace, with a stone cut sloping and placed on the inside. This plate has a notch on the top for the cinder or scruff to run off, and a place at the side to discharge the metal at casting.

The Shaft of a wheel is a large round beam having the wheel fixed near the one end of it, and turning upon gudgeons or centres fixed in the two ends.

The Furnace House I take to be what we call the casting-house, where the metal runs out of the furnace into the sand.

The Bridge is the place where the raw materials are laid down ready to be thrown into the furnace. I conceive that it had its name (which is still continued) from this circumstance—that in the infancy of these works it was built as a bridge, hollow underneath. It was not at first known what strength was required to support the blast of a furnace bellows; and the consequence was that they were often out of repair, and frequently obliged to be built almost entirely new.

Bellows Board: Not very different from the present dimensions.

Water Troughs: Scooped out of the solid timber. This shows the great simplicity of these times, not 150 years ago.

The Hutch, or as it is now corruptly called the Witch, a wide covered drain below the furnace-wheel to carry off the water from it usually arched, but here only covered with timbers to support the rubbish and earth thrown upon it.

Cambs are iron cogs fixed in the shaft to work the bellows as the wheel turns round.

Cinder Shovels, iron shovels for taking up the cinders into the boxes, both to measure them and to fill the furnace.

Moulding Ship, an iron tool fixed on a wooden handle, so formed as to make the gutters in the sand for casting the pig and sow iron.

Casting Ladles, made hollow like a dish, with a lip to lade up the liquid iron for small castings.

Wringers, large long bars of iron to wring the furnace, that is to clear it of the grosser and least fluid cinder which rises on the upper surface, and would there coagulate and soon prevent the furnace from working aright.

Constable, a bar of very great substance and length, kept always lying by a furnace in readiness for extraordinary purposes in which uncommon strength and purchase was required. I suppose this name to have been given to this tool on account of its superior bulk and power, and in allusion to the Constable of St Briavels Castle, an officer heretofore of very great weight and consequence in this Forest.

Cinder Hook, a hook of iron for drawing away the scruff or cinder which runs liquid out of the furnace over the dam plate, and soon becomes a solid substance, which must be removed to make room for fresh cinder to run out into its place.

Plackett, a tool contrived as a kind of trowel for smoothing and shaping the clay.

Buckstones, now called Buckstaves, are two thick plates of iron, about 5 or 6 feet long, fixed one on each side of the front of the furnace down to the ground to support the stone work.

Iron Tempe is a plate fixed at the bottom of the front wall of the furnace over the flame between the buckstaves.

Tuiron Plate is a plate of cast iron fixed before the noses of the bellows, and so shaped as to conduct the blast into the body of the furnace.

Tuiron Hooke, a tool contrived for conveying a lump of tempered clay before the point of the tuiron plate, to guard the wall from wearing away as it would otherwise do in that part, there being the greatest force of the fire.

Shammel Plate, a piece of cast iron fixed on a wooden frame, in the shape of a ⨽, which works up and down as a crank, so as for the camb to lay hold of this iron, and thereby press down the bellows.

Firketts are large square pieces of timber laid upon the upper woods of the bellows, to steady it and work it.

Firkett Hooks, two strong hooks of square wrought iron fixed at the smallest end of the bellows to keep it firm and in its place.

Gage, two rods of iron jointed in the middle, with a ring for the filler to drop the shortest end into the furnace at the top, to know when it is worked down low enough to be charged.

Poises, wooden beams, one over each bellows, fixed upon centres across another very large beam; at the longest end of these poises are open boxes bound with iron, and the little end being fixed with harness to the upper ends of the firketts are thus pressed down, and the bellows with it, by the working of the wheel, while the weight of the poises lifts them up alternatively as the wheel goes round.

The surveys of 1635 provide much information on forges. Schubert[184] pointed out that after 1600 the forges comprised 3 fineries, 1 chafery, and 2 power hammers. This was so, in 1635, at Parkend, Whitecroft and Bradley. However, Soudley and Lydbrook comprised 2 fineries, 1 chafery and 1 hammer.

The surveys of 1635 also provide much information on furnace construction and profile. Schubert wrote: [185]

Both the vertical basement and the height of the stack, which varied from 22 to 24ft, indicate that a development of the English furnace had taken place within the period of about 120 years, following the introduction from France shortly after 1490. Emanuel Swedenborg, who as a young man was in England from 1710 to 1712 and visited furnaces in the district of Stourbridge, remarked on the outer casing or shell being different from those of other countries, as the outer walls were parallel, ie vertical, from the bottom up to one-third of the total height and then converging. If he had been in the Forest of Dean, he would have noticed the same peculiar shape.

Unfortunately, there is no evidence of the dimensions of the English furnace before the inventory of 1635. However, some conclusions may be drawn from the countries, such as France and Belgium, in which this type of furnace originated. As late as 1775, the height of the French blast-furnace generally was 17–20ft and in Belgium it did not exceed 17ft before 1800. From this it may safely be concluded that the earliest English blast-furnaces were about 17ft high or less. The height of 22–24ft referred to in 1635 therefore represents a remarkable improvement.

The shell of the furnace was supported by a stone buttress which, at Lydbrook, was 10ft square. A further support was supplied by a framework of strong wooden beams embracing the outer walls at certain intervals,. They are the 'bindeinge beames' of the furnace at Parkend. They were intended to prevent cracks in the walls caused by a combination of moisture from rain or snow and the heat penetrating from within.

The British blast furnace up to about 1611 was stone-built, with a square or pyramid shaft, and stone-lined. Although in the building of Dean's furnaces in 1612–13 advantage would have been taken of known improvements, their design may have been substantially as hitherto. However, the rapid wearing away of the stone-lining between the crucible (or hearth) and the bosh, would have led to the amending of the form of the hearth and bosh.[186] The next amendment was to use a circular crucible, as evidenced c1651 at Coed Ithel in Monmouthshire,[187] but it is not known when Dean's furnaces followed in shape. (The rounded shape returned to square in later years, in particular in coke blast furnaces; later they took the round form again.)

Wheel and wheelshafts in Dean in 1635 were:

	Lydbrook	Cannop	Parkend	Soudley
Diameter of wheel	23ft	22ft	22ft	22ft
Number of cams		6*	6	6
Iron hoops	6	7	7	7
Gudgeons	2	2	2	2
Brasses	2	2	2	2

*6 iron cams weighing about 4cwt.

The bellows were depressed alternately by three cams set on each of two rings on the water-wheel shaft, which was some 15–20ft from the tuyere arch. The enormous leather bellows in the Forest furnaces in 1635 were 18ft long and 4ft wide. The cost of their maintenance was high.

By as early as 1631, roasting kilns (termed myne kilns) were used in the furnaces at Lydbrook, Cannop, Parkend and Soudley, viz:[188]

Lydbrook: 'A myne kilne defective, with 6 pieces of cast iron in the draught holes, of about 5 c. weight, built about 4 years since (ie 1631).'

Cannop: 'A myne kilne not in repair wherein are 5 pigs of iron'; and 'A cabin for the myne cracker.'

Parkend: 'The myne decayed in the inside, and the pigs of iron taken from the draughts thereof.'

Soudley: 'A myne kilne wherein are 10 pieces of rawe iron, in repair.'

The roasting kilns resembled ordinary lime kilns, walled in all round, leaving only a small door at the bottom for kindling the fire and withdrawing the calcined ore. The walls were strengthened with pigs of iron built into them (see above). The fuel was wood and/or small charcoal (called 'braise' or 'braize'). The objective of the roasting was to remove carbon dioxide and thereby to make the iron more reducible, and, second, to make it more friable and therefore more easily broken up to a consistent size. By roasting, the ore suffered a loss of weight. The operation was continued at least to 1677–8, when Henry Powle wrote of Dean:[189]

> After they have provided their ore, their first work is to calcine it, which is done in kilns, much after the fashion of our ordinary lime-kilns. These they fill up to the top with coal and ore, *stratum super stratum*, until it be full; and so putting fire to the bottom, they let it burn till the coal be wasted, and then renew the kilns with fresh ore and coal, in the same manner as before. This is done without fusion of the metal, and serves to consume the more drossy parts of the ore, and to make it friable—supplying the beating and washing which are used to other metals.

By that time, pit-coal, not charcoal, was used in the roasting. Some old roasting kilns are extant at Ruardean (Plate 3a).

Even after roasting, the ore did not lose its bulk, and because the ideal for the furnace were pieces of the size of a walnut, breaking by hand-hammer was resorted to, and later crushing by stampers moved by a water-wheel.[190] The stampers may also have crushed bloomery slag (cinders). After crushing, the smallest particles were separated from the rest by coarse sieves. Crushing by stampers was done in the late seventeenth century and subsequent centuries at Aylburton,[191] Parkend, Redbrook (two), Tintern and Bishopswood. In later times, some of these stampers were used for stamping not of ore but of blast furnace slag ('scruff') for the Glass Industry—described in Chapter 4.

Of smelting in Dean, Powle wrote in 1677–8:[192]

> From the kilns they carry the ore to their furnaces, which are built of brick or stone, about 24ft square on the outside, and near 30ft in height; within, not above 8 or 10ft over, where it is widest, which is about the middle; the top and bottom having a narrower compass, much like the shape of an egg, as in my Figure (A the tunnel, C the furnace, B the mouth of the furnace): [fig 4, p. 52].
>
> Behind the furnace are placed two huge pair of bellows whose noses meet at a little hole near the bottom. These are compressed together by certain buttons, placed on the axis of a very large wheel, which is turned about by water, in the manner of an overshot-mill. As soon as these buttons are slid off, the bellows are raised again by the counter-poise of weights; whereby they are made to play alternately, the one giving its blast all the time the other is rising.

At first they fill these furnaces with ore and cinder intermixed with fuel, which in these works is always charcoal; laying them hollow at the bottom, that they may more easily take fire: but after they are once kindled, the materials run together into a hard cake or lump, which is sustained by the fashion of the furnace, and through this the metal, as it melts, trickles down into the receivers, which are placed

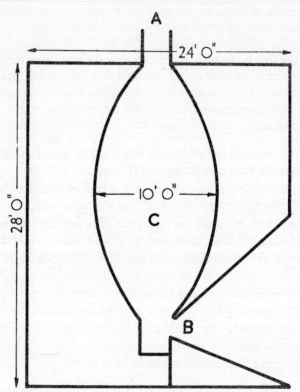

Fig 4. Section through a blast furnace in Dean (after Henry Powle, *Philosophical Transactions of the Royal Society*, 1677–8, 12/137, 31–5).

at the bottom, where there is a passage open, by which they take away the scum and dross, and let out the metals as they see occasion.

Before the mouth of the furnace lies a great bed of sand, wherein they make furrows of the fashion into which they desire to cast their iron. Into these, when their receivers are full, they let in their metal; which is made so very fluid by the violence of the fire, that it not only runs to a considerable distance, but stands afterwards boiling for a good while.

After these furnaces are once at work, they keep them constantly

11 (above) Lower Soudley coke iron blast furnaces (Great Western Iron Works) c1830; *(below)* today's remains

12 *(above)* Cinderford Ironworks, a coke iron blast furnace c1875; *(below)* 'Whitechapel Row' (demolished c1960) at Cinderford, which was originally the stables of Cinderford Ironworks

employed for many months together, never suffering the fire to slacken night or day; but still supplying the waste of the fuel and other materials with fresh, poured in at the top.

Several attempts have been made to bring in the use of sea-coal in these works, instead of charcoal; the former being to be had at an easy rate, the latter not without great expense: but hitherto they have proved ineffectual—the workmen finding by experience that the sea-coal fire, how vehement soever, will not penetrate the most fixed parts of the ore, and so leaveth much of the metal unmelted.

It is noteworthy that Powle does not mention that the cinders were included not only to be re-smelted for their residue of iron but also to act as a form of flux. Nor does he mention any addition of limestone as a flux. Much limestone may have been used in Dean, although its ores have a high lime and low silica content, and tend to be self-fluxing. Dean sent large quantities of cinders in the 1730s to North Lancashire, where its good fluxing characteristics were realised. Powle in 1677–8 went on to give a description of the process conducted in the forge: [193]

From these furnaces, they bring their sows and pigs of iron (as they call them) to their forges. These are of two sorts, though standing together under the same roof: one they call their finery, the other the chafery. Both of them are open hearths, on which they place great heaps of sea-coal, and behind them, bellows like to those of the furnaces, but nothing near so large. Into the finery, they first put their pigs or iron, placing three or four of them together behind the fire, with a little of one end thrust into it. Where softening, by degrees they stir and work them with long bars of iron, till the metal runs together into a round mass or lump, which they call a half-bloom. This they take out, and giving it a few strokes with their sledges, they carry it to a great weighty hammer, raised likewise by the motion of a water-wheel: where applying it dexterously to the blows, they presently beat it out into a thick short square. This they put into the finery again, and heating it red hot, they work it out under the same hammer, till it comes into the shape of a bar in the middle, with two square knobs in the ends. Last of all, they give it other heatings in the chafery, and more workings under the hammer, till they have brought their iron into bars of several shapes and sizes; in which fashion they expose them to sale.

All their principal iron undergoes all the aforementioned preparations: yet for several purposes, as for the backs of chimneys, hearths of ovens, and the like, they have a sort of cast-iron; which they take out of the receivers of the furnace, so soon as it is melted, in great

F

ladles, and pour it into moulds of fine sand: in like manner as they cast brass and other softer metals: but this sort of iron is so very brittle, that being heated, with one blow of a hammer it breaks all to pieces. Though this fault be most found in this sort of iron, yet if in the working of their best sort they omit any one process, it will be sure to want some part of its toughness, which they esteem its perfection.

At the time, mineral coal, not charcoal, was used in the forges, but not in the finery and furnaces.

It is not known at what date in Dean, or at what furnace, the change took place from the quadrangular to the circular shape of the tunnel and boshes. Powle shows that the change occurred by 1677–8, yet when the furnace at Guns Mill was rebuilt in 1683, it was still of the more typical square-sectioned shaft with the widest part about 7ft from the bottom.

By the close of Dean's first charcoal blast furnace era its iron possessed a good reputation, and had become a source of supply much drawn upon by the Midland trades. Andrew Yarranton,[194] a Worcestershire man with personal acquaintance with the iron trades, visited the Forest about 1677 and noticed 'what infinite quantities of raw iron is there made, with bar iron and wire'; and 'the infinite number of men, horses, and carriages which are to supply these works, and also digging of ironstone, providing of cinders, carrying to the works, making it into sows and bars, cutting of wood and converting into charcoal'. He drew attention to 'a most great benefit to the Kingdom in general by the sow iron made of the ironstone and Roman cinders, for that metal is of a most gentle, pliable, soft nature, easily and quickly to be wrought into manufacture, over what any other iron is, and it is the best in the known world.' Most of the sow iron was sent up the Severn to the Midlands, where it was made into bar iron, and further manufactured. Yarranton asserted that Dean was 'as to iron, to be compared to the sheep's back as to the woollen; nothing being of more advantage to England than these two are; let there be one ton of this bar-iron made of Forest iron, and 20s will be given for it.' But as a projector or promoter some exaggeration is likely in Yarranton's statements,[195] and guessing wildly, he asserted that 60,000 were employed directly or indirectly in the Forest's iron industry. Controversially, Paul Mantoux[196] has written:

> If we can believe Andrew Yarranton, the Forest of Dean under the Restoration still supported a numerous population of miners and black-

smiths. But is the evidence anything more than an echo of ancient fame? The fact is that between 1720 and 1730 this district, like Sussex, did not contain more than ten blast-furnaces, which often, instead of smelting ore from the mines, made use of the slag from the Roman foundries. And we may look in vain in all England for a more important centre.

Nevertheless, Dean's iron industry had been and remained of the utmost importance to the economy of both the Forest and the nation.

The few remnants of the foregoing ironworks, many of which sites were utilized in later times, have been mentioned when describing the individual works. Almost all the buildings were obliterated by subsequent activities, particularly at Lydney, Whitecroft, Parkend, Cannop, Lydbrook, Soudley and Redbrook. There are abundant evidences of ponds, dams, races and sluices, and occasionally are found portions of furnace-stones or bricks coated on the inner side with slag and scoria. Except for an almost undisturbed mound at Upper Soudley of slag from the 1612–50 furnace, slag-heaps have disappeared, though numerous pieces can be picked up almost anywhere throughout the Forest, particularly on woodland roads. The slag from the furnaces, of a siliceous nature and showing a bottle-green to green-grey glossy fracture, often with entrapped pieces of charcoal, and small particles of iron which did not separate from the molten slag, has been used either as an ingredient in the bottle-glass manufacture (qv) or for road-making. That from the forges, a dark, brown-black, relatively heavy slag containing in the order of 30 per cent iron, usually in large form, has probably been used for re-smelting.

References to Chapter 1

1 Tylecote, R. F. *Organon*, 2, 1965 (Poland), 165.
2 Hart, C. E. *The Free Miners*, 1953, 24–33.
3 Scott-Garrett, C. *BGAS*, 75 (1965), 199–202; see also Morton, G.R. and Wingrove, J. 'Technical Aspects of the Roman Bloomery Process' *Trans Worc Arch Soc* 3rd Ser, 2, 1968–9, 92–7.
4 Bridgewater, N. P. 'Ancient Buried Roads in South Herefordshire', *WNFC*, 36 (1959), 218.
5 Ibid, *Bulletin HMG*, 6 (1966), 4; 2 (1968), 76; *WNFC*, 38 (1966), 125–35.
6 *Vict C Hist Glos*, II, 216, 217.

7 Hart. *The Free Miners*, 158.
8 Personal communication from R. F. Tylecote.
9 Singer, C. (Ed.), *A History of Technology*, II, 1956, 68.
10 Hart. *The Free Miners*, 12, 13.
11 Hart, C. E. *Royal Forest*, 1966, Ch. I.
12 Ibid, 48.
13 Schubert, H. R. *History of the British Iron and Steel Industry*, 1957, 93.
14 Bridgewater, N. P. *Bulletin HMG*, 8 (1967), 46, 47.
15 Hart. *Royal Forest*, 65.
16 Ibid.
17 Ibid, 69.
18 Ibid, 74.
19 Ibid.
20 Court, W. H. B. *The Rise of the Midland Industries 1600–1838* (1938), 52.
21 *BGAS*, 14(II), 221–84.
22 Hart. *Royal Forest*, 78, 79, 82.
23 Nicholls, H. G. *The Forest of Dean*, 1858, 228. (This book is referred to hereafter as 'Nicholls *History . . .*')
24 Hart. *Royal Forest*, 83.
25 Schubert, H. R. 'The King's Ironworks in the Forest of Dean, 1612–1674'. *Jnl Iron and Steel Inst*, 173, Feb 1953, 153–62.
26 Donald, M. B. *Elizabethan Monopolies*, 1961, 100, 132.
27 GRO D421/T22.
28 Ibid.
29 Schubert. 'The King's Ironworks . . . ', op cit, 153.
30 Ibid, 153, 154.
31 Hart. *Royal Forest*, 89, 90.
32 Morton, G. R. 'The reconstruction of an industry', *Jnl Lichfield and South Staffs Arch and Hist Soc*, 1966, VI, 1.
33 Ibid, 6.
34 The life of the hearth and inwalls, and sometimes the availability of ore and charcoal, determined the length of time the furnace was in operation at a stretch, ie the campaign.
35 Schubert. 'The King's Ironworks . . . ', op cit.
36 Hart. *The Free Miners*, 172.
37 Ibid, *Royal Forest*, 95.
38 Ibid, 101.
39 Ibid, 102, 103.
40 SP16/282.
41 E178/5304.
42 Ibid.
43 Hart. *Royal Forest*, 112, 113.
44 Schubert. 'The King's Ironworks . . . '; Bodl Liby Bankes Papers 5/50; North Family MSS (East Suffolk Rec Off Ipswich); HMC 55/14, Earl of Guildford MSS 187.
45 SP16/282.
46 Hart. *Royal Forest*, 116–18.
47 Ibid, 119.
48 Ibid, 124, 125.
49 Ibid, 129.

50 Ffoulkes, Charles. *Gun-founders of England*, 1937.
51 Hart. *Royal Forest*, 130.
52 LRRO 5/7A.
53 In 1643: Roy, Ian 'The Royalist Ordnance Papers 1642–1646', Pt I, Oxfordshire Record Society (1964), 36, 109, 110. In 1646, 'shells for granadoes' were supplied from Dean for the siege of Goodrich Castle (*The Wye Tour*, 1885, 36).
54 Roy, op cit, 36.
55 Ibid.
56 Corbet. 'Military History of Gloucester', in *Bibliotheca Gloucestrensis*, 1825, 89.
57 LRRO 5/7A.
58 GRO D421/E9.
59 Hart. *Royal Forest*, 131–33.
60 Ibid, 135.
61 Ibid, 137.
62 Ibid, 140.
63 SP Interr 62, f67.
64 Ibid, f157B.
65 Hart. *Royal Forest*, 146, 147, 148.
66 SP Interr 1655, 444.
67 Hart. *Royal Forest*, 149, 150.
68 Ibid, 150.
69 Cf, Schubert. *History . . .*, 232.
70 HMC 7th Rpt, 94; HLC 7 June 1660.
71 GRO GG 1557.
72 HRO Foley Papers.
73 Hart. *Royal Forest*, 154.
74 Ibid, 157, 288.
75 Ibid, 181, 288.
76 Ibid, 158.
77 Ibid, 175.
78 HRO Foley Papers F/VI/DCC/1.
79 North MSS, op cit.
80 Mushet, David. *Papers on Iron and Steel*, 1840, 387.
81 *Encyclopaedia Britannica*, plate LXXXVIII, Supplement to 4th, 5th, 6th Edn, Edinburgh, 1820, and vol V, 124, 125, Edinburgh, 1824. See also Schubert 'The King's Ironworks . . .', Fig 1, 159; and Osborn, F. M. *The Story of The Mushets*, 1951, plates 5, 7.
82 Schubert. 'The King's Ironworks . . .', 159, 160.
83 SP 16/282.
84 North MSS, op cit.
85 Schubert. 'The King's Ironworks . . .', 161.
86 SP Interr 157B, quoted by Schubert *History . . .*, 233.
87 Hart. *Royal Forest*, 155.
88 Ibid, 158.
89 Ibid, 175.
90 GRO D421/E6.
91 Nicholls, H. G. *Iron Making in The Forest of Dean*, 1866, 53.
92 North MSS, op cit.
93 Johnson, B. L. C. 'New light on the Iron Industry of the Forest of Dean', *BGAS* 1953, 135.

94   E134/4 Chas I/Easter 40; E134/Supplem 902/24.
95   E134/39 Eliz Hil, 23.
96   E134/4 Chas I/Easter 40; E134/Supplem 902/22.
97   GG 784–820.
98   Bodl Liby Gough Glos I, f61d.
99   GG688; Bodl Liby Gough Glos I, f61d; E134/44 Eliz/Trin 3.
100 GG688; C66/2173; LR 12/35/1271.
101 GG 688.
102 Bodl Liby Gough Glos I, f61d.
103 GG821, 867, 950, G24/14.
104 HRO Foley Papers.
105 GG 619.
106 GG 654.
107 E112/83/351.
108 GG 676.
109 BM, Court Books of the Mineral and Battery Works, III, ff6, 26, 29v, 32, 72.
110 SP 16/307/6.
111 GG 780.
112 BM Harl 4850, f47d.
113 GG 821, 867, G24/14.
114 HRO Foley Papers.
115 E178/3837 10 Jas I.
116 Schubert. 'The King's Ironworks . . .', 161.
117 North MSS.
118 E178/6080, Pt I, m20d; SP16/491/50.
119 LRRO 5/7A.
120 SP23/136/219.
121 GRO D421/E6, b, c.
122 E 178/3837 10 Jas I.
123 E 134/4 Chas I/Easter 40; E 134/Supplem 902/22.
124 North MSS.
125 E 178/6080, Pt I, m20d; SP16/491/50.
126 LRRO 5/7A.
127 SP 23/136/219.
128 North MSS.
129 Nicholls. *Iron Making* . . . , 42.
130 Hart. *Royal Forest*, 155.
131 GRO D421/E6.
132 SP 16/282.
133 North MSS.
134 Roy, op cit, 109, 110.
135 SP 16/282.
136 North MSS.
137 Ibid.
138 Ibid.
139 SP 16/282.
140 HRO Foley Papers F/VI/DCC/1.
141 SP 16/282; GRO D421/T23.
142 Hart. *The Free Miners*, 103.
143 Ibid, 79, 80.

144   HRO Foley Papers F/VI/DAC/1.
145   Ibid.
146   Ibid.
147   Ibid.
148   Hart. *The Free Miners*, 103.
149   SP 16/282/127.
150   E178/5304, 4 Chas I.
151   Bodl Liby Gough Glos I, f62; BM Harl 4850, f48.
152   North MSS.
153   Tylecote, R. F. 'Blast Furnace at Coed Ithel, Llandogo, Mon', *Jnl Iron and Steel Inst*, vol 204.
154   SP 16/282.
155   GRO D421/E9.
156   LRRO 5/7A.
157   Ibid, GRO D421/E9.
158   Ibid.
159   GRO D421/T22.
160   Ibid.
161   Ibid.
162   *The Lismore Papers*, 1st Series, II, 282.
163   SP 16/282.
164   GG 800.
165   GRO D421/T22.
166   LRRO 5/7A.
167   GRO D421/T18, 22.
168   E178/5304; E159/425; GG 654.
169   GRO D1677; GG 784; E178/5304.
170   SP 16/429/94.
171   HRO Foley Papers; E407/50.
172   MRP 879.
173   SP 16/282.
174   Ibid.
175   GRO D421/E9.
176   GRO D1667; GG 1557.
177   HRO Foley Papers F/VI/DB/2.
178   Johnston, op cit, 132.
179   GRO D1677; GG981.
180   Hart. *The Free Miners*, 90.
181   Ibid, 103.
182   GRO D1677; GG1031.
183   Nicholls. *Iron Making* . . . , 38–40.
184   Schubert. 'The King's Ironworks . . . ', 161.
185   Ibid.
186   Tylecote, R. F. *Organon*, 2, 1965 (Poland), 170.
187   Ibid, 'Blast Furnace at Coed Ithel . . .', op cit.
188   Schubert *History* . . . , 217; North MSS, 1635 Survey.
189   Royal Society *Philosophical Transactions*, 1677–78, 12/137, 931–35.
190   Schubert 'The First Stamp Mills in English Industry', *Jnl Iron and Steel Inst*, 157, 1947, 344.
191   From about 1784 to 1789 David Tanner rented from the Bathursts of Lydney 'the old stampers mill in Aylburton' (GRO D421 E53, 55); it was let to the Pidcocks in 1793. The mill probably stood on the

Plain Tree Valley Brook, which had several weirs on it. The brook now runs through a housing estate named Millbrook.

192   Royal Society *Philosophical Transactions*, op cit, 933, 934.
193   Ibid, 934.
194   Yarranton, Andrew. *Improvement of England by Sea and Land*, Pt I, 57.
195   Court, W. H. B. op cit, 81.
196   Mantoux, Paul. *The Industrial Revolution in the 18th Century*, 1907.

13 *(above)* Cannop Hill Foundry, now demolished; *(below)* Lydney Foundry, now demolished.

14 *(above)* Inside Tingle's Foundry, Cinderford c1907 (now demolished); *(below)* Bilson ('Gas Works') Foundry, Cinderford

15 *(above)* Inside Steam Mills Foundry, Lower Cinderford (Teague & Chew) c1907; *(below)* Cullamore casting house, near Ruspidge, from the south

16 *(above)* Bromley Hill (Oakwood) Foundry from the east (now demolished); *(below left)* David Mushet (1772–1847); *(below right)* Robert Forester Mushet (1811–1891)

Two
The Charcoal Iron Industry
to 1794

The second Blast Furnace Period
(1680-1794)

INTRODUCTION   Following the Dean Forest (Reafforestation) Act 1667, and the demolition seven years later of what remained of the King's Ironworks, 'timber-trees' and 'stores' to replenish them were conserved for future naval and commercial ship-building. Charcoal was still the only suitable fuel for smelting (experiments in using coal had been unsuccessful). Tens of thousands of old and decayed trees, and a large acreage of coppice and underwood best suited for charcoal, assured supplies of cordwood to the ironworks on the fringe of the woods, to complement the abundant ore and cinders.

Activity increased in the ironworks at Lydney, Rodmore, Rowley, Barnedge, Redbrook, Lydbrook, Bishopswood, Flaxley, Soudley, Longhope, Blakeney, and Guns Mill (rebuilt 1683). An account of them is given later. Further afield, the works at Tintern, Whitchurch, St Weonards, Elmbridge and Linton, received some ore and cinders from Dean. In 1638, Commissioners urged the Crown to build a furnace and two forges, at a cost of about £1,000, to utilise its cordwood.[1] The assumptions were:

Charcoaling of 5,400 cords annually would maintain the furnace while making about 1,200 tons of raw iron, costing as follows:

	A ton of raw iron		
	£	s	d
4½ cords of wood will make a ton of iron and will cost at 8s a cord	1	16	0
Cutting and cording		12	0
Charcoaling		6	8
Carriage to works		8	0

61

	A ton of raw iron		
	£	s	d
Ore and cinders		18	8
Workmanship		2	6
Salary of a clerk for the wood, a clerk for the iron, and a stocktaker		2	0
Repairs, and sacks to carry the charcoal etc		4	0
	£4	9	10

The value of the iron would be £5 10s 10d, a profit to the King of about £1, or £1,200 annually. If the raw iron was wrought into bar iron the total cost would be:

	A ton of bar iron		
	£	s	d
26cwt of raw iron will go to a ton of bar iron		7	3	0
Carriage from furnace to forge		2	0
Charcoal	3	12	6
Carriage of the charcoal		8	0
Workmanship	1	0	0
Carriage of the iron to the Severn		4	6
Salaries of clerks and stocktakers		2	6
Repairs and utensils		2	6
	£12	15	0

The value of bar iron is £15 10s, a profit to the King of £2 15s: two forges would make 360 tons a year. The King would thereby be furnished with all sorts of bar iron for his Navy, for which at the time he paid ready money; and it would be 'commonly better iron, for that of the Forest is esteemed the best in England'. All kinds of shot and iron guns for the Navy could be made and cast there, as in 'the late ill times'.

Instead of pursuing the proposal the Crown decided to sell the cordwood to ironworks in Herefordshire and Monmouthshire. In 1688 Dean had spareable trees equivalent to 50,000 short cords, convenient to be sold at the rate of 4,000 a year. In 1692 a contract was made with John Wheeler and Richard Avenant, partners of the Foleys, for 60,000 short cords of '2-foot wood', whereby £20,000 was raised by the Crown over seven years. Sales were also made to the ironworks owned by Mrs Boevey at Flaxley, Lady Winter at Lydney, and George White at New Weir on the Wye. Sporadic sales of cordwood continued.

As noted in Chapter 1, the Foley Partnership controlled several iron-works in Dean from 1671. In 1691 the shares in their 'Ironworks in Partnership' were held by Paul Foley ($\frac{1}{6}$) Philip Foley ($\frac{1}{6}$), Richard Wheeler ($\frac{1}{6}$), John Wheeler ($\frac{1}{4}$), and Richard Avenant ($\frac{1}{4}$).[2] Their furn-aces included Blakeney, Bishopswood, Guns Mill and Redbrook, and they also had an anvil works at Gatcombe. Richard Knight, who had the furnace at Flaxley, joined by 1707, and William Rea in 1704, from which year he managed Redbrook furnace. In February 1705, Paul Foley obtained a contract from the Crown for 8,000 short cords for six years at 6s, having argued that Mrs Boevey had but one or two forges at most, whilst he was concerned within or adjacent to Dean in seven furnaces, besides forges. In 1725 the partners were Thomas Foley senior, Thomas Foley junior, John Wheeler junior, and Mrs C. Lane.

Dean had for long been the principal source of tough pig iron and had concentrated on its manufacture. A high percentage of cinders was used, together with a variable, sometimes negligible quantity of iron ore. The fact that from 1717 Lancashire ore was sometimes used in the Forest furnaces suggests that easily won supplies of local ore were running low. Yet there would seem to have been ample supplies of cinders in as much as quantities were sent in the 1730s to North Lancashire for fluxing purposes. The pig iron was sent chiefly to the Midlands (the Stour Valley in particular), the bulk being shipped from the nearest Severn ports—Ashleworth, Newnham and Gatcombe. By sea, supplies went to Blackpool Forge in Pembrokeshire. Although pig iron was the main product of the furnaces, a small portion of their make was firebacks, pots, plates, weights and troughs—in the form of light castings. The commonest functions of the Forest forges were the refining and drawing out (in charcoal-burning hearths) of merchant bar-iron, which was sold in Bristol, and in the Severn towns of Glouces-ter, Tewkesbury, and Bewdley. Lydbrook Upper Forge, at least until the 1730s, had a specialised function which set it apart from the normal run of Forest forges: a large part of its production of refined metal was in the form of *Osmond* iron or wire iron, which used more charcoal and required more working than merchant bar iron and which was mostly sent to ironworks at Tintern and Whitebrook.[3]

Of the partnership furnaces aforementioned, financial accounts are extant for Blakeney, 1692–1706, 1707–15; Bishopswood, 1692–1706, 1707–17, 1725—7, 1728–33, 1748–51; Guns Mill, 1705–6, 1710–12, 1730–3; Redbrook, 1697–1706, 1707–17, 1725–7, 1728–33; of forges in the partnership—Barnedge, 1701–6, 1707–9; Rowley 1703–4; Bishopswood (new forge) 1748–51; Lydbrook (2), 1708–17, 1725–7, 1728–31, 1748–51; of the anvil works at Gatcombe, 1695–1705.[4]

The output (in tons) of the furnaces from 1688–1751 was:[5]

	Blakeney	Bishopswood	Guns Mill	Redbrook
1688–9	—	—	—	—
1692–3	273	739		
1693–4	925	488		
1694–5	810	753		
1695–6	1047	537		
1696–7	794	777		
1697–8	697	684		
1698–9	995	656		
1699–1700	725	825		616
1700–1	1251	695		
1701–2	508	522		
1702–3	922	674		158
1703–4	574	575		913
1704–5	917	810		531
1705–6	441	740	779	836
1706–7	—	—	—	—
1707–8	866	779	Nil	704
1708–9	553	Nil	Nil	678
1709–10	869	726	Nil	450
1710–11	628	532	562	862
1711–12	1066	489	153	775
1712–13	435	526	—	899
1713–14	625	409	—	532
1714–15	614	150	—	633
1715–16	—	535	—	418
1716–17	—	201	—	513
1725–7	—	250	—	28
1728–9	—	—	—	657
1729–30	—	—	—	409
1730–1	—	—	467	317
1731–2	—	—	401	537
1732–3	—	—	—	478
1746–8	—	—	—	—
1748–9	—	482	—	—
1749–50	—	Nil	—	—
1750–1	—	474	—	—

Nil = No make.   A dash = absence of information.

Additional to the above tonnages were: 1717—Blakeney 600, Bishopswood 600, Guns Mill 200, Redbrook 600; and 1717–18: Guns Mill 620; 1718: Guns Mill 353¾.[6]

From 1701 the output (in tons) of bar iron from the forges was:[7]

	Lydbrook (2)	Barnedge	Rowley
1701–2	—	24	—
1702–3	—	25	—
1703–4	—	24	33
1704–5	—	19	—
1705–6	—	29	—
1706–7	—	—	—
1707–8	—	18	—
1708–9	184	Nil	—
1709–10	169	—	—
1710–11	203	—	—
1711–12	162	—	—
1712–13	188	—	—
1713–14	136	—	—
1714–15	161	—	—
1715–16	161	—	—
1716–17	198	—	—
1725–7	219	—	—
1728–9	170	—	—
1729–30	194	—	—
1730–1	152	—	—
1731–2	178	—	—
1732–3	230	—	—
1748–9	91	—	—

Nil = No make.   A dash = Absence of information.

Figures of output complementary to the foregoing are:[8]

Output of the Furnaces and Forges in England and Wales between 1717 and 1750: a year:

Furnaces		Forges	
	Tons		*Tons*
Lydney	250	Lydney (2)	150
Blakeney	600	Blakeney	80
Redbrook	600	Lydbrook (2)	160
Guns Mill	200	Rowley	40
Flaxley	700	Barnedge	80
		Rodmore	20
		Newent (3)	120

Consolidation Table of Forges

	List A 1717	List B 1736		List C 1750
		Past Output	Present Output	
Lydney (2)	150	300	160	350
Blakeney	80	—	—	—
Lydbrook (2; 3 in 1750)	160	260	160	350
Rowley, Barnedge and Clanna	120	100	80	—
Rodmore	20	60	60	—
Flaxley	—	100	80	150

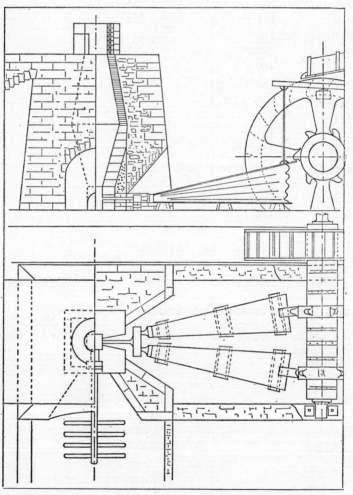

Fig 5. Reconstruction of a blast furnace (after G. R. Morton).

Charcoal was still the exclusive fuel in the furnaces and in the finery forges—with the one exception that at Redbrook the furnace in 1716–17 cast four tons of pig iron 'that was made with stone coal', previously 'charked'. The coke-smelted pig iron was priced at £6 a ton, compared with £7 15s for that smelted by charcoal.[9] In 1761, Lord Gage was warned by his steward of the competition to be expected from coke-smelted iron.[10] Attempts to smelt by coke at Lydney in about 1773 were unsuccessful—'from the bad quality of the iron therewith made'.[11]

Although the Foley Partnerships had almost a monopoly in Dean from 1691 till the 1750s, other ironmasters tried, some successfully, to intrude. Lydney ironworks were let to John Ruston of Worcester in 1723, and to other assignees in 1733. In 1740 Rowland Pytt took a lease of Lydney furnace and forges, and in 1742 of Redbrook furnace and two forges at Lydbrook. In 1747, there was an abortive proposal by Thomas Daniel and Richard Reynolds, ironmasters of Bristol, to erect a furnace at Barton Hill near Mitcheldean.[12] The local iron trade was good up to about 1758 but thereafter became depressed partly because of the war in 1761.[13] It had further declined by 1767.[14] After the 1770s, the Tanners, Partridges, Daniels and Pidcocks entered the field; Homfray and Platt had done the same in the 1760s but only as trustees of the children of Rowland Pytt, junior. Some of the ironmasters, eg Hanbury, Reynolds and Pidcocks used Dean's works only as subsidiaries. An account of the operations of these ironmasters is given later in this chapter.

After the mid-eighteenth century, supplies of cordwood were less plentiful. In 1742 the lessees of Redbrook furnace and of two Lydbrook forges obtained important cordwood concessions from Lord Gage's estates in and around the local Highmeadow Woods. In 1768 the lessees of Lydney furnace and forges persuaded Thomas Bathurst, the local squire, not only to reserve to them most of the cordwood from his extensive 16–18 year old coppices, but also to use his best endeavours to get as much cordwood from Dean. In 1775 Bathurst asserted that the price of cordwood, 7s 3d, should be increased to 8s—'the rise of the price of wood cannot be doubted, the new scheme of making iron with pitcoal apparently coming to nothing from the bad quality of the iron therewith made'.[15] Dean's cordwood continued to help to sustain neighbouring works, some £17,000 worth being sold during 1761–86. In 1788, cordwood was sold at 6s to 11s 6d a cord to Sir Thomas Crawley-Boevey, Bt, John Partridge and David Tanner. The furnaces at the time were '20 to 30ft high, of gritty stone found in the locality, and were generally built against a bank'.[16] The charge was first 10 baskets of charcoal, then 10 of cinders, and lastly 10 of ore. The 'make' at Flaxley was about 20 tons a week.

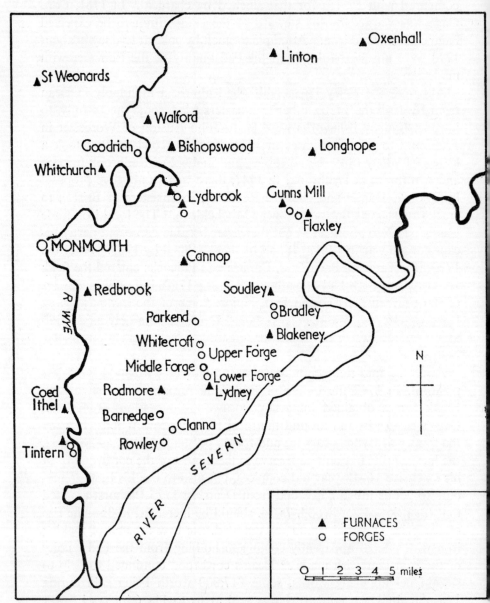

Fig 6. Map of charcoal blast furnaces and forges in Dean and its vicinity during the seventeenth and eighteenth centuries.

17 *(above)* The Titanic Steel & Iron Co's Works (Mushets'); *(below)* another view

18 (above) Lydbrook Tinplate Works c1937; *(below)* Inside Lydbrook Tinplate Works c1910

Writing in 1780, George Wyrall of Bicknor Court recorded information on the ores, cinders and smelting methods: [17]

> The ores of our Forest are of great variety: some of them being
> much more rich, as well as capable of producing better iron than
> others of them: and they are sometimes so ill gotten and adulterated
> by the miners as to be of little value.
>
> The cinders, too, are very different, as they are found in different
> places, some being light and porous, and yielding little metal, and others
> heavy and abounding in metal; and of these latter some are more brittle,
> may be broken into small pieces by slight blows of a hammer, and are
> more easily brought into fusion; whereas others, but little if any richer in
> metal, are more obdurate, and require a greater strength of fire to melt
> them. It is observable that these differences in the banks of cinders are
> commonly preserved through the whole of each; and that those which
> are found in the respective villages, or places, have a resemblance, so
> that whether it be owing to their being worked from the same particu-
> lar mines, or to some peculiar mode or process in the working of the
> bloomeries, the peculiarity seems to have continued the whole time in
> which the works were going on there.
>
> These ores, when judiciously chosen and used, I have had some
> reason to believe are capable of making better and more solid-bodied
> iron when worked alone without any mixture of cinders. But this has
> been found to be a matter of difficulty, so as to prevent many trials
> being made. Even the best of the ores are hard to be worked in the
> furnaces by themselves, owing, probably, to the quantity of hetero-
> geneous matter contained in them. They appear to require a certain
> proportion of other ingredients,[18] exempt from those matters, to bring
> them into perfect fusion, without which the scoria (which must be freely
> separated and drawn off) becomes not sufficiently fluid, and the labour
> to the men is exceedingly hard to keep the furnaces clear. This work
> has, therefore, been attended with great toil and some hazard. Perhaps
> future experiments may find ways to obviate this difficulty. The intro-
> duction, some years since, of Lancashire ore into the county to be used
> with ours, instead of cinders, on their becoming scarce, appears to have
> had a good effect, and to have caused much addition to the profits of
> the furnaces.
>
> It seems to be owing to the causes alluded to that no attempts
> have hitherto proved successful to blow our furnaces with the pit-coal
> of the Forest, these coals abounding in sulphur, and not being, in their
> nature, sufficiently absorbent to reduce the ores which are so replete
> with noxious substances.

A traveller in 1781[19] noted that wood in Dean was still plentiful

G

'notwithstanding the frequency of the iron furnaces, whose smoke impregnated the air, felt to me very wholesome and agreeable'. All the charcoal blast-furnaces except Flaxley, Lydney and Redbrook, and all the forges except Lydney, Lydbrook and Flaxley, were closed by the end of the century. The furnace at Flaxley ran to 1802, Lydney to 1810, and Redbrook to 1816. When the Industrial Revolution inaugurated a new period in the history of Britain, the Forest, despite closures, was the chief area of charcoal iron production—some 2,600 tons a year.[20] The long distances over which much of the ore had now to be brought to Dean, chiefly by sea from Whitehaven, was compensated by all the other essential elements being within easy reach—limestone-flux, water power, and charcoal. However, by that time, coke was replacing charcoal in smelting. The works at Lydney, Lydbrook and Redbrook, gradually enlarged and improved, together with new works at Parkend and Cinderford, later entered the coke-furnace, wire and tinplate eras—all dealt with in chapters 3 and 4—but first the history of the earlier individual works are outlined:

GUNS MILL　The derelict furnace[21] was rebuilt in 1683—the date on the cast-iron upper lintel-beam above the casting aperture. In 1701–2 'the mill' there, comprising two grist mills and a fulling mill, were mortgaged to Thomas Foley for £100.[22] The furnace was in the Foley Partnership account 1705–6, with a make of 779 tons,[23] and made 562 tons in 1710–11, 153 in 1711–12, 467 in 1730–1, and 401 in 1731–2. Information is lacking for the interim years. By 1743 it was a papermill (qv), the wheel being supplemented by a steam-engine (Plate 7a).[24]

When this furnace was rebuilt in 1683, it appears that the rebuilding was based on the earlier design. It has a square section about 28ft inwall with slight curvature on the faces. Although the hearth is missing, the remains suggest that there was no attempt to fit a circular bosh and crucible as at Coed Ithel, but that the original square hearth was retained. It is therefore the best remaining furnace of the earliest phase of British blast furnace practice. It would seem to have been 22ft to the charging floor, 7ft across the bosh, and to have a capacity of about 530cu ft. The casting floor lies to the south and the bellows room to the west, and adjacent to this is a capacious wheel-pit. The original overshot wheel was driven by a water supply contained in ponds to the west. Samples of charcoal blast furnace slag and bloomery cinders have been found on the site.

The now ruined furnace, much covered with ivy which makes it difficult to ascertain its exact state, is of the more typical square-sectioned shaft with the widest part about 7ft from the bottom. The cast-iron lintel beam mentioned above is in situ. The bridge house is probably not original; they were not very common, and that at Guns Mill appears to have been altered to serve as a barn, or built as one on the disused furnace. Also extant is picturesque half-timber framing surmounting the furnace but hidden by the ivy. Plans have been drawn by the Gloucestershire Industrial Archaeology Society. In 1968 the old furnace was subjected to a Building Preservation Order. If the structure is not to collapse soon it needs urgent attention.

RODMORE   This furnace which stood near the source of the Cone was probably out of use by 1680. By 1717 a forge stood on or just below the site, with an output of about 20 tons a year, increasing to about 60 tons by 1736.[25] At one time, Henry Thomas had some connection with this and other nearby forges.[26] It later became a paper-mill (qv), and afterwards a corn-mill (qv). Slag was found there in 1925,[27] and a little is still around. The mill buildings are extant.

BARNEDGE   A forge of this name stood east of the Cone, probably near the alder bed (or the now dry ponds below it) SE of todays Barnedge Farm House. From 1701 to 1709 it was within the Foley Partnerships with an average annual output of about 25 tons.[28] By 1775 the forge had passed to the Higfords (John Higford, lord of the manor of Alvington, died 9 April 1706) and later to the Parsons and Davies. It was leased 25 March 1775 to David Tanner for 99 years at a rent of £15 15s which included the Rowley and Clanna forges.[29] On 24 December 1789 Tanner assigned the lease to Thomas Daniels, John Fisher Weare, John Scandrett Harford, and Thomas Daniels junior, all of Bristol, who 8 November 1790 assigned (with Lydney furnace and forges) to the Pidcocks (John, Robert, and John junior) glassmasters of Staffordshire. There are no remains other than the sites of the ponds mentioned above.

CLANNA   This forge, on the Cone about halfway between the Rodmore and Rowley works, is mentioned in 1717 and 1736.[30] Its interim and subsequent working is obscure, but its later history is as outlined above for Barnedge Forge. The dam, pool and buildings have disappeared, but extant are the more recent pool and huge dam built to serve the Clanna Weir paper mill (qv) and later to provide power for a turbine to drive a nearby sawmill, and for a dynamo to generate electricity for Clanna House (now demolished), one-time home of the Marlings.

ROWLEY   This forge, lower down the Cone, produced 33 tons for the Foleys in 1703–4, and 40 tons in 1717.[31] The interim and subsequent working is obscure, but its later history is as outlined above for Barnedge Forge. Below the pool can be seen the wheel-pit and sluice system, but only fragmentary remains of walls mark the site of the forge buildings. Iron slag can still be found on the site. In 1797 the premises were advertised for sale, and thereafter were converted to a paper-mill (qv).

SOUDLEY   The King's furnace (in 1937 a sewage works was built on part of the site) was demolished in 1674 along with the King's forge (at Camp Mill—the site of a succession of ironworks in and after the eighteenth century). A map (believed to date from the early eighteenth century) indicates a forge at Camp Mill, while Drivers' map of 1787 shows there an 'Old Forge', and Bryant's map of 1823 a 'foundry'. No details of the earliest of these have been found, but they apparently stood on property belonging to the Jones family of nearby Hay Hill.[32] From 1824 to 1828 works there, or at the (later) tunnel mouth, or lower down the Ayleford Valley, were held by Browning, Heaven & Tryer (or Tayer); and in 1828 by Todd, Jeffries & Spirrin, who converted part of the premises to a paint and brass works, which lasted for about four years [33] (see ochre in Chapter 5). From at least December 1838 the Camp Mill premises became Samuel Hewlett's foundry (qv). His lease shows that previously they were an 'iron foundry' with tool-house and millhouse.

BRADLEY   This forge, on the east of the Soudley brook is believed to have been derelict by 1646. Taylor's map of 1777 indicates a forge in the vicinity—doubtless a new one. In the eighteenth century it formed part of a complex of wireworks (qv). From about 1810–12 Samuel Hewlett merged the premises with a foundry enterprise (qv) which he probably carried on there until he moved higher up the valley to Camp Mill. This Bradley forge-cum-foundry lay immediately to the east of today's Bradley House, either just north or south of the present dam wall which served to hold water, and to carry the tramroad to its termination a few yards below. The large supporting wall to the house may have formed part of the forge-building. The brook skirts it on the east, and to the north lies a small field showing remnants of embankments of the pool.

AYLEFORD AND TWO BRIDGES   The valley of the lower Soudley brook below the Bradley hamlet, now named 'the Ayleford and Two Bridges Valley', has from the thirteenth century had interesting but sometimes obscure industrial connections. Descending the valley, Brook Cottage on the east has a shallow retaining wall alongside the brook, some reconstructed outhouses, and a rectangular earth platform supported by stone facings. The occupants of the cottage reported unconvincingly hearing it was formerly a foundry; certainly in about 1800 a building and a pool stood nearby. Other local evidence suggests fairly recent construction, with a purpose unknown, but not industrial.

Downstream, a few hundred yards ENE of Two Bridges, evidence of a mill rests on the tradition of a water-wheel—the buildings are indicated on an early eighteenth-century plan and on a c1800 plan, as also on Bryant's map of 1823, which shows a little lane leading to it. There is now no pool, no fall of any significance, and no slag or substantial stonework. It may have been a small corn-mill, or a wheel for operating the sluice-gate of a leat, noted later. At the 'two bridges' (on one of the stone arches is set an iron plate 'Hewlett 1856'), the nineteenth-century cottages, some derelict, have no tradition of connection with industry.

Just below, at Lower Ayleford, new queries arise. Here (at *Erleyeforde*) in the thirteenth century, stood primitive forges (qv).[34] Later, in the sixteenth century, there were wireworks (qv), and other wireworks (qv) in the eighteenth century. Undoubtedly this valley has many historical secrets, including the precise site of a paint works (see ochre in Chapter 5.

BLAKENEY This furnace stood at Nibley, west of Blakeney on the Blackpool Brook. It is mentioned in 1680[35] in which year it had come into the Foleys' hands, for which their partners Richard Avenant and John Wheeler were purchasing cinders from English Bicknor.[36] The furnace was still within the Foley Partnerships in 1691 but it was in such a condition that it needed to be 're-erected or rebuilt'.[37] On 30 September 1692, it was willed to Thomas Foley by his father Paul Foley, who it seems had purchased the furnace from the Barrow family.[38] It served the Partnerships well until 1751,[39] with an output of 1,251 tons in its best year, and a weekly average around 20 when in blast. Only a third of the charge was ore—a fairly constant proportion in all the Forest furnaces at the time. The pig iron was sent from Gatcombe Pill on the Severn to Bristol and Bewdley.

The furnace ceased before 1777 (Taylor's map of that year shows 'Old Furnace') and the Drivers' map of 1787 simply shows upstream the old ponds. In 1795 a Guide[40] to the locality makes no mention of the furnace but, in calling Blakeney 'a small village of mean houses, seemingly studiously crowded into obscurity, deeply environed with hills', goes on to refer to 'a considerable stream which, after various embarrassments, makes its way from the forest lands above to the river Severn beneath'. The furnace was in absolute ruin by 1800.[41] 'Old Furnace Bottom' still exhibits much slag, and evidence of the harnessing of the brook, including a small weir and slight water-fall. There was a malthouse and premises close to it in 1864,[42] and today can be seen buildings which were formerly 'The Malt Shovel Inn', a malthouse, and a 'Wire-making house'.

LONGHOPE   This furnace was still standing in 1680.[43] A new lease of it was made to Paul Foley from Nourse Yate of Painswick 27 June 1682— for 15 years at £60 a year.[44] Foley agreed to repair the furnace, and to rebuild a coalhouse lately burnt down. A traveller in 1682 wrote of the works:[45]

> From Ross we went to Longhope, and turning a little out of the road saw the furnace or kiln where they melt iron. The bellows, being very great, which gave furious blasts to the fire, are driven like an overshot mill with water, having a great wheel divers yards in diameter. The fire to melt the ore in the furnace made of stone, which may be 7 or 8 yards from bottom to top in height, is made of charcoal, burning day and night for some months, viz: so long as the water, which is but a small stream, and commonly dry in summer, doth last. The flame mounts fiercely a good height above the furnace. Here is also at the bottom of the furnace a hole as big as that of an oven which lets the dross run away in fiery streaming flames from the melted metal or ore, which metal once in 4 hours is let run into bars or other forms of iron, but the dross when cold becomes a green glassy stone, of which they have vast mounds or heaps about the house, and good for nothing but to mend the highway; the heap of charcoal was also great, and the men work day and night in their turns.

LYDBROOK   No furnace remained at Lydbrook after 1674, but there is much evidence of the Upper Forge (previously called the Middle Forge) and the Lower Forge. On 20 June 1702 they were leased for 15 years by Benedict Hall to Richard Avenant of Shelsey Walsh, Worcestershire, and John Wheeler of Woolaston Hall in the same county. The plant taken over was:[46]

Upper Forge
Comprising a Chaffery, Upper and Lower Fineries, and hammerman's clerk's houses:

	T	C	Q
Cast iron fire plates in the forge floor		11	0
In the Chaffery seven plates, one old hammer, two hammer brasses		15	0

	T	C	Q
In Upper Finery, two other plates, one loop plate	1	0	0
Lower Finery three plates, two brasses, one loop plate		18	0
One hammer, one anvil, one hurst, two boyts [ie bearings for gudgeons] in use		18	2
Two barring plates		4	2
Weights in the pig beam		10	0
Five half hundreds and small weights belonging to iron beams		3	1
Two plates in the hammerman's house		5	0
Three plates in the clerk's house		5	0
	5	10	1

| Working tools with wood helves weighed | | 5 | 2 |

Two pairs of Finery bellows and one Chaffery
One iron beam and scales; one pig beam and scales

Lower Forge
(Comprising a Chaffery, Upper and Lower Fineries, finer's and stocktaker's houses):

	T	C	Q
Working tools with wood helves weighed		5	0
Six cast plates in Forge floor		10	0
In the Chaffery nine plates, an old hammer and boyte	1	2	0
Upper Finery 12 plates, 2 loop plates, one hammer brass	1	2	0
Lower Finery 14 plates, an old hammer and meese plate, one half hundred, one loop plate	1	10	0
One hammer, one anvil, one hurst, two boyts in use		18	2
Two barring plates		4	2
In finer's house 4 plates bar and cheeks		5	0
In stocktaker's house 4 plates		4	0
Weights on the pig beam		10	0
Five half hundreds and small weights to iron beam		3	0
	6	14	0

One pig beam and scales; one iron beam and scales.
Two pair of Finery bellows, one pair of Chaffery.

The Upper Forge appears to have been of the pre-1600 set-up of 2 fineries, 1 chafery and 1 hammer; thus the post-1600 3 finery and 2 hammer set-up was not used. The 'old hammer' probably refers to the previous occupant of the forge, not to a second hammer. The forge specialised in the manufacture of *Osmond* iron for the wireworks at Tintern and Whitebrook, though it also made bar iron. The tenants of the two forges, partners with the Foleys, held to at least 1751, producing on average about 175 tons a year.[47] During their tenure some Lancashire and 'Scotch' pig iron was received.[48]

From about 1702, Lydbrook had three forges working—the Upper (ie the Middle Forge of the previous decade), the Lower and the New Forge.[49] The last, site unspecified, was a finery only, refining pig iron from Bishopswood and sending the 'anconies' or blooms to Lydbrook forges which both refined pig iron and drew it and the 'anconies' into bars in the chafery. The quantities handled were not great, eg Lydbrook in 1748–9 refined 45 tons and hammered out 87 tons into bars. Most of the bar iron went to merchants in Bristol and South Wales—Messrs Roberts and Hanbury, William Chinn, and Samuel Partridge. An account book for the year 1728 shows that Thomas Foley and Partners paid (through Gage) to 'The Trustees of Lord Londonderry and other Annuitants' £300 rent for the Lydbrook ironworks and £867 11s 8d for 2,602¾ cords.[50]

Some of the Foley's accounts, purporting to be of Lydbrook forges for 1746–51, appear to have been wrongly dated. Although it is not certain when they quit Lydbrook, it is known that Lord Gage's two forges (with his furnace at Redbrook) were let 29 September 1742 to Rowland Pytt, from the previous 24 June, for 21 years at £200 annually.[51] The terms included a supply of cordwood for charcoal (see details under Redbrook furnace). Pytt died in 1756, and in his will made in 1753 he styled himself as 'Rowland Pytt the Elder, of the city of Gloucester, ironmaker'.[52] Pytt's son, Rowland, was still tenant in April 1761 when Lord Gage was being urged by his steward, Creed, to renew the lease to Pytt:[53]

> If the present trade was in the same situation as it was about two or three years ago, and that there was a prospect of its so continuing, I should not think your Lordship any ways to blame in desiring to advance your works, and I believe your proposals might have been complied with, but your Lordship upon the most strict enquiry will find that the trade never was in a worse pickle than it is at present, nor ever was there such a prospect as now of its still growing worse without the least hopes of its mending.
>
> A peace will bring foreign iron into this Kingdom in such quantities that all the markets will be full of it, and let the quantity of it be as t'will it must sink the price of English iron and always will keep it down so long as it continues to be imported, and that will be to the end of time your Lordship may rest assured.
>
> Another thing to be observed is the new method of making iron in

England with stone coal, a scheme that succeeds beyond expectation, and great numbers of furnaces are erected within these few years that blow with no other sort of coals, and the iron they make is little inferior to that which is by wood, and I am informed it sells for as much money per ton into 20s. What prospect then my Lord is there that the English iron will ever bear the price it has hitherto done, and upon these considerations I can't but think Mr Pytt's offer (to continue the works upon the old footing) a very good one.

And although these reasons may clash with your Lordship's views, I think it nevertheless my indispensable duty to lay them before your Lordship at the same time desiring your Lordship to consider whether letting the works to another man at an advanced rent for a few years will gain your Lordship any advantage in the end and whether Mr Pytt (who all the world acknowledges is a very good judge of the iron trade) would let the works slip through his fingers if he could get anything by them at your Lordship's terms.

That Mr Pytt is a person well beloved in this country (every individual of which is the better for him) and consequently can make as much of the works as any man in England, I regard not so much as to mention as his having been in every sense of the word an extreme good tenant. When he repairs any part of the works he minds no expense and does everything as though the premises were his own. At the time of the General Calamity when the Hail Storm broke down the forges at Lidbrook and did him other considerable damage he built it more substantial than it was before, and I dare say the whole loss and expense amounted to upwards of £1,000.

What offers your Lordship may have had I do not know. I hope they may answer your earnest wishes and I beg your Lordship to believe that what I have said is purely for the sake of truth and justice, and that I shall always have at heart your Lordship's real interest.

Pytt junior died about this time, because Creed soon after prepared a statement of 'New Buildings etc on the estate of Lord Viscount Gage at his ironworks, by the late Rowland Pytt deceased': [54]

At the Lime Kiln Pool
Part of the bay head.
The other pools much damaged and filled almost level with rubbish
    which was removed and repaired at great expense.

At the Finers Forge
New coal house ⎫
New smiths shop ⎭ Built with stone and covered with Forest tile.
One side of the Forge stripped and new tiled.

New troughs and substantial stone arches from the flood gates.
New walls to the coal yard, and new gate.
New drome, chipsill, poppet, and dogs, etc.

At the Hammer Mens Forge at Lydbrook
A new carpenters shop.
Two cellars for the workmen.
New stable.
Brewhouse.
Part of the bay wall, new.
Walls round the coal yard.
New walls to the throw of the back brook.
New arch through part of the timber yard.
New flood gates.
New penstock.
Waterpost, chipsill, poppet, and dogs, part of the chaffery trough.
A new gate and rails to the timber yard, and rails by the road to
    fence the ditch.
A new pigs cott.

On 1 September 1762 Viscount Gage let both forges (with the Redbrook furnace) for 21 years at £300 to Richard Reynolds of Bristol
and John Partridge senior and John Partridge junior of Ross-on-Wye.[55]
The lease gives the following estimate, dated 11 June 1762, of repairs
required to the two forges at Lydbrook:

Upper Forge

	£	s	d
Making one hammer beam, wheel fall and race, repairing 2 finery shafts and one finery wheel	27	14	0
Sawing work, nails and ironwork	12	0	0
Timber for above: 14 tons at 42s	29	8	0
Hauling same	5	12	0
Tyling and materials of all kinds for that part of the repairs	13	5	6
Mason work, house adjoining	2	12	0
Carpenters work and materials exclusive of timber	18	4	0
	108	15	6

Lower Forge

	£	s	d
Repairing the hammer beam and making the hammer wheel, fall, race, and water wall, and chafery wheel and fall	30	0	0

	£	s	d
Sawing work	5	0	0
Nails and ironwork	6	0	0
Timber for the above work: 10 tons	21	0	0
Hauling same	4	0	0
Tyling and materials of all sorts for that part of the repairing at Haddocks dwellinghouse	26	4	6
Carpenters and materials exclusive of timber	9	2	0
Timber for Lidbrook's buildings: 14 tons	29	12	0
Hauling same	5	12	0
	136	10	6
Dam heads at the pools at the Forges	3	14	0
Dam heads at the pools in the Forest	7	0	0
	10	14	0

The pools 'in the Forest' were those on the How (Hough) Brook (Plate 1b).

The Lower Forge was that referred to in 1769[56]—'A company at Bristol have lately erected a forge near Lydbrook, and had 500 loads of timber for that building and a water-wheel, and are now employing a great number to dig cinders or slag left by the ancient bloomeries'. On 25 March 1788 Messrs Harford, Partridge & Co, ironmasters of Bristol, obtained a renewal of a lease of the forge from William Vaughan, for 21 years at £12 10s a year.[57] The proprietors of the company were: James Harford the elder, John Partridge the younger, Richard Summers, Philip Crocker, Trueman Harford, and James Harford the younger.

In 1792 reference is made to the 'extensive ironworks' of Harford, Partridge & Co.[58] This apparently relates not only to the forge rented from Vaughan but also to the two forges (Upper and Middle) rented from Gage. The lease from Gage ended 5 July 1793, and the two forges were let (with Redbrook furnace) to David Tanner;[59] one of them had an aqueduct built over land owned by a Mrs Clarke. Within five years Tanner was in financial difficulties and in arrears with his rent. He sub-let the two forges to a Dr Hobbs and a Mr Ellaway; they too were soon in arrears with their rent. Tanner became bankrupt in 1798, and Gage brought an action against the sub-lessees and took possession. He leased the two forges (with Redbrook furnace) to his steward

James Davies and his partners, after Davies had pointed out in February 1800 that the following repairs were required (in addition to 'some little repairation to be done to two dams in Dean Forest'): [60]

Upper Forge
A new flood gate and 37yd of new troughing at Lime Kiln Pool.
Mason work from the pool to troughing leading to finery wheels.
Troughing from the acqueduct to the finery wheels.
The finery wheels to be properly repaired.
Flood gate at Upper Forge Pool, new.
The drone in Upper Forge to be repaired and a new dog to be put in.
The roofs and inside of the forge and three coalhouses with seven dwellinghouses to be repaired.

Lower Forge [Probably Middle Forge]
A waterpost and prickpost to be put new.
Mending a pair of bellows.
A new chaffery wheel and the timber under the penstock and troughing to be new.
The flood gate to be repaired and a part of it to be made new.
The roofs of the forge, house adjoining and timber house etc with stone coalyard to be properly repaired.

Davies and his partners held until 1805. Thereafter, the forges (with the Redbrook furnace) were let to Robert Thompson.

Meanwhile Harford, Partridge & Co continued to rent the Lower Forge, which in January 1808 was put up for sale as 'a very convenient forge for the manufacturing of iron, with an excellent pool of water for working the same, at Lydbrook within a few yards of the Wye'.[61] Their lease was due to end at Lady Day 1809, and it appears that they took the opportunity of purchasing the freehold. The Upper and Middle Forges were held by Thompson until about 1816. When Gage sold the freehold to the Commissioners of Woods in 1818, Henry Davis was the tenant.[62] The Commissioners sold the property to the Partridges that year—thus that family owned all the ironworks at Lydbrook, comprising three forges and their ancillary works. In 1818, or perhaps in the previous year, Thomas Allaway became tenant of at least some of the works and they became integrated with other premises for the making of tinplate—discussed in Chapter 4. Part of the Lower Forge later became a corn mill (qv).

FLAXLEY   The watercourse which flows from the Westbury Iron Mine area and from St Anthony's Well, becoming successively the Westbury

Brook and the Flaxley Brook, powered the Guns Mill furnace (qv) and, downstream, powered in 1680[63] a furnace (about 300 yards below the abbey) and two, possibly three, forges.

The furnace and forges were held in 1674 by the Foley Partnership, and their accounts are extant for 1686–7. In 1695 and 1710[64] the furnace was held by Richard Knight, who also owned ironworks in Shropshire. By 1712 all the Flaxley ironworks were owned by Mrs Catherine Boevey,[65] and in 1717 her furnace produced about 1,700 tons.[66] Her forges produced on average 100 tons annually pre-1736, and about 80 thereafter, rising to about 150 in 1750. Large quantities of cinders were delivered by the Wemyss family of Mitcheldean to Flaxley in 1741, 1742 and 1743, at 4s a dozen bushels.[67] The Wemyss's paid 8d to 18d a dozen to those who collected or dug the cinders from their Mitcheldean lands. The same family in 1767 sold large quantities of cordwood for charcoaling to Thomas Crawley-Boevey.[68]

By 1802, Flaxley's iron was 'esteemed peculiarly good—but its goodness does not arise from any extraordinary qualities in the ore, but from the practice of working the furnace and forges with charcoal, without any mixture of pit-coal'; however, the quantity of charcoal required was so considerable that the furnace 'cannot be kept in blow or working more than nine months successfully, the wheels which work the bellows and hammers being turned by a powerful stream of water'.[69] Lancashire ore, brought to Newham by sea, furnished the principal supply—the Forest ore 'being either too scanty to answer the expense of raising it, or when raised too difficult to fashion, and consequently too consumptive of fuel, to allow the common use of it'. To smelt a ton of Lancashire ore, 15 or 16 sacks of charcoal were required. The 20 tons of pig iron produced each week was carried to the forges, where about 8 tons a week 'were hammered out into bars, ploughshares, etc ready for the smith'.[70]

The furnace, one of the last locally to use charcoal, closed early in 1802.[71] The forges continued for a while longer. In the 1850s, 'aged people of the neighbourhood well remembered when the furnace was in blast, and told of the cinders, and of the pickings of the old mine holes, being taken down to it'.[72] By 1858 the ironworks had 'long since been discontinued, and with the removal of the furnace and forge buildings, and with the draining of the pools, the whole appearance of the valley changed—for the better,[73] and a solitary heap of Lancashire ore alone remained'.[74]

The stream, which turned the wheels for the bellows and hammers, is now of small proportions and much of it is out of sight underground. The site of the furnace and, upstream, one of the forges, cannot be found with certainty, but the names 'Furnace Yard', 'Mill Field', 'Forge Cottage', 'Old Pool Cottages', and one of the dams, bear witness to the past (Plate 6a, 6b). The furnace probably stood at the right-angle bend near the pound on the NW of the narrow road almost opposite Waldron Cottage (1878), now a farmhouse. It is believed to have been supplied with water by a leat cut into the hillside. The one certain forge site is adjacent to the above farmhouse, and was noted by Bryant in 1824 as 'Lower Forge'. The narrow road crosses the stream, and passes over the dam of a former pool—now a large field. The arched culvert passing beneath the dam is well preserved, and the tapering channel (to increase the velocity of water), and the large chamber, are noteworthy. Remains of buildings (the end wall of the present dairy is dated 1693) to the south of the road, now farm buildings, were part of the lower forge, and the channel leading from the former wheel-pit can be distinguished. In 1925 a fireback dated 1633 stood in the Flaxley estate workshop, and another dated 1685 in the abbey, while in the garden of the estate foreman was a cast-iron block, $11\frac{1}{2}$in $\times$ $5\frac{1}{2}$in $\times$ $5\frac{1}{2}$in, lettered 'Flaxley Woods, 1812'—presumably a weight (90.44lb).[75]

LYDNEY The demolition in 1674 of the King's ironworks within Dean's woods, probably gave an impetus to the Winters' furnace and three forges, then held by Sir John's son William, but all mortgaged —a penalty of the father's unhappy connections with the Forest.[76] By 1680 supplies of at least some of the ore still came from Dean.[77] In the 1690s Lady Frances Winter purchased cordwood from the Forest. Later the furnace was managed for her by William Johnson, in whose name there is a summary account[78] covering the campaign beginning 11 September 1699 and ending 6 May 1700, ie 7 months, $3\frac{1}{2}$ weeks. The account shows that cinders were bought at prices ranging from 5s 4d to 8s $7\frac{1}{2}$d a dozen; some came from as far away as Staunton. Ore from Clearwell (12 bushels to the dozen) cost 3s a dozen and from Red Hill in Lydney (13 bushels) 4s a dozen. Charcoal came chiefly from the Forest at 31s $5\frac{1}{2}$d to 35s 10d a load; Mr Catchway at Bigsweir supplied at 35s 9d; and wood from Somerset, charcoaled at Lydney Pill, cost 37s 2d. Sow iron made during the campaign, some 616 tons, was consigned chiefly to the Winters' forge; some went as fire-backs. The income from the campaign was £3,713 16s 7d, the expenses £3,219 7s 1d, and the profit £494 9s 6d. Particularly interesting among expenses of the furnaces are:

Taking out old hearth and supplying and fixing the new—£4 10s

26 tons of bosh stone—£2 7s 8d

Wages—usually 15d a day

Putting in and hewing 2 new 'dams'—2s

A pair of new bellows woods—£4

Building the end of the house over the bridge next the furnace—£1 7s 4d

Scouring the furnace ditch—£1 11s

6 bull hides etc (for bellows)—£11 5s

Scouring the witch and watercourse in Whitecross orchard—8s 2d

Pitch, tar and occham used to caulk the wooden water troughs—£6 13s

Tin and glue used for the bellows woods—£3 19s

60lb of tallow etc—£1 6s

Some bushels of hair: no separate sum

Charcoal baskets and cinder baskets: no separate sum

24½ dozen of mineral coal at 9d

230lb of hoggs licqor at 4d

Charcoal borrowed from Mrs Boevey (Flaxley): no separate sum

64 dozen Hamslaw (ie Hammer slag from the forge) at 23½d per dozen

On 3 June 1714, Thomas Talboys, steward to Lady Winter and her husband the Hon Thomas Nevill, made an agreement to sell to John Taylor, ironmonger of Bristol, 800 tons of bar iron to be delivered at the rate of 80 tons a year for ten years.[79] The price was to be regulated by that at which Samuel Wallis and Richard Taylor (father of John Taylor) sold iron in their Bristol shops. Early in 1718, Richard Taylor having died, a lawsuit was mooted to decide upon specific performances of the agreement. The previous year, 1717, Lady Winter's furnace produced about 250 tons of pig iron, and her two forges about 150 tons of bar iron.[80] In 1718, heavily in debt, she sold the whole of the Lydney estate to mortgagees who in 1723 (prior to the sale that year of the estate to Benjamin Bathurst) leased the ironworks to John Ruston of Worcester on terms which included:[81]

A repairing lease for 21 years at £200, of the Lydney furnace [near the site of White Cross House] and the Pill [Lower] Forge and New [Middle] Forge, the workmen's houses, a piece of land adjoining that Forge, 'Old Furnace Pool',[82] the Forge Pools, and all ways, waters, water-courses, etc, including the following:

(a) 2,000 short cords to be cut each year by the lessor at 7s a cord.
(b) Liberty to sink the waste of the Slitting Mill [Upper Forge] Pool 2ft lower than it now is, and to set up floodgates 4ft high and to shut and draw at pleasure, and to raise it higher if the lessee

obtains liberty for so doing from George Gough who owns the land adjoining part of the pool.

(c) Liberty to take stone and tile from Pailwell Quarry.

(d) The lessor to deliver cinders at 7s a dozen bushels, or 6s if the lessee raises them.

(e) Liberty for the lessee to draw the Furnace Pool, for the use of the Furnace when occasion requires in a dry time, 3ft below the waste.

(f) Lessee to pay £1 7s 6d a load for charcoal, or 20s for braizes [small charcoal], left at the Furnace by the lessor.

(g) Lessee to be allowed the timber cut for a hammer beam and three pairs of bellows boards, and to have £200 to repair the forges, etc.

The lease was not affected by the sale that year, 1723, to Benjamin Bathurst. John Ruston, some of whose accounts for cordwood are extant,[83] surrendered his lease in 1731.[84] On 25 September 1733 Bathurst made a lease (possibly by way of mortgage) to Sir John Eyles, Bt, William Bowles, William Giles, Phillip Roberts, and William Goostry:[85]

Repairing lease for 21 years at £200 a year, of the Pill [Lower] Forge, the New [Middle] Forge, and the Water Corn Mill or Milling Mill and Bakehouse in Lydney (late tenant, John Walter), including the following:

(a) Liberty to improve the properties, and to rise and dam up the water in the Slitting Mill [Upper Forge] Pool leased by George Gough to John Ruston and assigned by him to Benjamin Bathurst, paying £20 a year.

(b) The lessor to deliver all braizes from his Furnace at 20s a load.

(c) The lessees to take 1,000 tons of coal a year at 5s a ton.

The lessor reserved to himself the Lydney furnace; and the Upper Forge was not in work. The lease gives a schedule of 'goods, tools,, and utensils':[86]

New [Middle] Forge

16 plates in the air furnace [ie structural plates]

 2 bridge plates [These would bridge the openings from which red-hot blooms were taken]

11 plates in the finery [ie structural plates]

 1 cinder hole plate

 1 bottom hole plate

 2 old working hammers

 4 cast weights, ten hundred weight

 3 boyts [ie bearings for gudgeons]

 3 bloome tongs [ie tongs for holding blooms for forging]

19 (above) Site of Parkend Tinplate Works; (below) dwellings called 'The Square' in Parkend, now demolished

20 *(above)* Lower Redbrook Tinplate Works c1851; *(below)* Hawkwell Tinplate Works c1905 following the conversion to a brickworks

12 shingling tongs [ie tongs for holding blooms for shingling—pre-forming before forging]
1 small tongs
2 large chimney plates for the finery
2 pairs of working finery bellows
1 iron furnace in the house
1 iron beam and scales
5 half hundreds; one quarter do.; ten small weights
4 bottoms in the houses [ie furnace bottoms]
1 new hammer gudgeon
1 new wheelbarrow
2 large sledges
1 small sledge
2 furgon hammers [ie hammers for early forging]
2 hand hammers
2 large ringers
4 furgons [ie tools for raising and working the pasty mass of iron in the furnace]

Pill [Lower] Forge
13 plates in the ground [ie cast iron plates on the floor of the finery]
10 working plates in the chaffery [ie cast iron plates on the floor of the chaffery]
2 boyts
1 hammer gudgeon
1 cheek of a hammer
1 scale beam, scales and weights belonging, three hundred weight and a quarter
1 brays tub
1 hammer hurst

The lessees entered into possession and paid one year's rent, but in July 1735 Bathurst began law proceedings relating to the enforcement of the repair and other clauses.[87]

No records have been found for the subsequent 5 years. However, for 14 October 1740 there is 'An Inventory of the stock, working tools and other implements of Benjamin Bathurst at his furnace and forges and by him sold to Mr Raikes and Mr Pytt as they are now valued by Richard White and Thomas Pendrill':[88]

At the Furnace

	£	s	d
232 tons of pig iron at £6 5s per ton (Mr Bathurst to deliver the same at the Upper Forge)	1,450	0	0
Pig beams and scales, and a ton weights	8	0	0

H

	£	s	d
Iron scales and 1c 3q 14lb weights	1	0	0
3 new sacks		15	0
14 old sacks	1	15	0
6 dozen and 10 bushels of cinders at 6s 6d	2	4	5
22 dozen of small ore at 5s	5	10	0
11 dozen of small ore at 5s	2	15	0
8 loads of charcoal at £1 10s	12	0	0
5 tons of castings at £7 5s	36	5	0
9¾cwt of old castings at £5	2	8	9
12¼cwt of old wrought iron at 12s	7	9	0
7¾cwt of crop iron		7	9
	£1,530	19	11

At the New Forge

	£	s	d
Pig beams and scales and 10cwt weights	4	0	0
Iron beam and scales and 3cwt weights	2	5	0
48 loads of charcoal at £1 10s	72	0	0
2½ tons of old cast iron at £5	12	10	0
17¼cwt of old wrought iron at 12s	10	9	0
Working tools	1	17	6
A plate for the drooke: 18cwt	4	10	0
	£107	11	6

At the Pill Forge

	£	s	d
60 loads of brays (small charcoal) at 15s	45	0	0
3 tons 11½cwt old cast iron	17	17	6
9½cwt old wrought iron at 12s	5	16	0
Working tools	3	3	0
Iron beam, scales and weights	2	0	0
New hammer and anvil	5	12	0
4 new boyts and 1 new brass wt, 3cwt	1	2	0
2 old anvils and 1 old hammer and 1 standard	7	1	3
3½cwt old wrought iron at 12s	2	2	0
8 dozen of forge cinders at 2s		16	0
	£90	9	9

At the Storehouse

	£	s	d
Iron beam, scales and 3cwt weights	2	5	0
Old pair of chafery bellow woods	1	0	0
208 cords of wood at 4s	41	12	0
	£44	17	0

Total £1,773 18s 2d

No records have been found of any joint working of the ironworks by Pytt and Raikes, Pytt however, was doubtless Rowland Pytt who in 1731 is described as 'of Lydney, ironmaster', and in that year took a lease of Ynys-ygerwn Tin Works near Aberdulais, Glamorganshire.[89] In 1742 he took a lease of Redbrook furnace and two forges at Lydbrook.[90] It was the same Rowland Pytt, or his son of the same name, who on 16 February 1747 [91] obtained a lease from Benjamin Bathurst, for 21 years as from Michaelmas 1746 at £120 annually of Lydney Furnace and the Pill [Lower] Forge and the New [Middle] Forge together with their buildings, tools and plant, and other premises, namely: a house near the furnace called the Gatehouse and the waste land adjoining; all the workmen's houses and gardens belonging to the furnace and forges; a parcel of land adjoining the New [Middle] Forge; a pool called the Old Furnace Pool and the Forge pools; the dwellinghouse in the possession of Benjamin Taylor with the stable, garden and orchard thereto belonging and adjoining; the dwellinghouse now or late in the possession of Joseph Tamplin; a storehouse called the New Storehouse; a piece of meadow or pasture ground called the Storehouse Leaze; a small parcel of land inclosed in the possession of the said Benjamin Taylor; the orchard lying near the furnace called White Cross Orchard now or late in the possession of George Gorigh, gentleman, as tenant thereof; and the wharfage of Lydney Pill.

Benjamin Bathurst was to supply cordwood at 6s a cord, to be charcoaled and carried by the lessee with muzzled horses; the lessees were to be allowed wood for hurdles and cabins necessary in the charcoaling. Bathurst was to put in order the trough or water-course leading to the furnace wheel; and to permit the lessee to take ore at 6s a dozen, or 1s a ton, and cinders at market prices. The lessees were given permission to take, free of charge, stone and tile from Snead and Kidnalls woods, hearth stones and bosh stones from the quarries at Pailwell and Aylburton Common, and limestone from Red Hill quarry. The lessor agreed to supply, free of charge, timber for bellows boards, hammer beams, and roofs.

Some years before the end of the lease, Benjamin Bathurst gave the property to his son Thomas. Pytt died in 1766 demising his lease and assets to his children through two trustees—Francis Homfray, iron-master, of Wollaston, Old Swinford, Worcestershire, and John Platt, ironmaster, of Monmouth.[92] Mr Wyrhale (perhaps the person who was an authority on the local iron industry) assisted the trustees and their solicitor in negotiations which began for a new lease in February 1767.[93] Acting for Thomas Bathurst was Robert Pyrke, solicitor, of Newnham. The trustees referred to 'the present declining state of the trade'. Eventually Bathurst leased the ironworks to the trustees on 24 June 1768 for 21 years at £200 annually.[94] He agreed to fell all his coppices when within the ages of 16 to 18 years, and to supply there-from cordwood at 7s 3d a short cord—8ft 4in long × 4ft 6in high × 2ft 2in wide—reserving only produce to make rind hoops and smart hoops, and poles and stakes for himself and his tenants. He further agreed to use every endeavour to obtain for the lessees as much cord-wood as possible from the Forest of Dean—an indication that supplies were not plentiful.

In 1774 the trustees (who had in about 1773 used coke there for smelting ore, but it had been 'found not to answer'[95]) tried to obtain better terms for their leasehold. They asserted 18 January 1775[96] that the rent was too high 'because the furnace is not likely to work again during the remainder of the term, and there is hardly wood sufficient to work the forges only'; and the wood was 'considerably too dear'. The lessor countered 21 January that the rent was not too high, 'because the furnace is as likely to work and may be now as well sup-plied with wood as ever it was'; and the wood was not too dear, 'from their situation being very convenient and a certainty'. Thomas Bath-urst then (9 April 1775) advertised the property:[97]

> To be let and entered upon at Michaelmas next for a term of years if required, Lydney ironworks adjoining to the Forest of Dean, which have been occupied by the late Rowland Pytt, his father and repre-sentatives for near 3 or 4 decades, consisting of a furnace and two good forges, and several messuages, tenements, buildings, lands and other appurtenances most conveniently situated for carrying on the same to great advantage together with an annual fall of about 2,000 cords of coppice wood of 16 and 17 years' growth within 1½ miles carriage of such works, also several ponds and plenty of water, well adapted for

Slitting Mills and other purposes, and any quantity of iron ore and good coal to be had within the distance of $\frac{1}{2}$ mile, and the iron conveyed by water by one man and boat from the Upper [ie Middle] to the Lower Forge not 300 yards from Lydney Pill adjoining to the River Severn where vessels of large burthen may come in to load goods from Bristol, Gloucester and other ports. For further particulars inquire of Mr Robert Pyrke, attorney at law, at Newnham; and William Garland of Lydney will show the premises.

The following month, 17 May 1775, a survey was made of the dilapidations on behalf of Bathurst: [98]

The works are in a ruinous condition particularly the west side of a coal house lying open and wants stripping, and likewise furnace walls, stack and funnel head of the furnace ought to be taken down and rebuilt. The wheel, casting house and potthouse, and bellows house and the little tenements adjoining are in bad condition. The furnace pool and old pool heads, the witch (?twitch), and inside and outside walls and trough leading the water to the wheel, and the wheel on the west side of the forge are in great decay and one wheel destroyed. Also the floodgates and waste walls, the lace and cills and water post and the ground cills and finery wheels and troughs on the east side of the forge are in great decay and one leak in the pine end. The slitting mill pool gates are entirely gone, and a floodgate with a frame is wanting in the brook leading to Newerne. The chaffery wheel and arms and a new hammer beam are wanting at the Lower or Pill Forge.

The cost of repair was estimated at upwards of £500.[99] The lessees, 13 June 1775, agreed with the lessor for a joint survey of dilapidations to be made.[100] Thereafter the trustees of the late Rowland Pytt ended their connection with Lydney. It appears that 'Lydney Forge' (whether it was the Lower or the Middle is not known) was for a few months of that year, 1775, held by Reynolds, Getley & Co, ironmasters, of Bristol; a letter from them dated 23 February states: 'It is very uncertain our keeping these works longer than next Michaelmas'.[101] On 2 August that year, 1775, Thomas Bathurst let all his ironworks for 21 years to David Tanner, ironmaster, of Tintern;[102] his father, ironmaster, of Tintern and Monmouth, had recently died.[103] On 10 March that year, 1775, Tanner had taken a lease of Rodmore, Clanna, Rowley and Barnedge ironworks—the first three on the Cone and the fourth nearby.[104] The lessor agreed 22 November 1775 to pay to the lessee £400 towards the cost of the repairs, namely: [105]

The Lower or Pill Forge [This, later, became part of Lydney Tinplate Works]
The floodgates, hammer beam, wheel and plumber blocks, and fall and penstock and droome beam and laces for prickpost, and chaffery wheel and trough leads to the chaffery wheel, and outside carriage, and plumber blocks and one crooked and one straight leg to be all new and complete.

The grate and bay head to be made good, some part of the forge and dwelling houses to be stripped and new tiles, and the rest to be repaired.

A new door frame to the iron room and a loft in the forge wants repairing, and a new stairs and the back part of the coal house wants tiling.

The house that Richard Tamplin senior lives in and warehouse to be repaired, and the bark house to be stripped and repaired, and the house in Lydney where Mr Garland lives to be repaired.

The Upper [*ie Middle*] *Forge*
The water post, cheap sill, dogs and droome beam and laces and sills for ditto, and carriage for the cheap sill to be all new.

The hammer beam and water wheel and standard sill to be repaired.

A water wheel and tale and shaft and carriage for ditto and new bellows frame and shammey beam and shammey and carriages and plumber blocks and poizes all to be new.

The trough and penstock and side walls of the trough and chimney and bellows to be repaired.

The roof at the upper end of the forge to be stripped and new timbered and tiled, and the lower end to be repaired, and the beam in the coal house to be repaired, and new props to be put under the beams.

A new cap to floodgates and sill if requisite, and gates and side walls to be repaired. A new grate and the floodgates leading to the hammer wheel to be repaired and (?) mosse and pointed.

A new floodgate and frame below the forge leading to Newerne.

A waste ware to be erected in a substantial manner at the slitting mill and the bay head repaired if wanting.

The Furnace and adjacent
The shaft and wheel and carriages and plumber blocks to be all new, and the troughs leading to the wheel on the wall and bellows frames and shammeys and shammey beams to be repaired.

A new hearth and the stack and charge and fence walls to be repaired.

The roof over the casting house, moulding house and tenements adjoining to be new; and the bellows house, coal house, and bridge part to be sufficiently repaired.

The floodgates at the top of the long trough to be new. The bay-heads at the furnace pools and the bridge adjacent to the lower pool, and the troughs and floodgates in the Park all to be repaired, and made good, and all other pools and bayheads expressed in the lease.

Half of the £400 was to be paid by the lessor within fourteen days and the remainder at Michaelmas 1776, together with an allowance of 35 tons of timber 'exclusive of what has been already delivered'.

Thomas Bathurst had tried, unsuccessfully, to raise the price of cordwood from 7s 3d to 8s—asserting that 'the rise of the price of wood in general cannot be doubted, the new scheme of making iron with pitcoal apparently coming to nothing from the bad quality of the iron therewith made'.[106] On 8 April 1778, he gave a new lease to Tanner of Rodmore, Clanna and Rowley Ironworks. The repairing lease for 99 years at £280 a year included: [107]

(a) Lydney furnace, with the dwelling called the Gatehouse, waste land, and White Cross Orchard nearby.

(b) The New Storehouse, and the Storehouse Leaze.

(c) The Pill [Lower] Forge, with workmen's houses.

(d) The New [Middle] Forge, with workmen's houses. (Plates 4a and b.)

(e) A piece of land adjoining the Middle Forge, and a piece of land (late in the possession of George Wyrall) through which the Forge Brook runs.

(f) The Slitting Mill [Upper Forge] House, and the Slitting Mill Meadow. (Plates 5a and b).

(g) The ponds called 'Slitting Mill Pool', 'Old Furnace Pool',[108] 'Pill Forge Pool', 'Furnace Pool', and 'New Forge Pool'.

(h) All working tools, implements and utensils belonging to the furnace and forges, as per schedule [missing].

(i) Liberty to take ore, sand, clay, stone, and coal from the Lydney estate.

(j) Liberty to take cinders at market price, and cordwood at 7s 3d a short cord of 8ft 4in × 4ft 6in high × 2ft 2in wide.

(k) Liberty to work the coal-level already made in or near Kidnell's Wood.

(l) Liberty to make a navigable canal (later known as The Cut—made c1800 by the Pidcocks) from the Slitting Mill [Upper Forge] Pool to Lydney Pill, and to have the use of the Pill.

Tanner also paid £4 a year for 'the Old Stampers Mill in Aylburton'.[109] When he paid his rent in 1781 it included rent for 'Pill [ie Lower]

Forge now a Tin Work'.[110] Thus possibly tinplate (qv) was being made there. During the first ten years of his lease, Tanner built 'divers erections, buildings and conveniences for the better carrying on of the trade'.[111] A traveller in 1781[112] stated: 'At the end of Lydney stands an iron forge [for furnace], the water to which is brought from some distance through meadows on a pillared aqueduct.' The furnace stood between the site of the ruined White Cross House (indicated today by a walled and derelict field) and the Grammar School. The old Furnace Cottages are extant (Plate 7b). The stream (now reduced in volume) which powered the water-wheel of the furnace still runs, at its original level, down the side of the lane serving Red Hill House. To the north of the stream was a marshy area in which people dumped their rubbish; thus, when the new RDC offices were built in 1955 the site yielded Saxon, Norman, and up to Queen Anne, pottery etc. The water was carried over the South Wales road by a pillared acqueduct (a few remains of the pillars, now more like a broad wall, can be seen on the north side of the lane). The outfall from the water-wheel was channelled into an underground culvert which still exists, and finally debouched into the open just below the old wall of White Cross House on the east side of that site. Today in wet weather the old culvert discharge can be seen as a trickle of water oozing out of the wall. The culvert crosses the bottom of the Grammar School Playing Field. During one excavation of it, Dr C. Scott-Garrett was able to walk upright along the well-built arched passage (twitch) with a thick layer of mud at the bottom.

By 1789 Tanner had laid out a considerable sum of money and was 'possessed of a stock in trade consisting of iron, sand, iron ore, draught horses, wagons, carriages, tools, utensils, implements and other things'. He and his brother William had contemplated accepting Thomas Daniel and others as partners, and 'Articles of Co-Partnership' were drawn up.[113] However, on 5 August that year, Tanner assigned his Lydney lease, and his Cone Valley lease, with stock and goodwill to Thomas Daniel, John Fisher Weare, John Scandrett Harford, and Thomas Daniel the younger, all of Bristol, the Daniels taking one-third, and each of their two associates one-third.[114] Tanner was already indebted to the new lessees for £11,209 9s 11d; they paid him £6,019 7s 3d—making the full consideration £17,228 17s 2d.

The Daniels and their associates held only to 8 November 1790 on which date for £13,050 10s 3d they assigned their lease, stock and goodwill to John Pidcock, Thomas Pidcock, John Pidcock the younger, and Robert Pidcock, 'glassmasters' of Stourbridge, Staffordshire.[115]

In 1793 the Pidcocks obtained a lease of land called the Terrett, in Lydney, and of 'the mill, or site of a mill now in ruins called the Stampers Mill in Aylburton'.[116] By 1795 'the introduction of sundry iron works had latterly multiplied the inhabitants'; the church was 'neat . . . a good ring of bells, and an organ.'[117] The New Ground, was 'supposed to be obtained when the water deserted its ancient track for a more easterly course; for the inhabitants have a tradition . . . that the tide of the Severn once reached a bank of earth called the Turrett, which is near the church, and that a large ship was built near the place, now called the Turrett Well.'

By c1800 the Pidcocks had completed a navigable canal (now known as 'The Cut') alongside the Newerne Stream from near the Upper Forge to the New Storehouse near Lydney Pill.[118] For part of their tenure they appear to have been in partnership with Jeremiah Homfray.[119] About 1803, much ore was reduced at Lydney furnace, but 'where pitcoal is used the iron is allowed to be of inferior tenacity and ductibility'.[120] By 1810 the furnace had ceased to work, but the other ironworks being run by the Pidcocks comprised:[121]

Upper Forge—'now worked as a stamping forge, containing 3 charcoal fineries, and one running-out fire; with iron helve, and blowing machinery.'

Middle Forge—'with balling and other furnaces, but now used as a drawing-out forge for uses, etc.'

Lower Forge—'with puddling and balling furnaces and iron helve, now used as a plating[122] forge, with blowing machinery.'

A Mill—'capable of rolling 50 tons of merchant bars weekly.'

The Lydney tinplate era had arrived or was imminent—a subject discussed in Chapter 4.

BISHOPSWOOD   This furnace within the Foley Partnerships (probably on the Lodge Grove Brook) was still in being in 1680 as evidenced by the 600 dozen bushels of ore delivered to it from Dean in that year.[123] In 1685 Paul Foley assigned the furnace to Wheeler and Avenant for 7 years at £7 a year; in 1691 it was still within the Foley Partnerships. In 1699 Foley left it to his son Thomas Foley junior.[124] A contract for cinders in 1692 fixed prices when delivered to Bishopswood furnace.[125] Iron from it was taken overland to Newnham for transportation up the Severn to the Midlands.[126] Foley records are available of output to 1717; then, after a gap in the records, figures are available for 1725–7, when there is another gap, for 1728–47.[127] From

1746–51 the furnace was probably part of a privately managed group of works, still using cinders, Forest ore, and charcoal.[128] While supplying the Foleys' other works, it also sent pig iron to the Midlands, to George White at New Weir, and to Thomas Daniel & Co at Lydney, Tintern and Monmouth.[129]

The furnace probably ceased production in 1751. Taylor's Map (1777) shows 'Dam Pool' and the tithe map of Walford Parish (1840) which, despite there being no suggestion of any activity in the vicinity from the 1750s, shows on the brook three dams and, nearby, 'Furnace Farm' and 'Furnace Grove'. The 1st Edn 6in OS 1878 shows 'The Dam', 'Dam Wood', and 'Furnace Wood'.

Subsequently a new furnace and a forge were built on the Lodge Grove Brook, down whose valley runs an old trackway by which ore may have been brought from the Wigpool district, and perhaps roasted-ore from the kilns (still extant) at Ruardean. The furnace shown on Taylor's map (1777) stood about 150 yards from the Wye (some of its foundations, a deep stratified layer of early blast-furnace slag, and charcoal were found during excavations in 1964.[130]) Bloomery slag was also found, evidence that it was a traditional iron-smelting site. The forge stood about 300 yards further up the brook. There were three ponds; the lowest near the furnace (to which water was taken from the brook by a leat) is long and triangular, the middle pond just above is rectangular, and far upstream is a small triangular pond. Plans of 1805[131] and 1810[132] confirm the position of the furnace. Bryant's Map (1823–4) marks the works between the lower and middle ponds as 'Forge', while the Walford tithe map (1840) shows this area as 'Carpenters Yard' (with some adjacent buildings) and, nearby, 'Forge Meadow'.

William Gilpin[133] noted the furnace in 1770, and S. Shaw visited it in 1788.[134] Scrivenor[135] mentions it among the charcoal furnaces for 1790, while Rhys Jenkins[136] said it produced 947 tons in 1796, when owned by John Partridge. Samuel Ireland[137] noted the furnace in 1797, while in 1805 it is referred to as being worked with Lancashire ore and ancient *scoriae* (ie cinders) which were stamped with powerful engines.[138]

The importance of the furnace by 1810 is shown by the s&w Rly Co's Act of that year which authorised the Bishopswood extension 'to or near a place called or used as the Cinderhill, at Bishopswood Furnace, with necessary wharfs at the termination'. Their Plan of 1811[139] shows the furnace, with the authorised s&w tramroad terminating between the road and the furnace, and by which coke, coal, etc were brought in, and bar iron despatched. On 12 April 1814 the s&w Rly & C. Co minuted that their agent (Sheasby) was to settle the accounts of Mr Partridge and the Bishops Wood Co allowing them the reduction of half-tonnage on bar iron going to their works from Lydney along the rail road. This buying-in of bar iron suggests that by 1814 the furnace was out of blast. Soon, the s&w prabably regretted their outlay—on 23 July 1816 Sheasby was ordered by his company to dispose of the 'Finers metal' taken by distress from the 'Bishopswood Company' for the best price he could obtain. This indicates that the local company, with separate accounts from those of the Partridge family, was in a bad way in mid-1816, and there is no evidence that it worked thereafter. The forge probably continued, but the only suggested evidence for this is an application 9 April 1822 by James Price of Bishopswood 'Furnace' (for forge) for leave to carry goods on the railway upon credit.[140]

In c1821–2 William Partridge, ironmaster, built his pretentious mansion, Bishopswood House, near the site of the abandoned furnace—an indication that the most noxious activities at any rate were no longer taking place. Fosbrooke wrote in 1826:[141] 'On the Wye are Bishop's Wood Iron Works and Coal-Wharf, behind which is Bishop's Wood House, the seat of John Partridge, Esq.' This does not necessarily mean that the furnace was working (though the forge and coal-wharf were probably active) because there were two earlier editions of his book, and it was based in part on Gilpin's observations in 1770, previously noted. The forge probably ceased about 1840 (the 1st Edn 25in OS 1878 marks it as 'Old Corn Mill').

In 1873 Bishopswood House was totally destroyed by fire[142]; John Partridge had lived there for over fifty years.[143] As late as 1885, 'there lay close by the remains of ironworks, and some of the huge bellows are preserved on the spot as relics of the bygone industry of the place'.[144] Jacob Chivers of the Hawkwell Tinplate Works purchased the site of the house and furnace in 1874,[145] but if he intended to build there he never accomplished it. There must have been a thorough clearing-up at the works and wharves at some time during the eighteenth century, because the site today is so clean.

A portion of the underground premises of the old corn-mill was later adapted as an 'ice house', probably for Bishopswood House—the kiln-like structure is brick-lined, and nearby is an arched water-channel. The area abounds with slag, and a stone built bridge (span 8ft, width 5½ft), fast deteriorating, stretches over the run-off channel; it probably carried the 'iron rail road' shown on Bryant's map of 1823 as running up the valley to the forge. The upper pool, now dry and planted with poplars, has a well-defined dam, 6–7ft thick, and a stone water-channel; alongside, on the south, the brook still passes through a well-built stone sluice, with a now broken wooden gate. The middle pool is in use for driving an hydraulic ram to supply spring water to neighbouring houses. The lower pond, now dry, has a well-defined dam and sluice channel. By the Wye, where stood the old wharf, masses of slag appear in the bank.

REDBROOK The lower furnace (its site now forms part of a little hamlet known as 'The Foundry') was still being worked by Benedict Hall in 1693[146] and on 20 June 1702 he let it (with his two forges at Lydbrook) for 15 years at £90 to Richard Avenant and John Wheeler.[147] The inventory in the lease reads:

> Working tools with wood helves weighed 7cwt.
> Two plates at Tunnel head weighed 5cwt.
> One pair of furnace bellows and hammer.
> One pig beam and scales, and one ton of weights.
> One iron beam and scales and small weights.

The furnace was now within the Foley Partnership and from 1702–3 under its direct management through their manager William Rea.[148] Avenant and Wheeler held at least to Michaelmas 1710.[149]

In one technical detail of operation the furnace was unique among the Forest furnaces of the time: possibly independently of other iron-masters, possibly at the suggestion of Abraham Darby with whom the Foley partnership had some commercial dealings, Redbrook produced in 1716–17 4 tons of coke-smelted iron worth £6 a ton, compared with £7 15s for charcoal-smelted iron.[150] The discontinuance of the practice suggests that the experiment was unsuccessful, commercially, or technically. At that time, the furnace was capable of producing 600 tons of pig iron a year. It remained in the partnership until 1725.[151]

This furnace having come to an end, the Gage family built on or near the same site a new furnace which 29 September 1742 was let (with two forges at Lydbrook) by Lord Gage to Rowland Pytt, from the previous 24 June, for 21 years at £200 annually.[152] The terms included:

> The lessor to provide annually 2,000–3,000 short cords at 6s to be cut by him out of his coppices of 16 years and upwards, at a cording cost of 3d. The lessee to do the charcoaling and to have liberty to dig

turf and earth to make cabbins, coal hearths and other things necessary for that purpose.

The lessor to provide annually 600–2,000 dozens of cinders to be delivered at 5s a dozen bushels—washed cinders to be reckoned at 12 bushels to the dozen, but when foul and unwashed at 14 bushels— to be measured by the bushel used at Redbrook, the dimensions being 22in wide at the top, 21in at the bottom, and 8in deep.

The lessee to have liberty to take iron ore from the lessor's lands, paying 6s a dozen or 1s a ton.

The lessee to have one good fat buck and one doe in season out of the lessor's woods.

On 26 January 1757 the furnace was mortgaged by Viscount Gage to John Probyn.[153] Rowland Pytt junior was tenant (his father having died in 1756). In April 1761 Lord Gage was being urged by his steward, Creed, to renew the lease to Pytt,[154]—the reasons have been given earlier under 'Lydbrook forges'. Pytt died before a renewal was effected, and on 1 September 1762 Gage leased as from 5 July 1763 the furnace (with his two forges at Lydbrook) for 21 years at £300 to Richard Reynolds of Bristol and John Partridge senior and John Partridge junior of Ross-on-Wye.[155] The works had been 'lately occupied, by Rowland Pytt'. The lease gives the following estimate, dated 11 June 1762, of repairs required to the furnace:

	£	s	d
One waterwheel and shaft and trough to convey water to the wheel, and Bellows seats and Bosh, and sawing	37	5	0
Nails and ironwork	6	0	0
Timber for the above, 16 tons	33	16	0
Hauling timber	6	8	0
Tyling and all materials for that part of the repairs	17	12	4
Mason at the Furnace buildings	4	1	0
Carpenters work and materials inclusive of timber	7	16	0
Timber for buildings, 2 tons	4	4	0
Hauling timber	6	16	0
A new charge and repairing the bridge	20	0	0
	£143	18	4

Taylor's map (1777) shows the furnace together with the foundry which was run in conjunction with it, and from which 'ballast' was shipped in *The Monmouth* in November 1778 to be delivered at

Deptford Yard.[156] A traveller in 1781 referred to the works thus:[157]

> Hence the road [from High Meadow House] twines by a brawling stream, overhung by woods, to the village of Redbrook; and in my way, passing by an iron furnace, I entered therein, and was well received by the devils' who can bear the infernal heat, which soon drove me forth: they showed me the iron melting, and the immense bellows moved by water, eternally keeping alive the monstrous fire; for they work day and night, and make about 4 tons in 24 hours.

In 1792 we hear of the 'very extensive ironworks of Harford, Partridge & Co, of Bristol'[158]—presumably the furnace and its ancillary works. A traveller, writing in 1797, observed:[159] 'Some of the iron ore used here comes from Coleford and other places in the neighbourhood of the Forest of Dean, but the greater part is brought from Lancashire.'

The lease from Gage to Harford, Partridge & Co ended 5 July 1793, and the furnace was let (with the two forges at Lydbrook) to David Tanner.[160] Within 5 years Tanner was in financial difficulties and owing rent. He sublet the two forges to a Dr Hobbs and a Mr Ellaway but there is no evidence that he also let to them the Redbrook furnace. James Davies, steward to Gage, wrote to his master 11 March 1798 regarding Tanner's arrears of rent and informed him that little was done in the works at Lydbrook and that the furnace at Redbrook was never in blast:[161]

> They melt some pigs there which Partridge calls one of his whims; the Rolling Mill is much out of repair; and some of the furnaces are taken down and they never use that at all. [This refers to what remained of the old Upper Copper Works—though not used for copper since about 1730.]
>
> I saw Mr Wyndham the other day and told him you had said Ned might have the works if Tanner would give them up, and he immediately said he would engage Mr Cowsher, who would recommend a man that would manage it for him, and that the iron trade was the best trade in the Kingdom: for all the War the Ironmasters got plenty money now. But I told him to trouble himself no more than to ask what was the probable profits of a furnace and two forges, six or seven miles distant and each about a ¼ mile from a navigable river. I also told him not to mention that Tanner rented them, as all Ironmasters know something of each other.

On 20 September 1799 Davies wrote that Tanner was bankrupt and had sold machinery, including that in the Rolling Mill which he had no right to sell. Davies asked his master for a lease of the furnace (with two forges at Lydbrook) for 21 years, at the old rent (because the Rolling Mill was gone). The following month, Davies stated that £6,000 was needed to carry on the works. Mr Dighton was to loan him £4,000, James Hall was to advance £1,000 and Mr Pittman £1,000. Hall was to have £100 a year for managing; Pittman was to have £50 a year for looking after the wood and superintending the charcoalers (a post he had held for 30 years under the Partridges). On 11 December 1799 Davies advised that the capital was to be in eight shares—three held by members of the Gloucester Bank, three by himself, one by Hall, and one by Pittman. He pointed out in February 1800 that the following repairs were required: [162]

Furnace [This provides the first indication that a forge stood near the furnace]

A new inwalls, boshes, caves and hearth with a Chimney at Tunnell Head.

A new pair of Bellows (or cylinders which appears cheaper than bellows) a new wheel and shaft and gearing with pipes etc.

Stripping and tiling or repairing the Bridge House, Mine Shed, engine house and cast house.

Stripping, tiling and repairing three dwellinghouses adjoining the coal houses.

Stripping, tiling and repairing two dwellinghouses adjoining the cast house.

Stripping, tiling and repairing the stable, smithshop and buildings adjoining.

Repairing and putting the Stamps in order and all troughing belonging to the Furnace and Stamps.

Scouring, cleaning and repairing $5\frac{1}{2}$ pools with the repairation of flood gates etc.

Stripping, tiling and repairing two charcoal houses and carpenters shop adjoining etc.

Forge [This provides the first reference to the forge]

Tiling and repairing the forge, and repairing the machinery etc.

Erection of a chaffery wheel and appendages belonging together with the troughing to and from it.

Tiling and repairing a dwellinghouse betwixt the forge and pool.

Stripping, tiling and repairing the Great House and two houses adjoining.

Stripping, tiling and repairing the roof of the brick stove, and repairing the inside kiln etc.

Stripping, tiling and repairing two dwellinghouses in the back lane.
Stripping, tiling and repairing the carpenter and blacksmith shop.
Stripping, tiling and repairing one dwellinghouse and buildings adjoining.
NB An office, small brew house, and small stable with five or six small houses will be wanting and a small planishing forge and hammer with an air furnace; also a coal yard, a weighing machine for weighing of stone coal; and erection of a bay head near the furnace yard for a new pool.

Gage granted the lease, and Davies replied that he hoped to have the Redbrook furnace in blast by July 1800. By 1802 the ironworks (unlike the closed tinplate works) were busy, and 'the vale was filled with columns of dark smoke . . . and the noise of massive hammers'.[163] The partners ran the furnace (and the two Lydbrook forges) until 1804 when on 19 May Davies approached his master on the possibility of surrendering the lease, and of obtaining a longer lease if a sub-lessee could be found. Gage complained of 'the poor return to landlords of ironworks', and was not impressed. However, in February and April 1805 Davies hinted that Robert Thompson would take over from the partners if Gage would grant a lease for 21 years and sell his cordwood at 7s 6d a cord, cutting all his woods on an 18-year rotation. The proposals were : [164]

Robert Thompson is to advance £6,000 by instalments of £1,000 quarterly, the first payment to be made the first day of July 1805. In consideration of advancing the above sum in manner aforesaid, the present partners under the firm of James Davies & Co are to transfer ⅜ths of all the property belonging to the said partners under the firm of James Davies & Co including book debts and property in every place whatever belonging to the partnership concern to him.

James Davies originally advanced £3,000 as his proportion of capital in the said partnership of James Davies & Co and for which he had ⅜ths of the concern, and he has or will purchase of Sir Edwin Jeynes and Robert Morris the share they had in the said concern which was ⅜ths and for which they originally advanced £3,000, and his capital in the concern shall then stand at £6,000 for which he is to hold ⅜ths of the concern but no interest to be charged on the original advance from the commencement of the concern to the 1st July next.

James Hall originally had ⅛th share of the concern and advanced £1,000. He is to continue to hold ⅛th of the concern and to advance £1,000 more to make his capital equal in proportion to the share that he holds, to the sum to be advanced by Robert Thompson and James

21 Lydney Tinplate Works: *(left)* part was originally the 'Lower Forge'; *(below)* pickling and tin-plating buildings

22 (above) Lydney Tinplate Works: rear of tinning premises; *(below)* tinworkers' houses (three storey)

Davies but interest is not to be charged on his original advance till the 1st July next.

John Pittman originally had ⅛th share in the said concern, and another partner to be taken in if one can be found or Pittman's share to be disposed of in a manner mentioned at the end of this sheet.

James Hall to be manager and to reside at Upper Redbrook, and to have a house, firing, and all taxes allowed him and to receive a salary of £120 a year, until otherwise ordered by a majority of the partners, his own vote to be excluded, but not to make any new erections or alterations without the consent of James Davies and Robert Thompson given in writing. Partners to have access at all times to all books, papers, and correspondence whatever belonging to the concern, which are at all times to be kept in the compting houses belonging to the Company and at night locked up in bookcases provided for that purpose. The correspondence, purchases, sales, payments and receipts to be made by James Hall only so long as he is continued Manager, having proper assistants under him, and regular entries to be made of all transactions whatever, and monthly accounts to be regularly made out and sent to each partner requiring the same. Neither of the partners to borrow or lend money on the account or use of the partners without consent of all the partners in writing, or be bound for any person on the partnership account. No contracts to be made for more than 6 months but by a majority of the votes of the partners. Accounts to be made up annually and signed by all the partners with usual clauses for not being so, and £5 per cent per annum interest to be allowed on the capital of each partner in the trade and the profits (if any) afterwards to be divided. No part of the gains to be applied in any extension or increase of the said works or stock in trade without consent of James Davies and Robert Thompson. No partner to sell or dispose of his interest in the concern without consent of all the other partners, or shall any of the partners be concerned in any other ironworks of any description without consent in writing of all the other partners, except the said Robert Thompson, or unless the said James Hall is discontinued as Manager and is willing to dispose of his share to the other partners at the rate settled in the last settlement in the books. Upon the death of any of the parties, Executors, etc to stand in their place. And differences to be settled by Arbitration.

Lord Gage to engage by letter to grant a new lease of his Works and Woods for 21 years at the expiration of the first seven years from the commencement of the first lease granted to James Davies & Co, or when a tinplate manufactory is at work making tinplate. Lord Gage to engage by letter to cut into cordwood all his woods on his estates in Gloucestershire and Monmouthshire when they are 18 years growth and

I

not younger, without the consent of James Davies & Co in writing, and deliver it to the said James Davies & Co in the woods with liberty to coal it there at 7s 6d per cord, as also all the tops and lops of timber trees fallen on the said estates and to engage that nothing but wood hoops are to be taken out of any of the woods cut or from the tops and lops of timber trees as aforesaid. Lord Gage paying for recording the wood as usual. The Rolling Mill has not at present sufficient power to do work to any advantage and a very considerable sum of money will be necessary to make it sufficiently powerful: in consideration of the tenants doing so, the rent of the Rolling Mill to be reduced from £182 to £100 a year.

Gage added a note that the stipulations in regard to his woods were 'totally rejected in a personal conversation with Mr Davies about the 18 June 1805'. He was determined to manage his woods in his own way.[165]

Davies and his partners, and Gage, accepted the remainder of the proposals. Davies wrote to Gage 17 July 1805[166] that he had 'every reason to think your great kindness to me has saved me from ruin'; and on 24 July—'We are now out of debt'.[167] Thompson intended turning the old rolling mill site 'to the making of tin, as they do at the Lower Works'.[168] Davies wrote 7 September 1805, that Thompson had paid £1,000 and was to pay the remainder quarterly, 'but he never professed to set out in a large way at first, and blamed James Hall for going into such expense when his capital was so small'. Thompson had 'a man well skilled in tinplating to advance £2,000 for one share, who will live in the works and have a salary'. He had sent some iron to his brother who liked it very well, and had given another considerable order.[169]

A cash account of 'wages and refined and bar iron' is extant for the period 9 November 1798 to 14 June 1799,[170] which reveals that the following piecework rates etc were paid:

Pudling at 15s 6d per ton.
Rolling at 5s per ton.
Repairing furnace—3s.
Cleaning flues—2s.
Mending flues—3s 6d.
Melting at 4s per ton.
[Char] Coaling at 6s 6d per load.
Carrying at 6s a cord.
Cleaning boilers—2s 6d.
Getting sand—5s 4d.
8lb of Candles—6s 8d.

The total cash paid out by William Lane was £74 1s 1d. Refined iron totalling 31 tons 15¾cwt was delivered 19 January to 16 March 1799 to Cowley & Co and Messrs Corder. Bar iron totalling 117 tons 10¾cwt was delivered 7 January to 14 June 1799 to Cowley & Hatheway, and to others named. About that time the furnace and adjoining forge were used jointly with or as a foundry (qv). A plan of 1808[171] shows an outline of the 'complex', marked 'Upper Redbrook Furnace and Foundry'. Rent paid to Gage by 'The Redbrook Co' for the year to 5 November 1814 amounted to £373.[172]

According to Thomas Burgham, writing in 1864 (he was ironfounder at the 'Redbrook Iron Foundry' from about 1828 to 1870): [173]

> The furnace was supposed, from the cinders that have been made, to be in work for 500 to 600 years or more [probably c200 years]. It used to melt the Forest Iron Ore, and also the Lancashire Ore, with charcoal. The furnace to my knowledge worked up till the year 1816.

This date, 1816, for the demise of the furnace was after the building of the Monmouth tramroad, and there is no evidence that the furnace was ever served by the tramroad. It is likely that the furnace, with its long established lines of supply, and probably struggling economically, was unwilling to engage in the expense of a lengthy siding and the cost involved in lowering its materials down the incline; while if it was receiving ore from the Wye, the short haul was hardly worth the trouble.

In 1818, when Henry Davies was tenant, Gage sold the freehold to the Commissioners of Woods, who in turn sold to Henry Davies; the furnace was not used after 1816, but Davies probably ran the remainder of the complex (ie the forge-cum-foundry). He sold it in 1828 to Thomas Burgham, ironfounder—who ran it as a foundry (qv); he also used the Stampers, just below, for crushing blast furnace scruff for the bottle-glass industry (qv).

Thus Redbrook furnace, using charcoal (not coke) held out even longer than that at Flaxley (1802) and that at Lydney (c1810). The site now forms part of a little hamlet known at 'The Foundry'.

ANVIL WORKS The Foleys, in partnership with others from 1692, engaged in another minor branch of the iron trade in the Forest—the making of anvils, the normal blacksmith's anvil weighing on average 150lb. They had two anvil works: at Lydbrook, probably working to about 1694 and 'standing idle' from 1695; and near Gatcombe, working from 1695 to 1705, though in 1710–11 the premises were converted to a cornmill.[174]

The techniques of anvil making are not clearly described in the Foley Partnerships accounts, but two stages in manufacturing have been suggested by Johnson. The first, 'moulding' the anvil from 'loop' iron cast at the works from scrap iron and cinders; and the second, the 'steeling' of the anvils for which about a tenth of the weight of the anvil was required. The steel came from Bewdley. Pit coal appears to have been the sole fuel used. Of 87 anvils made at Gatcombe in 1699–1700, 31 went to Bewdley and 42 to Bristol. John Hatton, 'the head workman' received £25 a year, Thomas Pritchett, 'a caster of loop iron', 12d cwt plus 12d a day 'helping to put anvils together', and John Morgan, presumably a smith, 6d a week for 'smiteing'.

Another anvil works stood at Ruardean,[175] but apparently had no connection with the Foleys; and yet another at Aylburton.[176]

THE SITES TODAY Throughout this chapter information has been given on remnants of the works and on the appearance today of some of the sites. Later chapters will recount the subsequent history of industries which arose on some of the abandoned sites. Of the buildings of the second charcoal blast furnace period (1680–1794) there are a few remnants, eg at Guns Mill and Lydney. However, most of the buildings have been removed and the foundations of many have been obliterated by subsequent works, eg at Lydbrook and Soudley. There is abundant evidence of slag of the period, and occasionally there can be found stones and bricks coated on the inner side with slag and scoria. Most in evidence are the remnants of sluices, races, dams, pools and ponds. Strangely, there is no evidence of cast iron grave slabs and firebacks. Yet many place-names recall works which have disappeared; examples include: at Cannop, 'Old Furnace Level'; at Upper Redbrook, 'Furnace Wood and Furnace Hill'; at Blakeney, 'Foundry Bottom'; at Lydney, 'Old Furnace Cottages'; and at Longhope, 'Furnace Mill'. All bear witness to the local charcoal iron industry which virtually ended towards the close of the eighteenth century—to be followed by the period of the coke furnaces, discussed in Chapter 3.

Copper Works (Redbrook):   1690-1730

Rhys Jenkins in his history of the two Redbrook Copper Works,[177] did not give any reason why Redbrook was selected c1690 for the industry. There is no evidence of calamine, or copper ore being found in or near the district; thus ore had to be brought from Cornwall to

Chepstow and then up the Wye. Perhaps there was some advantage due to the import of ore being 'back-carriage' in otherwise empty boats. The selection of Redbrook may have been influenced by the availability of abundant wood, charcoal and mineral coal; also by streams ample for power, and by facilities on the Wye for loading and transport. Buildings were also available: for the Lower Copper Works and for the Upper Works there were premises (uses unknown) shown on a map of 1608.[178]

The Lower Works (earliest reference, 1692) stood near the mouth of the Valley Brook, partly on the lower section of the site later used by the Lower Tinplate Works, and partly a little nearer the Wye where stood the 'Coperas' House—a pantile-roofed building (now the site of a petrol filling station). The Upper Works (earliest reference, 1691), in premises at one time a paper-mill, stood near the mouth of the Newland-Redbrook stream not far from where it enters the Wye; the site later became that of the Upper Tinplate Works.

LOWER REDBROOK COPPER WORKS   This was begun c1691–2 by The Company of Copper Miners in England, in conjunction with Thomas Chambers. The year of commencement may have been earlier: in 1690, 50 tons of ore were sent from St Ives to Chepstow. In 1691 53 tons arrived and in 1692 502 tons, increasing in 1697 to 986 tons, brought in vessels from Plymouth and Fowey.[179] The first record of copper produced is that of 30 tons exported to Gloucester and Bristol via Chepstow in 1693.[180] In 1694 the Dean Free Miners fixed the price of firecoal to be delivered to both works.[181]

According to Swedenborg,[182] there were at Redbrook c1700 'two buildings, one consisting of 10 melters for smelting the ore, and 6 burning furnaces or calcining kilns, and 4 clotters for smelting the copper stone; 2 furnaces with a breast *(pectore)*; and 4 refining hearths'. The process was:

> In the ovens of the reverberator, which is called a Melter, the ore was smelted in the same manner as has been described; but the copper stone obtained here was crushed by rammers and the dust was conveyed thence to the calcining kilns, which were exactly like the common ovens of the reverberator, in order that the dust might be reverberated by the flame. Four hundred lb of copper stone were calcined each time, and the work was effected within 12 hours: an equable and moderate heat was employed, so that the pulverised copper stone should not melt; the redder it appeared, the better; wherefore also it was kept constantly stirred during the calcination itself. It was necessary

to mix ashes with the coal, as has previously been told, namely, in order that the fire might be tempered thereby. It [? the copper stone] was then conveyed from the calcining kiln into the ovens called clotters, of similar construction to the former, so that the smelting might be begun therein. They did not employ a greater degree of heat than was necessary to melt the stone; wherefore also it was not stirred as before, but as soon as it began to melt like a clot it was taken out even if the pieces were of very rough shape. If, however, the mass was less fluid, some portion of sand was added, which was of assistance when it was to be drawn off. These pieces were broken up into smaller ones of the size of eggs, and put into the breast *(pectorali)* furnace, as it is called, and thus they were smelted into coarse copper. This furnace was 4 feet high from the bottom. Neither were the charges put in at the front part, as is the custom at other places, but at the side through a certain hole, that is, at the site allotted to the bellows; at the front or breast *(pectore)* of the furnace there was an orifice designed for tapping the copper. The furnace was of equal breadth both above and below: from the tap-hole to the side wall it was 2 feet, and from the bellows side to the opposite side, where the charges were put in, the distance was 22 inches: above the furnace (was a chimney) which was called the stack, leading to the chimney or passage for the smoke; this structure therefore, for the better attraction of the draught was narrower, namely 16 or 18 inches in breadth, and it was carried obliquely towards the said chimney; and it was 14 or 15 feet high. The furnace was built of stones; the sides were smeared over inside with Stourbridge clay; the hearth was made of stone offering the utmost resistance to the fire. The hole for tapping the scoriae was situated by the hole for tapping the copper: it was only 6 or 8 inches high. As a general thing, the quantity of measures of coals were put in through the furnace was twice as great as the quantity of copper stone, so that 6 measures of coals were put in to 3 of copper stone. One ton of copper stone was passed through the furnace within the space of 12 hours. They used fossil coal *(carbone fossili)*, which however had previously been burnt and as it was calcined [= coke]; but the greater portion of the sulphur was expelled therefrom by calcination. The scoriae produced from the furnace during the smelting of the ore were used as a menstruum. The refining has previously been treated of. In this place the best kind of copper was produced: 3 tons of fossil coals *(carbonum fossilium)* were said to be consumed to obtain 1 ton of copper.

In 1708 we hear that 'the famous Copper-Work that turns so much to the advantage of the nation, and the benefit of the undertakers, is managed by Swedes and other foreigners'.[183] In 1716 the company advertised to sell or let 'the lease for the Cupilo, or Copper Works at Lower Redbrook', and it was taken over by Thomas Chambers junior, acting as a nominee for his uncle Thomas Chambers, until 1720 when the company was reconstructed. Thomas senior, who later became its Governor, died in 1726, and the Redbrook property passed to his daughter who in 1748 sold it to the company. By 1725 the works, fuelled by coal, comprised 16 'furnaces'—this number being necessary because of the many operations involved.

Writing c1734, Swedenborg[184] observed that 'At Redbrook there are at the present day 6 reverberating ovens for smelting ore; 3 melters for smelting the copper-stone, 1 slowing or setting-furnace or refining kiln, 2 smelting hearths for the spreading or beating out of the copper into plates.' Of the process being used he wrote: [185]

There is not much difference from the method previously described, except that the copper stone is crushed to dust by crushing hammers, and afterwards in a mill similar to that used for crushing wheat, and then calcined for the space of 24 hours; it is then smelted in the melters; and thus is changed into copper, which is then refined. When calcined copper stone is fused into copper, the scoriae flow out and are kept apart or separate, and are usually passed through a common fusing furnace, and fused by the aid of burnt fossil coals, which are called charcoals.

R. F. Tylecote has commented on the above: [186]

The furnaces used by Agricola (c1556) were small shaft furnaces, and for the complex series of operations required, many of this type were installed in one plant. The furnace operations described by Agricola are: (1) the separating of the sulphide from the gangue to give a matte (mixed with iron and copper sulphide), (2) the roasting of the matte to give an oxide and the slagging of the iron, and (3) the reduction of the copper. The last two operations were very slow and were therefore conducted in a large number of furnaces. At Keswick in 1564, 10cwt of dressed ore yielded about 3cwt of matte which finally gave 1cwt of copper. The smelter had only six furnaces, of which not more than four were in use at any one time. The matte was then roasted with peat which took eight days and gave black copper (oxide) which was reduction smelted once a month to give an impure copper. This operation could be done inside in shaft furnaces or outside in 'stalls'. So far peat and coal were the fuels, and limestone was needed as a flux. For the final refining which was done eight times, charcoal was needed since at this stage the elimination of sulphur was one of the aims. Again, many shaft furnaces were used for this purpose. By the beginning of the eighteenth century, reverberatory furnaces (or cupolas) were gradually replacing blowing houses for tin in Cornwall, and I suspect had already replaced most of the shaft furnaces for copper smelting. These furnaces worked by natural or induced draught, and therefore did not need water power for blowing. Furthermore, they could use coal for heating at all stages of the smelting of copper, although small quantities of raw wood were needed for refining, as indeed they are today. The capital cost was a good deal higher than that of the large number of comparatively simple shaft furnaces. It is clear that the changeover was a gradual process—as shown by the retention of some shaft furnaces at Lower Redbrook after the cupola had been installed.

The industry at the lower works probably ended a few years later, though in 1741 the Dean Free Miners were still fixing the price of coal to both works.[187] In 1771 the company leased the premises to Townshend and Wood for the making of tinplate (qv). How long this lease and manufacture continued is unknown, but in 1790 the company sold the property for £2,750 to David and William Tanner of Tintern and Monmouth, when it comprised: [188]

All that freehold copper work consisting of furnaces, forges, foundries, mills, utensils, implements, erections and works for calcining, smelting, refining, hammering and manufacturing copper ores and copper, together with three large ponds or reservoirs for supplying the work . . . water grist mill or tucking mill near adjoining a water grist mill formerly of Warren Jane, then in the tenure of William Carter, but since converted into a copper work . . . also that messuage or tenement in Lower Redbrook late in the occupation of Thomas Chambers deceased, formerly a water corn or grist mill, but converted into a large copper work.

The sale also included two dwellinghouses, built for the accommodation of the managers, one occupied by John Taylor and the other by John Wright, 'refiner of copper' (who in 1756 obtained a patent for his 'method of raising steam for working fire engines'). One of the premises may have been built partly of copper slag blocks, with the date 1771 over the doorway, which stood below the Tinplate Works but was demolished in 1943 to make room for an extension to the premises. Further evidence of the blocks of slag, particularly as wall coppings, are to be seen throughout Lower Redbrook and in the walls of the nearby Highbury Farm. The surfaces of the blocks are convoluted, as in iron slag, and their colour is black and dark green. Analysis of a specimen showed the content to be Cu, 0·5 per cent; Zn, 0·9 per cent; Sn, 3·2 per cent and lead 0·9 per cent.[189] There is no doubt that the ore giving rise to this material was, in view of its high tin content, of Cornish origin. The remainder of the specimen was mainly silica, with FeO 17·7 per cent and CaO 6·0 per cent; it contained visible pieces of quartz which had not dissolved in the slag.

The subsequent history of the site and premises is discussed in Chapter 4 under the Lower Tinplate Works.

UPPER REDBROOK COPPER WORKS   This was begun before 1691. On 25 March that year, John Coster (1647–1718), late of the parish of Augustines, in Bristol, but of a family originating from the Forest of Dean,[190] took a lease for 60 years at £20 yearly from Henry Benedict Hall, of:[191]

> All that Mill or those Mills formerly used or imployed as a paper mill, and now converted into a Copper Works with the appurtenances together with the dwelling house, stables, smyth's shop and several outhouses with the gardens and backs, courts, yards and other appurtenances—all c one acre and in Upper Redbrook, which are and for several years have been in the occupation of John Coster and are bounded by the highway from Highmeadow towards the River Wye and Monmouth on the northwest, a grist mill called the Kings Mill on the northeast, an old roadway between the said demised premises and the lands now or late of George Wyrhall on the southeast and a little tenement in the tenure of Mary Palmer and another tenement in the tenure of John Howell (alias Jones) on the southwest.

Kings Mill and other features shown on the map of 1608,[192] prove that the works were on the site later used by the Upper Tinplate Works.

Although members of the Coster family had been connected with both the Forest of Dean and Cornwall, John Coster in 1685 (aged 38) had been 'chief agent and workman and a sharer therein' to Sir Clement Clerke and his son, Talbot, of Bristol. In 1694, the Dean Free Miners fixed for the works delivered prices for fire-coal.[193]

In 1709 John Coster surrendered his lease for a new one made by Benedict Hall (only son of Henry Benedict Hall deceased) to him and Edward Colston, merchant, of Mortlake in Surrey.[194] The new lease was for 99 years on the survivorship of either of two of Coster's sons, Thomas and John, or of John Tompson of Redbrook. The rent was £20 per annum, plus a 'fine' of £1,600.

The following year, 6 March 1710, there is a reference to 'Surrender of premises to Benedict Hall by the Committee for the Management of the present stock of the Copper works at Upper Redbrook'; the premises comprised 'a mill formerly used as a paper mill, and now converted into a Copper Works with house'.[195] On the same day, Hall leased the property to John Coster senior for 99 years at £20 annually.[196] In 1711[197] John Coster junior purchased for £300 from George Wyrall and others 'the Kings Mill and several lands, tenements and hereditaments lying near the Upper Copper Works some of which extend to and lie contiguous with the Cinder Hill [slag bank] appertaining to the furnace of Benedict Hall'. The land ran up the east side of the road from Kings Mill (later rebuilt as Quicks Mill) to a large deposit of slag (cinders) just below the stampers mill—ore-crushing plant (qv)—which itself lay just below Hall's blast furnace.[198] John Coster senior carried on and, according to his will made in 1716, he owned 74 shares in the Upper Works and also had some interest in the 'Upper Stampers' (the stampers mill mentioned above). After his death, 13 October 1718 (*vide* a mural in Newland Church) his eldest son Thomas controlled the works, which in 1725 had 26 'furnaces'. Of the other two sons, John seems to have devoted himself to mining in Cornwall (he died in 1731 at the age of 43, and was buried at Newland); Robert lived for some time in Cornwall (he died at Bristol in 1736 at the age of 39).

Thomas Coster, the most important of the three brothers, had from about 1712 been in charge of the Bristol Brass Company. He ran the Upper Redbrook Copper Works from 1718. In 1730 he leased works at Neath, and throughout much of his life he was also engaged in copper mining in Cornwall. He assigned the Copper Works c1730 to the Brass Work Company of Bristol, and he settled in that city, for which he was one of the Members of Parliament from 1734 to his death in 1739.[199] The assigning of the lease of the Copper Works led to much trouble between Thomas Coster and Viscount Gage on whose behalf it was later asserted that the Brass Work Company had taken to the works 'with no other view than to ruin and destroy them, they being then in great repute, and by that means bring their trade from thence to their own work at Bristol'.[200] In 1735, witnesses on behalf of Gage estimated the necessary repairs at £1,980; witnesses for Coster and the company estimated them at £500 to £600, and that year workmen employed by the company 'on pretence of mending and covering the works did considerable damage by pulling down the main chimney stacks belonging to the 25 furnaces, and covering them over with tiles'.

In 1737 Gage brought against Thomas Coster an action which ensued for seven years. On 29 December 1739 four local craftsmen viewed the works at the request of William Gough, agent to Gage, 'and found them in a most ruinous condition, being an entire heap of rubbish, not one of the 25 furnaces for melting of copper left standing complete, but for the greatest part of them all levelled to the ground, all the hearths of the furnaces and most of the chimney stacks being pulled down and destroyed, and likewise most of the iron works and iron plates belonging to the furnaces carried away'. Furthermore, 'all the wheels, shafts, bellows, trows, sluices, and other necessaries thereto belonging were gone into an almost total decay, as also the dwellinghouse and the other buildings belonging to the Copper Works'. The craftsmen gave the following estimate of necessary repairs: [201]

	£
Repair of 25 furnaces for melting copper	1,125
Repair of 4 wheels, shafts, bellows, troughs, sluices, and other necessaries, with timber, iron and other materials for same	220
Repair of the several chimneys or stacks with materials and iron cramps for doing the same and other mason work	350
Repair of the timber work in the roofs and other timber work	5
Other repairs not above specified	10
Iron work, viz: cast plates for flooring, and other cast iron taken away about 40 tons at £7	280
Repair of the dwellinghouse	25
Repair of the lower hammer house	10
	£2,025

In the same year, 1739, William Cook, agent to the Brass Work Company of Bristol for the Upper Copper Works, informed William Williams, Clerk to the company that William Gough, agent to Viscount Gage, had demanded possession of the works the lease of which the late Mr Coster had assigned to the company. Cook handed over the works on Williams' instructions, at which time 'all the works, wheels, engines, and buildings were in a most ruinous condition, except the tiling part of the roofs, and all the hearths of the furnaces destroyed'. Furthermore, 'all the iron plates, charging plates, anvils, working tools and other iron work belonging to the furnaces and copper works had been carried to Bristol'. Cook had been paid by Thomas Coster for hauling the implements down to the River Wye.

Thomas Coster died that year, 1739, and soon afterwards Tompson (the last of the 'three lives' in the lease) also died, whereupon Gage took possession and levied his suit against Coster's heir—Robert Hoblyn—with the Brass Company[202] involved as sub-lessees.[203] About 1740, Thomas Viscount Gage gave a lease of his works to another tenant at £25 a year 'but could not obtain any fine by reason of the charges the new tenant was to be at for putting the works in repair, though the said tenant had in his lease several hundred pounds worth of copper slag granted to him'.[204] The name of the new tenant (name not given) was probably Rowland Pytt to whom from 24 June 1742 was leased Gage's furnace.[205] The lawsuit was settled in 1744 when Coster's executors paid £500 to Viscountess Gage (daughter of Benedict Hall).[206] Branches of the Coster family continued to live at Coleford during the eighteenth century.[207]

Viscount Gage on 26 January 1757 mortgaged to John Probyn the manor of English Bicknor including 'the works for making copper in Upper Redbrook'.[208] On 1 September 1762 Gage when letting his Upper Redbrook furnace (with two Lydbrook forges) to Richard Reynolds of Bristol and John Partridge senior and John Partridge junior of Ross-on-Wye, gave them 'liberty to use the Stampers belonging to the Upper Copper Works without paying rent until Lord Gage shall let the Copper Works or want it for his own use'.[209] The premises of the Upper Copper Works in the year 1786 were included in a list of the establishments of the Bristol Brass Company, but they had not been used for copper since about 1730. David Tanner took a lease of them as a small adjunct to his tinplate-making (qv) in 1793: the north-eastern part of the premises were owned by Jane Quick of Bath, widow, who that year leased to Tanner thus: [210]

> A mansion or dwellinghouse at Upper Redbrook lately occupied by John Green, also the Brewhouse and Outhouses, and the old mill-place heretofore called the Upper Hammer Works [presumably the Upper Stampers], and the ground whereupon the old grist mill called the King's Mill did formerly stand together with the water grist mill and flour mill [Quick's mill] thereon erected; also all that old Copper-house formerly used for the making or working of copper, all which premises were in the tenure of William and John Green.

The remainder (western) part of the premises (previously part of the Upper Copper Works) was still owned by Viscount Gage. They reverted to him after Tanner's bankruptcy in 1798, and he leased them in 1800 to his steward James Davies and his partners in connection with the Upper Redbrook furnace (and two forges at Lydbrook). The partnership (discussed in Chapter 2) lasted until 1805, when the premises were let to Robert Thompson, who may have done some tinplating there before 1818—when Gage sold his Gloucestershire properties to the Commissioners of Woods. The Commissioners offered the Redbrook property for sale in July of that year, when it was occupied by Henry Davies and described as 'The Redbrook Tin Works, Rolling Mill, etc, 3r 13p'.[211] The premises were dilapidated and were soon demolished. By 1818–28[212] a row of cottages stood on that part of the site lately owned by Gage, while just above stood the property of the Quick family (including their corn mill—earlier, the Kings Mill). On the lower part of the site a brewery stood from 1825 to 1926.

References to Chapter 2

1 Hart. *Royal Forest*, 181.
2 Johnston. 'The Foley Partnerships: The Iron Industry at the End of the Charcoal Industry', *Econ Hist Rev* 2nd Ser, 4, 1951–2, 322–40.
3 Ibid, 324.
4 Ibid.
5 Ibid, 338.
6 Schubert. *History . . .* , op cit, 350, 351.
7 Johnston. 'The Foley Partnerships . . .', 339.
8 Hulme, E. W. *The Statistical History of the British Iron Trade from 1717 to 1750.*
9 Johnston. 'New light . . .', 137.
10 GRO D1677; GG 1473.
11 GRO D421/E45.
12 GRO D36/E16.
13 GRO D1677; GG1473.
14 GRO D421/E44.
15 Ibid, E45.
16 Rudder, S. *New History of Gloucestershire*, 1779.
17 Wyrall, George. 'Observations on the Iron Cinders found in the Forest of Dean and its neighbourhood', *BGAS*, II, 1877–8, 216–34.
18 Probably Wyrall had in mind the use of limestone.
19 *The Torrington Diaries*, ed C. B. Andrews, I, 1924, 18, 19.
20 Scrivenor, N. *A History of the Iron Trade*, 1854, 86.
21 Hart. *The Free Miners*, 103.
22 Information from Dr Jennifer Tann.
23 Johnston. 'The Foley Partnerships . . .', 338.
24 Information from the late Rhys Jenkins.
25 Hulme, op cit.
26 Nat Liby Wales, Mynde MSS, 2099.
27 Information from the late Rhys Jenkins.
28 Johnston. 'The Foley Partnerships . . .', 339.

29 GRO D421/T104.
30 Hulme, op cit.
31 Ibid.
32 Nicholls. *History* . . . , 228; *Iron Making* . . . , 59.
33 Nicholls. *History* . . . , 228.
34 Hart. *Royal Forest*, 44.
35 Hart. *The Free Miners*, 103.
36 Nicholls. *Iron Making* . . . , 53.
37 HRO Foley Papers F/VI.
38 GRO D2184, Foley Abstract donated by C. E. Hart.
39 Johnston. 'The Foley Partnerships . . .', 338.
40 Anon. *A Picturesque Guide through Wales and the Marches*, Edn 1795, II, 21.
41 MS *penes me*.
42 Ibid.
43 Hart. *The Free Miners*, 103.
44 HRO Foley Papers F/VI/DAC/1.
45 HMC 13th Rpt App II, 292: MSS of the Duke of Portland II, Thomas Baskerville's Journeys in England, temp Car II (1682).
46 GRO GG1557.
47 A note in Aris's *Birmingham Gazette*, 8 April 1751 reads: 'We hear from Lydbrook in Gloucestershire, that on the 27th past in the morning, the wife of Samuel Bashick, belonging to the Forge at that place, cut her throat in so terrible a manner, that, though Mr Steel, a Surgeon in Coleford, was sent for, who sewed up the wound, she expired in two hours after. This unhappy woman and her husband were Methodists; and which is worthy observation, they had just been very earnest in their Devotions before she committed this rash act. She has left seven children, the last of which she lay in with about nine weeks ago.'
48 Johnston. 'New light . . .', 142.
49 Ibid, 143.
50 GRO D421/Z4, Gage A/c Book, f36.
51 Ibid, E44.
52 *The Collected Papers of Rhys Jenkins, Trans Newcomen Soc* 1953, 224.
53 GRO D1677, GG1473.
54 Ibid.
55 Ibid and D637.
56 Shelbourne MSS, 104; Hart. *The Free Miners*, 234.
57 GRO D637/III/8.
58 *British Universal Directory*, 1792.
59 GRO D1677, GG 1545.
60 Ibid, 57, 57a.
61 GRO D637/II/8.
62 Ibid, VII/7.
63 Hart. *The Free Miners*, 103.
64 Johnston. 'New light . . . ', 137.
65 *Flaxley Cartulary*, 34.
66 Hulme, op cit.
67 GRO D36/E12 ff 128–129.
68 Ibid, E7/2.

69   Rudge, T. *History of Gloucestershire*, II, 96; Nicholls. *Iron Making* . . . , 55; *Flaxley Cartulary*, 34.
70   Ibid.
71   See deliveries in Hart. *Royal Forest*, 191.
72   Nicholls. *History* . . . , 190; *Iron Making* . . . , 55.
73   *Flaxley Cartulary*, 35.
74   Nicholls. *Iron Making* . . . , 55.
75   Information from the late Rhys Jenkins.
76   GRO D421/T18, 22.
77   Hart. *The Free Miners*, 103.
78   GRO D421/E9.
79   Ibid, L15.
80   Hulme, op cit.
81   GRO D421/T18, L15, E53.
82   This lay midway between the Lydney Upper and Middle Forges. In 1802 the tenant of the 'Old Furnace' site was Richard Symonds (PRO Map of 1802).
83   GRO D421/E53.
84   Ibid, L15.
85   Ibid, T69, L15.
86   Ibid, T69.
87   Ibid, L15.
88   Ibid, E45.
89   Brooke, E. H. *Chronology of the Tinplate Works of Great Britain*, 1944, 74, 166.
90   GRO D421/E44.
91   Ibid, L20, T45, E44.
92   Ibid, E44.
93   Ibid.
94   Ibid.
95   Rudder, S. *'New History of Gloucestershire'*, 1779.
96   GRO D421/E45.
97   Ibid, E44.
98   Ibid.
99   Ibid, 120.
100 Ibid, E44.
101 Brooke, op cit, App, 1949, 203. In 1786, the company, nearly all of whose six partners were Quakers, was joined by John Partridge: the firm later became Harford, Partridge & Co.
102 GRO D421/E45, D2166.
103 St Pierre Documents, Mon Rec Office, D501, 473/4.
104 GRO D421/T104.
105 Ibid, E45.
106 Ibid.
107 Ibid, T104. The GRO D421 sources have been used for this and some later references, but many of the originals of the deeds are to be found in GRO D1329.
108 See Reference 82 *supra*.
109 GRO D421/E53.
110 Lydney Park Estate Office Rental MSS, 1781.
111 *Trans Newcomen Soc*, XVIII 1937–38, 200.
112 *The Torrington Diaries*, 1781, ed C. B. Andrews, I, 1924, 310: The

Hon John Byng (later Viscount Torrington) in his Tour of the West in 1781.

113   *Trans Newcomen Soc*, op cit, 199.
114   GRO D421/T104.
115   Ibid, 'In 1796 in Stourbridge were two Glass Houses of Pidcock, of the Dial Houses' (Court, op cit).
116   GRO D421/T76.
117   Anon. *A Picturesque Guide* ..., op cit, II, 21.
118   GRO D421/T105; PRO Map of 1809–10; PRO Map of 1802.
119   Rudge, op cit, II, 122. In c1789 Homfray was operating in Ebbw Vale, and in April 1791 he entered into partnership with Harford, Partridge & Co (Brooke, *Chronology* ..., 50, 51).
120   Rudge, op cit.
121   *Gloucester Journal* 21 May 1810; GRO D421/E46.
122   The reference to 'a forge used as a plating forge' has no connection with tinplating, but to the welding together of a small piece of steel and a larger piece of iron. Steel was expensive, yet necessary for the cutting edge of tools, such as scythes, spades, etc. So a piece of steel was fire-welded to the end of a piece of iron to form the cutting-edge, which could be hardened.
123   Hart. *The Free Miners*, 103.
124   GRO 2184, f10.
125   Nicholls. *Iron Making* ..., 53.
126   Johnston. 'New light ... ', 135.
127   Ibid, 136, 141, 142.
128   Ibid, 142.
129   Ibid, 143.
130   Bridgewater, N. P. 'Report on Archaeology', *WNFC* 38(1), 1964, 89.
131   GRO Q/Rum: when William Partridge & Co had a wharf.
132   E17/140.
133   Gilpin, William. *Observations on the River Wye*, 1st Edn 1782.
134   Shaw, S. *A Tour to the West of England*, 1789, 195.
135   Scrivenor, op cit, 1841, 361.
136   Information from the late Rhys Jenkins.
137   Ireland, Samuel. *Picturesque Views on the River Wye*, 1797, 88, 89; 'A considerable iron furnace in the vicinity'.
138   Wedlake E., and Britton J. *The Beauties of England and Wales, VI*, 1805, 527.
139   E17/40; copy in GRO.
140   Severn & Wye Railway Minute Book, 9 April 1822.
141   Fosbrooke. *Wye Tour*, 3rd Edn 1826, 34.
142   *Forester* (newspaper) 5 Dec 1873.
143   A letter from John Partridge regarding roads in 1827 is in GRO Q/SRR 1827B/4.
144   *The Wye Tour*, by the Editor of the *Ross Gazette*, 1885, 2nd Edn, 109.
145   Cooke, W. H. *Collections ... History of the County of Hereford*, 1882.
146   GRO D1677, GG 1031.
147   Ibid, GG 1557.
148   Johnston. 'New light ... ', 136.
149   GRO GG 1557.

23 (above) Lydbrook Ironworks: remains from the north; (below) Lydbrook Cable Works in course of construction, alongside the River Wye, c1912

24 (above) Richard Thomas (1837–1916), founder of Richard Thomas & Co whose first Tinplate Works was at Lydbrook; *(below)* Harold Smith, founder of the Lydbrook Cable Works

150 Johnston. 'New light . . . ', 136; 'The Foley Partnership . . . ', 331.
151 Johnston. 'New light . . . ', 141.
152 GRO D421/E44.
153 Ibid, D1677, GG 1121.
154 Ibid, D1677, GG 1473.
155 Ibid, D1677, GG 1123, 1545, 1557, D637.
156 Ibid, D326/Z4.
157 *The Torrington Diaries*, op cit, 1954, 37.
158 *British Universal Directory*, 1792.
159 Ireland, Samuel, op cit, 1797, 128.
160 GRO D1677, GG 1545.
161 Ibid.
162 Ibid, D1677, GG 1545, 56, 57A.
163 Manby, G. W. *An Historical and Picturesque Guide . . . through Monmouthshire*, 1802, 248.
164 GRO D1677, GG 1545, 104A.
165 Ibid, D1677, GG 1545, 96, 97, 104A.
166 Ibid, GG 1545, 106.
167 Ibid, 107.
168 Ibid, 92, 108.
169 Ibid, 108.
170 Ibid, D326/Z4.
171 Ibid, Q/Rum/30.
172 Ibid, D1677, GG 1545, 1149.
173 Letter from Thomas Burgham 25 Feb. 1864 *penes me*.
174 Johnston. 'New light . . . ', 140.
175 Schubert. *History* . . . , 312.
176 GRO D421/T45: '1750: Millen Mill or where an Anvil Works have formerly been erected in Aylburton.' Its right to water was restricted to when the same was not required for the ironworks rented to Rowland Pytt.
177 Jenkins, Rhys. 'The Copper Works at Redbrook and at Bristol', *BGAS*, 63, 1942, 145–67.
178 MR 879/D3152/3.
179 Waters, Ivor. *About Chepstow*, 1952, 21; BM, Add MSS 21567.
180 Jenkins, Rhys, op cit, 148.
181 Hart. *The Free Miners*, 114.
182 Swedenborg, Emanuel. 'Treatise on Copper', *Regnum Subterraneum, sive Minerals de Cupro*, Dresden and Leipzig, 1734: Published in 3 vols typescript, 1938 by British Non-Ferrous Metals Research Association (BM Cup 124719, 138).
183 Rogers, Nathan. *Memoirs of Monmouthshire*, 1708.
184 Swedenborg, op cit, 139.
185 Ibid.
186 Information from R. F. Tylecote.
187 Hart. *The Free Miners*, 132.
188 Jenkins, Rhys, op cit, 159, 160.
189 Information from R. F. Tylecote.
190 Jenkins, Rhys, op cit, 150.
191 Nat Liby Wales, Mynde MSS 1923.
192 MR 879/D3152/3.
193 Hart. *The Free Miners*, 114.

K

194   Nat Liby Wales, Mynde MSS 1923.
195   GRO D1677, GG 1092.
196   Ibid, GG 1093.
197   Nat Liby Wales, Mynde MSS 1269.
198   GRO D2166, Map c1818–28.
199   Jenkins, Rhys, op cit, 156.
200   GRO D1677, GG 1355.
201   Ibid, D1677, GG 1352.
202   Soyres, D. de. *Trans Newcomen Soc.*
203   Lincolnshire Rec Office, Holywell MSS 35/1.
204   GRO D1677, GG 1357.
205   Ibid, D421/E44.
206   Bristol Rec Office, Jarrit Smith Papers, 168, no 12.
207   Nat Liby Wales, Mynde MSS 1923, 1517–19, 1727–31, 1269, 2092–116, 2681; GRO D637/II/2/T1.
208   GRO D1677, GG 1121.
209   Ibid, GG 1557, D637.
210   Ibid, D2166.
211   Ibid, D627/VII/7, I/37.
212   GRO D2166, Map c1818–28.

Three
The Coke Iron Industry
(1795 - 1894)

INTRODUCTION While in the eighteenth century blast furnaces using charcoal were producing pig iron on the fringe of Dean's woods at Lydney, Redbrook, Flaxley, and Bishopswood, other parts of Britain were experimenting with coke-smelting. Subsequently the iron industry no longer depended so much on charcoal, but more on an abundant supply of good coke, which soon became the major factor of location, thereby making the coalfields the centres of the iron-smelting industry.

Dean, not working seams of coal suitable for producing good coke, was unaffected by the inventions. The coking properties of the coal being worked in the Blainau and Merthyr districts were far superior to the coking properties of Dean's outcrop and other easily worked coal (the better coals lay at a greater depth in the basin). Furthermore, there was not the incentive near the Forest to adopt coke-smelting, because the abundant supplies of wood for charcoal and water for power induced the neighbouring ironmasters to adhere to the old process for many years—indeed, the furnace at Flaxley used charcoal until 1802, while Redbrook and other furnaces followed suit for many more years. Coke had been tried at Redbrook in 1716–17,[1] also in about 1773 at Lydney where it had been 'found not to answer'.[2] In 1761, Creed, steward to Lord Gage at Redbrook, observed to his master 'the new method of making iron in England with coal'.[3]

When coke-smelting was eventually used in Dean, furnaces once more arose both within and almost adjacent to the wooded area— in 1795 at Cinderford, in 1799 at Parkend, and in the same year one was planned for Whitecliff, to be followed by others at Darkhill, Soudley and Bromley Hill (Oakwood). They are described later. At the Lydney furnace in about 1803, much ore was smelted by coke, but 'where pitcoal was used the iron was of inferior tenacity and ductibility'.[4] The furnaces procured coke by 'charking' coal in heaps in the

119

open in a somewhat similar manner to that employed for the production
of charcoal. Contemporaneously steam power raised by small coal overcame the unreliable supply of blast by water and wheel, though at
Parkend a huge water-wheel continued to assist with blast until about
1827.

The use of coke, and the introduction of the steam engine and blowing cylinders in place of bellows, led to new designs in blast furnaces.
At Parkend, Whitecliff, Darkhill, Soudley, and Bromley Hill sites were
chosen where the terrain provided a natural point for charging the
furnace. At Cinderford presumably an incline from ground level had
to be introduced, up which the charge, loaded in small wagons, was
pushed—a development which later became mechanised. Evidence is
lacking of the shape of the furnaces at Cinderford (1795) and Parkend
(1799), but there are remnants, described later, of those at Whitecliff,
Darkhill, and Bromley Hill. As to furnaces in general, according to
Morton: [5]

> Modifications were applied to the square stone built charcoal furn-
> aces, and many of the characteristic features of that period remained
> well into the 19th century, eg even when the external shape of the furnace
> changed from square to round, the arched fore-hearth with a dam over
> which the molten slag flowed continuously still existed.
>
> Because of the quantity of heat carried through the furnace by the
> ascending gases, and in particular by the large volume of inactive
> nitrogen, an endeavour to reclaim some of this heat tended towards
> taller furnaces, and the general limit of 20ft high extended to 30ft or
> more. With increased blast availability, the number of tuyeres increased
> to three (one on each of three sides of the square outside shape), with
> a consequent rise in output—thus it became necessary to tap the iron
> at more frequent periods, usually once in each twelve hour shift. The
> hearth, bosh and sidewalls continued to be made from best quality
> sandstone, but the tendency towards higher lime slags placed a limit
> on this type of refractory material, and higher refractory fireclay bricks
> were introduced. With the development of the brick industry the out-
> side shape above the level of the top of the bosh, began to change from
> the square stone structure to that of a round section made from brick
> and supported by iron bands.

The higher temperature available caused the reduction of silica to
silicon which dissolved in the molten iron, and which on solidification
of the sow and pig iron tended towards a coarse grained graphite iron
generally unsuitable for the production of castings when used direct
from the blast furnace. Thus re-melting units became a necessity, in the

form of air furnaces and cupolas. Usually it was a foundry which had the cupola.

The bottle-green acid slag of the charcoal blast furnace suffered an important restriction by its inability to accept sulphur in solution. To remove this element high lime slags were necessary, and because lime raises the melting point of slag, a higher temperature in the bosh became an essential requirement. Therefore the coke blast furnace with its higher bosh temperature enabled higher lime slags to be used, with the result that a less pure ore could be used, and the sulphur contained in the ore and fuel could be effectively accommodated by the slag.

The re-establishment of iron production in Dean in the early nineteenth century led to much development of industries that used iron as a raw material—in particular the industries of tinplate and wire, discussed in Chapter 4. Although deposits of easily won ore in Dean were dwindling, and supplies were having to be brought from Lancashire, there followed large-scale integration of iron, coal and tramroad (later railway) interests, described in Chapter 4. Dean's coke blast furnaces are noted more fully below:

CINDERFORD IRONWORKS (Plate 12a) In 1795 the first furnace in the Forest to use coke for smelting iron-ore was erected almost half a mile north of Cinderford Bridge (modern Ruspidge)[6] on a site now occupied by caravans. The date '1795' was to be found on an inscription-stone in 'no 1 furnace' of the works.[7] Ore was brought in on mules' backs from Edgehill and other mines, while coke was made in the open at nearby Broadmoor and brought on a narrow canal: much of the embankment is extant. Pig iron of good quality was made there, but production did not reach 20 tons a week, and inability to compete with iron from South Wales and Staffordshire caused the furnace to soon close—probably in 1806.[8]

In November 1827[9] the Office of Woods (the name given to the Commissioners of Woods) were informed that Thomas Teague wished to re-establish and extend the ironworks. The site with some of the buildings was used for a new works by the first Cinderford Iron Company, formed by Moses Teague with William Montague (who had a foundry in Gloucestershire), Church and Fraser. William Bishop joined the undertaking when the foundations were laid, and later became clerk to the company. The plans envisaged 'two blast-furnaces, a powerful blast-engine, finery, forge, and rolling mill, designed to furnish about 40 tons of tinplate a week, with collieries and mine work'.[10] Building began late in 1827, and in the following May negotiations for a weighing machine began with the Forest of Dean Railway. Lack of finance delayed completion until about October 1829, but despite the depression in the iron industry the works operated until October 1832, though tinplate was not among its manufactures.

Three years later, 1835, Teague induced William Allaway (who with his sons Stephen and William was engaged in the tinplate trade at Lydbrook) to join with William Crawshay of Cyfarthfa, William Montague, and John Pearce (partner of Allaway at Lydbrook), in forming the second Cinderford Iron Company to resuscitate the works. Crawshay took a three-twentieth interest in the partnership.[11] Much bar iron was sent to Lydbrook, but in 1837 a crisis arose, evident in a letter of 11 January from Crawshay to Allaway:[12]

I have your letter of the 6th inst, and as Mr Teague had informed me that he intended being here as last night, I have thought best to see and consult him, before I replied. We have gone into the matter of the Cinderford works most fully, and we are of opinion that nothing but the most decided conduct of its owners can save that concern from ruin. Among the difficulties to contend with as to coal, is the present danger of Mr Protheroe's collieries being drowned by the water accumulating in Bennett's collieries. There is not a day in which this event may not happen, and the very existence of our Cinderford works is threatened.

You may think we look at the gloomy side of the question. If so, and you can see your way clearer than we can for the carrying on of the Cinderford works upon the present system, we entreat you to release us upon the same terms we came in, and we will retain the working of the mines, and supply your three furnaces with ore regularly, and when we do not do so, you shall be at liberty to take to our mine works as already stipulated. Thus if we are wrong in our view of the dangers of the Cinderford works as to coal, we leave it to you to take the advantage of your better opinion. If you decline to do so, we must either release ourselves in some other way, or we must urge upon those parties differing in their views with us, the necessity of a widely different conduct of the concern to the present system.

I am desirous in all matters of avoiding disputes and litigation, and I had hoped that the expression of our wishes, coupled with Mr Montague's, and as I stated with Mr Pearce's too, of the preceding evening, that you would readily have allowed your son Stephen to reside at and manage the Concern instead of William, and Mr Teague and myself feel much disappointed at your unwillingness to make this change, which we think so necessary for the welfare of the Concern.

I regret to have to repeat that we are by no means satisfied with the present management of the Concern, or with the result of last year. Mr Montague fully joins us in the feeling.

You state in your letter of the 6th inst that there is an account made out between the Lydbrook and Cinderford Concerns to the end of the year, by which Cinderford owes Lydbrook One Thousand Pounds, and that you wish a meeting of the Partners to advance a further capital. I shall not hesitate to express my determination not to accede to this proposal upon the present system between the two Concerns at Cinderford and Lydbrook. There ought to be an entire separation of the two Concerns in every way whatsoever, and it must be done immediately. It was agreed by all parties, that we ought to have our own Bankers. That our Books should be kept upon the spot, and that we ought to have our own responsible Clerk. The young man, I looked to, has re-engaged himself at his present place, and I think we had better at once advertise for another. You allude to the Lydbrook works paying at the end of the quarter like other customers. This we are quite desirous of, but we do not admit that any advantage has accrued to the Cinderford works from the contrary system. The constant supply afforded Lydbrook from hand to mouth, without any stock being kept, has been a convenience to Lydbrook more than commensurate to the inconvenience of payment, and our own Bankers would be willing for our account to be under any reasonable advance of money.

I think it is indispensible that the two Concerns should be as distinct as though the Parties belonging to each were not the same, and even more so; and at our next meeting, I shall propose to the Partners that a Manager be appointed for the Cinderford works, totally unconnected with either of the Parties, and I shall see what fate this proposal meets.

I would much rather than enter into all these unpleasant discussions, retire from the Concern, and leave you and your sons to carry it on as you think proper. But I cannot, and will not, remain in it upon the present system. The Concern can never prosper, and a year, or month, or day, may see it wholly suspended for want of coal. Mr Teague and myself beg you will give the whole subject of this letter your immediate consideration, and we are ready to attend a meeting of the Partners whenever you think proper to call one. I send Mr Montague a copy of this letter.

I have so many memorandums of the different sums to be paid, that I am quite confused as to which it is, but I think it is £4,761 1s 5d to you. I enclose my cheques for the £4,761 1s 5d dated 1st February and for £59 10s 3d for the interest from 1st November until that day. Pray acknowledge the receipt to me as soon as you have them.

Changes were made. Furthermore, on 13 April 1838, Thomas Prichard of Ross agreed a nominal lease with a view to a sale to Wil-

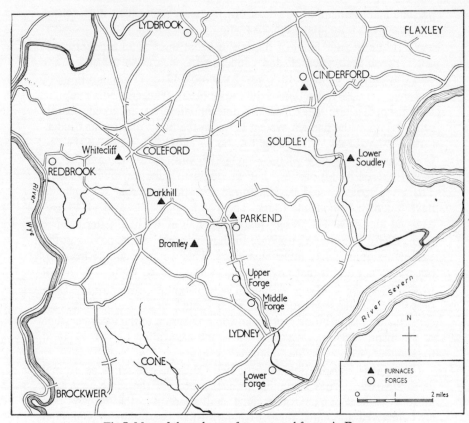

Fig 7. Map of the coke era furnaces and forges in Dean.

liam Allaway, William Crawshay and other subscribers, of fourteen acres bounded on the west by Cinderford Brook on which stood the furnaces, forges, mills, engines, buildings and houses, called the Cinderford Ironworks. The other parties relevant to the agreement[13] were John Pearce, ironmaster, of Larkfield Lodge, Richmond; William Montague, ironmaster, of Gloucester; Moses Teague, ironmaster, of Cinderford; the Rev William Leigh, of Pulham Rectory, Norfolk; John Willim, of Bilston; Helen Fraser, of Baring Crescent, Exeter; Edward Protheroe of Hill House, Newnham-on-Severn; Peter and James Teague, Free Miners, of Coleford; Abraham Thompson, of Stanfield House, St Johns, Bredwardine; the Rev J. C. Egginton, of Cheltenham; and Edward Prichard, banker, of Ross-on-Wye. On the same day,[14] Peter and James Teague agreed to a lease with a view to a sale, to Allaway, Crawshay, and the above associates, of the coalmine and 'gale' called

Water Engine near Daniels Ford (together with the iron furnace, and all erections and buildings thereon, forming part of the Cinderford Ironworks) 'formerly or now standing' in the name of John Addis in the Gale Books, and also the share formerly belonging to Philip Robinson, deceased, afterwards to Edward Protheroe and thence in trust to Peter and James Teague. The sale was also to include 'the veins of coal of the Lower Bilson Colliery (Edward Protheroe's) named the Lowery Delf, Twenty Inches or Little Delf, and Smith Coal Delf (to be won by the engine belonging to Lower Bilson), and two pits already opened named Links Delight and Coal Pit Green Engine Pit near Oiley Hill Inclosure'. The two deeds are complex but it is clear that the land on which the ironworks stood was owned partly by Prichard and partly by the Teagues, and that it was leased with an intention of sale to the proprietors of the Iron Company in order to render their tenure more secure.

The new manager was James Broad who for twenty years made iron 'of quality and in quantities which had never been anticipated'.[15] In March 1841 the works, said to be owned by 'Crawshay & Sons' (but still partly owned by Allaway) comprised 'three blast-furnaces with a 54in double power steam engine, blowing; and a melting finery for scraps and runners'.[16] The annual output of iron, during the two years to 30 June, 1840, was 12,000 tons. There were twenty-eight workmen's houses, counting-house, smith and carpenter's shed, a range of stables, agent's house and 'bate' shop, and a surgeon's house in the yard. Many of these premises appear in a photograph taken many years later (Plate 12a). Coal, chiefly for coke, was being supplied by Edward Protheroe & Co from the collieries named Gainall (Crump Meadow), Old Bilson, and the The Winner. Crawshays themselves owned only Haywood Colliery, but they were sinking Lightmoor.

Accounts to 30 June for the years 1847, 1848 and 1849[17] show that William Crawshay and William Allaway each held 50 per cent of the shares in the prosperous concern, of which Crawshay's second son, Henry, was in charge.[18] The fully detailed costs and sales, with creditors, debtors and stocks, show the integrated and varied assets of the company—part of William Crawshay's local 'empire'. According to David Mushet junior[19] 'the Cinderford cold-blast iron brings a high price in the market—its tenacity adapting it, in a high degree, for cast hardware, and tinplate.'

There does not seem to have been any connection between the Cinderford works and the Crawshay concerns in South Wales; they were carried on as independent enterprises, though William, who transferred his half share to his son Henry in 1854,[20] was four years later purchasing from his son Forest ore at 14s a ton, delivered at Cardiff.[21]

By 1858 there were four blast furnaces at Cinderford, three always in blast; and a new 'blast-engine of considerable power' was in course of erection, in addition to the old engine which had been working for 28 years.[22] Each blast furnace had a height of 43ft, an extreme breadth of 14ft, that of the hearth being 6ft. Together they made each week 500 tons of the finest hot-blast iron.[23] The ore came chiefly from the Shakemantle, Buckshraft, and St Annal's mines on the eastern side of the Forest, and from the Milkwall district on the west. The furnaces had become the centre of a network of tramroads over which horses brought in the raw materials. Railways were added to the network; a Neath Abbey Iron Co drawing of October 1855 shows a sectional elevation plan and cross-section of an 0-6-0 locomotive with 12in cylinder, 20in stroke, and 4ft diameter wheels, for the Cinderford Iron Co.[24]

In a letter 30 August 1861, William Crawshay asserted that Henry's 'pits, engines, and collieries are the most perfect in the Kingdom',[25]—which was praise indeed, even from father to son! But the partnership was not free from financial difficulties, and Henry, with the help of his father, in 1862 bought the entire interest of his partners for £50,000.[26] The following year the company had the rare distinction of having a book dedicated to it—*A Practical Treatise on Mining, Land and Railway Surveying, Engineering etc*, by H. D. Hoskold of Cinderford, inventor of the Miner's Transit Theodolite, and who undertook much work for the company. In 1858 William Crawshay paid Robert Mushet the very high compliment that a piece of iron submitted to him was 'the very best I ever saw in my life!'[27] Crawshay died in 1867, having built up an 'empire' in South Wales and Dean—'His quickness of perception and unhesitating readiness of decision made his success as an ironmaster when railways were first introduced; states wanted railways—he found the means, repaid himself in shares, and large profits soon fell into his hands'.[28]

Three furnaces were in blast at Cinderford in 1864[29] and in 1871–3, but only two in 1876–9.[30] Henry Crawshay died in 1879, but the following year his family were erecting two furnaces 'on a modern principle'.[31]

Early in 1882 the Crawshays sent samples of iron from Cinderford to the USA, and thereafter received offers to accept, on approved quotations, half the output for steel rail manufacture: a cablegram was received from New York in May, offering a contract for 10,000 tons of 'Forest of Dean Bessemer pig iron'—but the price offered was too low for acceptance.[32] Eight years later only one furnace was in blast, and that only to one quarter of its capacity,[33] and much plant was sold,[34] the works finally closing 9 April 1894.

The premises were demolished soon afterwards, and the stables were converted to dwellinghouses known as 'Whitechapel Row' (Plate 12b), themselves demolished in 1960. Two rows of other houses remain; also 'Furnace Pool'; and scattered nearby lie huge blocks of slag thrown out by the furnaces.

PARKEND FURNACES (Plate 8a and b)   A furnace using coke built in 1799,[35] stood just north of the railway station. By 1807 it was worked by a steam engine,[36] and run by a Mr Perkins. The outline of the premises is shown on a plan of 1809–10.[37] The plant was later sold to John Protheroe who in 1824 passed it to his nephew Edward Protheroe (one-time MP for Bristol), proprietor of extensive mines in the neighbourhood. In April 1824 Edward Protheroe was proposing re-opening his (probably improved) furnace following a successful experiment by Moses Teague in smelting with a coke of Low Delf coal at David Mushet's first furnace at Darkhill.[38] It became necessary for the s&w to lay a branch tramroad to convey ore to the works.[39] Protheroe asked the Office of Woods for permission to use a watercourse[40] (see *infra*), and in the same year leased the premises and plant to the Forest of Dean Iron Company, then comprising William Montague, Benjamin Whitehouse, and Moses Teague.[41] In January 1825 the company were permitted to make for their works a dam-head about $1\frac{1}{2}$ miles up the Parkend-Cannop Valley, against the embankment of the s&w tramroad leading to Bixslade, to form a reservoir (this became the lower Cannop Pond).[42] By October 1826 there were complaints that the damming had seriously reduced the water in the Lydney Canal, and the company proposed, but had to abandon as illegal, to form a well or cistern to receive the water after it had passed the Parkend wheel, and then to pump the same back for re-use.[43]

In 1826 Montague, with John James of Lydney, became the lessees, and had Moses Teague as their manager. By early the following year, they had erected a second furnace, and an undershot water-wheel of 51ft diameter and 6ft wide, weighing 60 tons, and said to be nearly the largest in the kingdom; the components were cast at Gloucester.[44] Each furnace was 45ft high, $9\frac{1}{2}$ft diameter at the top, 14ft across at the bosh, and the hearth 5ft diameter.[45] From the reservoir above Bixslade, formed by damming the Newerne Stream, water was directed to the Parkend furnaces by a leat about $1\frac{1}{2}$ miles long, crossing the Brockall Ditch by a wooden aqueduct, and thence going under the Moseley Green-Parkend road. The leat is extant along much of its length. This source of power for blast proved unreliable and inadequate: by May 1827 the works had been stopped twice and the men discharged.[46] A new steam-engine of 90hp was erected, to supplement the power from the water-wheel. Permission was sought from the Office of Woods in April 1829 to improve the watercourse and to make a reservoir (presumably the upper Cannop Pond).[47] Sopwith's plan of 1835 shows the Parkend works in detail. A feature of them was a short overhead artificial tunnel, the 'covered way', erected because the s&w tramroad was at the foot of rising ground, and the furnaces were fed from lines which passed over it. The two furnaces were not worked together. In March 1841 only one was in work, its blast being by water in summer (a tribute to our English summer!), and steam-engine in winter.[48] There was a 'melting finery', besides four good houses for workmen, a stable and building, a beer house, counting house, agent's dwelling, and carpenter's, smith's and other sheds; six out of eight of the cottages 'under the bridge house' were occupied.[49] The make of iron for the year to 8 December 1840 was 60 tons a week, for the last 6 months 70 a week, for the week ending 21 February 1841 101, and on average about 3,640 tons a year. Coal, chiefly for coke, was coming from Fetterhill Pit and Protheroe's Parkend Pits.

By April 1843 the ironworks had been out of blast for $1\frac{1}{2}$ years, but re-opening was planned.[50] They were certainly in use by 28 December 1846 when David Mushet junior wrote[51] that 'at Parkend furnace the style of filling is to keep the burden circularly round the walls, leaving a centre of bare cokes; and the large weekly quantity of 120 tons, from a moderate-sized furnace, places in a conspicuous light the intelligence of the management'. On 3 July 1847 Mushet wrote[52] that 'the Parkend hot-blast iron possesses amazing strength. Mr Montague, of Gloucester, the proprietor, has cast railway girders of most unusual power, in proportion to their scantling: I have seen pigs of his iron deflect from 1 to 2 ins ere repeated blows could produce a fracture.' The same July, application was made to the Office of Woods for land on which to build workmen's houses.[53]

Following Montague's death that year, James became sole lessee. In 1849 he installed an 80hp steam-engine, but though coke was used, he was still buying cordwood from the Crown in 1851.[54] He purchased the freehold from Protheroe in 1854, and thereafter both furnaces were worked together under the management of Charles Greenham of Highfield, Lydney, managing partner of The Forest of Dean Iron Company. Meanwhile, James and Greenham had completed the building, near the furnaces, of a new enterprise—iron forges, rolling mills and tinplate works (qv). Selling agents were appointed for the Midlands.[55] An S&W Railway Plan of 1852[56] shows the layout of the works, and indicates 'coke hearth, blast furnaces, casting houses, engine houses, boilers, workshops, etc.'

By February 1864, The Forest of Dean Iron Company was producing about 280 tons of pig iron a week, consuming in the same period about 350 tons of coke, and 600 tons of iron ore obtained from the neighbouring Oakwood and China Engine mines, and from the Perseverance and Findall mines to the east.[57] The ironworks and the iron mining gave employment to about 300 men, 'besides those engaged as colliers';[58] and the foundation of another furnace was being laid.[59] In 1871 all three furnaces were in blast, but one for only three months, while in 1871 to 1875 two only were working.[60] The iron produced was chiefly used for the manufacture of Bessemer steel rails, and tinplate.

In 1875 Edwin Crawshay purchased the Parkend plant, including the tinplate works, for a sum reputed to be £120,000.[61] The three furnaces, of which George Belcher of Parkend Cottage was manager, 'with all modern appliances such as utilising waste gas, etc' were capable of producing 600 tons of pig iron a week.[62] However, trade slumped: in 1876 two of the furnaces were in blast for 7 months, and one for 5 months; and in August 1877, after only one furnace being in blast for 7 months,[63] the works were closed.[64] The depression had been accentuated by a fault in the China mine.[65] Crawshay had purchased Robin Hood mine, northwest of Coleford, but haulage by cart had increased production costs.

The furnaces were demolished in 1890,[66] and the 'covered way' removed in 1898. The last stack was thrown 13 February 1908 (Plate 8a). In the same year, the engine house was converted into a Forester Training School, and is still used for this purpose (Plate 8b).

WHITECLIFF FURNACE (Plate 9a)   Towards the close of the nineteenth century, Samuel Botham, a Quaker residing in Uttoxeter, was in partnership with the brothers Bishton of Shifnal, Shropshire. He and his wife Ann were the parents of Mary Howitt, poet. In 1798 his partners induced him 'to exchange his share in the very advantageous iron-forges in which they were concerned for a principal share in some iron-works in Gloucestershire'.[67] Late in that year Botham arrived to reside in Coleford where, at nearby Whitecliff, had begun the erection of a coke-smelting blast-furnace. Considerable capital was invested in the project, all furnished by Botham.

The works were sited on the west of Thurstan's Brook which runs through Coleford to Newland and continues, as the Valley Brook, to Lower Redbrook and the Wye. Much progress had been made in the erection when in 1799 deep snow fell, followed by such heavy rains that the brook swelled, flooding all the buildings, and in one night wrecked much plant. Botham's associates in South Wales refused to help, and having lost his investment he withdrew from the undertaking and by 1801 he had returned to Uttoxeter. His associates together with Thomas Halford and Moses Teague took over the works and eventually completed them:[68] 1804 is the date on the extant furnace, which is free-standing, but buttressed back to the hill by a membrane wall to facilitate charging from above. The blast was by steam raised by coke.

The furnace was the reason for the coming to Dean of a brilliant Scot and early metallurgist, David Mushet (Plate 16b) who, with his eldest son, was to bring fame and notability to themselves and the Forest. Mushet, born in Dalkeith 2 October 1772, and the discoverer in 1801 of the Blackband ironstone in Scotland, while working at the Clyde Ironworks near Glasgow began to experiment on the scientific determination of various properties of iron, but his work terminated suddenly when his employers pulled down his small experimental furnace. He moved to the Calder Ironworks, and then to Derbyshire. In 1809 he entered the association at Whitecliff, and in 1810 his family moved to nearby Coleford where he had purchased Tump House, later renamed Forest House, which still stands.

Only for a short time did Mushet help to run the Whitecliff iron-works; 'he had grave reasons for being most dissatisfied with his partner, and he withdrew'.[69] Thomas Halford became bankrupt in February 1816.[70] The works were dismantled, except the furnace, which is still standing though devoid of the hearth and ironwork; a large quantity of the castings including blast apparatus, were taken to the Cinderford blast furnace in 1827.[71] CMU & PR Rly plans of 1852 show the furnace as 'old ruin', but the outline suggests that a fore-part or covering over the approach to the hearth then existed; a warehouse was adjacent.

Whitecliff furnace was designed for smelting with coke and had a capacity of about 1,200cu ft. Thus it is considerably larger than that at Guns Mill. It represents the latest practice at the time of its building, and presumably its financial failure was connected with the high price of coke and ore at that time relative to those elsewhere. The furnace was 40ft in height, with a highline about 50ft above the casting floor. There are two tuyeres; the small opening opposite the tymp arch was for some other purpose. It was steam blown and the shaft was lined with firebrick. The shaft, bosh and crucible would all have been circular. The casing is of square plan, 40ft wide by 45ft in the side, and most of the external masonry is intact, although the keystone is missing—this probably having been loosened by the heat from the taphole. The hearth and bosh system are missing, but an illustration[72] depicts what the hearth *ought* to have looked like. A small building situated to the east of the casting floor may have been a pattern shop, and the engine house was probably behind it.

In 1968 the furnace was subjected to a Building Preservation Order. If the structure is not to collapse soon it needs urgent attention: the fore-part arch is broken; the lining of the stack, which is in very good condition, is apparently only held in by friction—it is in effect a tapered plug, ready to fall out at any moment and needs shoring up at least, as a temporary measure.

DARKHILL FURNACE (Plate 10a) In 1810, David Mushet severed his connections with the Whitecliff Furnace (qv), but continued to reside at Forest House in Coleford. A hundred yards up the road from his home stood a large stone barn (Plate 10b), where he (and later his eldest son, Robert) carried out numerous experiments with iron—the building becoming the scene of many discoveries.[73]

On 17 July 1815 Mushet took out a patent on a process of producing 'refined iron' direct from the blast furnace without the refinery. He succeeded in producing an excellent quality of refined iron, practically free from phosphorus and sulphur, superior to that obtained in the ordinary refinery.[74] He was soon benefiting financially from some of his patents, as evidenced by a letter written by him 7 January 1818 to Josiah John Guest:[75]

> My patent embraces every sort of cast or pig iron to be made or manufactured by the means or processes set forth in the specification. My terms are to you the same as those agreed with Mr Crawshay, viz: £1,000 for each blast furnace working and to work, but not subject to the delay required in your letter, as to your assent or dissent from this proposition, lest by your present operations I may sanction the

infringement of my own patent. I would recommend that you at once
by all means to make finers' metal from the blast furnace. You would
in so doing carry at least 25 per cent of additional burden and save
all the subsequent waste and labour of the common refinery. To do this
you would require merely to take up the dam and build a thin brick wall
under the Tymp with a plate and tapping hole, and use water tue irons
or twyres, then bring up the burden by adding mine and slags, together or separately, till the metal was as high as it was wanted. You
might still, if thought necessary, run it into a prepared refinery and blow
upon it for a short time.

Mushet delayed commercially testing some of his theories until the
latter part of 1818 or the beginning of 1819,[76] when he built a 'furnace'
some two miles south-east of his home, at Darkhill near Fetterhill, between Milkwall and Parkend. He had obtained the land 13 June 1818
by Deed of Exchange from the Commissioners of Woods.[77] He records,
'I erected a cementing-furnace which was capable of containing $2\frac{1}{2}$
tons, and in which, from first to last, I made a good many batches, not
only with the rich ore of Dean Forest, but also with the ore obtained
from Cumberland'.[78] Additional light on the subject is shed by a letter
from David Mushet junior:[79] 'My father . . . [in about 1818] . . . had
a patent for manufacturing finer's metal direct from the blast furnace:
to practice it he erected a cupola . . . [which he worked for about two
years] . . . and tried to introduce the new process in Staffordshire and
Wales; but it was not then adopted, nor has it been taken up since the
patent-right expired.'
Mushet only used his 'cupola' (in effect, a lightly constructed furnace) for a year or two:[80] by April 1824 Moses Teague had successfully
made coke-smelted iron 'in the cupola formerly used by Mr Mushet'.[81]
Thereupon, 'after an experiment in smelting with a coke of Low Delf
coal at Mr Mushet's furnace', Edward Protheroe proposed to re-open
his Parkend furnace.[82]
Mushet well before this time had invested in coal and iron mines,
brick-making, and tramroads. He expressed his faith in Dean's tramroads at the earliest practical stage, by being amongst the subscribers
listed in the original Acts of Parliament for the Lydney & Lydbrook
Rly (1809) and the Monmouth Rly (1810). As early as 1810, he was
sufficiently well thought of to be asked by the s&w Committee to
find an engineer to superintend the Mirystock cutting and other works,
while by 1812 he was on the Committee, and in the forefront of the
company's internecine politics by preparing a circular in defence of

25 *(above)* A Free Miner's sword inscribed: 'Eustace Hardwick, Esq., 1697, Free Miner of ye Forest of Dean'. On the reverse side is: 'Miner against Miner, and Miners against all other men'; *(below)* 'An Ancient Free Miner' (a brass effigy in Newland church—'The Cathedral of the Forest'). The miner carries a mattock implement, a wooden hod is strapped to his shoulder, and his mouth holds a stick to which is attached a piece of clay to hold a candle

26 *(above)* 'The Miners Lawes & Privileges'—the first page of the 1673 transcript. The earliest known copy is dated 1610; *(below)* a Mine Law Court order, No 14, dated 12 November 1728 and signed by forty-eight Free Miners and five Officials

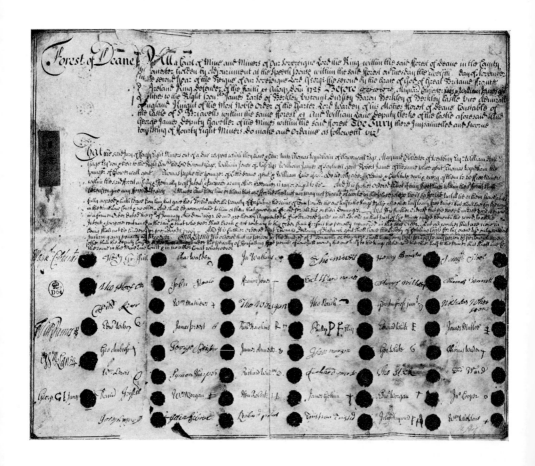

constructional policy, in answer to that of Atherton and Whitworth, two disgruntled shareholders.[83] In November 1813 an attempt to enter the Port of Bristol with a cargo of coal was planned, for the purpose of testing the enforcement of the Coastwise Duty, and to Mushet fell the dubious honour of supplying a trow full of small coal. It is unlikely that this particular attempt was made, but clearly Mushet was 'in business' as a coal-owner. In June 1815 the s&w unanimously resolved to request Mushet's acceptance of £100 'for services rendered to the Company by a journey of his on the Company's business to Swansea, and great trouble and loss of time which he had undergone in his long attendances on legal consultations.'

The scale of Mushet's mining activity can be judged in 1822, when he was amongst traders offering to 'lease their own rates'—ie to pay a sum instead of piecemeal tolls for transport on the s&w tramroad: Mushet offered, in line with John Trotter & Co, £800 per annum for his tonnages; The Park End Coal Co offered £4,000 per annum.

In March 1823 Mushet was chairman of the s&w Committee, but this may have been only on one occasion. He appears to have been a 'minute man', a capable but normally quiescent trooper who emerged at times of need, when some problem threatened the organisation.

In 1825 Mushet secured a licence for the Oakwood Tramroad. In the same year he commenced driving an old and a new ore adit (level) at Oakwood, but in winning 40,000 to 50,000 tons of ore, not more than 300 tons of 'steel ore' were produced.[84] The same year he received a licence from the Office of Woods to erect branch railways. In 1834 he leased to William Allaway, Moses Teague and John Pearce (trading as The Cinderford Coal & Iron Company) Oakwood Mill Upper Mine Level. He owned the Level in 1841 as well as Park Hill Iron Mine Work, including Dark Hole Level Gale.

Of coal works, Mushet by 1841 held Old Furnace Level Gale, Howlers Slade, Deep Engine, Protection Level, Bixslade Level, Bixslade Upper Level, Dark Hill, and Shutcastle.

As to tramroads and railways, Mushet emerged as one of the chief crusaders against 'the third railway'—the Purton Pill scheme. In January 1831 he was one of two men chosen to meet Protheroe of the Forest of Dean Rly Co to arrange a plan of opposition to 'Mr Teague's intended railway'. The other delegate was Henry Davies, the chairman, who wrote to Mushet from the Bank, Monmouth on 15 March 1832, enclosing a pro-Purton Pill pamphlet, Davies wrote: 'It gives me great pleasure to observe by your last letter, that you are better pleased with

L

the conduct of the Office of Woods than you have been'; and he added
post scriptum, 'It is reliance upon you I presume that causes the apathy
of our proprietors'. Mushet, the willing horse—it was ever thus!

Later, Mushet had at Darkhill 'a small cupola blast furnace, of about
1,000 cubic feet capacity' (see *infra*). He was recognised as an authority on iron, of which he wrote profusely,[85] though he had his detractors
and his advice (quite often sought) was not always taken.

In May 1845 David Mushet gave his Darkhill ironworks in equal
shares to his three sons, William, David and Robert.[86] It comprised
'Blast furnace for the smelting of iron, with the blowing engine, boiler,
machinery, casting house, buildings and appurtenances; also the coke
yard, furnace yard, and water ponds or reservoirs; part being a brickyard and a workman's house; total 5a 3r 17p'.[87] In addition there were
the Darkhill and the Shutcastle coal levels.[88] The details of the ironworks were: [89]

> A blast furnace, with steam cylinder of 24 inches, and a blowing
> cylinder of 60 inches diameter.
> A small cupola blast furnace, of about 1,000 cubic feet capacity, much
> worn and wasted [Possibly the 1818 'cupola' noted above].
> A casting house.
> A water regulator.
> A bridge or filling loft.
> An office in the yard.
> A round boiler.

The 'blast furnace' (improved, as noted later) is that of which the
remains have recently (1968) been excavated. Its steam engine would
have been of the Boulton and Watt beam type: on one side of the beam
would be the steam cylinder, 24in diameter, and on the other the blowing cylinder, 60in diameter; thus at each stroke of the engine $\pi D^2/4$
length of stroke = volume of air pumped into the water regulator. The
worn and wasted cupola blast furnace 'was probably a round iron-
cased furnace, of small size even for that period: it probably had
three tuyeres. The water regulator was a common device of the period
when people were concerned (unnecessarily, as we now know) with
equalising the blast from the blowing cylinder to be as pulseless as
possible. There was more than one type. The 'water' regulator, used a
water cistern to act as a sort of accumulator, the water absorbing the
air pulses and giving them out smoothly. The bridge or filling loft was
simply a building at the top of the furnace, covering the men (the fillers)
who worked there doing the charging. The 'round boiler' could have

been a haystack boiler (later evidence shows that it was inadequate, new boilers being necessary). The casting house was a building erected over the fore hearth of the furnace, with a sand floor to which the sows and pigs were cast, and possibly where castings were made.

In November 1845, a partnership agreement was drawn up for the three brothers, whereby Robert was the sole manager of 'The Darkhill Iron Co' styled 'Robert Mushet & Co'.[90] Soon William's one third share was mortgaged to Gratrex & Co, Bankers, of Monmouth, as a security for his debts.[91] By the same year, 1845, Robert Mushet and his brother David (but without the aid of William), had 'recently laid out about £1,000 in enlarging and improving the blast furnace property and the apparatus belonging to it, and were about to complete other improvements thereto at a cost of at least £3,000 more'.[92] The blast furnace was to be repaired, and the following additions were to be made (the water regulator, casting house, and office would remain the same):

2 new boilers 36 feet, each of 4 feet diameter.
2 stoves for heating the air, to contain 35 perpendicular, besides the horizontal, pipes: the whole will weigh 40 tons and when completed will cost £600.
Weighing machine.
Considerable extent of new walling in the coke yard.
Enlarged bridge loft or filling house, nearly new.

The two new boilers were cylindrical egg-ends, very common in the iron trade. The two stoves were probably of the syphon-pipe pattern. It appears that up to this time the furnace was blown by cold blast, and that the two Mushet brothers in 1846 improved the performance by fitting hot blast. David Mushet junior, wrote of the furnace,[93] 'The Darkhill pig iron is not made by any peculiar process: there is no difference, except in the construction of the furnace, which I built, under an unpleasant opposition, on the scientific principles of Mr J. Gibbons; their efficacy was proved by producing, at our first cast, fine foundry iron—an event unheard of with the refractory ores of the Forest of Dean'. Gibbon's process was well known at the time.[94]

By 1846 David Mushet was living at Monmouth, and his eldest son Robert resided at Forest House, Coleford. The father, in the late evening of his life, viewed from afar the desultory efforts of his three sons to carry on the ironworks which had been part of his life. But strife was rampant between the three brothers: letters show the hatred of David junior for his brother William, an apparent bigamist; and other letters show the preference of David senior for his son Robert.[95] Contemporary letters written by David junior[96] indicate his disagreement with Robert; they also provide much information regarding the Darkhill Furnace (in particular that it was a hot-air, hooped furnace, 8ft at the top):

28 Dec. 1846

After some months struggle with prejudice, I introduced the following mode of filling. It produced in the yield an immediate change from $14\frac{1}{2}$ tons of high-blown scrap iron to 26 tons of Nos. 1 and 2 in successive weeks. The effects were developing with great rapidity, and the make was at the rate of 40 to 50 tons in the beginning of the third week, when the blast pipes were cut down by parties connected in the management to less than half their area. The full effect was destroyed, but sufficient proof of its high value remained as the furnace alternated 28 and 32 tons for some weeks, in place of the former miserable yield, and thus saved us from ruin. The style of filling is, to heap the burden circularly round the walls, leaving a centre of bare cokes . . . Our furnace is 8ft at the top.

12 Jan. 1847

I built the furnace upon the principles of Mr J. Gibbons, as far as I could, under much obloquy, and I have found a proof of their truth; for it has withstood, through six months, a degree of torture, misusage, and ill management, that would have set fast 10 furnaces of the ordinary construction.

19 Jan. 1847

There is nothing better known to practical men than the kind of coal safe to use raw in the blast furnace. The following is the result of an act of great ignorance or mischief—the use in the blast furnace of the 'Coleford High Delf' coal. After a number of charges, without mixture of coke, amounting to nearly the contents of the furnace, great difficulty supervened in keeping the tuyeres. One failed in spite of every effort, and, for near a week, the chief part of the iron flowed over the cinder notch of the most infusible kind—the hearth being set level over. The dust was prodigious; the furnace worked by slips 8 or 10ft in depth, until, at length, from 8 am to 4 pm, the materials were not seen to move. They then set exploding like a volcano, to the great danger of the structure—a hooped furnace. Dust and small ore, rising with a lofty emission of flame, covered the platform 8 or 10 inches in depth, and, falling below, set fire to the workmen's clothes. No fillers or others fortunately were entered on the platform, or loss of life would have inevitably occurred, and made more serious this warning on the use of improper coal. It is true, that, in addition to its defective quality in the best state, I have seen barrows of small coal and coal-dust filled in as if a blast furnace were only a depository for rubbish; this no doubt aggravated the effect.

22 Jan. 1847

In establishing a hot-air furnace last year we used cast-iron tuyere-irons with wrought-iron spiral tuber, both for safety, and as needing a less supply of water, of which we are deficient. Our ingenious manager, J. Walkinshaw calculated with nicety the most economical construction of irons for our supply, but they scarcely had a fair trial. The furnace was started with deficient blast which, unable to heat the materials upwards and ascend through them, blew forward, cracked a ring, and did great damage. This danger was no sooner escaped than the preposterous burden of 9cwt of materials on 2½cwt of coke was laid on. This caused the inevitable amount of scouring and action on the sides, so that the tuyeres burned every day. After a dreadful calamity, where three lives were lost through incompetence in the engineers, and a stand of 12 days, we blew in with the old-fashioned plate-iron of the finery; but the glass of iron from that monstrous burden closed too immediately. They remained closed nearly two months, until the rains began, and the solitary tuyere was supplied with no great difficulty; but in the summer it will be a different question to supply three. Information respecting the use of the more economical tube tuyere-iron, would therefore be of value. So far as I have seen, an effective jet against the breast, to prevent their burning back, their peculiar failing, is the best preservative. In the furnace itself the tube stands with greater safety than the more copious reservoir, which may set the hearth level almost before the burning is detected. I have thought of economising the water by passing it from one to the other, making the stream supply successively two or even three of the chambered tuyere-irons.

1 March 1847

I have a furnace fitted with two hot-air stoves of 20 pipes each—the internal area of the 'A' pipes, 27in. The air enters the stoves from a water regulator through 12in pipes, and the horizontal pipes of the stove are about 3ft above the top of the air chest. The blast is divided to the tuyeres through three 6in pipes—the two side pipes in a part of their circuit touch the ground, and are sometimes sprinkled with water from the tye-irons and breasts. When the perilous derangement took place, which I have recorded as an instance of the effects of an improper raw coal, the parties who had during months inflicted a series of unparalleled disasters, differed with me in opinion, and attributed that disorder to the effects of water blown into the furnace.

A letter 27 May 1847 from the Mushets' manager, J. Walkinshaw, adds information about the furnace:

Having constructed the water-regulator, and arranged the position of the blast-pipes, I beg leave to correct the following errors in Mr R. Mushet's reply to 'an Old File', in your Journal of the 22nd inst: Mr M. says—'The cold-blast from the blowing cylinder passed into a water-regulator at one side, and passed out into the stove at the other side.' If this had been the case, there would have been some colour to his assertion, of water getting into the furnace; but the arrangement of the blast-pipe was designed to prevent the chance of even the vapour of the water getting there. The blast goes direct from the engine to the stove along a straight and nearly horizontal pipe, laid some few inches above the top of the air-receiver; and this pipe is furnished with a branch leading downwards, and screwed to the receiver—the pipe and branch resembling the letter T—so that the blast going to the stoves cannot enter the regulator, which becomes quite filled on the first starting of the engine, and so continues until it stops—acting there merely as a spring, to keep up uniformity of pressure. Again, he says—'There is too much water in the regulator.' This could not be the case for any great length of time, there being a pipe so placed as to carry off any excess which might chance to occur. He further says—'At the turn of each stroke the water rose, and some of it passed into the eduction blast-pipe, and was carried by the blast, etc.' Looking at the fact of the blast-pipe going direct from the engine, what does Mr M. mean by 'the water passing into the eduction blast-pipe?' If the water could possibly have got there, how came it that there still continued to be 'too much', seeing that the regulator was never supplied but at intervals, when found to require it? And yet he says, that 'Some water was thus carried by the blast 30 times every minute for months!' Having shown the true position of the blast-pipe to be above the regulator, I next proceed to inform you, that the surface of the water usually stood 4ft below the said pipe while the engine was at rest—that the density of the blast was equal to a column of mercury 6in high—consequently, the surface of the water in the interior of the regulator would be so much more depressed. I would now beg leave to ask, by what miracle the confined air could, at the same instant, both depress and elevate the water, in order that 'some of it might pass', etc? Or, is it more in accordance with nature, to suppose that 'some of the water, becoming tired of its confinement within the narrow limits of the receiver, had thrown off its allegiance to gravitation, and thus stripped of ponderosity, had joyously leapt up so many feet and inches for the mere pleasure of possessing liberty.' In conclusion, I would recommend Mr M. to look at things before he describes them; and, by thus disabusing his own mind, I should hope he will cease to abuse those he appears to consider guilty of what in my view, seems an impossible offence.

Meanwhile, Robert Mushet had been experimenting in the making of 'grey cast-iron from an air furnace'. On 18 January 1847 he wrote:

Many years ago, my father, Mr D. Mushet, made a series of experiments upon artificial materials, prepared for use in blast furnaces. His object was to form a compound of rich ores of iron, with clay, lime, and carbon, in a state of comminution, which should admit, through the adhesive nature of the clay, of being made up into rough lumps for fusion in the blast furnace. The discovery of hot-blast rendered the smelting of rich ores a matter of no further difficulty, and the subject was for that time dropped. Reverting lately to these experiments, and following them up by others, I succeeded in combining rich ores with clay, lime, and carbon—so that, when made up into rough lumps, by the addition of water, and subsequently dried, these materials produced, by fusion in a small air furnace, a highly carburetted grey cast-iron.

In April 1847 Robert set down two costings: [97]

Week ending 3 April 1847
Cost of pig iron made at Darkhill Furnace, per ton,
  delivered at Lydney:
Percentage of ore used, 23·8 per cent

	Tons	Cwt
Quantity of ore, per ton of iron	4	4

Cost of ore, average 4s 10d per ton

	£	s	d
Cost of ore, per ton of iron	1	1	4

	Tons	Cwt
Quantity of coke used, per ton of iron	1	4

	£	s	d
Cost of coke, 12s 6d per ton			
Cost of coke, per ton of iron		15	0

		£	s	d
Cost of labour		1	0	0
Cost of ore	per ton of	1	1	4
Cost of coke	iron, upon		15	0
Sundry expenses	33 tons		6	9
Haulage and tonnage, and dues			3	6

Cost per ton, long weight, at Lydney	£3	6	7

Cost per ton, short weight, at Lydney	£3	2	2

Quality of iron made and proceeds to be derived from its sale:

	Tons
Foundry iron nos 1, 2 & 3 long weight	19
Dark and Bright Forge iron long weight	14
Total	33

or 35 tons 7cwt short weight,

	£	s	d
Sale of 35 tons 7cwt at 80s	141	8	0
Cost of producing this iron at the before mentioned price of £3 2s 2d per ton	109	17	7
Profit upon the week's make	£31	10	5

9 April 1847

Estimate of the cost of iron made at Darkhill Furnace and delivered at Lydney on the supposition of capital being found to enable the adjacent supplies of [coal for] coke and ore to be fully taken advantage of (based on an output of 50 tons a week): [98]

	Per ton		
	£	s	d
Ore 3 tons 5cwt at 4s 10d		15	9
Coke 1 ton 5cwt at 10s 4d		12	11
Labour per ton		13	10
Limecoal for stoves etc		2	9
Charges		2	0
Haulage to Lydney		1	6
Tonnage on Railway		1	6
Cost per ton, long weight, at Lydney	£2	10	3
Cost per ton, short weight, by which the iron is sold	£2	6	10

The present regular burden of the furnaces is 7cwt of ore upon 2cwt of coke.

The average sale price of the iron has been 83s 6d per ton since the blowing in of the present furnace.

The outlay required to render the present colliery capable of yielding an adequate supply of coking coal, would be about £180, and the outlay upon ore-mines attached, would permit to £340 to £400 so as to open up complete supply of ore of good quality. These sums would not however require to be laid out at once, but gradually, as circumstances should point out the best mode of procedure.

Three extensive ore-mines might be at once secured on very moderate terms, all within a mile of the furnace, in addition to the
present sources of supply already secured by lease.

With the iron-ore thus opened up, the make of Pig Iron would be 50
tons on an average per week, and upon this quantity the above
calculations are founded.

The contemporary letters in 1846 and 1847 of David and Robert
indicate that both could write fluently and knowledgeably on matters
relating to iron and steel. David displayed some literary wit; and he
took a great interest in the improvement of ventilation in mines, and
in the pumping of water from them.

David Mushet senior died at Monmouth 7 June 1847 at the age of
75, and was buried at Staunton. (On 24 September 1967 the Historical
Metallurgy Group laid a wreath on his grave). He passed away with
the expectation that one or more of his sons, particularly Robert,
would equal or emulate his work on iron and steel. Unfortunately his
death emphasised some of the family feud. A letter in *The Times*
21 June 1847 from John Upton, mining engineer, seeking recognition
for the deceased and soliciting financial aid for some of the dependents,
drew an angry reply (22 June) from David junior to the editor of *The
Times*:

An advertisement in your Journal of yesterday appeals to public
benevolence in behalf of the widow and grandchildren of my late
father, as the discoverer of the blackband ironstone. This paper is unauthorised by his family; and if intended, as stated, to be the effort of
friendship, it wears more the character of a spurious insult to his
memory. He left the individuals alluded to considerable property of
increasing value. To show the complete misunderstanding of the
parties as to facts, I have to state that my lately deceased father has
not two, but four, grandchildren, and that their parents are living.
The benefits Mr Mushet has conferred on his country are undoubted;
but his family is not in a condition to appeal to public sympathy. I trust
your sense of justice will give insertion to this letter.

Upton countered 25 June 1847:

I have observed an advertisement in your paper, by one of the sons
of the late David Mushet, Esq, requesting you not to insert again the
advertisement drawn and inserted by me; which I have done at the
request of his mother, and the virtuous part of his family, for their
exclusive benefit. As considerable sums have been already paid as sub-
scriptions, whose names are not appended—one for no less than £500
alone—permit me, therefore, in the honesty of my principles, and as

a sincere friend to justice, to request you to repeat the advertisement, the truth of which I am willing to defend with my life, for the sake of my own reputation.

Upton also praised Mushet senior's accomplishments (23 June 1847): [99]

The late lamented and illustrious David Mushet showed how to produce very pure strong fibrous iron, from the blast furnace, of great homogenity, wanting no refinery process, and which he proved only deteriorated the metal. By this method the iron only requires, for certain purposes, to be reheated, with the addition of a small portion of ore; and shingled, or rolled, into bars of amazing nerve, fibre, and cohesion. He was a man of great meakness and suavity, who did not consider that he came into the world to benefit himself exclusively; and published from time to time, many valuable methods of operation in iron making. The above plan he used at Coleford many years since, which cost him considerable time, labour, and expense, to reimburse himself for which he took out a patent. This patent, however, was invaded by a man of such enormous wealth, as to be able successfully to set both honourable dealing and law at defiance—one who could afford to expend £10,000 per annum in law to defend his encroachment, easier than Mr Mushet could afford £100. I think Pope mentions a man, who was 'for law too mighty grown' etc, and I know at this time more than one or two such in the iron trade in the City of London. About three weeks previous to his death Mr Mushet sent me a large piece of his Darkhill pig-iron for my opinion. It is the production of his faithful and virtuous youngest son, Mr Robert Mushet, under his father's direction and rules; and I am bold enough to assert that, being now 72 years of age, during which time I have had much experience in iron and steel making, that this pig-iron is the best ever yet produced by any man with mineral fuel. It possesses great hardness, density, cohesion, and amazing natural fibre, chiefly gained in the process of reduction; for I agree with Mr Mushet, in considering pig-iron, and not refined metal, as the true source of hardness, fibre and stability in bar-iron, particularly when cold; and that, were the ironmasters to proceed according to the rules which he published for them, the great evil of lamination, so very injurious to the durability of railway iron, would be prevented. It is quite true, that crystallisation in the railway bars is constantly going on, for the continued vibration caused by the ponderous vehicles, travelling at such amazing volocity, causes the iron rails to become brittle, and, in some cases, to exfoliate rapidly, because there is not a sufficiency of strong natural fibre in the pig-iron before rolling it into bars, which operation only gives a portion of the strength by condensation; but can never impart that strong natural cohesion of particles, which all good iron should possess in its first reduction from the ore. The latter are the qualities which all iron should have, intended for cannon, steam-engines, cranks, axles, chain cables, railway bars, girders, and for every description of iron bridges; and if the Chester Railway engineer had adopted the use of Mushet's Darkhill iron, the late fatal accident would not have occurred, nor others elsewhere. I know very strong doubts have been expressed, touching some of the ironmasters being favourable to the rapid decay and weakness of iron; and really the suspicion does not appear groundless, when it is proved they refuse to avail themselves of effecting a saving, but also of producing a very much stronger and more durable article; therefore, let all the engineers take care of themselves.

Mr Mushet's iron possesses all the good qualities mentioned, in a superior degree to any other in England. Himself and son were very particular in making good coke. The ore they worked was calcareous and very good, but poor in yield, and obtained under great disadvantages, although they possessed an extensive quantity; yet for want of pecuniary means, were unable to avail themselves of it. Added to these perplexities, Mr Mushet was visited with some extremely heavy and most unnatural family afflictions for several years up to his death; but for which, notwithstanding the infringement and robbery committed on his patent right, his iron-works at Coleford would have produced him a competent fortune. He is now at rest, and died in peace, and in the possession of a good conscience.

David junior, undeterred, wrote in the *Railway and Commercial Gazette Supplement to the Mining Journal* 28 June 1847:

It is sad indeed my father's memory should be exposed to the eulogiums of Mr Upton. To bear any testimony to his solid reputation, requires some acquaintance with his merits. I know nothing of this person; and it is surprising he should dare to intrude upon a subject, on which, whatever his interest, he has no information. It is my duty to correct a mass of mis-statements contained in his letters to your last number. The Darkhill pig-iron (which works were the property of myself and brother, and not of Mr Mushet, senior as stated erroneously by Mr Upton) is not made by any peculiar process; there is no difference, except in the construction of the furnace, which, as already alluded to in your Journal, I built under an unpleasant opposition on the scientific principles of Mr J. Gibbons. Their efficacy was proved, by producing, at our first cast, fine foundry iron—an event unheard of with the refractory ores of the Forest of Dean; the strength of our iron is (as frequently occurs) the result of those refractory ores. The

Cinderford cold-blast iron brings a high price in the market—its tenacity adapting it, in a high degree, for cast, hardware, and tin-plate. The Parkend hot-blast iron, made with the same ore, possesses amazing strength. Mr Montague of Gloucester, the proprietor, has cast railway girders of most unusual power, in proportion to their scantling. I have seen pigs of his iron deflect from 1 to 2in ere repeated blows could produce a fracture. As proprietor of the Darkhill works, these avowals are not to my interest; but it does not consist, with common honesty, to appropriate to a private process what is the characteristic of the district. Mr Upton's information, on my late father's patents, is equally incorrect; he has some confused notion of two distinct processes. My father had, 30 years since, a patent for manufacturing finers' metal direct from the blast-furnace. To practice it he erected a cupola, which he has not worked for 28 years, and tried to introduce the new process in Staffordshire and Wales. It was not then adopted, nor has it been taken up since the patent-right expired. Mr Mitchell's letters on cast-iron, in your columns, I think, throw some light on the causes why it might not succeed. Twenty years after, my father took out quite a different patent, to abolish the refinery operations. This consists in puddling grey pig-iron with rich ore—the absorption of carbon from the iron, to deoxidate and revive the ore, performs an important abridgement of the process, and the wrought-iron has remarkable toughness. This economical practice would, perhaps, have extensively prevailed, but at the same period 'boiling' was introduced, or the puddling pig-iron with the cinder of the different furnaces—an act identical in principle, and only deteriorated by the usual qualities of cinder iron. My late father has stated to me his uncertainty whether these practices were simultaneous, or if the one suggested the other. These two different patents Mr Upton confounds as practised at Dark-hill—whereas, neither are practised there. His version, that pig-iron, merely reheated with ore, is rolled out, is the greatest nonsense ever printed; it does not appear he has any knowledge of the manufacture of iron. I never said the 'fibre' of cast-iron, and the 'nerve' of any kind of iron, is rather a novelty. Iron, likewise, is the production of the furnace, not of the proprietors, as he has it. A patent which has expired cannot be encroached on; this passage of confusion alludes, probably, to the latter patent. This has been used, with great improvements, by Mr Hill, of the Plymouth Iron-Works. If this be the ironmaster Mr Upton endeavours to attack, I can only state, my late father informed me, two years since, that Mr Hill had so improved, and entirely altered, his idea, that a new patent would be required to secure it; I likewise know it as a fact, that Mr Hill, at that time, offered a sum to purchase the remainder of my father's term.

In reply to Mr Upton's beggarly and impertinent account of my father's circumstances and capacity for business, I have to state, that, for the last 20 years his income ranged from £2,000 to more than £4,000 per annum; he was totally unconnected with the Darkhill Iron-Works, and he divides to his widow, children, and grandchildren, property cheaply estimated at £80,000.

Mr Upton avows himself the author of the unparallelled advertisement, and I shall take legal advice on his conduct. It was correctly stated in the *Mining Journal* of the 19th inst, that Messrs Bald, Macintosh, and others, considered the Scottish proprietors, who derived great wealth from Mr Mushet's discovery of the blackband ironstone, would honour themselves by a public testimonial to the inventor; but this is no fraudulent appeal to destitution—and if it be fact, which I am not aware it is, that any one has betrayed my mother's advanced years into the sanction of a step, which would have been as deeply mortifying to my late father, could he have anticipated it, as it is distressing to his relations, the act is truly infamous. The annoyances which my father suffered for five years, and which Mr Upton, with abominable indecorum, drags before the public, he is, perhaps, as well acquainted with as with the other details. My father, likewise, did not die at Coleford, as stated in the advertisement, but at his residence, in Monmouth: I advisedly believe this error is intentional, with an obvious object by certain parties.

Robert Mushet held a different viewpoint (30 June 1847):

To clear Mr Upton from the imputation which has so unwarrantably been laid upon him, I beg leave to state, that he had the full consent and approbation of the widow of the late David Mushet, in undertaking that which has been by him transacted, and which has so much offended the sickly posthumous delicacy of a party who might, had he attended my father's funeral, have learnt more accurately how matters really stood with his widowed mother. I regret being thus compelled to clear the character of a sincere friend at the expense of a relation so near to me as Mr Upton's accuser; but it is due to Mr Upton, who has been actuated by the best and kindest motives, without the slightest intention of giving offence to any person. Mr Upton has nowhere stated that Mrs Mushet had been left unprovided for; neither has he claims as a charity that which is due rather as a token of respect, than as a mere eleemosynary tribute, to the widow of his departed friend. I really do not see why my mother should not have a testimonial of respect to her husband's memory, even though she were in affluent circumstances, which is very far from being the case. Mr Hudson's wealth was no sufficient argument against the levy of a testimonial of respect in hard cash—and what has Mr Hudson ever done to earn such a mark of popular esteem? or what has my father not done to deserve, in tenfold proportion, such a tribute granted to the meritorious promoter of his country's best interests, not to the mere accumulator of wealth? Surely the man who, by his early labours, advanced the science of iron-making at least half a century in improvement, deserves as much, at the hands of the British nation, as the overgrown speculator in railways, or the most celebrated cantatrice of the present day, for whom a testimonial has been recently in contemplation.

By his will (dated 15 April 1847)[100] David Mushet bequeathed 'Parkhill Mine and Coal Gale' to his son William, 'Upper Mine Level at Oakwood Mill' to David, and 'Deep Mine Level at Oakwood Mill' to Robert. His tramroad ('Oakwood Mill Branch', about two miles in length) he left to David and Robert as tenants in common; and his five shares in the s&w Rly to Robert. His coal levels of Bixslade (Lower and Upper), Howlers Slade Deep Engine, and Old Furnace Level (Cannop), together with 'all other mineral and coal property in the Forest of Dean, and stocks of carts, trams, tools and implements' were entrusted to three trustees, eventually to be given to William (4/9ths), Robert (3/9ths) and David (2/9ths). His Darkhill brickworks and house, to be dealt with likewise, are discussed in Chapter 7.

A valuation of the personal property of David Mushet, made July 1847, included: [101]

At Darkhill Carpenter's Shop:

	£	s	d
30 yd new trunks 12 x 10 at 3s yd:	4	10	0
30 new sleepers at 3d		7	6
7 cast iron strickers at 15s	5	5	0
Also sundry oak, elm and pine board.			

At Darkhill Blacksmith Shop:

1 good bellows	3	0	0
1 inferior bellows		10	0
2 anvils	4	0	0
1 big iron		7	6
1 vice		15	0
1 stock with 3 sets of dies	1	0	0
1½ tons wrought iron rods, new	15	0	0
½ ton scraps	2	10	0
6 hammers average 5lb each		15	0

	£	s	d
		£	s	d
2 sledges		5	0
6 rounding tools 1½lb each		5	0
1 dozen cliffs and punches ¾lb		5	0
18 pair tongs average 3lb each	1	5	0
2 sets coal boring tools		15	0

Other parts of the valuation included the plant etc at Howlers Slade and Bixslade coal levels, Oakwood ore levels, the Brickyard and house, and at Lydney Wharf.

A few days after his father's death Robert minuted that 'owing to a disagreement amongst the partners and a consequent deficiency of capital' it was decided to sell the Darkhill property and the two coal levels. On 16 June, he wrote to the Rev George Roberts, a trustee of his father's will: [102]

> There are 98 tons of iron at Lydney, whereof 57 are sold to Messrs Thorneycrofts for cash, at about 80s per ton at Lydney. The whole of the iron will be sold, and the acceptance met long before the time when it falls due. Messrs Thorneycrofts will remit as soon as the iron reaches them.
>
> Messrs Ridlers account is exactly what I have stated subject, as I remarked, to any deduction by payments made through the Lydney Cash Book which I have not seen for 4 weeks.
>
> As to giving up possession of this house [Forest House] I cannot do it, as I have no other place to go to, and no means of paying for another. If Miss Mushet [his sister] had had the common courtesy to inform me 2 months back that Mr James and my father had not agreed for 3 years more on lease of the house, I might have gone out, as I should have had time to seek employment elsewhere. As it is, however, I cannot consent to turn out my wife and children into the streets at a week's notice, and though I am desirous of giving no offence to anyone, I must if the worst comes to the worst keep possession for 3 or 6 months in spite of Mr James. I shall see Mr J. about it on Friday.
>
> I am getting forward the books as fast as possible. Mr Gratrex's [banker in Monmouth] plan is a very good one.

Robert tried to hurry up the sale[103]—'I hope there will be no delay in fixing a day of sale for the Darkhill property. I have struggled to keep the furnace in blast until any sale should be effected . . . I cannot much longer continue the struggle . . . in vain . . . without capital, and with a host of old liabilities.' On 13 July 1847, the ironworks and two coal levels (The Darkhill and The Shutcastle) were offered for sale. Part of the Sale Particulars reads: [104]

The newly erected and valuable blast furnace for the smelting of iron, called Darkhill Furnace, with the engines, machinery, apparatus, hot blast stoves, casting-house, carpenters' and blacksmiths' shops, and other buildings, coke-yard, furnace-yard, water ponds, reservoirs, lands and appurtenances thereto belonging and adjoining, the site whereof comprises in the whole 5a 3r 17p, situate within a few yards of the S&W Railway. The blast furnace is capable of making from 50 to 70 tons per week of pig iron which can be manufactured and delivered at the shipping port of Lydney for a cost, including every expense, not exceeding 55s a ton. An abundant supply of excellent iron ore can be obtained at a price ranging from 5s to 7s per ton delivered at the furnace-yard; and firebricks are made in a brickyard adjoining the property.

A sale was not effected. By deed dated 17 September 1847 David and Robert dissolved partnership.[105] At that time each held a one-third share in the furnace and in the Darkhill and Shutcastle coal levels; they also held in equal shares their brother William's one-third. After paying off a mortgage and other debts, David was to own the ironworks, and the Darkhill and Shutcastle coal levels and the Easter iron mine; Robert was to be manager of the brickyard, and of the coal levels of Bixslade, Howlers Slade and Old Furnace. The furnace was probably never again in blast (the remnants of firebricks within its base are as new). Robert soon went into partnership in a new venture, 'R. Mushet & Co', Forest Steel Works—later 'The Titanic Works'—discussed in Chapter 4.

The Darkhill premises stood idle. A plan of 17 October 1866[106] shows the outline of the furnace, with a long smith's shop to the north and two extensive ponds to the south. On that date, Robert Mushet and Goodrich Langham were given licence by the Office of Woods to continue to use water-pipes 'to buildings at Darkhill, used as a smith's shop, and part formerly a brickworks'.[107] Langham sold to the S&W Rly which by March 1874 was discussing tenders for the sale of materials from the furnace and other buildings, also for tramplates and blocks about to be removed.[108] The following month, the s&w minuted its willingness to accept £420 from Vernon & Shepherd, iron merchants of Smethwick, for the furnace, which they wished to retain for smelting.[109] Whether or not the deal was completed is unknown; no smelting was done. By mid-1874 the sandbed and ancillary buildings to the south of the furnace were obliterated by the embankment made for the s&w railway (opened for mineral traffic in July 1875). The

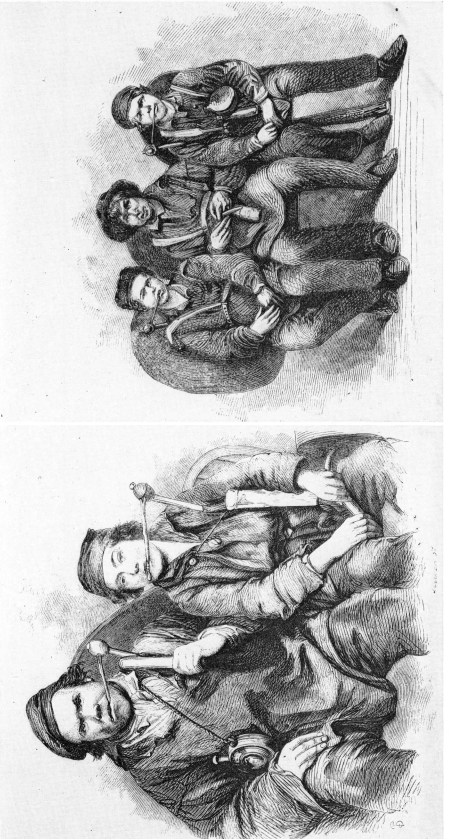

27   Two portraits of miners of iron ore in their working dress, c1830

28 *(above)* Shakemantle Iron Mine c1900, now demolished; *(below)* Wigpool Iron Mine c1940, now demolished

premises are shown as disused on the OS Map of 1877–8. Thereafter the buildings gradually deteriorated.

Today, excavations by A. K. Pope and others are being pursued to
ascertain and record details of some of the buildings and plant.

LOWER SOUDLEY IRONWORKS (Plate 11a and b) From the eighteenth
century there had been industrial buildings, at one time part of a wireworks (qv) consortium, just below where in 1853 the Bullo tunnel's
mouth in Lower Soudley was driven. In 1837 coke-furnaces were
erected there by Edward Protheroe & Co (Protheroe was one-time MP
for Bristol) at a cost of upwards of £10,000,[110] and by October two new
furnaces 'of the usual size' and two steam engines were completed.[111]
The Protheroes, with Mr Broad as manager, worked the coke-furnaces
for four years, but the works were idle in March 1841.[112] and 1842.[113]
In August 1850,[114] Sale Particulars and Plan of the Hay Estate, the
property of Edward Owen Jones, shows the land and premises occupied
by 'Sewdley Iron Works', 13a 0r 36p, including Rolling Mill Patch on
the west of the stream. The premises included the works at the tunnel
mouth and those at Bradley (which Samuel Hewlett had once used as a
forge-cum-foundry (qv). In 1857, Benjamin Gibbons of Staffordshire
purchased the works, and kept them in blast for a year or so;[115] they
were idle from 1856 to 1860. He sold to Alfred Goold in 1863, but in
1864[116] and 1866 only one furnace was in blast, producing about 20
tons of Forest iron at each cast.[117] South Wales coke was used; William
Trafford was manager, and there were eighty employees.[118] Goold
Bros tried to sell the works by auction at Gloucester 15 November
1866, but they were withdrawn at the highest bid, £8,000.[119] Goold's
still held the works in December 1870[120] but apparently sold them to
Maximillian Low.[121] One furnace was in blast from 1871 to 1875,[122]
when the Great Western Iron Co acquired the works, and made
improvements, 'successfully introducing waste gas utilisation plant'.[123]
Pig iron was produced 'absolutely without coal for raising steam or
heating the air, which is required at 800 degrees; with the engine working at 40lb, steam is blowing at 4lb pressure of blast; and at present
only one of the two furnaces are put in blast, and the daily saving
with the new system is at least £10 a day'.[124]

The managing director was A. D. Morrison, and the general
manager J. Yorke Jarrett. The works were under lease to Morrison,
Beauclerk & Co, who had opened them that year,[125] but in 1876 and
1877 only one furnace remained in blast,[126] and the whole plant was
idle by September 1877. Bradley Villa, opposite on the west side of the

M

stream, was, according to its iron plate ('1876 J.Y.J.'), built by or for the general manager of the Great Western Iron Co. The top step up to the crossing-keeper's cottage on the north side of the railway is lettered 'S.I.Co', ie Soudley Iron Co.

In January 1891, the two furnaces were reported as 'under careful supervision' but 'the rooks are the only sign of life'.[127] By 1895 The Cinderford Crushing Co (speciality, slag for concrete) had purchased the 'slag heap' adjoining the furnaces and set up crushing apparatus there[128] and continued to at least May 1898. There were three sidings, used to clear slag for ballast purposes; they were removed, by (and probably well before) 1920.[129] The chimney-stacks were felled c1900. Plate 11b shows the remains.

BROMLEY HILL (OAKWOOD) FURNACE (Plate 9b) The first we hear of this furnace is the indication in the Parliamentary Deposit Plan, 1852, for the DF, Monmouth, Usk and Pontypool Railway, of 'Oakwood Furnace, Ironworks, of John Passand Litchfield and the Bromley Hill Company'. By 10 July 1856 the Ebbw Vale Co (who had acquired Bromley Hill Iron & Coal Co)[130] were about to put the furnace in blast,[131] and it probably worked until c1865–70. Evidence given in connection with the Coleford Railway Bill 1872 shows that the 40ft high furnace was not in work—and had not been for many years— but that the Ebbw Vale Co wanted ironstone carried to South Wales, and coke brought back for use at the Bromley furnace. The company was opening ore mines in the Oakwood Valley, and would build a second furnace when the railway was authorised. Edward Wilson stated he had laid out railway lines to let about five tons of ore, coke and limestone into the top of the furnace without hoisting (high line), and to take one ton of iron from the bottom by means of a steeply-graded siding. The Proposed Development Plan, 1872, indicates 'Pit, furnace, chimney, shaft, engine house' of the Ebbw Vale Steel & Iron Works Co Ltd. The plans for the furnace did not mature. It was certainly out of blast during 1871–80[132] and not even acknowledged as existing in 1877–80.

Some of the remnants are visible (Plate 9b). It was a three-tuyere furnace contained in a square casing, 40ft by 34ft in plan, built into the hillside to the north. The charging-point foundations can still be seen, about 40ft above the casting floor, which lies to the south. The northern and eastern tuyere-arches are blocked, whilst the hearth and fore-hearth area is filled with rubble. The lining and most of the external stone facing has gone.

The blast was by engine, housed a little to the east but not immediately adjacent to the furnace. The slag heap has been removed, but there are traces of ore, limestone, coke, charcoal and iron. A mixed fuel of charcoal and coke is indicated. The type of slag suggests a cold-blast operation. No slag heap appears to exist; this accumulation must have been taken away for other uses, such as roadmaking. Analysis of a cast-iron plate and a wrought-iron bolt have been reported upon.[133]

It has been noted that the coke blast furnace period began in Dean in 1795, and ended in 1894—thus bringing to an end a history of iron smelting there which had begun before Roman times. The intermittent life of the coke iron industry covered: at Cinderford the years 1795 to 1894, Parkend 1799 to 1877, Whitecliff c1807 to c1815, Darkhill 1819 to c1862, Lower Soudley 1837 to 1877, and Bromley 1856 to c1865. Concurrently, coke was used in forges at Lydbrook, Lydney and Redbrook.

Few records of output are available, but it is known that in 1806 two furnaces, Cinderford and Parkend, produced 1,629 tons of coke pig iron.[134] In 1839 two furnaces at Cinderford and three at Parkend produced about 18,000 tons (in 1857 their output reached 30,000 tons);[135] in 1856 there was a total output of 24,132 tons from Cinderford, Parkend, Darkhill, Bromley Hill and Soudley. The eight furnaces in Dean in 1856 produced 'upwards of 24,132 tons'.[136] The maximum number of furnaces existing at any one time was ten, and the largest number in blast was seven (in 1870 and 1871). From 1871 to 1880 the production of pig iron was:[137]

	Cinderford (Crawshays) In blast	Parkend (Forest of Dean Iron Co) In blast	Soudley (Goold Bros) In blast	Tons
1871	3 of 3	3 of 3(*a*)	1 of 2	99,957(*e*)
1872	3 of 4	2 of 3	1 of 2	46,226
1873	3 of 4	2 of 3	1 of 2	44,049
1874	3 of 4	2 of 3	1 of 2	43,139
1875	3 of 4	2 of 3(*b*)	1 of 2	27,088
1876	2 of 4	2 of 3(*c*)	1 of 2	28,108
1877	2 of 4	1 of 3(*d*)	1 of 2	25,602
1878	2 of 4	nil	nil	43,351(*f*)
1879	2 of 4	nil	nil	40,000(*g*)
1880	2 of 4	nil	nil	37,351(*h*)

(*a*) One furnace for 5 months.
(*b*) One furnace for 11 months.

(c) Two furnaces for 7 months, and one for 5 months.
(d) For 8 months only.
(e) Includes the production of five furnaces in Wiltshire and one in Somersetshire.
(f), (g) and (h) Include the production of two furnaces in Wiltshire.

From 1874 the industry declined, especially after 1878, when only two furnaces were in operation, both at Cinderford—evidence that Crawshays alone seemed capable of survival, and indeed in 1880 they were erecting there two blast-furnaces 'on a modern principle'; whether they were completed is unknown, but by 1890 only one furnace was in blast, and that to only one-quarter of its capacity.[138] Crawshays' furnaces were finally blown out on 9 April 1894. Thereafter no smelting was done in Dean: the cause of the collapse can be partly explained as follows. Until 1856 Dean's iron-smelting industry slowly adapted itself to the changing conditions brought about by the great inventions of Darby, Cort and Watt. In that year Bessemer discovered a method of converting specular cast iron into steel, but the process demanded the use of an ore with a low phosphorus content. Very little of such ore exists in Britain, but a process of R. F. Mushet, using manganese, in the compound *spiegeleisen*, to remove the occluded oxygen, obviated the need for ores with very low phosphorus content. Thus Dean (whose ore was of that low content) no longer held an advantage. Furthermore, improved processes made it possible to utilise low grade iron ore in other parts of the country, putting Dean's ore still less in demand. Later, when much ore required to be imported, the most favoured ironworks were those located on or accessible to the seaboard and within easy reach of the coalfields; Lydney, situated so much farther up the Severn Estuary than the ports of South Wales, and with very limited facilities, being geared mainly to coal-exporting, was at a disadvantage. Concentration on the production of Bessemer steel took place between 1865 and 1870. Within two decades Dean's iron-smelting industry was virtually extinct (Cinderford furnaces closed in 1894), and only its tinplate works (qv), wireworks (qv), and foundries (qv) survived. It was for Dean's iron that demand fell, and not a shortage of ore—yet it left Dean's mines to compete against cheaper Spanish ore, and caused their closure in 1899. Doubtless it was her small scale of iron production, coupled with indifferent transport facilities, which led to decline. The furnace units in Dean were fewer and probably smaller in dimensions than those elsewhere; and failure to modernise and mechanise had ill effects (Soudley did not introduce a locomotive until c1875). Transport facilities were delayed for many years (it seems significant that Cinderford, the biggest unit, with railway facilities from 1854, and with the most energetic management, was the longest lived).

References to Chapter 3

1   Johnston. 'New Light . . . ,' 137; 'The Foley Partnerships . . . ,' 331.
2   Rudder, S. *New History of Gloucestershire*, 1779.
3   GRO D1677, GG 1473.
4   Rudge, T. *History of the County of Gloucester*, 1803.
5   Morton, G. R. 'The Early Coke Era', *HMG Bulletin*, 6 Jan 1966.
6   GRO Q/Rum 106: A Plan of 1825 indicates the location.
7   Nicholls. *History* . . . , 226.
8   Information from the late Rhys Jenkins. Outram's report in 1801 on proposed railways in Dean mentions that there were two furnaces for making iron: one of them at Cinderford, the other at Parkend.
9   F3/608.
10 Nicholls. *History* . . . , 226.
11 Addis, J. P. *The Crawshay Dynasty*, 1959, 142, 143
12 Nat Liby Wales, Cyfarthfa Papers, Letter Book 3, ff 172–5.
13 GRO D1987/2.
14 Ibid.
15 Nicholls. *History* . . . , 226.
16 GRO Q/Rum/175.
17 Cyfarthfa Papers, loc cit, Box XII.
18 Addis, op cit, 142.
19 GRO D637/II/7/B6 3 July 1847.
20 Addis, op cit, 143.
21 Cyfarthfa Papers, loc cit, Letter to R. F. Mushet, 3 March 1858.
22 Nicholls. *History* . . . , 226.
23 Nicholls. *Iron Making* . . . , 61
24 Glam Rec Office DD/NAI/L7.
25 Cyfarthfa Papers, loc cit, William Crawshay to Robert Crawshay, 30 Aug 1861.
26 Ibid, also F3/608: circular from Henry informing his customers and suppliers.
27 Ibid, Letter to R. F. Mushet, 3 March 1858.
28 *Dict of National Biography*.
29 Letter from Charles Greenham to H. G. Nicholls, *penes me*.
30 Insole, H. R. and Bunning, C. Z. 'The Forest of Dean Coalfield', *Jnl British Soc of Mining Students*, VI, no 5, 1881, 61–94.
31 Insole and Bunning, op cit, 87.
32 *Engineering* (Jnl), 5 May 1882.
33 *Iron* (Jnl), 23 May 1890.
34 Ibid, 21 March 1890.
35 Nicholls. *History* . . . , 227; *Iron Making* . . . , 57.
36 F3/147.
37 F17/9.

38 S&W Min Bk, 14 April 1824.
39 Ibid.
40 F3/147 14 Oct 1824.
41 Ibid.
42 S&W Min Bk, 5 Jan 1825.
43 Ibid, c18 Oct 1826.
44 Counsel, G. W. *The History and Description of the City of Gloucester*, 1829, 214.
45 Letter from Charles Greenham, 23 Feb 1864, *penes me.*
46 F3/147.
47 Ibid.
48 GRO Q/Rum/175.
49 Ibid.
50 F3/223.
51 Letter in *Supplem to The Mining Journal*, 28 Dec 1846.
52 GRO D637/II/7B6.
53 F3/147.
54 F16/36.
55 GRO D2175 (1863, 1867, 1874).
56 BM.
57 Nicholls. *Iron Making* . . . , 58.
58 Letter from Charles Greenham, 23 Feb 1864.
59 Nicholls. *Iron Making* . . . , 58.
60 Insole and Bunning, op cit, 88.
61 *Engineering* (Jnl), Aug 1877.
62 *Kelly's Directory* 1876.
63 Insole and Bunning, op cit, 88.
64 *The Forester* (Newspaper), 2 Aug 1877.
65 Paar H. W. *The Severn & Wye Railway*, 1963, 47.
66 *Iron* (Jnl), 21 March and 23 May 1890.
67 Howitt, Mary. *Autobiography*, 1889, I, 36, 39.
68 Rudge, op cit, II, 104, records: 'At White Cliff is an iron blast furnace belonging to Messrs Teague & Co.'
69 Osborn, F. M. *The Story of the Mushets*, 1952, 24.
70 GRO D192/4.
71 Nicholls. *History* . . . , 225.
72 Gale, W. K. V. *The British Iron & Steel Industry*, 1967, 22, fig 1.
73 'Mushet's Barn' was demolished in 1966, whereupon a commemorative plaque was erected.
74 Osborn, F. M. *The Story of the Mushets*, 1951, 25; GRO D637/II/7/B6.
75 *Iron in the Making: Dowlais Iron Company Letters 1782–1860*, ed. M. Elsas.
76 On 14 April 1819 the S&W Rly agreed to provide 300 yards of tramroad facilities to Mushet's works (S&W Min Bk, 14 April 1819).
77 GRO D637/II/7/B3.
78 *Papers on Iron & Steel*, 1840, 551–2.
79 *Railway and Commercial Gazette*, 28 June 1847.
80 GRO D637/II/7/B6.
81 Nicholls. *History* . . . , 225.
82 S&W Min Bk, 14 April 1824.
83 Information from H. W. Paar.

84 *Papers on Iron & Steel*, 1840, 551–2; GRO D637/II/7/B3.
85 Ibid; see also bibliography in the *Royal Society of London Catalogue of Scientific Papers*, 1800–1863, 560, 561.
86 GRO D637/II/7/B3.
87 Ibid.
88 Ibid, David Mushet senior also owned or had a share in the Bixslade, Howlers Slade and Oakwood collieries (GRO D637/II/7/B1, 2, 3).
89 Ibid, B3.
90 Ibid, B2.
91 Ibid.
92 Ibid, B3.
93 *Railway and Commercial Gazette*, 3 July 1847: David Mushet junior, to the Editor.
94 Gale, W. K. V. *Black Country Iron Industry*, 57, 58.
95 GRO D637/II/7/B3, 4.
96 *Supplements to Mining Journal*, 1846, 1847.
97 GRO D637/II/7/B3.
98 Ibid.
99 *Supplement to Mining Journal*, 1847.
100 GRO D637/II/7/B7.
101 Ibid, B7, 9.
102 Ibid.
103 Ibid, B5.
104 Ibid, B2.
105 Ibid.
106 F15/8.
107 Ibid.
108 S&W Min Bk, 5 March 1874.
109 Ibid, 14 April 1874.
110 *Mining Journal*, 21 Nov 1866.
111 Nicholls. *History* . . . , 228; *Iron Making* . . . , 59.
112 GRO Q/Rum/175.
113 *Mining Journal*, 1842, 53.
114 GRO D637/VII/23.
115 Nicholls. *History* . . . , 229; *Iron Making* . . . , 59.
116 Letter from Charles Greenham.
117 Nicholls. *Iron Making* . . . , 60.
118 Ibid.
119 *Mining Journal*, 21 Nov 1866.
120 GRO D265/Z3.
121 *Iron* (Jnl), 11 July 1875.
122 Insole and Bunning, op cit, 88.
123 *The Forester* (Newspaper), 9 Dec 1875.
124 Ibid.
125 *Iron* (Jnl), 23 Oct 1875.
126 Insole and Bunning, op cit, 88.
127 *Iron* (Jnl), 2 Jan 1891.
128 GRO D265/Z3.
129 Paar, H. W. *The Great Western Railway in Dean*, 1965, 66.
130 GRO EL/172/18.
131 S&W Min Bk, 10 July 1856.

132   Insole and Bunning, op cit, 88.
133   Bridgewater, N. P. and Morton, G. R. 'Bromley Hill Furnace', *Bulletin HMG* 1968, 43–6.
134   Information from the late Rhys Jenkins.
135   Turner, G. 'The Iron Industry of England', *The Ironmonger*, 22 Aug 1908, 359.
136   Nicholls. *History . . .* , 229.
137   Insole and Bunning, op cit, 88.
138   *Iron* (Jnl), 23 May 1890.

Four

The Iron-working Industry in the Late Nineteenth Century and the Twentieth Century

With Dean's Coke Iron Industry, which began about 1795 and ended about 1894 (see Chapter 3), there were the partly contemporaneous industries of stamping of slag (cinders), foundries, steel, tinplate and wire. Their history is discussed in this chapter.

Stamping of Blast Furnace Slag for the Glass Industry

It was noted in Chapter 2 that crushing of iron ore, and possibly of bloomery slag (cinders), was done for the furnaces by stampers powered by a water-wheel; this practice continued throughout the eighteenth and part of the nineteenth centuries. However, in the latter century these stampers, or improved successors to them, were engaged at Parkend, Redbrook (two) and Tintern to pound or crush blast furnace slag ('scruff') for the glass industry, particularly bottle-glass. George Wyrral referred to this in 1780 when he described scruff ('shining, glass-like cinders') thus: [1]

> The scoria which rises upon the surface of the metal by the present method of melting the iron-ore in large furnaces . . . quite destitute of metal, and consisting of a vitreous substance more or less mixed with the impurities carried off with it in its fluid state.

He went on to say:

> The best of it is used as an ingredient in the making of common green glass, for which purpose it is picked out and reduced to a fine powder by pounding with large stamping engines, and at the same time washing away the lighter substances by a stream of water. There

157

is also found amongst the scruff, on stamping, considerable quantities of granulated iron, and also of ragged lumps, which are called shot and scrap iron. These, in the clearing of the furnaces, are thrown off with the grosser and less fluid scoria, and, after being separated by the stampers, are taken to the forges and worked up with pig iron.

Thus the stampers provided an ingredient in glass-bottle manu-facture, and salvaged iron which would otherwise have been wasted. For the manufacture, bloomery slag (cinders) was apparently not used, because the iron content, some 40 per cent, was far too high. Perhaps only charcoal blast furnace slags (dark green glass) and cold blast coke slags (lighter green to cream glass) were suitable; the iron content of these slags would be less than 30 per cent.

It is not known in how many places in Dean stamping for glass was carried on. It certainly took place by 1810 at Parkend when the Office of Woods gave Isaac and Peter Kear licence to erect there 'a stamping mill to reduce the powder, slag and cinders from the iron furnaces, for the use of the Bristol bottle-glass manufacture.[2] Four years later the Kears were licenced to erect there 'a water-wheel in connection with a mill for pounding slag'. The licence included permission to use both the 'Mound of cinders' and the Newerne stream with its tribu-taries.[3] The plant was situated a short distance above the present road-bridge over the Newerne stream, on or just below the site of the blast furnace erected for the King in 1612 and of that erected for the Com-monwealth in 1653, which together had left behind thousands of tons of cinders, slag and scoria; as late as c1826 David Mushet noted there 8,000 to 10,000 tons.[4] For several decades, the material from Parkend was sent to Bristol; Mushet, writing some time before 1840 says:[5]

> The superior quality of the Bristol black bottles has been attributed to the immemorial use of a portion of the slags of the charcoal furnaces from the neighbourhood of Dean Forest. The consequence of this long-standing practice has been to carry from the furnaces not only the old slags [of the charcoal period] but those currently made [of the cold blast coke period].

On 11 June 1832 the Office of Woods granted to Anthony Hill a licence to 'search for, raise, and convert the slags, cinders and refuse of the ancient iron manufactures on Crown lands in Dean'.[6] The licence was for 31 years from 10 October 1831, the royalty being 1s a ton, with a minimum of £25 annually. No record has been found of any activity by Hill.

On 9 July 1834 s&w Minute Book notes the company's agreement to the Forest of Dean Iron Co being permitted to carry water from 'the stampers (wheel) above Parkend' to the water-wheel at the Parkend turnpike. The Kears being deceased, John Morse who had married Mary the widow of Isaac Kear, was running the Stampers in March 1841, when he was 'stamping ancient cinders with a 24ft water-wheel and 12 stampheads, capable of returning 700 tons if there was a demand for it'.[7] In April 1843, those holding an interest in the property were Morse, Mary Kear, James Ward and Elizabeth Holder; Ward and Thomas Holder had purchased their interest some twenty years earlier.[8] In applying to the Office of Woods for a renewal of their licence they said 'the trade had been very much reduced over the last few years, and the cinders were a great distance from the Stampers'; in the last four years they had erected a new water-wheel on the premises. The licence was renewed 21 November 1844 for 31 years from 10 October 1843, at £9 a year.[9] Morse informed T. F. Kennedy, Commissioner of Woods, 13 December 1853 that there had been no work there for two or three years; there had been 'no demand for the scruff for the last five years in consequence of a company at Redbrook working against us at a lower price than we can render it'. The works were idle and out of repair; if Kennedy would sanction a release of the current rent due, Morse would try to repair ready for next spring.[10] By 1855 Morse was the sole proprietor, subject to a child's interest. On 11 November 1863 he was re-licenced 'the Stampers at Parkend for grinding cinders and other purposes', for 31 years, at £9 a year.[11] The works did not survive long enough to be named on the 25in OS map of 1878. However, to the west still stands 'Stampers Row', a group of cottages. On the east is the site of Paynes derelict stone works. The only remains are abundant traces of slag and some signs of the damming of the meandering Newerne stream, now dotted with small islets.

As to the contemporary stamping industry, at Tintern in 1781[12] 'the dross, already a crystal, is sent to the glass houses of Bristol: much is employed in mending the roads'. At Redbrook there were the 'Upper Stampers', ore-crushing apparatus, which stood below the Furnace, and later 'The Foundry'; and the 'Lower Stampers', between the Upper and the Lower Tinplate Works, and for which the Duke of Beaufort received from Viscount Gage £4 a year from 1812 to 1814 (this included a Slag Bank).[13] John Coster of the Upper Copper Works held them in 1716. On 1 September 1762 Gage when letting his Upper Redbrook furnace (with two Lydbrook forges) to Richard Reynolds of

Bristol and John Partridge senior and John Partridge junior of Ross-
-on-Wye, gave them 'liberty to use the Stampers belonging to the
[Upper] Copper Works without paying rent until Lord Gage shall
let the Copper Works or want it for his own use'.[14] Such stamping was
probably to condition the ore or cinders for smelting or re-smelting. The
Stamp Mill is shown on a map (c1818–28). It was powered by a water-
wheel. Not till 1853 is there evidence for the stamping being done for
the bottle-industry, when the contemporary industry at Parkend was
complaining that a company at Redbrook had for the last five years
been competing at a lower price.[15] The company was the proprietor of
'Redbrook Iron Foundry', which stood just above the Stampers, and
25 February 1864 one of the partners, Thomas Burgham, wrote:[16] 'I
am stamping up some old cinders which I send to Bristol for making
glass bottles that came from a blast furnace that used to melt the Forest
iron ore, and also the Lancashire iron ore with charcoal'. The word
'cinders' was doubtless meant to describe scruff.

Foundries

A foundry was, and is, a building in which metals are formed by
casting. Although some casting into finished products (such as fire-
backs and cannon) was done direct from furnaces, the increasingly
widespread need for intricate machine parts, which could only be made
by casting, led to the growth of the foundry—Boulton & Watt's Soho
Foundry in Birmingham (1775) being an early and very large example.[17]
The Dean foundries of the nineteenth century were of modest proportions, casting for the local market such simple items as tram plates,
mile-posts and tram wheels, although small mechanical items were also
sometimes produced. Some of the foundries had a cupola—a vertical
coke-fired shaft furnace similar to, but smaller than, a blast furnace,
used for re-melting pig iron. An account of Dean's foundries is given
below.

BRADLEY   The site of this foundry was probably that of a seventeenth-
century forge (see Chapter 1), and in the eighteenth century, part of a
wireworks complex (qv). From about 1810–12, premises there were
used by Samuel Hewlett, carpenter and, possibly, blacksmith—a progressive local man who became an ironfounder. At that time, or later,
he lived in the adjacent Bradley House.[18] In 1809 he was a subscriber
to the Lydney and Lydbrook Rly Company. By about 1820 Hewlett

had resuscitated the forge premises as a foundry; and by 1821 a branch tramroad running down from Lower Soudley terminated at his works (see Metcalfe's Map). He must have erected a cupola in 1822 or thereabouts: sometime about 1823 the s&w resolved to use only tram plates made of 'foundry iron'. At least by 1838 (and probably by 1823) Hewlett had established a new foundry a quarter of a mile upstream at Camp Mill (see *infra*). He supplied much ironwork for the Forest tramroads, including tram plates and mile-posts.[19] In 1842 he was a member of the Committee of the Dean Forest & Gloucester Rly.

It is uncertain whether the two foundries, at Bradley and Camp Mill, were for a while run in conjunction with each other, but it seems likely that they were. In 1836 the tramroad is said to go to Bradley House, making no mention of the forge; whereas the 1850 PD Plan (SWR Bill) shows a branch to Bradley (syn 'Aylesford'), and the 1856 Plan names 'The Forge' without showing the tramroad branch. Hewlett's will (proved 5 October 1852)[20] suggests the foundry at Bradley Forge as at least in existence but the premises in 1850 were part of those occupied by the 'Soudley Iron Works'[21] and Hewlett occupied only a 3 acre pasture to the east of his earlier works. The only remnants are indications of the damming of the Soudley stream, a high wall (possibly associated with the works) now buttressing the grounds of Bradley House, and a wide stone-lined leat (in the 1635 inventory 76ft long by 18ft broad) or possible one-time sluice.

CAMP MILL (SOUDLEY) This site (the mill's name is derived from the Norman camp nearby) just below the dam-head of the lower Soudley (Sutton) Pond, was probably that of the 1625–35 forge (see Chapter 1). A map[22] believed to date from soon after 1674, indicates a forge there, while the Drivers' map of 1787 shows 'Old Forge'; Bryant's map of 1823 indicates it to be a foundry, as does Sheasby in 1825[23] and Sopwith in 1835. Samuel Hewlett established his new foundry in these premises, probably by 1823, and he was occupying them under some *ad hoc* arrangement by 1838, in which year on 19 December he leased from William Crawshay of Cyfarthfa (who had obtained the land from Sir Thomas Crawley-Boevey Bt of Flaxley Abbey) the 'iron foundry with the three cottages, sawpit, tool-house, millhouse, and all the erections and buildings', 3a 19p in extent, at or near a place which, though called 'Ayleford', is shown by a plan on the lease unquestionably to be the site of Camp Mill.[24] It is not known who erected the extensive buildings—most of which are extant.

From 1823 Hewlett had supplied the bulk of the s&w plates until

January 1833, when tenders were considered from other suppliers. He
continued to supply 'sundry castings', and in April 1839 the s&w agreed
to purchase from him 5 tons of plates, to be cast from an air furnace,
to be laid on the line for experiments as to 'ware and tare'.

In 1841[25] the foundry at Camp Mill was occupied by Thomas Hewlett. Nine years later,[26] Samuel Hewlett was occupying there a sawpit,
buildings, timber yard, warehouse with cottages over, turning mill,
foundry, and blacksmith's shop. In his will (proved 5 October 1852)[27]
he demised to his sons George and William possession of 'all that ironfoundry with the cottages, sawpit, coalhouse, millhouse, and all other
the erections and buildings, gardens and land'. He demised to the sons
'all his stock-in-trade and effects as an ironfounder, iron machinery, wood
and other patterns, tools, articles and other things (except timber)' in his
foundry at Camp Mill. On 6 October 1855 his executors assigned the
lease of the premises to his son George, 'ironfounder, of Ayleaford'.[28]

On 6 March 1861[29] Henry Crawshay of Oaklands Park, Newnham-
on-Severn, sold to George Hewlett of Bradley House 'the Soudley Iron
Foundry and five cottages, with the sawpit, toolhouse, millhouse,
workshops, etc, late in the occupation of Samuel Hewlett and William
Hewlett, and now of George Hewlett'. The following year, 27 September, George, still of Bradley House, sold the property to Peter Constance, wood turner, of Latimer Lodge, Cinderford, for £1,200; it was
mortgaged back to Hewlett two days later,[30] and in 1867 sold to
Henry Crawshay.[31] Subsequently the premises were used as a flour
mill (qv), a leatherboard mill (qv), a sawmill (qv), and is now (unfortunately from an amenity point of view) a scrapyard for old cars.

Meanwhile, before his death Samuel Hewlett had opened another
foundry, at Upper Bilson (see *infra*) some three miles away in a district
now known as Lower Cinderford.

UPPER BILSON (IN LOWER CINDERFORD)   Samuel Hewlett held this, his
third, foundry sometime after 1838 and certainly before 1852. It
stood at Holly Hill Green on a site which had been owned in 1833 by
William Wintle, engineer, of Littledean Woodside, and on which in
about 1838 Timothy Harris had erected 'certain buildings used by him
as an engine house, blacksmith's shop and casting house'.[32] The works
were probably 'the iron foundry at Upper Bilson' occupied by Timothy
Bennett in March 1841, which included 'one air furnace, one cupola,
stove, and a turning and boring machine driven by a 10in high pressure steam engine.[33] Bennett's Foundry was stated to be close to the
Paraguay Pits.[34]

In his will (proved 5 October 1852)[35] Hewlett demised to his sons George and William 'all those cottages or tenements and gardens with the building formerly used as an ironfoundry, engine house, blacksmith's shop and casting house, and all other the erections and buildings, steam engines and machinery, at Upper Bilson, and as the same are now in the respective occupations of myself and my trustees—Goold and Meadows—together with all stock-in-trade'.

The location of the works is believed to be the now derelict site behind 'York's Fish Restaurant' on the west of High Street in Cinderford. The site is marked on a plan of 1859[36] as 'Boiler Works', and doubtless had a connection with the nearby old 'Boiler Shop Row' demolished c1960. The same plan shows a 'Brush Works' (noted as 'Sawmills' in 1860) a little to the west of the 'Boiler Works'. It is believed that a brickworks later stood on or near the site, probably where stood a property called 'Forest Terrace', demolished c1935 for the Deancroft Housing Site.[37]

As to the boiler works, in 1856[38] there is a reference to 'William Cowmeadow, Steam Boiler Maker and Beer Retailer, Airy Hill' (modern Harry Hill or Harrow Hill). Perhaps this craftsman acquired the works from Timothy Bennett, and ran a public house in his spare time. In 1876[39] under the heading 'Drybrook' appears 'James & Joseph Cowmeadow, Boiler Makers and Engineers'. Later members of the Cowmeadow family remained in the boiler trade—one Arnold Cowmeadow in particular (pre-1930 or thereabouts) used to visit some of the local collieries repairing boilers.

LYDNEY (Plate 13b) In 1856, Talbot & Grice were trading as the s&w Foundry Co, when 23 October the s&w Rly Co authorised their clerk to affix their seal to a lease of 'Lydney Yard' to the s&w Foundry Co 'so soon as the conveyance of that property to the s&w Rly Co shall have been completed by Messrs Bathurst.'[40] Up to that time the railway company had only leased the property from Bathursts.

By 11 July of the following year, the foundry company had become bankrupt,[41] and on 21 April 1858 Keeling of the s&w was directed to effect an arrangement with the assignees of Talbot & Grice, bankrupts, for obtaining legal possession of the s&w Foundry premises.[42] In June 1859 Keeling reported a 'new foundry at Lydney in progress', and a tender to supply a steam engine (£80, excluding boiler) to be used there, was received from Richard Banks of Brierley Hill. Joseph Danks tendered to supply a non-tubular boiler, to be $\frac{7}{16}$in thick, 4ft diameter and 24ft long, at £16 a ton. Both tenders were accepted.[43]

In November 1872, T. G. Pearce was lessee of the Lydney Foundry under the s&w Rly Co, and the landlords were drawing up a new lease.[44] It is not known when this tenancy ended. On 19 April 1892 terms were agreed for Arnold Perrett & Co of Wickwar to lease the old foundry premises as a depot for beer, wine and aerated waters; they took possession late in the summer. At Michaelmas 1896 the Foundry House, formerly used as the s&w Rly Co's Engineer's Office, was rented to C. J. Woolf. Perretts held the foundry premises until at least 1904; they were demolished in 1969.

CANNOP HILL (HOWLERS SLADE) (Plate 13a) Trotter Thomas & Co (proprietor—John Trotter Thomas) in 1829 and 1833 tendered, unsuccessfully, to supply tram plates to the s&w Rly. It is not clear from where they were operating, because their Cannop Foundry, on Howlers Slade, is said to have started in 1835[45] (although its old name-plate, now at Bilson 'Gas Works' Foundry, reads 'Cannop Foundry 1874'). Possibly, prior to 1835 they were prepared to act as factors on behalf of another supplier (for instance, there was a small foundry at Mile End, where the Wades later resided).[46] In 1836 the company tendered again for tram plates and castings, to be cast from an air furnace, for three years at £6 a ton, on condition that the s&w sold them all their broken plates and castings at £3 12s 6d a ton. This was accepted, but a month later Trotter Thomas attended a meeting of the s&w and 'wished his offer abandoned by reason of his not understanding the quantity of old plates prohibited to be used in making the new tramplates'.[47] He was released from the contract, and the Yniscedwyn Company's offer at £5 10s a ton was accepted, also John James & Son's (of Lydney) offer of £3 15s a ton for old plates.

In March 1841[48] the foundry at Cannop comprised 'two air furnaces and stove; fitting shop; steam engine; turning and boring mill'. In 1847 Trotter Thomas & Co supplied castings to David Mushet.[49] An old tramway wheel (which may date from c1829)[50] in the Science Museum, was made for 'Bilson & Crumpmeadow' (and thus probably for Edward Protheroe) and has the name of the foundry as 'Cannopbrook' (the trade name used by Trotter Thomas & Co).[51] In June 1865[52] John Trotter Thomas and others were given by the Office of Woods licence for 31 years at £5 per annum for 2½ acres of land for a foundry and a stone planing and sawing machine in Howlers Slade. This was a renewal of an earlier licence. Trotter Thomas & Co were still in business there in 1887[53], but by 1891[54] the firm was simply 'Thomas & Co', and about that year Edward Thomas of Winalls Hill House (he had

29 *(above)* Edge Hill Iron Mine
c1930, now demolished; *(right)*
The 'Creeper', Waterloo Colliery,
1912

30 *(above)* F. B. Watkins, a talented engineer and industrialist who (like his father and grandfather before him) has provided much employment in Dean. It was said of his grandfather, Richard Watkins, that 'while Henry Crawshay had built Cinderford, Richard Watkins had built Bream'. The family owned several iron ore mines; *(below)* Colour Works at Milkwall

a coach-and-pair, and paid boys ½d to open gates) failed to pay his workpeople, became insolvent and prudently flitted to the USA. Thereafter the foundry was taken over by Richard Young of Berry Hill and Thomas Herbert—'Herbert & Young (Established 1893)—Engineers (iron and brass).' In 1902 we read of 'Coleford Foundry, R. Young'.[55] The partnership was dissolved 31 March 1930, and the business was carried on by Thomas Herbert until his death in 1942. It was then continued by his son Ewart B. Herbert until 1957, when he moved the business to the premises of the old Bilson Gas Works (see *infra*). The Howlers Slade site today is clear of foundry remnants, but much of it is taken up by the surface accoutrements of a coal level.

BILSON ('GAS WORKS') FOUNDRY (Plate 14b) In 1957 the Bilson Gas Works premises (which had been established in 1859) were taken over by Ewart B. Herbert to house the business which he transferred that year from the Cannop Foundry. Incidentally, on the new motorway at Whitchurch are cast iron man-hole covers by 'Wm Young, Cinderford'.

TINGLE'S FOUNDRY, CINDERFORD This foundry stood just off Station Street in Cinderford, east of the old premises of East Dean Grammar School (since 1968 part of the Technical College). The Tingle family owned the foundry by 1887—in which year we read of 'Mrs Hanabia Tingle, ironfounder'.[56] Subsequently Tingle Brothers ran it[57] until it was closed in 1924.[58] Three photos of the interior of the works (c1907) are extant (Plate 14a). The foundry was also part of an extensive engineering works. The site was later cleared and bungalows built thereon.

STEAM MILLS (LOWER CINDERFORD) Teague and Chew An engineering works which included a foundry was begun here in 1888 by the Teague family. In 1902 we read of 'Moses Edward Teague, engineering works, Steam Mills'.[59] He invented automatic expansion gear for steam engines which was used in many mines throughout the country. The OS Map of 1903 shows 'Haywood Engine Works'; a corn mill adjoined it. Later, Charles Teague and Arthur Chew formed Teague & Chew Ltd. Although the business always comprised a foundry and machine shop, the firm expanded and began manufacturing grey-iron castings, including dynamo castings, and machine tools, at one time employing 30 men. There are extant four photographs of the interior of the works (c1907), three of the pattern shop, and two of Teague's Expansion Valve (Plate 15a). D. M. Teague, grandson of the founder, now heads the company, which employs about 50 men.

THE FOREST VALE IRONWORKS, CINDERFORD This large establishment c1850 (see Chapter 3) included a foundry. It had three cupolas, and was probably used for producing pig iron of a size suitable to be handled in the puddling furnaces there, prior to going through the rolls, etc. The steam hammer there was quite a large one, and its sound could be heard for miles around; it gave the name to a nearby inn—the 'Forge Hammer'.

HEYWOOD (LOWER CINDERFORD) In the early 1900s Charles Wheeler worked for Teague & Chew Ltd (see *supra*) and in his spare time made brass castings at his home. He had small brass furnaces successively in premises at Cinderford—in Prospect Road, then near the Lydney & Crumpmeadow Company's offices at Bilson, and later at Hawkwell near the old Tinplate Works. His son, Eddie, also worked for Teague & Chew Ltd, and when in 1912 he had the house adjoining the foundry built he too installed a small brass furnace, and produced bearing castings and the like for local collieries and other industries. He continued his employment with Teague & Chew Ltd until the early 1930s, when on a full time basis he founded the present foundry at Heywood, and began casting iron as well as brass. His son, John, carries on the business, using iron only.

CULLAMORE FOUNDRY (SOUTH OF RUSPIDGE) This was probably the site of the building shown as a 'furnace' on Sopwith's plan of 1835, though he indicates quite a gap between the siding and the building as it is today. By 1878 it was in use as a colour mill (hence the name 'Cullamore') processing, for pigments, red, yellow and 'blue' ochre from Buckshaft iron mine (which closed in 1899). Later the premises were used by Henry Crawshay & Co (they may well have owned them throughout because they had connections with iron mines) as stables for the horses of their Lightmoor Colliery (to which they built a tram-road bridge—hence 'Cullamore Bridge'). On the closure of Lightmoor in 1940, the brass and iron foundry situated at that colliery was transferred to Cullamore, where castings were produced for Eastern United and Northern United Collieries. Up to c1945 Cullamore had a cupola, and was known as 'the Cast House' (Plate 15b).

Architecturally, the building has several interesting features, and has obviously been reduced in width and had some of its windows blocked. Bricks from a chimney stack which once stood at the SE corner are now scattered in the waste ground at the rear; also to be seen are pieces of furnace-lining, slags, coke-cinder and iron. It is unlikely that all these samples were associated with the cupola process: certainly the samples of blast furnace slag could not have been derived therefrom. A feature of the site is a badly robbed stone wall-like structure set into the bank behind the cast house—perhaps merely a retaining wall for the tramroad siding shown thereabouts on Sopwith's plan. The main building is now used as a private car-repair workshop.

BROMLEY (OAKWOOD)   This foundry in the Oakwood Valley bore on the west side a plaque with the date '1852'.[60] It made tram wheels for one of the collieries, and continued in use after the tramroad behind it ceased to work, closing about the time of the First World War. Thereafter, Charles Pearce, the manager, carried it on as a colour works, using ochre from the nearby Noxon Park mine. Later, it is believed, Pearce went to work at the Cannop Foundry. The walls were levelled to the ground in 1967 (Plate 16a).

UPPER REDBROOK   Part of the sites and premises at Upper Redbrook connected with two successive blast furnaces (qv) which had been in operation throughout much of the period 1604–1816, were for part of the late eighteenth century and early nineteenth century used jointly with a foundry. A plan of 1808[61] shows the outline of 'Upper Redbrook Furnace and Foundry'. Ten years later the Commissioners of Woods were owners of the Redbrook 'Upper Forge, Furnace, etc, 2a 3r 38p' and in July of that year the premises were sold by auction to the tenant, Henry Davis,[62] who was also tenant of the Tinplate Works. About the year 1828, Davis sold the property to Thomas Burgham, ironfounder.[63] In 1847 Burgham & Harris there, supplied tram wheels to David Mushet.[64]

Burgham in his will (dated 17 August 1850)[65] demised to his wife 'a property now in my own possession and occupation, consisting of a cottage or cottages with garden, Stamping Machine etc in Upper Redbrook, purchased by me of Henry Davies about the year 1828'. His trustees were to allow his wife sufficient capital to carry on 'the trade'— ie of an iron foundry. Burgham was still the ironfounder there in 1858,[66] and in 1864, when 25 February he wrote from 'Redbrook Iron Foundry':[67] 'I am not in the habit of using Forest ore in the Foundry Business. The pig iron I use is of different sorts and old castings.' Burgham also ran the Stampers (qv) nearby. A traveller on the Wye in 1885 noted: 'At Redbrook Hills the curling smoke issuing from the ironworks forms a pleasing accompaniment to the scenery, the inspiration of which it for a while suspends; below are Redbrook tin-works'.[68]

The foundry closed about 1874,[69] and the premises were later demolished. The whole site now forms part of a small hamlet known as 'The Foundry'.

Steel

The Forest of Dean witnessed two projects in the making of steel—a form of iron that has been subjected to complicated heating processes and contains a certain proportion of carbon. The two projects are discussed below.

THE CEMENTATION PROCESS By this process, which possibly dated back to 1556 in Italy or to 1613 in Holland[70] steel was produced from pig iron through the addition of carbon to wrought iron. In 1614 a patent for the process was obtained by William Ellyott and Matthias Meysey. Two years later they gained another patent, for carrying out their invention with pit-coal instead of wood. The patents were transferred to Sir Basil Brooke of Coalbrookdale, one of the lessees of the King's Ironworks in Dean who from 31 May 1615 had a lease of the two furnaces and two forges (qv) at Parkend and Soudley. He may have sent from Dean iron for the production of steel by the cementation process, and in 1635 he claimed that he had settled the new invention of making steel in the Kingdom. In 1622 he was spoken of as 'the great steel maker' in Gloucestershire.[71] The process may have spread to Dean—'the best steel is made about the Forest; it breaks fiery, with somewhat a coarse grain, but if it be well wrought, and proves sound, it makes good edge tools, files and punches, it will work well at the forge and takes a good heat'.[72]

FOREST STEEL WORKS (LATER THE TITANIC STEEL & IRON CO LTD) Shortly after the death of David Mushet (7 June 1847), his son Robert Forester Mushet having in September 1847 dissolved partnership with his brother David in Darkhill furnace (qv) went into partnership with Thomas Deykin Clare, a Birmingham merchant, in a new venture, 'R. Mushet & Co', Forest Steel Works.[73] This 'small experimental steelwork', situated a few hundred yards to the north-west of Darkhill, included 'a crucible furnace of ten melting holes, and a pair of wooden helves or old-fashioned tilt-hammers; the melting holes were square so as to hold four crucibles or pots in each'.[74] The walls of the structure were formed of local red grit stone. The process used by Mushet is on record.[75] The chief workmen were: a 'potmaker', to prepare, mould, and condition the clay crucibles; two forgemen, George Hancox and George Tomlinson; a young melter, William Phelps; Jim Brookfield, the head melter (the most important man in a crucible melting team); Lewis Joseph, the trusty handyman, stern and eagle-eyed, who helped

Robert to prepare and weigh up the materials for melting; and a young man named Turton, who was willing to turn his hand to any job. Subsequently Robert employed two Sheffield men, Morehouse and Bull, as melters. A man named Rook, a blacksmith, made hammers, chisels and other tools.

In 1856 Mushet with the aid of S. H. Blackwell of Dudley, added to the steel works 'a cupola for melting pig iron, a small Bessemer hearth or converter, 15in square by 5ft deep, and a blowing apparatus driven by a belt from a large pulley fixed on the end of the flywheel shaft which worked the tilt hammers; it delivered a blast of 8 to 10lb. The tuyers were made of $\frac{1}{2}$in gas piping, two being run into the sides of the furnace and one at the back through the firebrick'.[76] In that year Mushet was shown a sample of iron made by the Ebbw Vale Company, using the Bessemer process, and was asked by Thomas Brown, one of the Ebbw Vale partners, if he could improve it. Recognising the fact that excess oxygen was causing trouble, Mushet removed the oxygen by using a material known as *spiegeleisen*, a triple compound or iron, manganese and carbon, which, when melted and added to the blown Bessemer metal, deoxidised it successfully. In 1858 William Crawshay paid Mushet the very high compliment that a piece of iron submitted to him was 'the very best I ever saw in my life!'[77]

On 22 October 1862 The Titanic Steel & Iron Co Ltd was formed, promoted by Mushet to provide badly needed capital for expansion. They built large ornate works a few hundred yards WNW of the Darkhill premises. By 1868, Mushet was producing his self-hardening tool steel ('R. Mushet's Special Steel') much in demand in the Sheffield area. He made it by alloying it with the element tungsten, and it was an immediate success because of its hardness, toughness and durability, and its unusual property of hardening itself, without quenching. All that was necessary was to heat the steel, forge it to the shape required, and let it cool; it was then ground at the working point, to sharpen it, and could be used at once. The following report appeared in 1869:[78]

Mr Robert Mushet has started a steelworks at Coleford, Forest of Dean, for the manufacture of titanic steel. The influence of titanium upon steel and steel-manufacture is comparatively little known as yet; but to judge from the records of Dr Fairbairn's tests of steel, laid before the British Association in the last year, the steel of the Titanic Iron and Steel Company seems to be distinguished by an extraordinary amount of cohesive strength. The specimens of titanic steel tested by transverse strains have given some of the highest figures in Dr Fairbairn's table, both with regard to the value of the modulus of elasticity and to the value of the unit or working strength. We do not know whether it be the titanium, but we are quite certain it is Mr Mushet's great skill as a metallurgist to which such results are due.

The trade thereafter moved out of the carbon-steel field. Tungsten-alloy steels, more sophisticated now than in Mushet's day, but basically the same, are still made throughout Britain.

Mushet made and despatched some of the steel products under the greatest secrecy.[79] The iron base for the manufacture of the steel was processed at the 'brickyard', part of the adjacent site. In August 1870 the company was refused by the s&w Rly a reduction of tolls on blooms, to bring the rate in line with that on pig iron,[80] and in November of that year claimed about £6 for damage to iron plates on transfer from the broad gauge at Parkend, where they were unloaded.[81] All seems to have gone well with the Titanic Company until 1871 when the works was closed; the company was voluntarily wound up in August 1874.[82] About 400 tons of its old iron was purchased in December 1871 by Richard Thomas & Co of the Lydbrook Tinplate Works to whom the s&w Rly gave a special tramway tonnage rate of 1s.[83]

Thereafter the premises lay neglected. In 1908 the Office of Woods advertised the property for lease.[84] No enterprise was attracted, but by 1926 the property was on lease to Lydney District Brickworks & Collieries Ltd, who in 1928 sub-let to Milkwall Brickworks Ltd.[85] The buildings gradually further deteriorated. Photographs taken in 1935 and 1951 show some of the ornate arches and windows (Plate 17a). A gasometer on the OS plan was for storing producer gas for the heat treatment of steel. In 1964 the remnants, having for many years been open to the sky, and used for such humble purposes as a chicken run, were bulldozed level by the Forestry Commission. Only one small building, near a cottage, was saved (Plate 17b).

Tinplate

INTRODUCTION Tinplate is neither tin nor plate, but sheet steel (originally sheet iron) coated with a very thin protective layer of tin. Andrew Yarranton[86] on his return from a visit to Saxony in the 1660s to obtain information about tinplate making, canvassed the idea that the distressed condition of both the Cornish 'tin-miners' and the Dean 'iron-miners' could be relieved by the establishment of a tinplate industry in Britain. As an experiment, 'many thousand plates made of Forest of Dean iron and tinned with Cornish tin were produced, and the plates proved far better than the German plates, the true reason being the toughness and flectibleness of our Forest iron.'[87] However, experiment was not followed by commercial development until early in the eighteenth century, and even then, while charcoal remained the fuel in use, tin-plating was not generally introduced. Immediately after the Industrial Revolution most iron-smelting areas had tinplate works as a subsidiary industry.

By the nineteenth century (perhaps late in the eighteenth), tinplating, using charcoal, spread to Dean. One unsubstantiated source implies that the first local manufacture was in 1760 at Lydbrook;[88] another source asserts that it took place at Lydney in 1789,[89] while Redbrook may have begun manufacture in 1771.[90] Certainly tinplate was being produced at Redbrook by 1774, at Lydbrook by 1798, and at Lydney by c1810 (indeed evidence will follow of a 'Tin Work' there by 1781).

Early in the nineteenth century, new tinplate works using coke as fuel were begun in South Wales. Dean soon followed, with coke gradually replacing charcoal. The records of the five local works show that at Redbrook the manufacturers were Townshend & Wood, at Lydney the Pidcocks, or John James; and at Lydbrook the Partridges and the Allaways. Richard Thomas and his company followed in the early 1870s at both Lydbrook and Lydney. At Parkend, works were established by James and Greenham (c1853), and at Hawkwell by Chivers and Bright (1879). In 1880 the five works comprised 17 mills, of which 15 were at work:[91]

> In these works the iron is made from pig iron on the spot. At one of the works, the iron made in the Forest being too tough to be used alone, is mixed in equal quantities with pig from Middleborough or Bristol and is then puddled, rolled into plates, cleansed, annealed, tinned and packed into boxes. The thickness of the plate varies from 24 to 38 Birmingham Wire Gauge.
>
> The annual production may be calculated upon an average of 450 boxes per mill per week, giving for the 15 mills 351,000 boxes per annum, and as each box weighs a cwt, the weight will be 17,550 tons; in

the manufacture of which about 1,050 hands are employed. A great part of this production finds its way to the United States, the proportion of the Forest with that of Great Britain being one-seventeenth. No Terne plates (ie iron plates tinned with a mixture of tin and lead) are made in the Forest, but some Black plates (ie thin plates not tinned at all) are manufactured and sent to America where they are varnished and returned to England to be used for photographic purposes.

The tinplate works used sulphuric acid (much was made at the Cannop Chemical Works using sulphur from Sicily) to remove the ferric oxide and other impurities on the iron plates, previous to their being tinned.[92] Some of the acid was brought from Swansea, where it was made from pyrites, after the copper had been extracted; being a waste product of the copper works, it was cheaper than the acid made from sulphur, but contained impurities in which arsenic was a great objection.[93]

The histories of Dean's five works are given below:

LYDBROOK   According to Brooke,[94] in 1760 at Lydbrook 'a Tinplate Works is said to have been started'. There is some doubt about the year, because an early letter-heading of 'Lydbrook Tin Plate Works' says 'Established 1798'. Brooke is more likely to be nearer the truth when he stated[95] that tinplate works were erected at Lydbrook in 1806 by Thomas Allaway—tenant under the Partridges—and that tradition has it that he produced there the first tinplates in England (but a similar claim has been advanced, as noted, for Lydney). The Partridges' works were the Upper and Lower Forges, and it seems they converted them to early tinplate works, adding associated works in between the two forges. They leased them to Allaway in 1817 'at which time they comprised three forges, rolling and bar mills, and tin-house complete, capable of producing 100 to 150 boxes of tin plates per week'.[96]

Possibly Allaway had, as Brooke implies, begun in 1806 producing tinplate, and in 1817 had added to his holding by taking a lease of the Partridges' premises where they too had apparently been tin-plating. Materials and some fuel arrived by tramroad, but the tinplate was shipped at Lydbrook via the Wye to Bristol. In April 1820, when the firm was 'Pearce & Allaway', they appealed to the S&W for a reduction of the tonnage rates on soft coal and cokes used in their works.[97] From 1 January 1823 the firm had a new lease for 14 years at £580 a year.[98] Their works, rented from John Partridge, comprised:[99]

Upper Forge		*Lower Forge*	
Plan		Plan	
No		No	
1	Pool	57	Charcoal yard
2	Yard	59	Pool
3	Smiths Shop	60	Boiler
4	Yard	61	Engine house
5	Rolling Mill and Forge	62	Forge
6	Fly-wheel, water-wheel, etc	63	Charcoal yard, etc
7	Rolling and Bar Mill	64	Charcoal house
8	Tin furnace	65	Yard
9	Bloom furnace		
10	Coal yard		
11	Engine-house		
12	Boiler-house		
13	Boiler-house		
29	Shear shop		
30	Scale house		
31	Cold Rolls, water-wheel, etc		
32	Scouring house		
33	Tin house		
34	Wash house		
35	Store house		
47	Tin house yard		
48	Office, and warehouse under		
49	Carpenters shop		

On 23 October 1834, the Lydbrook Tinplate Works were put up for sale, the Particulars reading: [100]

The Extensive Iron and Tin Plate Works, freehold property for investment, singularly eligible for advantageous and safe investment, capable of making about 300 boxes of Tin Plates per week with one set of workmen only, and the produce may be doubled by employing a sufficient number of hands. They have been recently improved, and a considerable portion placed on an entirely new construction close to a capital rail road.

The great improvements in the making of iron lately introduced to the Forest of Dean will, it is hoped, in the event of their being satisfactorily brought to bear, add much by reducing the price of raw material, to the advantages which these works already possess, and under which they have been carried on so beneficially for many years past.

The property comprises: Steam Engine, Rolling Mills, Forges, Tin

Houses, Blacksmiths' and Carpenters' Shops, with the Agent's House, Workmen's Cottages, Gardens, Stables and Warehouses, with the machinery belonging to the works, and the workmen's tools now in use, and castings, and the 27 acres of land held therewith, as the same are all now in the possession of Messrs Pearce & Allaway, as tenants thereof under a lease for the term of 14 years from 1 January 1823, at the yearly rent of £580.

The proprietor was John Partridge, and viewing was to be done through 'Mr Pewtner of Bishopswood'. Whatever the result of the auction, the tenants in the period 1847 to 1849 were still Pearce & Allaway. William Allaway was in charge, assisted by his sons William and Stephen. By 1850[101] the name had changed to 'Allaways, Partridge & Co', and they were still buying cordwood for charcoaling from the Office of Woods.[102] In that year they informed the s&w that they wished to convey tinplates from Lydbrook to Lydney by tramroad, instead of by water via the Wye to Bristol. Negotiations were unsuccessful: in October 1858[103] the firm proposed that the whole of their tinplate traffic should go over the s&w if the tonnage rates did not exceed 1s 6d a ton, but it is most unlikely that this was effected, because the tramroad north of Mirystock was not carrying traffic by 1869.[104] In that year 600 boxes of tinplate a week were being produced, chiefly from Cinderford iron.[105] Neath Abbey Ironworks prepared drawings in July 1867 of 'part of a 34in engine for Messrs Allaway, Lydbrook'; and in August 'drawings for Messrs Allaway & Partridge'.[106]

In 1871 the works, comprising two mills and a forge, were leased to Richard Thomas (Plate 24a), who made a great impact on the Forest's industrial growth. Born 5 December 1837, at an early age he set up in Cardiff as a coal exporter and commission agent, which business he gave up in 1859 to become manager and accountant to a colliery and firebrick works at Briton Ferry in which his father was a partner. He relinquished this position in 1863 on being appointed accountant and sub-manager of the Melyn Tin & Iron Works at Neath, and four years later, with friends he restarted the Ynyspenllwch Tinplate Works which he managed till 1871. Thomas moved from Wales to 'The Poplars' at Lydbrook, and on 1 April wrote to prospective customers:[107]

> Lydbrook Tin Plate Works
> (Established 1798)
> Having taken the above old-established Works, which I need scarcely inform you are situated in the Forest of Dean, so noted for

its supplies of Charcoal, and the Malleability of the Iron made from its Ores, I have pleasure in introducing to your notice my different Brands of Tin and Terne Plates, and in doing so allow me to accompany each with a few explanatory remarks.

My 'KSI Best Stamping' Brand will represent the very best description of Charcoal Plate that can be manufactured; it will specially meet the large demand that has arisen for Plates of good stamping qualities of Iron; and it is my intention to spare no effort or expense to make this Brand at least equal to any in the trade.

The 'TOWYN' Brand will denote my second quality of Charcoal Plate—a kind of Plate, when fairly coated and made of regular quality of Iron, now much in request.

My 'MADOC' Brand will represent best Hammered Coke Plates, and every care shall be taken to make this class of Plate equal to any of a similar kind.

In addition to the above, under the Brand 'CEFN', I shall make a Coke Plate of a cheaper description to meet the present great demand.

The Forge Power at these Works being ample, I am able to make the whole of my Charcoal and other Iron on the Premises, thereby giving me every facility for producing it of uniform quality.

In conclusion, I may state that my experience of the Tin Plate Trade, having been learnt at Works where the following Brands of Plates are made, viz, 'KCB', 'MELYN', 'AFAN', 'KG', 'YNIS', 'THOR', 'HS', etc, is, I trust, a proof that any commands you may be good enough to favour me with will be carried out efficiently, and I hope to your entire satisfaction.

I am, dear Sir, yours obediently,

RICHARD THOMAS

Within a month he was pressing, unsuccessfully, for an extension of the s&w Railway from Serridge Junction to Lydbrook.[108] In March 1875 his company acquired the Lydney Tinplate Works. Five years later,[109] at Lydbrook there were five mills, four working, with an average weekly production from each mill of 450 boxes. A chimney stack was built that year by John Watkins,[110] some 125 to 130ft tall, 4ft thick at the base, and 14ft square (Plate 18a); when completed, several members of the tinworks' brass band were hoisted inside the stack, and played several tunes at its top!

In 1882 the company suffered much financial loss in litigation with Francis Brain and partners respecting water troubles in Trafalgar, Speculation, and Old Bobs Collieries.[111] Thomas bought the Lydbrook Colliery in 1877; later he owned Speculation and the Waterloo Colliery (known also as The Pludds), opened by him about 1882. By May 1883 the Lydbrook works were closed, and in July the company was in liquidation, with the Gloucester Banking Co mortgagees in possession. At the time of the closure the employees at night dislodged many tons of rubble on to the awkward rail approach, to prevent the company despatching 500 boxes of tinplate, already loaded, which the employees asserted as representing their wages.[112] By February 1884 the company was solvent,[113] and in September of that year Richard Thomas & Co, Lydbrook and Lydney Works, were registered as a limited company. Thomas was ably supported by his sons Richard Beaumont, and Frank.[114]

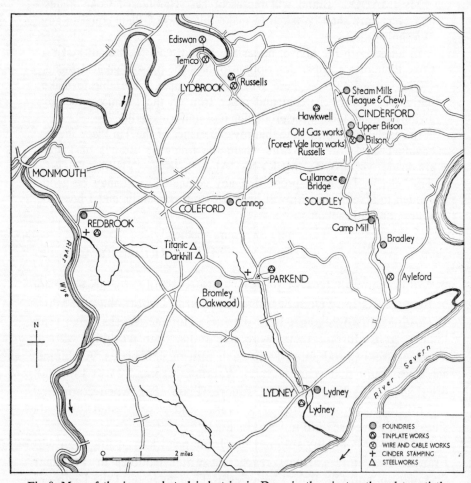

Fig 8. Map of the iron and steel industries in Dean in the nineteenth and twentieth centuries.

The company suffered a recession after the McKinley Tariff (1890) limited trade with the USA. In 1893 the plant comprised five mills, the brands being: charcoal, 'DEAN', 'LYDNEY', 'LB', 'ALLAWAY BEST', 'RT&CO', and 'KYRL'; coke, 'MADOC' and 'LYDBROOK'.[115] The works were closed temporarily in February 1899 due to 'dearness of coal and tin, and the cheapness of the manufactured article'. During their most prosperous years they employed almost 700 men. They closed during the First World War, and although the works were re-opened in 1919, they ceased operating in 1925.

Until 1930 the machinery was kept in repair in the event of the works restarting, but by December that year the plant was dismantled and removed.[116] Felling of the huge chimney stack took place 28 June 1938.[117] (Plates 18a and b.)

The early tin works and rolling mills (see Metcalfe's Plan of 1834) stood between the Upper and Lower Forges. The enterprise developed into the main Tinplate Works (of which only the rear retaining walls remain). The main site is now used for the premises of S. C. Meredith & Sons (Engineering) Ltd, and Lydwood Ltd. The associated site a short distance upstream, where stood the Upper Forge (adapted for a 'tin furnace and rolling mills') is occupied by Edwards Transport Ltd; underground is a stone archway through which a tramroad ran to connect the two sites.

LYDNEY The consortium of ironworks at Lydney and district has been described in Chapter 2. When for them David Tanner in 1781 paid to the Bathursts £280 rent it included rent for 'Pill Forge [ie Lower Forge] now a Tin Work'.[118] If this implied plating with tin, as opposed to making iron plates for that purpose, tinplate was presumably being made at Lydney in 1781—seventeen years earlier than the year (1798) when it has been asserted that the manufacture of tinplate there first took place.[119] Thus Tanner may have been in the trade well before the Pidcocks who on 8 November 1790 obtained the lease of the Bathursts' furnace near the site of White Cross House, and of their Lower, Middle and Upper Forges on the Newerne stream.[120] Certainly by 1810, when the Pidcocks put up for auction their lease of the works, there is evidence of 'buildings for the manufacture of tinplates'. This does not necessarily imply that they had already been used for this purpose, yet it is a fair assumption that the words 'suitable for' would have been inserted if tin plates had not actually been already made. One advertisement for the auction of the lease reads:[121]

Lydney Iron Works and Colliery

To be sold by auction at the Exchange Coffee-house, Bristol, on 1 June 1810. Consisting of Upper Forge, now worked as a stamping forge, containing three charcoal fineries, and one running-out fire; with iron helve, and blowing machinery. Middle Forge, with balling and other furnaces, but now used as a drawing-out forge for uses, etc. Lower Forge, with puddling and balling furnaces, and iron helve, now used as a shingling forge. One other forge, on the same head, used as a plating forge, with blowing machinery. One mill capable of rolling 50 tons of Merchant bars weekly. These works are upon one stream of water, and the extreme distance between them about 2 miles. One foundry, one charcoal furnace, not being worked, with charcoal houses and other buildings for the manufacture of tin-plates. One Clerk's house, 19 workmen's houses, and about 17 acres of good meadow and orchard ground.

The colliery consists of one 6ft and two 3ft veins of coal, over about 500 acres, at present worked by one level and 2 pits, there being a railway just finished through the collieries and works to the Severn, where the coals sell for from 12s to 14s per ton; the present price for getting the coal and delivering it to the Severn, through a private canal belonging to the works, about 5s 6d per ton.

Works and collieries held under lease from Rt Hon Charles Bathurst, about 67 years unexpired, rent £280 per annum free from Poor Rates and Tithe. In the lease Mr Bathurst covenants to cut and deliver all his underwoods, averaging 1,400 cords annually, of 16–18 years growth at 7s 3d per cord.

Also a farm, held under a lease (7 years unexpired), consisting of a good house, fit for the residence of a managing partner, with about 31 acres of land and orchard ground, rent £93 per annum. (Barker & Onett, Solicitors, Birmingham).

Another advertisement reads: [122]

Charcoal Iron Works, and Collieries

To be Let—All those Forges, Mill and Collieries situate at Lydney, upon the banks of the Severn, between Newnham and Chepstow in the County of Gloucester—The Iron Works consist of One Forge, containing 3 Fineries and 1 Running-out Fire, with Blowing Machinery complete; One Shingler's Forge, and a One Drawing-out Forge for uses; and a very good Mill, with a Plating Forge, all upon one Stream; the extreme distance from each not above 2 miles. There is also a Foundry.

These Works are well supplied with Contract Cordwood, at the very low price it bore 30 years ago; they have also advantages which no other Works possess, being situate so as to command the Shropshire and Welsh Hills, and by that means are capable of making the very best of Iron for Tin Plates, Wire, etc and therefore the best situation in the Kingdom for Manufacture of that sort.

Also, to be Let, upon Royalty, Very Extensive Collieries, near the above Works. These Collieries are worked by Levels, and are capable of supplying large quantities of Coal. There is a Rail-Road from the Forest of Dean through the Iron and Coal Works, and by a Clause in the Act of Parliament, these Works and Collieries have an exclusive privilege of passing upon the Rail-Road at One-Sixth of the Tonnage other Works pay; and by the Canal Act which unites the Rail-Road with the Severn, these Works are allowed to pass the canal free.

The present Proprietors would have no objection to retain a Share in these Works, if they were applied to the making of either Wire or Tin Plates, provided a proper Person, competent to the management, could be found to undertake the Business.

Apply to Mr G. Pidcock, at the Works, for a View; and Messrs Pidcock, Stourbridge, for further Particulars.

The reason for the Pidcocks wishing to sell their interests at Lydney is not stated. The property was withdrawn at the auction. The s&w Rly Co Act (50 Geo III c215) 21 June that year (1810) authorised the railway to 'cross the private canal of Thomas Pidcock, John Pidcock and George Homfray' twice by a drawbridge. Furthermore, Messrs Pidcocks and Homfray had the right to throw cinders and refuse into the Lower Brook, behind their works at Middle Forge, if not removed by the s&w within 7 days.

Following the unsuccessful attempt to sell by auction, negotiations ensued between the Pidcocks, the Rt Hon Charles Bathurst, and Thomas Waters, merchant of Carmarthen. A letter from Waters 11 November 1813, and draft Articles of Agreement, are extant.[123] Waters was to take a lease from Thomas Pidcock of Stourbridge, Worcestershire and John Pidcock of the Platts, Amblecoat, Shropshire, of the Upper Forge, capable of making charcoal iron from pig iron as heretofore; the Middle Forge for drawing out bar iron; the Mill for rolling tin bars; and the Lower Forge for shingling stamped iron. On 3 October 1813 John Pidcock wrote to Bathurst:[124]

Mr Waters knows the situation of the Lydney Works to be the best I may say of any in the Kingdom for the making of Tin plates, but seeing your anxiety to get a tenant, is treating with a seeming indifference as he did with us, thinking to make a good bargain. You and us stand in two very different lights, the one having a very serious repair of the furnace staring him in the face, the other having it in his power to do away these repairs altogether had it been proposed to us to concede these repairs by allowing the 400 cords of wood annually we should have readily accepted the proposal, and for this reason only I think Mr Waters' bargain will now be as good a one to him as though he purchased from us, and I really think he ought not to hesitate one moment, as you guarantee a thousand cords of wood annually, to take to the works at the £350 per annum and pay for all the stock as valued by Messrs Thompson & Browning.

As Mr Waters will want wood in his collieries it may be a great inducement to him, and I see no great injury to you to give him the option of cutting his cord wood into one length for the use of his colliery only, instead of confining him to 2-foot lengths for charcoal; again suppose you permit him to turn these works to any other purpose than iron, giving up to you the woods, except such quantity you may agree to cut him for the use of his own collieries. Were the works my own I should not be in a hurry to let them, for should former times come round again these works will let for a great deal more money.

I recommended Mr James of Redbrook to apply to you for the old iron which I told him I thought you would let him have at the valuation and also give him permission to work them up at Lydney; this is a nice chance of business whose lease at Redbrook will shortly expire, and I think was he to taste the situation and convenience of the Lydney Works he would be a very likely person to take them; these united with the Redbrook Charcoal would be very complete. Mr James informs me he saw Mr Ducker who told him you were in treaty with Mr Waters.

I have thus wandered very far from the question you put to me but it is trying in some measure to return the many civilities I have received from you is my excuse for my troubling you with my opinions; and believe me Dear Sir if at any future period I can render you any service I beg without the least hesitation you will command me.

There is one other matter I beg to remind you of and that is to replant your woods putting in the moist places willow or sally of the right sort; it grows quick and is the best cratewood and brings the best price; the thicker planted in reason the better; and care should be taken to keep out the sheep by having good fences.

P.S. If Mr Waters sees another person occupying the works it will bring him to his senses.

The negotiations with Waters proved abortive. On 29 November 1813, John Henzey Pidcock, George Pidcock, and John Pidcock, all of Staffordshire, assigned their Lydney interests to the Rt Hon Charles

31 (above) Trustees of the Free Miners for the 'Deep Gales': Top left to right: F. Jones, R. Brown, C. Hirst, B. Dobbs, J. Hawkins; Middle left to right: A. Sadler (auditor), T. Morse, G. Barnard, J. J. Joynes, T. Wright, C. Lees, J. Nicholls; Bottom left to right: M. Perkins (vice-president), S. J. Elsom (president), W. Meredith (hon sec), G. T. Stephens (hon treas), G. Jenkins; *(right)* a Free Miner's level

32 Six of Dean's collieries, all abandoned: (*a*) Arthur & Edward (Lydney & Crump-meadow Collieries), previously 'Waterloo'; (*b*) Princess Royal (Princess Royal Colliery Co); (*c*) Norchard (Park Colliery Co); (*d*) Lightmoor (H. Crawshay & Co); (*e*) Northern United (H. Crawshay & Co); (*f*) Eastern United (H. Crawshay & Co)

Bathurst,[125] who 1 October 1814 leased the property to John James, ironmaster, one of the two partners in the Redbrook Tinplate Works.[126] To enable James to accept the works, Bathurst had taken over from the Pidcocks their stock of castings, utensils, implements and fixtures, being given several years to pay for them (Bathurst was still paying off the debt and interest in November 1816,[127] when he asserted to John Pidcock that the bargain was likely to prove a bad one; he had been left with much unsaleable cordwood (*vide* Chapter 10) although the Pidcocks had retained an interest in at least one of his coalworks— the level at the Norchard).[128] The actual lease to James, 1 October 1814, has not been found, but later evidence[129] confirms that some of the terms were:

1. Tenure: to 25 December 1844.
2. Property: Lower Forge and Rolling Mills, Middle Forge, Upper Forge, Wharf and Warehouses at Lydney Pill, Land and Houses in Lydney.
3. Covenant that the lessee would take cordwood at 7s 3d a cord.
4. The lessee to keep the property in repair.

In October and November 1814[130] James sought permission from the s&w to make connections to the Upper, Middle and Lower Forges. In July 1818 he and the Bathursts were negotiating with the s&w for a branch of his rolling mill via his private railway, from the gate of Pill Meadow across the canal bridge at the tail of the lock nearing that mill.[131] There is no confirmation of a statement[132] that in this year, 1818, Thomas Allaway (of the Lydbrook Tinplate Works) had started a tinplate works at Lydney, although in this respect he may have had some connection with James.

By October 1823[133] James was proposing to build new ironworks on the Bathursts' land—the 'New Mills' erected by him in 1824 midway between the Upper and Middle Forges, on or near a site where had stood an 'old furnace', the site of which was in the tenancy of Richard Symonds.[134] The New Mills comprised[135] a large water-wheel, powered by the Newerne stream (there was a 7-acre pond, with a good fall, just above) which drove a 'rolling machine'. There was also a 'blowing machine', and a forge hammer and wheel. James also had a '60 Horse Engine with shaft to work when water is short'. Other property there included a puddling house with three fires, and three labourers' houses. The New Mills, of which part of the dam wall and sluice remain, stood just above the Norchard Colliery and the Electricity Power House (now demolished).

o

In March 1841 James's 'Middle Rolling Mill' comprised two pairs
of Tinplate Rolls driven by a water-wheel in winter, assisted by a
steam-engine in summer, capable of converting 20 tons of bar iron
weekly.[136] The lease to James was due to expire 25 December 1844.
An inventory made the previous month by Jacob D. Sturge, land
surveyor, of Bristol, shows: [137]

*Tin works called in the lease of 1 Oct 1814 'the Lower Forge and
Rolling Mills'*

These contain a large water-wheel driving a rolling machine.

Another for the blowing machine.

Another for the cold rollers.

A hammer wheel and hammer.

Together with wash house and scouring rooms for tinning the plates,
annealing rooms, workshops, carpenters shop, five labourers' houses
etc.

The inventory describes:

A hammer wheel with iron helve.

An anvil block.

Two standards.

Two iron crosses.

Wedges and wrought iron cramp.

A water-wheel, a main cog wheel, a spur wheel, a fly wheel and shaft.

The whole of this remains, and much more which has been added by
the lessee.

Middle Forge

This contains:

A hammer wheel working a large hammer.

A large water-wheel working a rolling machine.

A water-wheel working a blowing machine.

A foundry (2 fires), charcoal shed, workshops, 4 labourers' cottages
and about half an acre of garden ground.

The machinery comprises:

The whole machinery capable of drawing bar iron.

Poppett and frame.

Cast iron crooked leg and box and straight leg.

Blowing machinery and wheel for ditto.

All this machinery except the wheels has been taken out and new and
more effective machinery has been substituted for it; most if not all
the old is still remaining in the yard.

Upper Forge (Plates 5a and b)

The inventory describes:

A hammer wheel.

One bear helve.

One anvil block and plate.

Two cast iron plates under the block.

Two standards and plates.

Blowing machinery for these (? three) fires with two cylinders, pipes, cracks and iron beams.

All this machinery remains and is still in use with but little addition. The blowing machine is worked by a large water-wheel. There are ten labourers' cottages, about one acre of garden ground, and a charcoal house. The pond contains 13a 0r 39p and the fall is good.

The New Mills which have been newly built by the lessee within the last twenty years [in 1824] contain:

A large water-wheel driving a rolling machine.

A blowing machine.

A forge hammer and wheel.

There is a 60 Horse Engine with shaft to work when water is short. Also a puddling house with three fires.

There is a pond containing about 7 acres and the fall is good.

Three labourers' houses and 1½ acres of garden ground, also 1a 1r 6p of marshy meadow.

The machinery in this mill all belongs to the lessees.

Wharf and Warehouse

With a navigable canal and locks leading up to the Upper Forge. The goods shipped from the wharf are free of the Lydney Port dues.

Two closes of meadow land containing 11a 2r 23p.

Houses in Lydney consisting of a carpenters shop, two small tenements, and five larger tenements, with garden ground, the whole covering 0a 3r 2p. The houses are old and from their having been let in small tenements have a neglected appearance. The roofs etc appear to be substantially good.

The land surveyor, after setting out the foregoing inventory, reported:

There is a covenant that all the wood in the coppices of the lessor which shall exceed in quantity 1,000 cords per annum shall be taken by the lessees at 7s 3d per cord.

The lessee also covenants to put in good repair and at all times well and sufficiently repair, support, amend, maintain and keep in repair the forges, messuages, tenements or dwellinghouses and buildings which are now standing or hereafter may be erected, also the gates, fences, etc.

Also the canal pools and ponds, locks, gates, weir, stanks, banks, bridges and dams of the canal etc; and all including such as may be hereafter erected to be given up in good repair together with the fixtures and utensils in the schedule annexed to the lease.

The lessees are bound to leave the machinery as described in the inventory in good repair, and I doubt whether it would not cost them as much to restore the old as they could sell the new for, and thus I conceive it to be to their interest as it is undoubtedly the landlord's that the present should remain.

With respect to repairs, I did not observe but the buildings are substantially good. The tiling of the roofs wants general examination with some other things of not much importance. The lock gates near the Tin Works are in a bad state.

On the question of value, it is not easy to fix any very definite sum on account of the little competition there is for Manufactories of this nature, and the improvements which have taken place in machinery rendering the works of older date of less value. This kind of work is now also done without charcoal, which renders the situation near the Forest of less importance than heretofore. The following calculations may be considered as an approximation to the rental which ought to be obtained:

	£
Water power for 4 mills including the water-wheels	100
Buildings	
Machinery so far as it is the landlord's property, except water-wheels	130
Labourers houses and gardens	55
Meadow land at 45s an acre	26
Houses in Lydney	36
	£347
Deduct for repairs if all done by the lessees	37
	£310

Although this is a moderate rent for property of the extent, I consider it to be of great importance to make a fresh arrangement with the present tenants, and for that purpose I beg to suggest that it may be best to make a sacrifice in rent. The reasons I have before mentioned rendering it uncertain as to procuring a new tenant.

The covenant to take all cordwood above 1,000 cords at 7s 3d a cord, that being about 1s 3d a cord above the market price, is in fact an additional rent to the extent of the quantity which the woods may produce and may I am informed be estimated at 400 cords equal to £25 per annum. In a new lease I beg to suggest that *all* the cordwood be taken either at the price per cord which may be determined to be the present market value, or at a price to be annually fixed by two wood dealers or surveyors, one to be chosen by each party.

In case an Agreement cannot be made with the present lessees, I do not advise the landlord's taking to their machinery because a new tenant would probably object to take any which was not according to the most modern improvements. I would rather suggest that they might have the option of its remaining, to offer to succeeding tenants, or to take it away.

Following the above inventory and report, John James, by then of Highfield, Lydney, and Henry James, of Highfield Cottage, took a new lease of the property, for 12 years from 17 January 1845 at £225 yearly.[138] The property included:

(*a*) The Storehouse or Warehouse called the New Storehouse (later the Pill Storehouse) and the Storehouse Leaze.

(*b*) The Lower Forge (formerly Pill Forge for making bar iron) now known as 'the Lower Forge and Rolling Mills, with the Tin-works, Rolling Mills, Buildings, Yards, and Workmen's Houses'.

Plant:	T	C
1 hammer wheel, one iron helve at work	3	17
1 anvil block	3	0
2 standers	3	0
2 iron brasses	0	3
wedges and wrought iron cramps	0	1

(*c*) The Middle Forge (formerly New Forge for making bar iron), with yards and workmen's houses.

Plant:	T	C	Q	lb
1 cast iron hammer wheel in two parts	4	8	0	0
1 cast iron hammer beam	4	15	0	0
1 cast iron hammer beam ring	3	4	1	0
4 cast iron ditto arms in ditto		8	2	16
1 cast iron hammer		6	0	0
1 cast iron anvil		9	1	0
1 cast iron anvil-bit		1	0	18
1 cast iron anvil-block	2	10	0	0
1 cast iron bed-plate under ditto	1	11	3	1

	T	C	Q	lb
2 cast iron liners under ditto		1	0	25
1 cast iron breech plate to anvil		4	1	14
1 cast iron standard under hammer beam		5	0	11
1 cast iron flutter plate for hammer wheel		1	2	11
1 cast iron still plate under standard		6	0	14
6 cast iron sturts for hammer wheel		1	2	14
3 cast iron plates for the fall of ditto		17	2	7
2 cast iron side plates for ditto of ditto		8	1	7
1 wrought iron bar and key to standards			3	8
1 wrought iron hook round the anvil block		1	0	14

(*d*) The Upper Forge (formerly 'a tenement called the Slitting Mill House but for many years past used as a forge for making iron') with yards and workmen's houses.

Plant:

	T	C	Q	lb
2 brass bearers under gudgeons of hammer beam		1	1	6
1 hammer wheel and a beam helve	3	16	0	0
1 anvil block and plate	4	11	0	0
2 cast iron plates under the block	2	0	0	0
2 standards and plates	2	10	0	0

blowing machinery for these fires with 2 cylinders { 2ft 8in diameter, receiver, pipes, cranks, and iron beams.

(*e*) The Rolling Mill (formerly 'part of the Old Furnace yard together with the Mill for Rolling iron, two workmen's houses and other buildings'): This property, near the Lower Forge formed a separate lease of the same date, at £48 a year, and the extent was 1a 1r 19p.

Plant:

1 water-wheel, a main cog wheel, a spur wheel, a fly wheel, and a shaft.

(*f*) Meadow etc (formerly called 'the Slitting Mill Meadow but the greater part now covered with water, forming what is called the New Mill Pond'). The premises and machinery in the New Mills belonged to the lessee.

(*g*) Parts of those lands for workmen now occupied by the James's (formerly 'part of the land called the Brick Yard, formerly in the possession of George Whyrall, through which the Forge Brook runs').

(*h*) Ponds or pools called 'Slitting Mill and Upper Forge', 'Pill Forge or Lower Forge', and 'New Forge or Middle Forge'.

(*i*) Piece of land, part of 'The Langet' adjoining the Middle Forge Yard, 3 roods, on which to deposit cinders from the forge: The land was included in the separate lease of the same date, referred to in (*e*), above.

(*j*) Use of 'Pidcock's Canal' extending from near the Upper Forge to the New Storehouse at the Pill.

The James's surrendered their lease to Charles Bathurst 24 March 1847[139] who on the following 3 June re-leased for 14 years at £225 a year to the Allaways of Lydbrook Tinplate Works: William Allaway the elder, of Lydbrook, Stephen, of the Grange, Flaxley, Thomas, of Lydney, William the younger, of Lydbrook—all ironmasters and tinplate manufacturers—and James Allaway, of Ross-on-Wye,[140] of the banking firm of Allaway & MacDougall. Nicholls wrote in 1858:[141]

The Tinworks at Lydney are in the hands of Messrs T. & W. Allaway, and comprise three forges, mills, and tin-house, producing 1,200 boxes of tin plates a week, with the consumption of from 70 to 80 tons of Cinderford iron.

He added in 1866[142] (based on information given to him in 1864):

Similar works [to those at Lydbrook], only on a larger scale, are carried on at Lydney by Messrs Allaway & Sons. These are five in number, and bear the names of the Lower Mill, the Lower Forge, the Middle Forge, the Upper Mill [ie The New Mills], and the Upper Forge. About 400 hands are engaged at them, and turn out about 1,000 boxes of tinplate every week, besides a quantity of sheet iron. The materials supplied to these works from the Forest of Dean are pig iron, coal, fire-bricks and clay, fire-stone and fire-sand, and cordwood for conversion into charcoal.

Thomas Allaway informed Nicholls 16 March 1864,[143] 'we use a little iron as a mixture with the Forest iron—about two-thirds Forest and one-third Scotch or Welsh; we do not make pig iron in any way, either with charcoal or coke'. Two years later, Neath Abbey Ironworks prepared drawings for machinery for the 'Lydney Tinplate Co'.[144]

William Allaway & Sons surrendered their lease 9 November 1871,[145] and Richard Thomas & Sons, of Lydbrook, acquired the works in March 1875, when the plant comprised four mills, and the brands were: Coke, 'AWRE'; Charcoal, 'LB', 'LYDNEY', and 'ALLAWAYS'.[146] In 1877 Thomas complained to the s&w of loss of power at his water-wheel, because water in the s&w canal was being

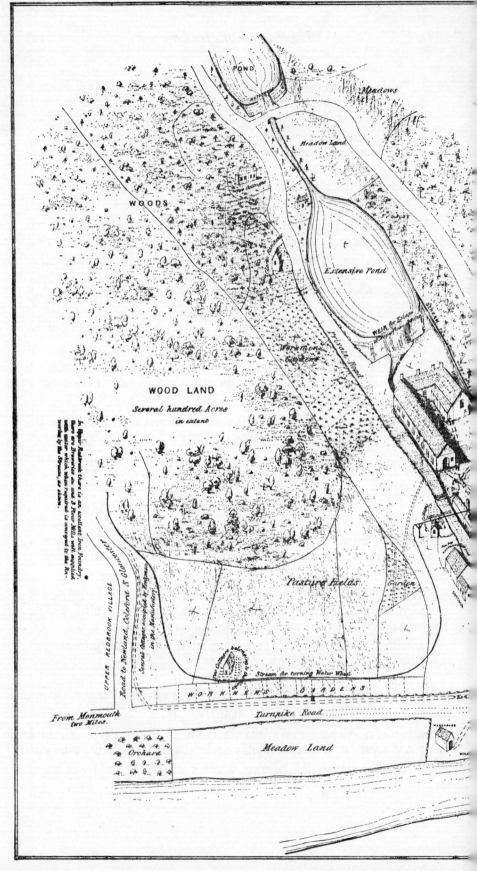

Fig 9. Panoramic sketch of Redb

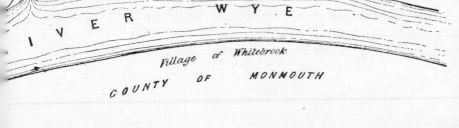

VIEW OF THE

REDBROOK TIN-PLATE WORKS

SITUATE TWO MILES FROM MONMOUTH,

IN THE PARISH OF NEWLAND,

and County of

GLOUCESTER

1848.

S.G. Gregg. Land Surveyor &c.
Highbury near Monmouth.

Tin-plate works in 1848.

kept at a low level. Three years later,[147] there were four mills, three working, with an average weekly production of 450 boxes at each mill.

In January 1882 Thomas was fined £1 in connection with smoke nuisance,[148] and that year he built a 164ft brick stack to abate it. In December he negotiated with the s&w to retain the part of the tramroad from Middle to Lower Forge which remained. However, early in 1883 the works closed due to Richard Thomas & Sons' financial difficulties. In May, Thomas was reported as contemplating re-opening the Lydney and Lydbrook works, and he suggested that the s&w should lay a narrow gauge tramway on the tinwork canal towing path, charging him the same tolls as before (on the tramroad) and giving him an option to purchase it. However, by July the company was in liquidation, and in August the mortgagees of the works, the Gloucester Banking Company, complained to the s&w about the removal of the tramroad, and proposed to build their own tramway from Middle Forge to Lower Forge, using the canal as a road-bed and passing under the s&w near Lydney Church. The creditors offered to accept a composition,[149] and by February 1884 Richard Thomas & Co were solvent again. The bankruptcy did not diminish the confidence of the creditors in Richard Thomas's ability, and he became managing director of the new firm formed to operate the Lydney and Lydbrook works. He was succeeded by his son, R. Beaumont Thomas in 1888, and thereafter the Thomas's tinplate manufacturing interests greatly expanded.

The last charcoal-iron for tinplate was rolled at Lydney in 1886;[150] steel for tinplate-making had taken the place of puddled iron. In 1887 the yearly traffic between the Upper and Lower Forges was about 4,200 tons in process of manufacture, and 5,200 tons of coal to or from the New Mills.[151] Down the Thomas's tramway from Lower Forge were conveyed tinplates in boxes to their wharf at the head of the canal, just south of the South Wales line, where the old ruined warehouse still survives. Horses worked the flat-bottomed waggons, and a small steam-boat, the *Black Dwarf*, carried the plates to Avonmouth, where they were shipped to places as far afield as Australia.[152] The Upper Forge was dismantled by 1890.[153] (The shell of the engine house, and walls of unidentifiable small buildings survive, occupied by undergrowth and trees; the dam wall, still serving the additional purpose of a carriageway, has been strengthened. To the east there is a spectacular spillway in a minor gorge.) Dismantling quickly followed of the Middle Forge, where blackplate was still being produced in 1891[154] leaving only a strengthened dam-cum-carriageway, and of the New Mills, leaving only a dam and a sluice.

Thereafter, production of tinplate, ever increasing, was carried on by Richard Thomas & Co Ltd at the Lower Mills in Lydney. A new lease to the company was made by the Bathursts 7 November 1889.[155] In 1893 the plant comprised eight mills, and their brands were: Charcoal, 'DEAN', 'L.B.', 'LYDNEY', 'ALLAWAYS BEST', 'RT & CO', and 'KYRL'.[156] A second stack, 170ft tall, was built in 1913.

In August 1941 the premises were requisitioned by the Admiralty. The works re-opened in April 1946, with W. H. Parry as manager, and O. C. Davis as assistant manager, but in March of that year the Tinplate Redundancy Scheme had sterilised five of the eleven mills, then under the control of Richard Thomas & Baldwin Ltd. In May of the following year, 1947, the enterprise was acquired by The Steel Company of Wales, Ltd. The works, of six mills, were finally closed in November 1957, when O. C. Davis had been manager since 1950. The buildings with the freehold reverted to the Bledisloes, as landlords. The two large stacks were felled in November 1958 (Plates 21a and b, 22a and b).

Subsequently the premises have been put to use by Watts Tyre & Rubber Co Ltd.

REDBROOK In 1771, according to Brooke,[157] the Company of Copper Miners in England leased to Townshend & Wood the Lower Copper Works with land on which they built a Tinplate Works [the Lower], and wherein they made tinplate in 1774. The property included the Coperas House (now the site of a petrol filling station). In 1790 the Company sold the premises for £2,750 to David and William Tanner of Tintern and Monmouth, when they comprised:[158]

> All that freehold copper work [the Lower] consisting of furnaces, forges, foundries, mills, utensils, implements, erections and works for calcining, smelting, refining, hammering and manufacturing copper ores and copper, together with three large ponds or reservoirs for supplying the work . . . water grist mill or tucking mill near adjoining a water grist mill formerly of Warren Jane, then in the tenure of William Carter, but since converted into a copper work . . . also that messuage or tenement in Lower Redbrook late in the occupation of Thomas Chambers deceased, formerly a water corn or grist mill, but converted into a large copper work.[159]

The Lower (main) Tinplate Works and the (smaller) Upper (previously the Upper Copper Works—just east of the junction of the

Newland and the Monmouth-Bigsweir roads) were run as one, and no records of their separate working up to 1800 have been found.

The tanners improved the plant and premises as well as the forge up the Valley Brook. (The forge is sometimes referred to as the Bigwell Forge, of which the only remnants are the Forge pool and the sluice in the dam wall. Below the pool stands Forge Cottage). The water came from around the Valley Brook: [160]

> A curious spring, adjoining the Lower Works . . . supplies the wheels . . . and issues at the bottom of a grand woody hill, and is formed by three distinct streams, which pour their contents into a basin, that empties itself into an adjoining pool . . . discharging a large and unceasing torrent at all seasons.

Finding that the water-wheel in the main works was not providing sufficient power, they installed a steam engine. Soon the Tanners were in financial difficulties, and on 29 June 1791 they mortgaged for £2,200 to James Sevier of Bristol, manufacturer of horsehair: [161]

> All that freehold ironwork lately used as a copper work [the Lower] and converted into an ironwork, consisting of furnaces, forges, foundries, mills etc, lately used for calcining, smelting, refining, hammering, rolling and manufacturing of copper ores and copper, together with three large ponds or reservoirs for supplying the work, and houses etc; also a water grist mill or tucking mill at Lower Redbrook being near adjoining to a water grist mill formerly of Warren Jane then in the tenure of William Carter but since converted into a copperwork and in the possession of the Governors and Company of Copper Miners in England; also the messuage in Lower Redbrook lately in the occupation of Thomas Chambers deceased whereon formerly a water corn or grist mill was standing but converted into a large copperwork.

On 20 September 1793[162] David Tanner leased from Jane Quick of Bath, widow, a dwellinghouse and the premises previously used as the Upper Copper Works (qv). This was to supplement Tanner's Lower Tinplate Works. For a short while Tanner progressed. A traveller on the Wye in 1796 mentions that 'some iron and tin works give animation to the romantic scene'.[163] Shipments of tinplate via Chepstow were 22½ tons in 1794, 27¼ tons in 1795, and 43 tons in 1796. Another traveller, writing in 1797, says: [164] 'Here a considerable manufacturing of iron and tin gives a new and pleasing variety to the scenery and bustle on our river.'

The Boulton & Watt Collection, deposited with Birmingham Public Reference Library, contains two drawings of the Rolling Mill at Lower Redbrook, one dated 1798 and the other 1799. One drawing shows drive by water-wheel, and the other by steam engine. The rolls were 14in diameter by 18in long.[165] Rhys Jenkins copied the drawings and commented thus:[166]

It would appear that by this time the mill consisted of two pairs of rolls, and that the rolls had increased in size; they were now 14in diameter and 18in long. The mill housings were, as in 1755, each composed of a pair of round wrought-iron uprights threaded through a pillow block and a cap block of cast iron, both top and bottom rolls were driven, and the pinions were mounted in separate housings. The bar shears were worked by water power, as they were in 1755.

Figs (*a*) and (*b*) in Plate 7 are the earliest scale drawings of tinplate rolling mills. One of the drawings—'A Plan of Lower Redbrook Tinn Mill' shows a mill driven by a water-wheel; the other drawing, headed 'A side view of a Steam Engine for Rolling Tin Plates, Ac.,' is not stated to be one of the Lower Redbrook Mills, but there can be no doubt that it does show the 'fire engine' mill at their works. Both drawings are signed by the same man. The engine shown is an atmospheric or Newcomen engine.

In 1789 David Tanner was declared bankrupt, and the Lower Tinplate Works were taken on from the mortgagees by William Cowley and John James[167] under a lease for 21 years from 25 December 1798 at £700 annually.[168] By 1802 the tin-works were 'all in gloom, and a mournful picture of misfortune'. Litigation was said to be the cause. Particulars of a sale to be held 28 July 1802[170] of 'Lower Redbrook Works now used as a manufactory for tin plates', included:

Managers dwellinghouse.
23 Workmen's houses.
22 acres of woods.
26 acres of pasture and orchards.
30 acres of rough land and brakes.
1 Forge with 2 Fineries and 2 Balling furnaces.
2 Rolling Mills, with 3 Bar Iron Furnaces, and 4 Tin Furnaces, for making Tin Plates.
1 large Shears for cutting iron, and two for shearing the plates.
A Steam Engine for working the Rolling Mill.
2 Shear Shops.
2 Scaling Houses with two furnaces for scaling, one Scouring Room, a Tin House and 2 Warehouses; with 6 Tin Pots, 4 Wash Pots, Grease Pots and Lesting Pots to match, for tinning and washing the plates.

A Set of Stamps.

A pair of small Rolls, and a Wheel for Rolling Clay.

A Stove and Brick Kiln for making and burning bricks.

2 Smith's Shops and 1 Carpenter's Shop, with sundry other Warehouses and Buildings.

3 large ponds or reservoirs to supply the works with water.

Also to be sold was 'the remainder of a certain term of years in a Turning Mill, now occupied with the before mentioned works'. The sale was to be subject to the following outgoings:

	Yearly rent		
	£	s	d
To Lord Sherborne for the Turning Mill and backage at the Wye	8	10	0
To Lord Berkeley a Chief Rent of	8	10½	
To Charles Edwin a Chief Rent of	5	4	
To Mrs Quick for the lower Mill pond	2	0	
	£9	6	2½

The 'Turning Mill' mentioned above apparently stood just below the Lower Tinplate Works, ie nearer to the Wye. It was owned by Lord Sherborne, who sold it 6 August 1802 as a 'Rolling Mill' to Edward Sayce;[171] it had been 'a water corn grist mill, heretofore in the possession of Elizabeth Jones but afterwards of Messrs Cowley & James, and now vacant'. Cowley & James were still making tinplate at the Lower Works in 1805, when they complained that water above their works was being diverted.[172]

The Upper Tinplate Works, always a small adjunct to the Lower, were idle by the time of Tanner's bankruptcy, 1798, and they reverted to the landlord, Viscount Gage, who in 1800 leased them (not for tinplate manufactory) to his steward James Davies and his partners in connection with the Upper Redbrook furnace and two forges at Lydbrook. The partnership (discussed in Chapter 2) lasted until 1805, when the premises were let to Robert Thompson, who may have done some tinplating there before 1818, when Gage sold his Gloucestershire property to the Commissioners of Woods. The commissioners offered the Redbrook property for sale in July of that year, when it was occupied by Henry Davies and described as 'The Redbrook Tin Works, Rolling Mill, etc, 3r 13p'.[173] The premises were dilapidated and were soon demolished. By 1818–28[174] a row of cottages stood on that part of the site lately owned by Gage, while just above stood the property of the Quick family (including their corn mill, earlier Kings Mill). Elsewhere on the site a brewery stood from 1825 to 1926.

John James, one of the partners at the Lower Redbrook works, acquired the Lydney Tinplate Works in 1814. Both works for a time may have been run complementary to each other, but by 1825 we read that the Redbrook works 'had been in a state of neglect since they were given up by Mr James on his taking to those at Lydney, though they have now been put in repair by B. Whitehouse who has also become the occupier of the forges at Monmouth'.[175] On 19 March 1828 Messrs Whitehouse took a lease of 'The Redbrook Tin Works' for a term of $27\frac{1}{2}$ years commencing 29 September 1827.[176] As suggested above, they had probably been in occupation since a few years earlier.

Around this period a stone culvert about 3ft $\times$ 3ft was built to bring water from Upper Redbrook southwards along the hillside to the first pond above the Lower Tinplate Works. (This remained in use until 1960.) About the same period an adit to supplement the water supply was driven northwards from the top of the first pond, some 200ft in length, 10ft high and 6ft wide. It was bricked and arched for the first 25ft, and from thence was in solid rock. (S. Horton has navigated the adit by boat for 180ft. Today the water from the adit is pumped to Upper Redbrook and from thence to West Dean Rural District.)

Although in 1841 Messrs Whitehouse were obtaining coal for Redbrook from their Speedwell pit in the vicinity, by 1842 the tinplate works had become the property of Philip Jones, and on 22 June they were offered for sale, and described as:[177]

> An excellent dwellinghouse, offices, rolling mills, furnaces, forges, and other works, and machinery adapted to the manufacture of tin-plates on an extensive scale, with 12 cottages or workmen's houses, and lands, in all 30a 3r 16p.

A plan of the property made that year by R. Gabb is extant.[178] Jones still owned the works.[179] A three-dimensional plan made that year by S. G. Gregg [180] shows much of the detail of the premises and its water supply (Fig 9). A drawing of about the same period by N. Daniels[181] (Plate 20) gives a view of the works as seen from the Wye. In the year, 1848, the stock and some of the equipment were sold by auction.[182] Much went to local ironworks, eg William Allaway & Sons of Lydney purchased backplate at £11 a ton and block tin at £64 a ton. Litigation relating to dilapidations ensued, and in 1855 an Action, between parties not stated, 'to recover damages for not quitting the premises at the expiration of the demise'; also 'for not leaving them with the buildings, erections, alterations and additions thereto, together with the machinery and other things thereto belonging, in good and sufficient tenantable and working order and repair and condition'.[183] The repairs required were:

Water Wheel—in very good condition requiring new driving wheel, planking etc.

Penstock—a new one required.

The machinery generally in bad order.

Steam Boilers—in bad condition.

Engine—requiring several things done.

Roof over Tinplate Mill—nearly falling and requires repairing with new timber.

Roof of Lower Mill—much out of repair.

Centre of Fly Wheel in Lower Mill—requires new blocking and wedging.

Penstock in ditto—rubs against water-wheel and requires raising.

Tin House; Roof out of repair.

No 1 Stack—flues require to be opened.

Fire bars—chiefly removed and all the fire doors and bars belonging to no 6 taken away.

Tin box and float—removed from heating boiler for picklers.

Annealing Furnace—doors and frames out of repair and fire grate bars all gone.

Top of one of the Stacks nearly falling.

Cold Rolls—spanners deficient and Standards require blocking.

Splash Boards—new planking required to prevent water from Wheel splashing Cold Rolls.

Tin Furnace Stack—out of repair.

Lime Kiln—ditto.

Ground Water Wheel—requiring new Stock ditto.

Small Lock Gate—destroyed.

Fencing—requiring around Cottage Gardens.

Masonry—walls, water courses, dwellinghouses and outbuildings much dilapidated.

Workmen's Cottages—a portion of them out of repair.

Upper pond—requires cleaning and Wall at the top out of repair.

The following machinery and articles had been removed:

A Steam Boiler nearly new.

A Turning Lathe.

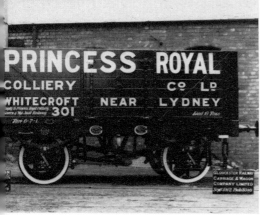

33 Six railway coal wagons used in Dean from c1910 to c1960

34 (above) Cannop Colliery c1930; (right) New Fancy Colliery c1930; (below) J. J. Joynes: manager of Cannop Colliery and chairman of the local branch of the National Association of Colliery Managers

Sheet Iron Shears.
Clock and Bell.
Several Cast Iron floor plates.
Cast Iron Trough for Scaling Bars.
Water Pipe.
Iron Trough from the pump, and the pump destroyed.
Two Copper Furnaces, one replaced with an imperfect iron boiler.

Subsequently the works re-opened.[184] In 1858 the manager was David Griffiths. By 1876, when there were still two rolling mills, the proprietors were The Redbrook Tin Plate Co, using as brands, for coke tinplate 'REDBROOK', and for charcoal, 'LRB'. Following the opening of the Wye Valley Railway in that year, 1876, the tinplate works were 'considerably enlarged' by August 1878.[185] In 1880 there were three rolling mills, all working, and each producing about 450 boxes a week.[186] A plan is extant showing the layout of the works throughout the years 1820 to 1883.[187] The works were closed by March 1883.[188]

In July 1883 the Redbrook Tin Plate Co was registered with £13,000 capital, subsequently increased to £43,000. Its directors were: J. Coventry (chairman; he died in 1918), E. Coventry, J. C. Robinson and A. F. Robinson. On the works re-opening in 1884, Daniel Horton became superintendent (he retired in 1915). David Nurse was managing director until 1887 when he was succeeded by Alexander Taylor. In 1893 there were still three rolling mills, using as brands, for coke 'REDBROOK' and 'PENALT', and for charcoal, 'LRB', 'REDBROOK' and 'NEWLAND'.

During the winter of 1898–9 the works closed because of the McKinley tariff; two of the mills were restarted in April 1899, when the manager was Edwin Beard (he retired about 1930). Rhys Jenkins was informed by a native of Redbrook in 1925 (then aged 50) that there had been a blast furnace and a cupola at the tinworks.

Taylor continued as managing director till his death in 1928, when he was followed in office by his son-in-law, W. G. Thomas whose co-directors in 1932 were E. Coventry (chairman), G. H. Robinson, H. Coventry (died 1934) and W. T. Horton (brother of S. Horton, who became manager in 1930 and joined the board in 1940). A plan of the works in 1941 is extant.[189] During 1941–5 the old pantile-roofed buildings were replaced by the present premises. In 1944, water and coal for power were dispensed with; mains electricity was installed to power motors from 1,000hp to $\frac{1}{8}$hp. Steam was raised by oil-fired boilers. In 1949 the works had four mills, with a total weekly capacity

P

of 4,350 boxes. A plan[190] of that year, shows the layout of the works, and a list of the motors, as they were from that year onwards.

Monmouthshire Tinplates Limited (incorporated in 1944) held an interest in the Redbrook Tin Plate Co, Ltd when the parent company went into voluntary liquidation in 1956–7.[191]

Redbrook made the world's thinnest (·0025in) steel sheet hot rolled. It was exported to almost every country. Records of output are available for the period 1924 to 1961,[192] when the works closed 31 December—the last victim of the modern giant strip mills. The wonder is that the works lasted so long, but this was partly due to it having specialised in thin gauge quality plate in which the large strip mills could not compete.

The large residence is occupied by Mel Morgan, one-time foreman at the works, to which S. Horton returns from time to time. Standing near the old wharf on the Wye is the warehouse, first mentioned some 160 years ago (Plate 20a). The premises stood idle from 1962 until in 1968 they were used for storage by the Birmingham Waste Co, Ltd and R. W. Kent (Waste Paper) Ltd.

PARKEND These tinplate works, sited about a hundred yards north of the blast furnaces and ironworks, were erected 'at a large outlay' by John James and Charles Greenham in 1851–3.[193] They comprised iron forges, rolling mills and tinplate works; twenty-four houses for their workmen were also built adjacent to the northern boundary of the works (the group of houses were later known as 'The Square').

By autumn 1854 the owner was Samuel Ries, and the tenant Nathaniel Daniels trading as the Parkend Plate Co.[194] In October 1854 Daniels purchased 4,500 firebricks at 63s per 1,000 from James Hall of Redbrook, proprietors of the Marion's Brickworks.[195] However, by December that year, Daniels was insolvent, his liabilities being between £9,000 and £10,000, and his assets £5,950 (£2,000 charcoal and wood, £700 tin, £1,500 iron, £1,500 sundries, plant, implements, oils, tallow and tools, and £250 cash). Thomas Gratrex of the firm of Bailey & Co, bankers, Monmouth, was appointed as Trustee to sell the assets.[196]

By 1857 the proprietors of the works were Thomas and William Allaway who had achieved success with their Lydbrook Tinplate Works.[197] They enlarged and improved the works at Parkend, 'and carried them on with much spirit and success'.[198] By 1866 some 200 work-people were employed, producing about 500 boxes of tinplate a week.[199] Two-thirds of the iron came from the Forest.

Edwin Crawshay acquired the works in 1875,[200] and by the following year was producing 700 to 800 boxes a week.[201] In 1878–9, Jacob Chivers & Co, proprietors of the Hawkwell Colliery (and, in 1879, of the Hawkwell Tinplate Works) were considering purchasing the Parkend concern from Henry Crawshay & Sons, but did not do so.[202] By 1880 the two mills there, both working, were on lease to Messrs Morris.[203] The brands were: Charcoal, 'PARKEND', and 'EAGLE'.[204]

The works closed in 1881,[205] and were demolished in the 1900s. The twenty-four houses at 'The Square' (Plate 19b) were an early example of industrial housing (even if of a most squalid kind in its later years). They were demolished in the 1950s.[206] (Plate 19a).

HAWKWELL These four-mill works on the north side of the GWR Churchway line were started in February 1879 by Jacob Chivers & Co.[207] Chivers, who held an interest in a tin works in Spain, had Thomas Bright as his working partner. The firm were proprietors of the Hawkwell Colliery about ¼ mile away.

In 1877, application was made by the Bilson Gas Company to the Office of Woods for a wayleave for a gas-main to the Hawkwell works.[208] Chivers & Co had been considering purchasing the Parkend Tinplate Works, idle for some time; early in 1878 they applied to the S&W to allow a rebate on coal from Bilson Junction to Parkend, and on tinplates from Parkend to Lydney. The proposed purchase fell through, and Hawkwell was developed instead. On 9 January 1879 the S&W agreed a rate for pig iron from Lydney Harbour to Bilson Junction.[209]

In 1880[210] there were three mills, all working. The brands were: Coke, 'NOFOLD' and 'HAWKWELL'.[211] The following year, Alfred Bright & Co were the proprietors,[212] and in 1894 they were granted a licence by the Office of Woods for a water supply to the works at £3 10s per annum[213]

The works closed in 1895, when A. C. Bright & Co ceased trading.[214] H. Spence Thomas, manager for Richard Thomas & Co Ltd, purchased the four-mill engine of the works for 26s a ton.[215] About the turn of the century, the premises were purchased and converted to a brickworks by the Coleford Brick & Tile Co (Plate 20b).

The tinplate era in Dean thus extended from about 1798 to 1961— some 160 years. The works at Parkend and Hawkwell were almost at an end by the 1880s, particularly through the local ore having been found unsuitable for Bessemer's process of converting specular cast iron into steel. Furthermore, competition from South Wales, and failing markets, greatly harmed the Forest. The tinplate works at Lydbrook, Lydney and Redbrook weathered the change successfully. The works at Lydbrook continued till 1925, while those at Lydney, although latterly depending for raw material on steel bars brought by rail from Scunthorpe, survived till 1957. The Redbrook works closed in 1961. The closure of the tinplate works at Lydbrook and Lydney, where they had been the staple industry on which hundreds of the inhabitants depended, was a severe blow to the local economy.

Wire and Cable

INTRODUCTION By 1565 wire from iron, some probably drawn by manual strength and some by simple machines powered by waterwheels, was being made at Tintern and Whitebrook by the Company of Mineral and Battery Works under the patent granted that year to Humfry and Shutz.[216] John Challoner had a lease of the Tintern wireworks from 1591 to 1594.[217] In Dean a small contemporary industry was being carried on at Soudley,[218] but the trade did not develop much in the Forest, though what little there may have been subsequently was by 1608 allied with that of nail and pin-making.[219] When in 1611 the Earl of Pembroke's nominees were empowered to build ironworks in Dean, wireworks were expressly excepted, but c1625 Thomas Smart was drawing wire at Lydbrook Middle Forge under licence from the Company of Mineral and Battery Works. In 1630 Sir John Winter, who had a slitting mill on the Newerne Stream towards Lydney was engaged for some time in making wire from *osmond* iron, using tools and methods of production allegedly modelled on those in use by the works at Tintern.[220] It was asserted by one of Winter's men that John Bisse, owner of a brass-works near Bristol, had bought 'a great store of nail-rods' from him for the making of wire. In defending himself in 1631 Winter stated that he 'made his wire with a brake, as many used to do, which he supposed might be lawful . . . No man could make wire but must draw it through a hole and, therefore, *worbles* (wortles) were such tools as had ever been in use for making wire and are, therefore, as free now as they were before the Company was granted its privilege . . . As for the use of *osmond* iron, Winter was unaware that it was an invention of the Company, as claimed, nor had he made wire with *osmond* iron or with any other iron to sell but for his own use'.

From 1672[221] Thomas Foley made wire at Tintern and Whitebrook, drawn from bar iron made in forges fuelled by charcoal. By then it was a trade diverse in the range of its products and its technical vocabulary.[222] Coal was used in drawing, and the wireworks also rolled and slit bars into nail rods as a sideline. The Foleys' interest in the trade persisted until at least 1712, when Thomas Foley certainly held Whitebrook works. By 1715, however, Thomas Dix (Dicks) was at the Tintern Works.[223]

AYLEFORD WIREWORKS   On 20 March 1765 John Purnell[224] of Dursley, proprietor of wireworks and ironworks there and at Fromebridge on the east of the Severn, leased for 20 years at £520 10s annually *inter alia*, property in the Ayleford valley to his son William, and John Purnell of Fromebridge and Joseph Faithorne of Dursley, ironmaster.[225] The Ayleford property comprised:

All that messuage, tenement or dwellinghouse together with the mill late a grist mill but now converting into a tilting mill, barns, stables, and several closes, pieces or parcels of meadow or pasture ground to the same belonging or in any wise appertaining, situate, lying and being at Ayleaford in the parish of Newnham, late in the possession of William Price as tenant thereof.

In addition the leased property included premises higher up the Soudley Brook, on its east bank and stretching northwards from the present Bradley House up to the, later, Bullo Tunnel mouth:

All that decayed messuage or tenement and all those four several closes, pieces or parcels of meadow or pasture ground adjoining together in the said parish of Newnham late in the tenancy of Jonathan Higgins, called by the several names of Glastonbury Grounds and Parry's Piece, containing about 25 acres bounded on the south by the Forest of Dean and Sowdley's Brook, and on the north-east by a grove or coppice belonging to William Jones Esq, called Glastonbury Grove, together with the several dwellinghouses, forges and other buildings lately erected and built on the said several demised premises or some part thereof.

A schedule to the lease sets out the following plant and equipment (some may relate to Frombridge):

In the old Wire Mills—the shaft wheel and benches which were removed from Dursley, and all hand-tools.

In the Forge—the bellowses, all the anvils and hammers and hand-tools.

In the New Wire Mill and Block Mills—all hand-tools only.

In the Tilting Mills—all bellowses, hammers, anvils, shears and hand-tools.

In the Smithy—the bellows, hammers, anvils, and all the hand-tools.

Thirteen years later (23 March 1778) the lease was renewed for 13 years to the three ironmasters, by which time the tilting mill at Ayleford had been converted to a wire mill. Five years later (7 August 1783) the landlord and the three tenants leased their wire works and other property to Simon Dobbs, ironmaster of Moreton Valence, and Thomas Taylor, ironmaster of Ayleford. Included in the lease were (*a*) 'the shafts, water-wheels and other appurtenances belonging to the wire mill, also the use of the tongs, gearing and tools then used and belonging to the wire mill', (*b*) 'the forge and tilting mill', and (*c*) all watercourses, ponds, dams, etc. The tilting mill here mentioned was probably that at the, later, tunnel's mouth, north of Bradley House. In some way the lessors became beholden to their agent in London, John Smith, ironmaster, for on 7 August 1786 they assigned to him as security £300 a year of Dobbs & Taylor's rent. In 1785 Dobbs & Taylor purchased huge quantities of cordwood for charcoal at 7s a cord from Maynard Colchester of the Wilderness, Mitcheldean.[226] The charcoaling was to be done by the purchasers.

How long the two wireworks continued is not known. As to those at Lower Ayleford (probably the 'Old Wire Mills' and 'the forge' mentioned above) Taylor's map of 1777 shows a water-wheel and a leat to it, and Bryant's map of 1823 shows there 'Hale Ford Wireworks', although by that time they were probably disused. The wireworks at Bradley and above may have closed early in the nineteenth century, because in about 1810–12 the Bradley premises were being used by Samuel Hewlett as a foundry (qv).

On 9 January 1830[227] Edward Jones of Hay Hill mortgaged 'lands in Ayleaford' including:

All those several mills, dams, millponds, mill streams, sluices, watercourses, messuages or tenements, cottages, gardens, meadows, etc known by the name of the Ayleaford Works and Lands, comprising all those messuages or dwelling houses, mill buildings and gardens belonging thereto called The Lower Mill containing 1a 1r 12p and in four several places; and Rolling Mill gardens; and the cottages and premises called the Wire Works containing 1a 2r 19p; and the Upper Mill and part of the Tilting Mill grounds.

It is disappointing that the conveyancer was not more specific, and that no plan was prepared. Apparently the Wire Works were those at Lower Ayleford; and the Upper Mill and Tilting Mill were at the foot of Tilting Mill Pond near the, later, tunnel mouth.[228] The Lower Mill was either that shown as a water-wheel near the Lower Wire Works by Bryant in 1823, or it may have been a mill (as tradition holds) at the point where a leat now leaves the main stream. There is today evidence of the leat some 550 yards long from the Soudley Brook above to an enclosed embanked pond (now dry) to the west of and at a higher level than the buildings of Ayleford Farm (owner, Mr Robbins)—reputedly the site of a wireworks, and of a much more modern era than those of the sixteenth century mentioned earlier. There is a run-off channel from the pond, which is believed to have formerly discharged into a channel underneath the farm buildings, thence to the Soudley Brook, locally called Forge Brook. Partly buried in the bank of the leat is a large slab of charcoal blast furnace cinder, 8ft $\times$ 2ft $\times$ 1$\frac{1}{2}$ft (c1$\frac{1}{2}$–2 tons)—evidence rather for a furnace than a forge, and whilst its presence at that spot seems whimsical, it would be even more difficult to believe it was brought any great distance. South of the pond, a recently excavated section of bank shows unconvincing grains of coked coal and charcoal, and from the spoil dump was recovered in 1967 an abraided rim of coarse red Romano-British pottery.

LYDBROOK WIREWORKS   In 1815, ironworks upstream of the Upper Forge (opposite the present Bell Inn) were purchased from Viscount Gage by the Crown. In 1818 the Crown sold the works to James Russell who had had some connection with ironworks at Flaxley (James's son Edward was born there), and he may have rented the works at Lydbrook prior to purchase. Russell considerably improved and enlarged the works[229] and added a wireworks a little downstream towards the Anchor Inn (now a private house) and opposite the present Beards' Bakery. Between the two works lay a pond (now dry).

In October 1820,[230] Russell appealed to the s&w for a reduction of the tonnage rates on soft coal and coke used in his works. In 1839 he contracted to take all s&w broken tram plates and castings for 3 years at £3 10s a ton, but the following year he was unsuccessful in his application for a reduction in the tonnage of iron from 4d per ton per

mile.[231] In 1851 he was still buying cordwood for charcoaling from the
Office of Woods.[232] By 1858 a tramroad connected the two sites and an
incline led to the s&w. When the railway was built, the incline was
diverted to an exchange siding. The horses which were stabled at the
Anchor Inn, usually hauled two trams of wire up to the railway each
trip.[233] By 1864 Russell's works were employing about 100 hands, and
run by his son Edward (his other son, James, owned the Cinderford
'Mill and Forge'), who wrote 23 February 1864: [234]

> We manufacture wire for fencing also for telegraph of which we
> can roll from 40 to 50 tons per week. We also make charcoal iron for
> horse nails and smith work. We are also makers of iron for agricul-
> tural purposes. We use a large quantity of pig iron from Cinderford,
> Shropshire, and Staffordshire, the principal portion being from the
> former.

On 5 March the same year he added: 'We do not make charcoal
iron from the ore but from the pig'; and 'the waste in making wire from
the pig through all its processes is about one-third'.

By 1880[235] about 50 men were employed. Some Dean pig iron was
used, the remainder coming from Middlesbrough, Cumberland,
Bristol and Wales. A little of the Middlesbrough iron was always
used, which acted as a flux for the tougher kinds in puddling. Some
50 tons of wire were produced each week, from 4 to 7/0 Birmingham
Wire Gauge. The principal market was Birmingham. The output could
be increased and employ 30 per cent more hands, but the trade was
spoiled by competition from Germany. On 25 February 1880 the
s&w ordered that their sidings at Lydbrook Junction be improved
to facilitate the handling of the wire.[236]

Later, Alfred J. Russell with his cousin George Russell managed
the enterprise, but George died when a young man. Alfred resided first
at Lydbrook, a well known figure often seen on his horse 'Lancer'.

Trade depression led to closure of the works between 1890 and
1900. Many of the workmen departed to Middlesbrough and elsewhere. Alfred, the last of his long line of local wire-makers, retired to
the Grange at Bishopswood (Partridge and Chivers had also used
Bishopswood as a retreat). He later returned to Lydbrook, and died
29 July 1932.

The premises fell into disrepair, and today their ponds are dry and
partly infilled. Portions of the retaining-walls and dam-heads remain,
as well as the shell of the engine-house (Plate 23a).

CINDERFORD WIREWORKS (FOREST VALE IRONWORKS) A plan of these works, higher up the Cinderford Brook near Lower Bilson, is shown on the East Dean Survey of 1856 (by Dibdin). The original proprietor or occupier is not known, but by 1864 the works, a 'mill and forge' were owned and run by James Russell, junior, brother to Edward Russell who ran the Lydbrook wireworks. James wrote 12 May 1864:[237]

> When I took to these works I thought I could turn the wheels to some good, but from the construction of them I have failed to do any good. I am now but partly at work until I can lay down another engine, which will take about three months. I have had 60 men at work but my number is now reduced until my works are more complete, when the number will be very much increased. At present I am making wire rods for making telegraph and other wire etc, and cable iron chiefly from Cinderford pig iron: from half to three parts Cinderford and the other portion from other parts to mix with it. The Forest iron is too redshort [brittle] of itself for Merchant Iron; it may do of itself for Tin Plates.

In 1880 it was a well-equipped factory with a foundry, rolls and shears (plan by Spearman),[238] employing 100, and using some Dean pig iron, the remainder coming from Middlesbrough. Cumberland, Bristol and Wales; a little of the Middlesbrough pig iron was always used, which acted as a flux for the tougher kinds in puddling.[239] About 100 tons of wire (from 4 to 7/0 BWG) were made each week, including 20 tons of charcoal iron. The principal market was the Midlands. The output could be increased, and employ some 25 more hands, but the trade was depressed by foreign competition.[240]

In September 1882 a substantial order for wire was obtained from the USA.[241] By 1887, Alfred J. Russell of Lydbrook was the proprietor. Trade depression before the end of the century led to closure of the works c1895. They were demolished c1900 all that remains being the office, and the stables, converted to private dwellinghouses and outbuildings.

THE LYDBROOK CABLE WORKS Cable making at Lydbrook grew out of experience gained around the turn of the century in making leads for fuses, wire-covering and allied developments at the Electric Fuse Factory (qv) west of Trafalgar Colliery. Harold W. Smith (Plate 24b), with much knowledge gained there under his father William J. Smith (he died in 1895 when Harold was 16) and Frank (later Sir Francis) Brain, having decided in 1906 that the cheapest way to insulate wires for the long fuse-leads was by extrusion, purchased from Germany a machine which covered with a layer of bitumen six wires at a time. (This machine was still producing at Lydbrook in 1954, and it is interesting to note that in a Government publication setting out ideas gleaned from the Germans after the 1939–45 war, the drawings of an almost identical machine were included as the most recent development for the extrusion coating of several hundred wires with PVC and other plastics, through one head.) This new business was begun in a very small way in some out-buildings at Trafalgar, which sufficed until 1912. By that year Smith and his colleagues had accumulated such a quantity of light cable machinery, and the demand for shotfiring machines and detonators had increased so rapidly, that land for a new factory was purchased near Stowfield on the Wye northwest of Lydbrook. Contemporary with his fuse-making (qv), for his cable manufactory Smith formed in 1912 H. W. Smith & Co Ltd, and selected a site in the 'V' of the Lydbrook Junction of the GW Ross-Monmouth line with the s&w Joint Railway (Midland and GWR) serving Dean. On this site—a 'poppy field'—in 1912, Mrs Smith, accompanied by her husband, with Mr Flewelling, a local builder, and David Nelson, one of Smith's handymen, cut the first turf for the foundations of the cable factory. Thereafter, Flewelling erected two steel-framed factory bays, making a building about 60ft wide by 75ft long, which soon became full, and in all out production. Other bays were added to a total of eight—some 240ft by 75ft (Plate 23b).

Scarcely had the factory started when the war came, 1914. Contracts were secured with the British, French and Belgian governments, and about 70,000 miles of field telephone cable were produced during those fateful years. Employees increased from 40 to 650, and double shifts were worked. During and just after the war, the factory extended rapidly. A new wire-drawing mill was built complete with modern tinning plant, as well as a substantial rubber mill. A large Lancashire boiler and house with an imposing brick stack were erected; also a power-house with a modern Musgrave steam-engine and generator; and a self-contained gas plant and sewage plant. Further additions were a two-storey block to accommodate engineering maintenance, modern test equipment, extended vulcanising area, bunching and laying-up machines. Goods Inwards Stores and Despatch Stores were added at the same time as the palatial office block, canteen, laundry and baths. A multitude of new processes, brought the manufacturing side of the factory up-to-date and capable of handling many new types of cable. An account of the works, 14 November 1919,[242] when 250 people were employed, reads:

The principal raw material employed is copper wire. It comes to Lydbrook Junction in coils with rough exterior, and is there drawn down to the required thinness, even to the fineness represented by five-thousandth of an inch diameter—scarcely thicker than the hairs of a woman's head. Stranded, insulated, and braided together, these fine strands form the substance of the familiar flexible wire utilised wherever electricity is available. The process is most interesting but finality has not been reached, and every month sees the scrapping of some not very old plant and the substitution of something else which saves labour and increases output. Probably the popular notion of the preparation of copper wire would be that it is pared down to the required size, and that the factory would be littered with shavings. The method is however by elongation, the wire being pulled through dies of a diameter slightly smaller than the wire before the process. If this is not a sufficient reduction the wire is drawn again through another smaller die, and so the process goes on all round the shop until the required degree of thinness is attained. The newest machines will pass a given wire through perhaps a dozen dies at one winding, thus reducing a wire from, say, 20 to the inch to 30 to the inch, instead of necessitating the use of several machines, and as many windings. Had Messrs Smith & Co nothing better to do with the copper wire they draw they could sell at this stage all they manufacture, and they are, in fact, contemplating making copper wire for electric tramway purposes.

The bulk of the copper wire produced, be it coarse or fine, is utilised for preparing telephone wires or electric cables, insulated with rubber and clothed with protective or decorative material. The rubber comes to the factory in practically a raw state and is there compounded with other ingredients, is callendered and cut in sizes and thicknesses, is vulcanised by a dozen processes which, not to abandon the intention formed at the outset to eschew technicalities, we pass over, except to say that it is all profoundly interesting to a stranger to watch.

In another section of these busy workshops the copper wire is ingeniously clothed with the rubber while still in its plastic condition. Then comes the vulcanising, and after that the clothing of the insulated wire with braiding of one or of as many different colours as there are hues in a rainbow. The process here is similar to that in the textile industry.

At present the works only produce cables of limited thickness. Between the production of 'Saturn' cables and flexible wires (the trade mark of Messrs Smith & Co is the planet over whose mysterious rings astronomers grow so eloquent) and the heavy electric cables which are buried in the streets of electrically serviced towns, there has been a wide gulf, but it is rapidly being bridged by the installing of new plant, which will enable the production at Lydbrook of larger cables, and by the beginning of 1920 the firm will be in a position to take up orders for the complete range of electric lighting and power cables ordinarily required.

A recent development is the engineering shop which is now being equipped in such a manner that it will probably be the best in or near the Forest of Dean. Mr Smith's experience teaches that it is incomparably better to construct a machine to one's own designs than to purchase of some engineers, who, after all, have not got to run the machine they make. Building operations continue although already the 540 square feet of floor space with which the works started has increased to 60,000. Latest additions are the provision of a despatch department and an upper floor of large dimensions on which to accommodate the braiding machines, at present occupying the ground floor, where room is much needed. Of these, 450 were running incessantly during the war.

The electric power house is a model of its kind, fulfilling the wise saying that a good machine is worthy of careful housing, but there is a revolution approaching here, and the plant will soon be for sale, inasmuch as Mr Smith has concluded terms with the Corporation of Hereford to take electricity from their economically produced supply 20 miles away at a rate which will reduce his works costs. It is interesting to note that the overhead lines by which this power will be conveyed will be made at the Lydbrook works.

The output of the works had been sold for some months ahead in telephone wire for the GPO, cables for Rumania and Belgium, wire for Egypt, and for the manufacture of submarine cables. However, the following year, 1920, serious financial difficulties arose as a result of the general slump which followed the end of the 1914–18 war, and creditor banks appointed an Official Receiver to run the plant, thereby ending Smith's connection with the factory. It eventually revived to be bought about 1925 by the Edison Swan Electric Company (Siemens Bros Edison Swan), a member of the AEI group, who held it until 1966, when they sold the premises to the Reed Paper Group.

'TEMCO' WORKS, LYDBROOK   Harold Smith quickly recovered from the personal blow received by the financial failure of the Cable Works, and in 1920 formed another company which was registered as a limited company in 1927. The firm built premises on the roadside below Offa's

Dyke, a short distance away from the earlier Cable Works. Smith soon showed his powers of resuscitation. Throughout his most trying periods he had redoubled his efforts on diversified products. He carried out some of the earliest experiments on the commercial production of pure electrolytic copper wire, by electrically depositing copper on to a fine spirally grooved cylinder, tearing this off in the form of a rectangular continuous strip, then reducing it by rolling and drawing it into the form of a round wire. He was early in the field in drawing very fine Nickel Chrome Alloys for tiny resistances, etc. This was also used in wire and thin tape form for heating elements. One of Smith's greatest successes was the development of stainless steel in fine sizes, reaching a diameter of half a thousandth part of an inch, whereupon he experimented further to flatten it into the form of an almost invisible tinsel. During the 1939–45 war stainless steel was used as a heating element for airmen's suits, aircraft cables and aerial wire. There was a growing demand also for this alloy in chemical industries, and in woven wire cloth. The wire, drawn through diamond dies, can be so fine that it takes seven wires bunched to become the size of a human hair. Due to its non-corrosive qualities, there was a gradual development in the use of stainless steel for orthodontic and surgical purposes. Out of these experiments and developments, with the help of his family, he built up a very substantial business in the production of stainless steel wire of all types, at the same time developing a notable diamond-die drilling and polishing shop.

Mr Smith's son, Conrad, and his daughter, Kathleen, helped much in the management. He died in 1959, in his eighties, but his factory still flourishes—truly a triumph over adversity, and a reward for endeavour. Temco Ltd is now a member of the BICC group of companies. Shortly after this development the Smith family severed its connection with the firm, continuing its interest only in the form of stainless steel for orthodontic and surgical purposes, operating from the Cell, Redbrook Road, Monmouth.

References to Chapter 4

1   *BGAS* 1877–8, 217.
2   Rpt of Commissioners of Woods . . . , 1810.
3   Ibid, 1814.
4   *Papers on Iron and Steel*, 1840, 386.
5   Ibid.

6   10th Rpt of Commissioners of Woods . . . , 1833, 24.
7   GRO Q/Rum/175.
8   F3/223.
9   Ibid.
10 Ibid.
11 42nd Rpt of Commissioners of Woods . . . , 1864, 101.
12 *The Torrington Diaries*, 1954, op cit, 40.
13 GRO D1677, GG 1545, 114a.
14 Ibid, GG 1557, D637.
15 F3/223.
16 Letter from Thomas Burgham *penes me*.
17 Gale, W. K. V. 'Soho Foundry: Some Facts and Fallacies', *Trans Newcomen Soc*, 34, 1961–2, 73; and *The British Iron & Steel Industry*, 1967.
18 A beam engine (? 1805) in Cardiff Museum is reputed to have been made by Hewlett. The earliest item otherwise made by him was a small hand-winch, inscribed 'Hewlett 1828', which stood at Wimberry Loading Bank for tipping trams into railway wagons.
19 Paar. *The Great Western* . . . , 28, 30, 32, 38, 65, 138.
20 Extract in East Dean RDC Muniment Room.
21 GRO D637/VII/23.
22 F17/7 D2633.
23 GRO Q/Rum/106.
24 Information from Stanley Joiner.
25 GRO Q/Rum/175.
26 1850: Proposed Development Plans for South Wales Rly Bill of 1851. Relevant parts of the Plan and the Book of Reference are in GRO Q/Rum/248.
27 Extract in East Dean RDC Muniment Room.
28 Information from Stanley Joiner.
29 Ibid.
30 Ibid.
31 Ibid.
32 Deposition, 28 Aug 1839, in East Dean RDC Muniment Room.
33 GRO Q/Rum/175.
34 Ibid.
35 Extract in East Dean RDC Muniment Room.
36 F3/176.
37 A useful map for Cinderford properties is the huge one of 'The Township of East Dean' by F. W. Dibdin, 1856, in the East Dean RDC Muniment Room.
38 *Kelly's Directory*, 1856.
39 Ibid.
40 S&W Min Bk, 23 Oct 1856.
41 Ibid.
42 Ibid.
43 Ibid.
44 Ibid.
45 Paar. *The Severn & Wye Railway* . . . , 53.
46 Information from E. B. Herbert.
47 S&W Min Bk, 1836.
48 GRO Q/Rum/175.

49 GRO D637/II/7/B9.
50 Science Museum, photo negative 7817.
51 *Slater's Directory*, 1858: 'Cannop Brook: Trotter Thomas & Co, ironfounders'.
52 43rd Rpt of Commissioners of Woods . . . , 29 June 1865, 100.
53 *Harris's Directory*, 1887.
54 Ibid, 1891.
55 Ibid, 1902.
56 Ibid, 1887.
57 Ibid, 1902.
58 Information from E. B. Herbert.
59 *Harris's Directory*, 1902.
60 Paar. *The Severn & Wye Railway* . . . , 50, 51.
61 GRO Q/Rum/30.
62 GRO D637/VII/7, I/37.
63 Ibid, IV/8.
64 Ibid, II/7/B9.
65 Ibid, IV/8.
66 *Slater's Directory*, 1858.
67 Letter from Thomas Burgham *penes me*.
68 *The Wye Tour* by the Editor of the Ross Gazette, 2nd Edn, 1885, 124.
69 The Wye Valley Rly Prospectus of 1874 mentions foundry works at Redbrook.
70 Barraclough, K. C., 'The Cementation and Crucible Steelmaking processes', *Bulletin HMG*, 8 Jan 1967, 24–34.
71 Fuller. *Worthies of Gloucestershire*, 1662.
72 Moxon. *Mechanick Exercises*, 2nd Edn, 1693, 54.
73 Osborn, op cit, 33.
74 Ibid, 33, 140.
75 Ibid, 33–5.
76 Ibid, 46, 142.
77 Cyfarthfa Papers, loc cit, Crawshay to Mushet 3 March 1858.
78 Kohn, F. 'Iron and Steel Manufacture', *The Engineer*, 1869.
79 Murray, John. *A Handbook for Travellers in Gloucestershire*, 1st Edn 1867, records: 'Edgetools and cutlery are manufactured at the Cyanogen Steelworks near Coleford'.
80 S&W Min Bk, 8 Aug 1870.
81 Ibid, 11 Nov 1870.
82 Osborn, op cit, 79.
83 S&W Min Bk, 9 Dec 1871.
84 F3/902; S&W Officials' Min, 20 Oct 1908.
85 F3/1093.
86 Yarranton, A. *England's Improvement* . . . , 1681, quoted by Minchinton, W. E., *The British Tinplate Industry: A History*, 1957, 6, 7.
87 Yarranton, op cit, Pt II, 173–4.
88 Brooke, E. H. *Chronology of the Tinplate Works of Great Britain*, 1944, 152.
89 Letter from Richard Thomas & Co Ltd, 2 Aug 1907 *penes me*.
90 Brooke, op cit, 99.
91 Insole and Bunning, op cit, 88, 89.
92 Ibid, 89.

93   Ibid, 90.
94   Brooke, op cit, 152.
95   Ibid, 153.
96   Nicholls. *History* . . . , 228; *Iron Making* . . . , 60.
97   S&W Min Bk, 12 April 1820.
98   GRO D637/VII/19.
99   Plan of 1834 by William Metcalfe, surveyor, of Monmouth (HRO Foley Papers).
100 GRO D637/VII/19.
101 S&W Min Bk, 1850.
102 F16/36.
103 S&W Min Bk, 22 Oct 1858.
104 Paar. *The Severn & Wye Railway* . . . , 59.
105 Nicholls. *History* . . . , 228; *Iron Making* . . . , 60.
106 Brooke, op cit, 153. The drawings have disappeared.
107 Copy in the possession of F. H. Treherne-Rees.
108 Paar. *The Severn & Wye Railway* . . . , 78.
109 Insole and Bunning, op cit, 88.
110 *Dean Forest Mercury*, 1 July 1938.
111 The present writer possesses a bound volume of technical reports relating to the dispute.
112 Paar. *The Severn & Wye Railway* . . . , 128.
113 S&W Min Bks, 7 May, 2 July, 8 Aug 1883, 22 Feb 1884.
114 In 1908 Richard Thomas and his wife placed in Lydbrook Parish Church a stained-glass window in memory of their deceased children.
115 Brooke, op cit, 152, 153.
116 *Dean Forest Guardian*, 4 July 1930; *The Times*, 20 Dec 1930.
117 *Dean Forest Mercury*, 1 July 1938.
118 Lydney Park Estate Office Rental MSS, 1781.
119 Letter, 2 Aug 1907 from Richard Thomas & Co Ltd, *penes me*.
120 GRO D421/T104.
121 *Gloucester Journal*, 21 May 1810; GRO D421/E46.
122 GRO D421/E46.
123 Ibid, E47.
124 Ibid.
125 Ibid, T104.
126 Ibid, E46; Lydney Rating Terrier 1814.
127 Ibid, E47.
128 In December 1815 John Pidcock was granted by the S&W Rly Co permission to make a turnout from one road to the other opposite his level at the Norchard (S&W Min Bk).
129 GRO D421/E46; Lydney Rating Terrier 1814.
130 S&W Min Bk, Oct and Nov 1814.
131 GRO D421/51.
132 Brooke, op cit, 1944, 74.
133 S&W Min Bk, Oct 1823.
134 Plan, 1802, of intended railway from Parkend to Lydney Pill (PRO).
135 GRO D421/E46.
136 Ibid, Q/Rum/175.
137 Ibid, D421/E46.
138 Ibid, T105.
139 Ibid.

35 *(above)* 'Oak' Stone Quarry (70ft deep), Cannop Hill, 1904; *(below)* Speech House Road Stoneworks c1909

36 (top) Mitchel-
d e a n Cement
Works, Stenders
R o a d c1910;
(centre) Hawkwell
Brickworks c1961;
(below) Pullen's
Stone Works

140 Ibid, The lease was repeated 13 Jan 1852 (Ibid), presumably because William Allaway the elder had died 16 June 1849.
141 Nicholls. *History* . . . , 228.
142 Nicholls. *Iron Making* . . . , 59.
143 Letter from Thomas Allaway, 16 March 1864 *penes me.*
144 Brooke, op cit, 1944, 74. The drawings have disappeared.
145 GRO D421/T105. Allaways were in liquidation in March 1878, when the three proprietors were: T. Allaway of Highbury House, Lydney; James Allaway of Moraston House, near Ross-on-Wye; and William Allaway of Walford House, near Ross-on-Wye.
146 Brooke, op cit, 1944, 74.
147 Insole and Bunning, op cit, 88.
148 *Foresters ½d Newspaper*, 7 Jan 1882.
149 Brooke, op cit, 1944, 74. In July 1900, all creditors were paid in full, with interest at 5 per cent, by means of Preference Shares in Richard Thomas & Co Ltd.
150 R. Beaumont Thomas. 'The Manufacture of Tinplates', *Trans Institute of Mechanical Engineers*, Aug 1906.
151 Paar. *The Severn & Wye Railway* . . . , 42.
152 Paar. *The Great Western Railway* . . . , 150.
153 Brooke, op cit, 1944, 75.
154 Ibid, Information from David Jones, who came to Lydney in 1891, and from 1906 to 1926 was secretary of Richard Thomas & Co.
155 Lydney Park Estate Office Muniments.
156 Brooke, op cit, 1944, 75.
157 Brooke, op cit, 1944, 99.
158 Jenkins, Rhys, op cit, 159, 160.
159 Probably the 'Coperas' House, a pantile-roofed building, now the site of a petrol filling station.
160 Heath, Charles. *Historical and Descriptive Accounts of Tintern Abbey*, c1801.
161 GRO D2166.
162 Ibid.
163 Brooke, op cit, 1944, 100.
164 Ireland, Samuel, op cit, 128.
165 Cookson, H. E. *Rolls and Rolling Mills 1933.*
166 *The Collected Papers of Rhys Jenkins, Trans Newcomen Soc*, 1936, 230, 232.
167 GRO D637/I/5.
168 Ibid, VII/22.
169 Manby, op cit, 248.
170 GRO D637/VII/22; Monmouthshire Record Office D10/12/76.
171 GRO D637/VII/22, I/77.
172 Ibid, I/5.
173 Ibid, VII/7, I/37.
174 Plan in GRO, c1818–28.
175 *Bath Chronicle*, 2 June 1825.
176 GRO D2166.
177 Ibid.
178 Monmouthshire Record Office NPT6292.
179 GRO D637/I/81.
180 Ibid, D639, photo negative 619.

181   The original, once the property of Taylor & Son Ltd, Britonferry, Neath, has disappeared.
182   GRO D637/I/81.
183   Ibid.
184   The CMU&P Rly Min Bk, 5 Jan 1857 records that a letter had been received from John Biddulph regarding conveyance of his traffic from Redbrook; the Company decided that it could not entertain the subject at the time. This may not have referred to tinplate.
185   Engineer's report, 30 Aug 1878.
186   Insole and Bunning, op cit, 88.
187   GRO D2166.
188   Wye Valley Rly Co's Directors' report, 20 March 1883.
189   GRO D2166.
190   Ibid.
191   GRO D2166.
192   External Liby Monmouthshire EL172.
193   F3/147; Nicholls. *History* . . . , 227, 228; *Iron Making* . . . , 58, 59.
194   GRO D637/II/5/B1.
195   Ibid.
196   Ibid.
197   There is no confirmation of the statement by Brooke (op cit, 1944, 155) that in 1853 a two-mill Tinplate Works was erected by Thomas and William Allaway.
198   Nicholls. *History* . . . , 228.
199   Nicholls. *Iron Making* . . . , 59.
200   Brooke, op cit, 155, asserted that the Allaways discontinued in 1872.
201   *Kelly's Directory*, 1876.
202   S&W Min Bks, early 1878 and 9 Jan 1879.
203   Insole and Bunning, op cit, 88.
204   Brooke, op cit, 1944, 155.
205   Ibid.
206   Information from W. Johns.
207   Brooke, op cit, 1944, 148.
208   F3/176.
209   S&W Min Bk, 9 Jan 1879.
210   Insole and Bunning, op cit, 88.
211   Brooke, op cit, 148.
212   Harris's Directory, 1891.
213   72nd Rpt of the Commissioners of Woods . . . , 54.
214   Brooke, op cit, 148.
215   *Proc South Wales Inst of Engineers*, XXIX, 1913, 203.
216   Jenkins, Rhys, op cit, 7; Nicholls. *Iron Making* . . . , 29, 30; Rees, W. *Industry before the Industrial Revolution*, 1968, Vol II.
217   Exch Deps by Coms, 39 Eliz, Hil 23; BM Lansdown MS 76.
218   Nicholls. *Iron Making* . . . , 28.
219   *Men and Armour for Gloucestershire*, 1608.
220   Rees, op cit, II, 612, 632.
221   Johnston. 'New light . . . ,' op cit, 132.
222   Ibid.
223   Ibid, 133, containing a list of terms and rates.
224   Around 1760, John Purnell was granted a patent for his 'new-

invented improvement for making iron and steel wire' (Rees, op cit, II, 651).

225 GRO D2913.
226 Ibid, D36/E7/3.
227 Ibid, D265/T22.
228 Sheasby's Plan of 1825 shows the Tilting Mill as just below the tunnel mouth (GRO Q/Rum/106).
229 Letter from Edward Russell 23 Feb 1864, *penes me.*
230 S&W Min Bk, 12 April 1820.
231 Ibid, 9 April 1839 and 14 April 1840.
232 F16/36.
233 Paar. *The Severn & Wye Railway* . . . , 62.
234 Letter from Edward Russell 23 Feb 1864, *penes me.*
235 Insole and Bunning, op cit, 90.
236 S&W Min Bk, 25 Feb 1880.
237 Letter from James Russell 12 May 1864, *penes me.*
238 Spencer W. Site Plan, 1880.
239 Insole and Bunning, op cit, 90.
240 Ibid.
241 *Foresters ½d Newspaper*, 30 Sept 1882.
242 *Dean Forest Mercury*, 14 Nov 1919.

Five
Mining of Iron Ore
and Ochre

Mining of Iron Ore

> Gold for my lady, Silver for the maid,
>   Copper for the coppersmith who's cunning at his trade,
> 'But', said the miner, picking up a fall,
>   'A big churn of Brush ore is better than them all.'[1]

INTRODUCTION The geological structure of the iron ore field (Figs 10, 15 and 16) has been described by Sibly,[2] Lloyd,[3] Trotter,[4] and Dreghorn.[5] The deposits occur chiefly beneath and around the coal-field in the form of a basin on the edge of which, in the outcrop of the Crease Limestone, early mining took place—certainly in earlier years and of a more intensive nature than did coal-mining.

Earliest evidence of iron ore mining in Britain is in Dean—the Roman mines (Fig 11) in the Lydney Temple settlement.[6] Less easy to date are numerous mining excavations called 'scowles', as at Bream and Noxon Park, in or near which have been found Roman coins, and large mounds of partly-smelted slag, termed 'cinders'. No satisfactory answer can be given as to the reason for the huge crevices and cavities at such places: were the spaces due entirely to the removal of ore? If the material removed was ore and rock, where was the rock dumped?

Undoubtedly mining took place in Dean through the first to fourth centuries AD; and after the departure of the Romans some reduced activity continued to the eleventh century, when the Normans intensified the iron industry. Well before 1244[7] the Dean miners were allowed to win iron ore, termed 'mine', on their own account, subject to dues in cash or kind made either to the forester-of-fee of the bailiwick (there were nine in Dean) or to the constable of St Briavels castle on behalf of the King. From 1246[8] receipts accrued to the King from the

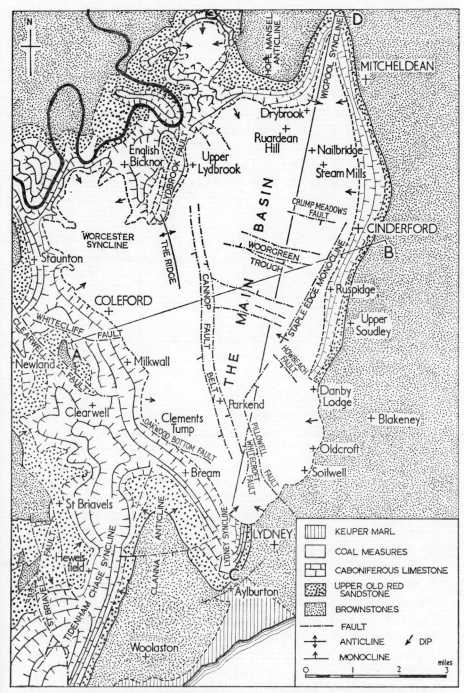

Fig 10. Geological map of Dean (after F. M. Trotter, *Geology of the Forest of Dean Coal and Iron ore Field*, 1942, fig 1).

sale of ore and cinders. By 1282[9] it was customary for miners to take trees 'to timber their mines'. By the same year[10] the foresters-of-fee of Abenhall, Bicknor and Blakeney claimed the ore in their bailiwicks, and the King received nothing except that in the first bailiwick he had six loads a week from each mine, for which he paid the miners 6d. The holder of The Lea claimed the ore there, but it was not known by what warrant. The Earl of Warwick claimed the same in his estate at Lydney, where the King received only a due of ½d on each load of ore taken out of the Forest. The King held the ore in the bailiwicks of Great Dene, Bearse and Staunton, but allowed the miners to win it

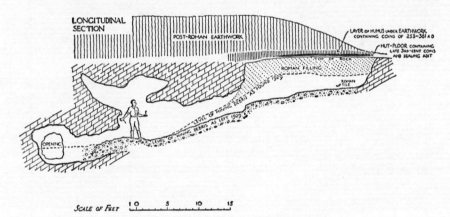

Fig 11.　　Section of a Roman iron ore mine at Lydney Park (after R. E. M. and T. V. Wheeler, *The Lydney Excavations*, 1932, plate VIII).

subject to payment of dues. Thus by the thirteenth century the miners were a somewhat 'free' and specially priviliged class of operatives, encouraged and patronised by the King and the foresters-of-fee, in return for revenue in cash or kind. Many difficulties were subsequently encountered by the Free Miners in retaining their privileges, and eventually rights[11] which extend to the Hundred of St Briavels (Fig 14)—a district which includes the present extent of the Forest.

No reliable estimate can be given of the quantities of ore mined, and of cinders dug to be re-smelted, but records of charcoal-burning, smelting and forging in the thirteenth to sixteenth centuries[12] suggest the amount was immense—probably hundreds of thousands of tons. Mining of ore from the weathered outcrop was by dislodging with small picks and mattocks, aided by hammers, wedges and wooden shovels (Figs 12 and 13). Bringing from the cavities to the surface was in baskets or hods—on men's backs—up primitive wood ladders; or by winding with ropes. The removal by 'quarrying' of large ore-bodies known as 'churns' (found by following small off-shoots, termed 'leads') was complemented by small bell-shaped surface workings, as evidenced in and near Noxon Park[13]

1600–1679 An impetus to mining was given in the last quarter of the sixteenth century by the establishment of voracious blast furnaces at Whitchurch, Lydbrook and Lydney, supplemented in 1612–13 by the establishment of the King's Ironworks throughout Dean. Demands for ore also came from other parts of the Kingdom, particularly Ireland. The total requirements were perhaps half met by the tens of thousands of tons of easily dug cinders of earlier centuries, made valuable by the improved methods of smelting. Yet in 1613 the local iron-masters complained of the miners that most of Dean's ore and cinders were exported.[14] About that year, 6,000 cartloads of 'iron myne' (ironstone) and ore (perhaps this had been 'roasted') worth 30s a load, and 6,000 of cinders worth 15s, went via the rivers Severn and Wye to Ireland and elsewhere:[15] the Dean miners were under contract to William Chessall (Cheinall or Charval), merchant, of London, who in 1606 had been granted a licence for 21 years to export ore to Ireland.[16] The miners asserted that they more than satisfied the wants of the local furnaces; furthermore, the King benefited by $1\frac{1}{2}$d a ton on all exported ore, and by 14s a ton on iron, whether exported or imported.[17]

The 'gale' or boundary for each mining concession was allotted by the King's representative—'the keeper of the gawle' or 'gaveller'; there was one gaveller for the east of Dean (referred to as 'Beneath the Wood') and another for the west of Dean ('Above the Wood').[18] The limits were small, but there were safeguards to the miners, as shown by the oldest extant copy (1610)[19] of their 'Laws and Privileges' (Plate 26a).

(34) The Pit shall have such liberties and franchises that no man shall come within so much space that ye miner may stand and cast redding [ie spoil] and stones so far from him with a bale as the manner is.

(38) Also ye pit shall have a windeway [? wayne or cart-way; or air-way] so far from him as is aforesaid.

(40) Also if a pit be made and upon adventure cometh another up another way within the ground and drulleth to [ie drives into] ye said pit, at what time he drulleth to ye said pit he shall abide till the other Fellowship [partners, termed 'verns'] of the said pit be

present at which time if the other Fellowship will not receive him he shall return again by the forebode and by the Law of the Mine. But if he drulleth to the said pit in a certain Myne then the said Mine shall be free to both parties which it dureth and afterwards each one shall come again to his own place Saving to each one ye place of others and after if one or the other do hurt to ye other he shall restore again so much to him if he dig and make ye pit fall he shall build it again and if he distrouble the other so that he may not travaile to win his profit and the Customs of the King he shall restore all the lost of the King and the Miner.

Obviously by 1610, and doubtless much earlier, it was not unusual for a working to meet another underground. Disputes were settled either by the gaveller or by the miners' own Law Court. By the same year,[20] the miners were accustomed to be given timber 'for the boothes for the mine', and for the workings, 'to make a lodge upon the pit'. The measure of ore was called 'Belleyes'.[21]

Much surface mining was still done, complemented by shallow though increasingly dangerous underground working, whereby the removal of large churns left vast caverns or chambers. (Many of them were enlarged or at least encountered in later centuries). New methods may have been tried—for example, lighting fires against a deposit until it became hot, and throwing water over it, thus causing the ore to yield; or using unslaked lime to break down the deposit.

Throughout subsequent leases of the King's Ironworks along with the minerals of the Forest, and during periods of alienation of much of Dean and its resources to Sir John Winter of Lydney (who had unfortunate connections with Dean's woods), the miners held tenaciously to their privileges.[22] They did likewise during the Civil War and the Commonwealth—one of the most active periods of the iron industry. Following the Restoration, a commission in April 1662[23] advised the Crown 'to lay on ore an imposition of 6d at first for fifteen bushels, as there is carried out yearly at least 4,000 dozen bushels, and there is now lying at Newnham a small vessel to transport some for Ireland'; and to prohibit carrying any cinders from the Forest, in case His Majesty's own works should in time need them. Yet in 1666 two vessels from Pembroke, laden with cinders from Dean for Ireland, were taken by the French or Dutch.[24]

The Dean Forest (Reafforestation) Act 1667[25] saved to the miners their privileges, as then exercised. But timber for mining, and charcoal for smelting, were having a disastrous effect on Dean's woods,[26]

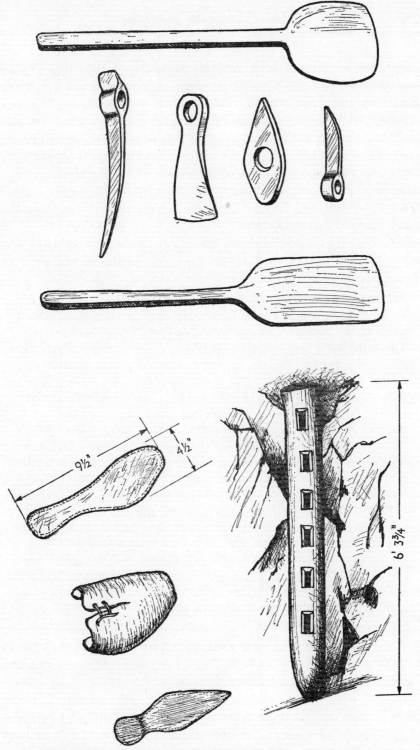

Fig 12. Miners' tools, shoes and ladder found in Dean's iron ore mines.

confirming most aptly John Evelyn's statement in 1663 that 'Nature has thought fit to produce this wasting ore more plentifully in wood-land than any other ground, and to enrich our forests to their own destruction'.[27] Consequently in 1674 the King's Ironworks were sold to Paul Foley for demolition, in order that trees should be conserved, particularly for ship-building. Henceforth the markets for Dean's ore and cinders were on the fringe of her woods, and in Herefordshire and Monmouthshire; complemented by much Forest ore shipped to Ireland from Brockweir and 'Wyes Green' on the Wye, and from Cone Pill and Lydney Pill on the Severn.[28]

1680–1794 The demolition of the King's Ironworks in 1674 was not a serious setback to iron ore mining in Dean, of which Henry Powle wrote in 1677–8: [29]

> The iron ore, which is the principal manufacture here, and by which most of the inhabitants subsist, is found in great abundance in most parts of the Forest: differing both in colour, weight, and goodness. The best, which they call their 'brush-ore', is of blueish colour, very ponderous, and full of little shining specks like grains of silver. This affords the greatest quantity of iron; but being melted alone it pro-duces a metal very short and brittle, and therefore not so fit for common use. To remedy this inconvenience, they make use of another sort of material, which they call their 'cinder', and is nothing else but the refuse of the ore after the metal has been extracted; which being mingled with the other in a due quantity, gives it that excellent temper of toughness for which this iron is preferred before any that is brought from foreign parts. But to understand this rightly, it is to be noted that in former times, when their works were few and their vent small, they made use of no other bellows but such as were moved by the strength of men: by reason whereof their fires were much less intense than in the furnaces they now employ. So that having in them melted down only the principal part of the ore, they rejected the rest as useless, and not worth their charge. This they call their 'cinder', which is now found in an unexhaustible quantity through all parts of the country where any former works have stood.

The Free Miners had their own Mine Law Court (Plate 26b). In 1674 they made regulations regarding loading and carrying of ore, and agreed that 'the constant future measure of iron-ore shall be accord-ing to the Winchester bushel, as by law is directed, and not otherwise, three of such bushels to be a barrel'.[30] They appointed six bargainers to treat with ironmasters 'for the sale and carriage of ore to their respective ironworks, and to the rivers of Severn and Wye at the best rates'. Yarranton[31] wrote in 1677 of 'the infinite number of men, horses, and carriages; and digging of ironstone, providing of cinders, carrying to the works; and great and infinite quantities of cinders (being the rough and offal thrown by in Roman times, they then having only foot-blasts to melt the ironstone), some in vast mounts above the ground, some underground, which will supply the ironworks for some

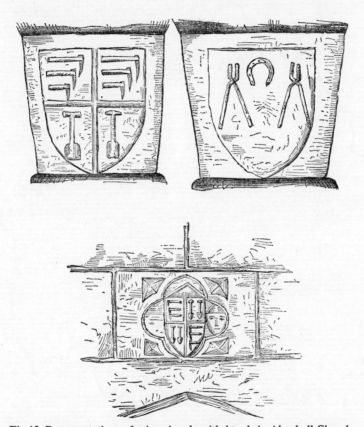

Fig 13. Representations of miners' and smiths' tools in Abenhall Church.

hundreds of years, and these cinders are they which make the prime and best iron, and with much less charcoal than does the ironstone.'

Ore continued to be shipped to Ireland from 'Conpill' on the Severn and Brockweir on the Wye.[32] The demand was great, but the prices were low, hence the miners in 1680 fixed minimum rates for ore 'per dozen of twelve Winchester bushels' delivered to ironworks in Gloucestershire, Herefordshire and Monmouthshire;[33] seven years later they cancelled the rates,[34] though in 1693 they fixed others for ore 'to be

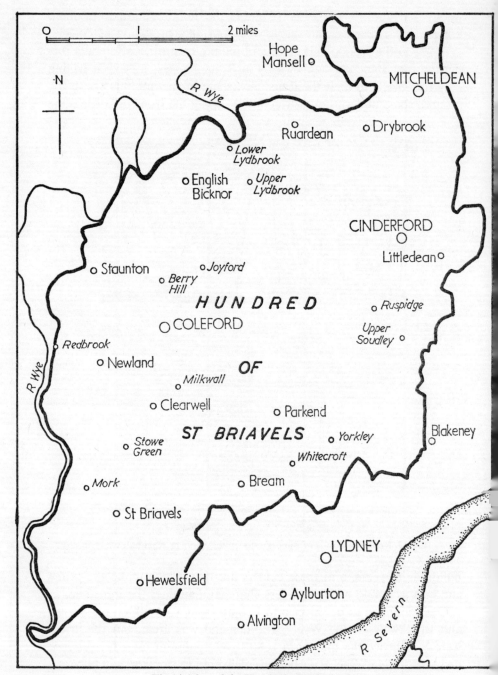

Fig 14. Map of the Hundred of St Briavels.

transported into the Kingdom of Ireland'.[35] A typical sale of cinders is one made in 1692 by Jephthah Wyrall of 10,000 dozen bushels at 10d a dozen ('6 heaped, and 6 even with the top') from English Bicknor, to be lifted and transported by the purchasers, Wheeler and Avenant[36]—'such of them as should be taken to Bishopswood or Parkend to be measured by the bushel used at Bishopswood furnace; or to Blakeney furnace by the bushel used there', Furthermore, the vendor was annually to raise and carry up to 250 dozens to Parkend at 4s a dozen. In the same year[37] Wheeler and Avenant were permitted to take cinders from within the Forest at 1s a dozen: in three years they paid £145.

Some surface-mining of ore was carried on, but it was during the hundred years from about 1675 that many of the 'old men's workings' underground were made—often limited in extent by water, and hindered by the method of granting 'gales'. George Wyrral (1780) wrote of these workings: 'There are, deep in the earth, vast caverns scooped out by men's hands, and large as the aisles of churches.'[38] Many were encountered by the nineteenth-century miners—in East Dean (in the Shakemantle, Buckshaft and St Annal's mines) there were found 'great voids formed by the old miners in which a few scattered tools have been discovered, left behind when operations were stopped . . . but not before the men had burrowed down some 150 yards';[39] also (in the Edge Hill—or Westbury Brook—mine) 'old men's workings remarkably extensive and searching, where all the ore had been cleared out to a depth, in some places, of 160 yards, and found to contain many ancient mining implements, such as plank-ladders, shovels, helves, etc, all of ash, as well as leather shoes, and mattock-heads'.[40] (Fig 12). In West Dean (in Old Sling mine) the 'old men's workings' were found 'to reach about 50 yards below the surface after they had worked over upwards of seven acres of the ore',[41] and there were recovered ancient picks and wooden shovels tipped with iron (Fig 12). Somewhat similar old workings were found elsewhere (eg in the Easter mine).[42] Contemporary workings, both open and underground, took place on the Lydney Park and Highmeadow Estates where during and around the period 1730–75 the Bathursts[43] and Gages[44] allowed the tenants of their furnaces and forges to take ore at 6s a dozen bushels, or 1s a ton.

Since c1717, some ore for Dean had come from North Lancashire. The local iron trade was good up to about 1758 but thereafter became depressed;[45] and in 1767 the trustees of Rowland Pytt were complaining to Thomas Bathurst in Lydney of 'the present declining state of the trade'.[46] By the last quarter of the eighteenth century, the demand for Forest ore had lessened; and easily accessible supplies were limited.

Cinders were still sought,[47] but it is uncertain whether they were the slag from the bloomeries, or that produced by the subsequent blast furnaces. (As late as 1820, some 8,000 tons lying at Parkend were acknowledged by David Mushet as being from bloomeries,[48] but they might well have been from a blast furnace.) The tonnage of cinders scattered throughout Dean was immense, and large quantities were also lying on the local estates of the Bathurst, Gage and Wemyss families. During and around the period 1730–75 the Bathursts allowed their ironmaster-tenants to take huge quantities of cinders at market price,[49] whereas Gage demanded 5s a dozen bushels (22in wide at the top, 21in at the bottom, and 8in deep), washed cinders to be reckoned at 12 bushels to the dozen, and unwashed at 14.[50]

A traveller in 1781,[51] while noting that wood in Dean was still plentiful, said that 'those men here who are not blacked by coals and furnaces are redded by the iron ore'. Yet only a small portion of the ore used was obtained locally; most supplies came by sea from Whitehaven in Cumberland—as late as 1780 a vessel carrying ore from Workington to Chepstow was captured by an Irish vessel:[52] it was probably cheaper, being easier to win chiefly on account of fewer troubles from water. By 1788[53] there was 'no regular iron ore mine work carried on in the Forest, but there were about 22 poor men who, at times when they had no other work, employed themselves in searching for and getting iron ore in the old holes and pits, which have been worked out many years'. Such work was chiefly in Parkend Walk, where there were 'eight mines of iron ore, in which are employed about 20 men, Free Miners, and three boys who are working their freedom'.[54]
1795–1893 The opening of a coke blast furnace at Cinderford in 1795, and the expectation that others would arise (as indeed one did at Parkend in 1799) led to a resurgence of iron ore mining in Dean. This development, complemented by an increase in coalmining for coke, steam-raising and domestic uses, made urgent the need for improved facilities for transport—which had always been difficult and expensive, particularly because of the poor state of the roads used as mineral outlets to the rivers. The Surveyor General of His Majesty's Land Revenues (chiefly concerned in the late eighteenth century with timber conservation) and its successors, the Commissioners of Woods

and Forests, deprecated expenditure on roads as encouraging their use for ore and coal transport, thus leading to the taking by the miners under custom of more timber and also to the ruination of routes used for the haulage of ship-timber. Such conditions kept the price of ore at a high level in markets outside Dean, with repercussions on the mines themselves. 'Foreigners', so-called, holding gales through Free Miners, had for many years been financially interested in the Forest's minerals, and were anxious to expand, while the coke furnaces at Cinderford and Parkend (followed in 1804 by one at Whitecliff) were requiring large quantities of ore, coal and limestone.

From 1799, pressure was brought by local and neighbouring industrialists for a tramroad network. Benjamin Outram, engineer, reported in 1801 his recommendations for tramroads throughout Dean to the rivers Severn and Wye—based chiefly on the potential of the coal-mines (see Chapter 6), but he also pointed out that his network would serve the coke blast furnaces at Cinderford and Parkend, and the Upper, Middle and Lower Forges at Lydney. There followed in the period 1809–1815 the establishment of three tramroads—Lydney-Lydbrook (Severn & Wye Railway & Canal Co), Cinderford-Bullo (Bullo Pill Railway Co), and Coleford-Monmouth (Monmouth Railway Co). By these tramroads (tracks composed of L-type tram plates, for the passage of horse-drawn wagons with flangeless wheels) much of the Forest was connected with the Severn (at Lydney and Bullo) and with the Wye (at Redbrook, Monmouth, Lydbrook and Bishopswood). Particularly useful were the many branch tramroads which provided access to minerals won in remote places—eg down Bixslade, Howlers Slade and Wimberry Slade, and in areas converging on Parkend (Ivy Moor Head, Brookhall Ditches, Milkwall-Darkhill, and Oakwood). In addition, scores of sidings and short branches increasingly served particular iron-mines, collieries and quarries. Many of the tramroads were later extended.[55]

The developments led to widespread integration of coal, iron and transport interests (at first tramroads, and later tramways and railways). Capitalists appeared as potential large-scale employers of labour and users of machinery. Subscribers to the Lydney and Lydbrook Railway Act 10 June 1809 (from 1810 the operators' name was changed to the Severn & Wye Railway & Canal Company) included the Protheroes (John, Edward and Philip), David Mushet (see Chapter 3), and Samuel Hewlett, local ironfounder. An example of the integration is in connection with the Protheroe family: John, like other proprietors of the

foregoing and of other tramroads (eg Bullo Pill), was obliged to become coal, ore and ironworks proprietor to help furnish traffic for his
line. In 1812 he sold for 20,000 guineas his collieries to his nephew
Edward Protheroe (one-time MP for Bristol). Edward in 1815 was
developing Whitelea Colliery, and after purchasing from his uncle
in 1824 the Parkend Furnace and associated ironworks, he began sinking iron mines near Milkwall. In 1826, when chairman of the s&w
Company, he purchased the idle Bullo Pill line and its Great Bilson
Colliery, and from the following year developed Birches Pit and
further increased his local empire by working Ivy Moor Head, Parkend
Main and Parkend Royal. By 1841 he controlled or leased some thirty
coalworks and about ten iron mines.

Another example of integration, was that connected with William
Crawshay (1788–1867), one of the greatest of the Welsh ironmasters,
who in 1832 acquired an interest in the Cinderford furnaces. By 1841
he owned or leased about ten iron mines. He and his son, Henry built
up the Cinderford ironworks and developed many iron mines to such
effect that Henry was widely known as 'the Iron King of the Forest of
Dean'. They owned Shakemantle and some other iron mines, and an
'empire of tramroads', particularly in the Cinderford district. Though
the Crawshay's, later including Edwin, were pre-eminent in the iron
trade, they also developed Lightmoor and Foxes Bridge collieries and,
later, Eastern United and Northern United.

Demands for ore and coke for blast furnaces (see Chapter 3) were
later increased by demands of local tinplate and wire works, particularly at Lydney, Parkend, Lydbrook and Cinderford. Thereupon was
inaugurated a period of deep mining in which pits were necessary as a
rule, though the valleys in the south-west of the Forest allowed the
driving of deep cross-measures adits—some were driven to win coal
from the coal measures in the first instance, and afterwards extended
into the Drybrook Sandstone or Carboniferous Limestone in search of
iron ore. A little outcrop-mining by means of opencast excavations,
slopes, and shallow pits continued as a desultory accompaniment to
deep mining.[56] Underground, the constricted earlier methods were
continued, but in the majority of cases the ore was conveyed for long
distances on tramways to the mine's bottom, whence it was usually
raised by steam-engines. Drilling and boring was by hand. Pumping
and steam-raising plant, and winding-engines were not as yet fully
developed.

In the east of the Forest, three associated mines—Shakemantle,

37 *(above)* Lime kilns alongside the Moseley Green to Blackeney Road, 1960; *(below)* Bixslade Stoneworks 1939. The block is of blue Forest stone, 7ft × 3ft × 4ft, weighing about 8½ tons

38 Charcoal burning
in Dean c1909 (1):
(above) constructing
the 'pit' or stack;
(left) the 'pit' awaiting
a covering of turf or
soil
(See also plate 39)

Buckshaft and St Annal's—were opened in 1829, 1835 and 1849 respectively; and Edge Hill (or Westbury Brook) was begun in 1837. In the west, Old Sling mine and Easter mine were opened in 1838 and 1852 respectively (all, as previously noted, meeting with 'the old men's workings'), and have been described.[57]

In 1831 a Commission was appointed to investigate the working of the Dean mines and other relevant matters. Their Fourth Report, of 1835,[58] resulted in the Dean Forest Mines Act, 1838,[59] in which the rights of the Free Miners were at last defined. Mining Commissioners appointed thereunder,[60] in 1841 made the Award of Iron Mines[61] which listed the persons then entitled to gales for the purpose of working them—many described in detail.[62] The foregoing and subsequent 'gales' are listed to 1877 by Wood,[63] and to 1919 in the Annual Reports of the Commissioners of Woods and Forests. Full records from 1841 to date are held in the Gaveller's Office, Coleford. (The Gaveller's Office also holds full records of the mining on the Highmeadow Estate, which has long been in the possession of the Crown, but comparatively little information concerning the so-called 'exempted lands', such as Noxon Park, and none relating to the Lydney Park Estate. These three regions of the iron-mining district are not subject to the Free Miners' rights. Fully 600,000 tons were estimated to have been won from 1841 to 1919 from the Lydney Park Estate and Noxon Park, chiefly the latter.) The assignees of the iron gales, their rights assured, and regulations made to obviate much of the earlier chaos, began to develop their works, and with like Awards of coal gales and quarries, made even more urgent the need for improved transport.

Even before 1830 the s&w tramroads fought against the incursion of the steam railway, and clung to the old methods and outmoded tolls, making only grudging concessions to public opinion, and this intransigence produced harsh criticism from the Office of Woods, other railway companies, and the industrialists.[64] Converting to railway the many miles of steep and tortuous s&w tramroads would have eaten into dividends! Not till 1868 did s&w convert to broad-gauge railway, quickly followed by the standard gauge; the tramroads were at last eclipsed, though many stretches remained till late in the nineteenth century. The company which sixty years earlier had instituted a system of tramroads through Dean, did the same with railways, albeit belatedly.

Meanwhile in 1854 the Forest of Dean Railway (previously the Bullo Pill Railway Company) was replaced by a broad-gauge railway, and

R

was later continued northward to join the Hereford, Ross & Gloucester Railway by the ill-fated Mitcheldean Road & Forest of Dean Railway, authorised in 1871 and completed, but only opened as far as Drybrook. In 1856 the Forest of Dean Central Railway was built, from New Fancy Colliery down to Awre on the South Wales line, but it too was ill-fated.

The tonnage of ore mined annually from 1841 is given in the Annual Reports of the Commissioners of Woods, and in records held by the Gaveller's Office. From 27,537 tons in 1842, the output rose to 192,080 in 1860, and to 203,502 in 1873.[65] The yield of each mine in 1864 and 1865 is on record.[66] Not much ore was sent out of the Forest (apart from Edge Hill ore to Dowlais, and Oakwood ore to Ebbw Vale)— partly due to indifferent transport facilities. Robert Forester Mushet had in 1858 tried unsuccessfully to sell Dean ore (through a Mr Hart) to William Crawshay of Cyfarthfa,[67] who said it was inferior to the ore from his son Henry's Forest mines, for which he was paying 14s a ton delivered at Cardiff. In Chapter 4 it was noted that Bessemer's process of steel production from about 1865–70 made it possible to utilise low grade iron ore, available in many parts of Britain, putting Dean's ore still less in demand. Yet in the 1850s faith remained in the local ore-mining industry: at Shakemantle 'the large pit now in work is 22ft 6in long by 11ft 6in oval shape; 72yd deep; cylinder 36in diameter, 8ft stroke power of steam is 50lb to the inch and from 6 to 10 strokes per minute, working two pumps 27in in diameter, four foot strokes at quarter centre of the beam'. Furthermore, 'there is a new pit been sunk at Shakemantle 19ft 6in by 11½ft wide, oval shape; at this pit the engine is to be differently constructed—60in cylinder 10ft stroke piston rod coming out of the bottom of the cylinder and attached to the pump rods; the mine at this works pitch at the bottom about 1 in 1 or 45 degrees at the top from 60 to 70 degrees.[68]

Much new machinery was necessary for the Dean iron mines: the following list of extant drawings made by the Neath Abbey Iron-works[69] gives an idea of what machinery was required:

Causeway Mine (Henry Crawshay & Sons)
1868: 21-inch winding engine.
Cinderford Iron Works (Henry Crawshay)
1875: Pair of 12-inch, 20-inch stroke, haulage engines.
1856: Girders for supporting a steam capstan and 15-inch engine.
1857: Winding roller for a 15-inch horizontal high pressure winch engine.

1851: 22-inch engine.

1865: 32-inch cylinder 6 foot 10 inch stroke, nozzles, etc for a blowing engine.

1845: 78-inch pumping engine.

1856: Wrought ironwork, centre piece, pillow blocks, tooth wheels etc for a steam capstan.

St Annal's Mine (Henry Crawshay & Son)

1868: Sundries for a 21-inch winding engine.

Shakemantle (Henry Crawshay)

1857: Piston, rod, cap and gudgeon for 34-inch engine.

Feed pump from pattern of 60-inch engine (No date).

Forest of Dean Iron Company, Lydney (? for Parkend).

Feed forcer for 15-inch engine (No date).

Wigpool Mine Works, Mitcheldean

1861: Beam, carriages and plates for a 12-inch pump, 6 foot stroke.

1861: Pump work.

For 1880, information is available on some of the principal pumping engines:[70]

	Diam. of cylinder in	Stroke in cylinder ft	Stroke in mine ft
Shakemantle:			
Bull Engine, High Pressure	60	10	10
Bull Engine, Auxiliary	30	5	5
Rotary Condensing Beam Engine (not working)	70	12	12
Edge Hill:			
Cornish Rotary High Pressure	45	8	5
Easter:			
Inverted Cornish Beam Condensing (not working)	42	10	9
Wigpool:			
Horizontal Rotary High Pressure	30	6	6

Many other details of the above pumping engines and their boilers are available.[71] Some of the boilers also fed the winding engine. At Shakemantle in 1882 'a ponderous double-acting pumping engine', designed by P. Teague, was made and erected by the Neath Abbey Ironworks.[72] The pit was 600ft deep, and every stone in the lining was dressed to template at the pit's mouth. There were three lifts of pumps. The cylinder was 70in diameter and 13ft 9in long, and the

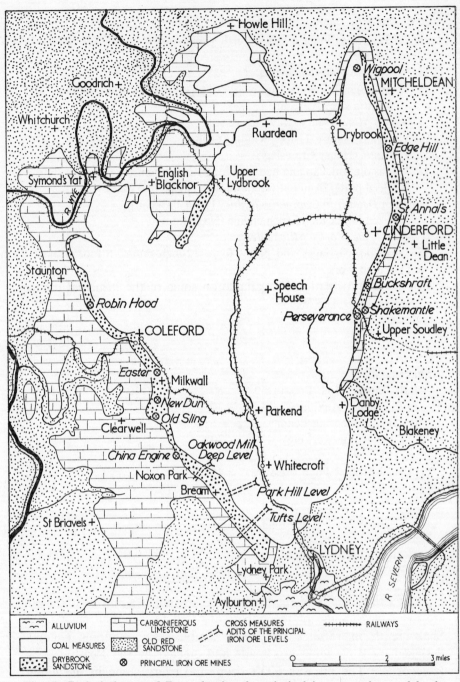

Fig 15. Geological map of Dean showing the principal iron ore mines and levels (after T. Franklin Sibly, *Special Reports on the Mineral Resources of Great Britain*, 1927, fig 1).

piston rod was 8in diameter. The condensing apparatus was of the usual jet construction. The length of the main beam to centres was 36ft, the depth at the centre 6½ft, and the weight over 30 tons. The engine was placed on a lever wall 6ft thick by 43ft high, above the basement of the engine-house. The flywheel was 20ft in diameter, and the weight about 32 tons.

So much for the machines, what of the miners? A traveller witnessed in 1880 on Bream Meend the following scene: [73]

> A miner under the lee of one of the whitewashed cottages sits in a chair; from the crown of his curley head to the sole of his boots, he is— hair, hands, face, bare arms, clothes and all—of the colour of a red-horn carrot. He is an iron miner rolled in ochre. Behind him, bearing over him, another stalwart miner, bare-headed, bare-armed and 'raddled all over' with the dust of his calling, is singeing his hair with a comb and spirit-lamp appliance: the very delicacy of the manipulation contrasted with the strong rough figures of the men and the wild surroundings is most comical.

Employment figures for the years 1873 to 1880 respectively were 2,322, 2,055, 1,860, 1,790, 1,814, 1,683, 1,627, and 1,758.[74] Mining of ore decreased towards the end of the nineteenth century—from 199,111 tons in 1871, to 90,497 in 1881, and to 63,748 in 1891.[75] It was said of West Dean in 1889[76] that 'iron ore, formerly sent in large quantities to Staffordshire and South Wales, is now but little worked, in consequence of the depression in trade, and the vast quantities imported from Spain.' Oakwood Mill and China, two large mines on the west of the Forest, were abandoned in 1884 and 1892 respectively, whereupon a local newspaper reported: [77]

> For many years past, the once famous Oakwood Valley has been particularly gloomy and quiet. While nature still preserves her charms, and the natural beauty of the spot remains unimpaired, the cessation of works has somewhat isolated the valley as a centre of commercial interest. Gone are the extensive mines, whilst its towering chimneys are fast going to decay.

On the east of Dean, Edge Hill (Plate 29a) was abandoned in 1893 (since 1843 it had produced 958,000 tons), and in 1899 came the closing of Shakemantle (Plate 28a) and its associated Buckshaft, St Annal's and Perseverance (the three first named had produced 1,650,000 tons from 1841). One of the chief reasons for the closures was the termination of the Cinderford Furnaces in 1894.

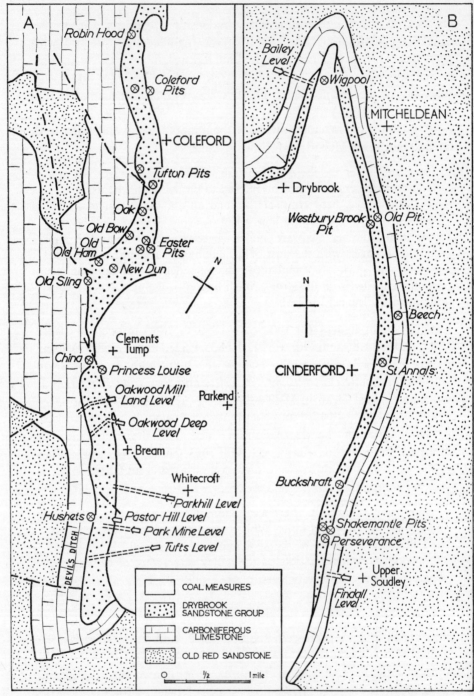

Fig 16. Plan of the western and eastern parts of Dean's iron ore field (after F. M. Trotter *Geology of the Forest of Dean Coal and Iron ore Field*, 1942, fig 14).

1894–1945 Mining continued to fall rapidly—the output in 1901 was 9,769 tons, and in 1911 5,830 tons. There was a temporary resurgence during the 1914–18 war, and by 1917 seven mines were at work, the output (22,990 tons) coming chiefly from the Easter, New Dun, Tufts, and Wigpool mines.[78] In 1921 the output was only 1,727 tons; and during the period 1918–25 only 38,000 tons were won, chiefly from Birch Hill (503 tons), British (2,739), Easter (2,102), Highmeadow (7,535), New Dun (20,875), Old Ham (1,353), and Bailey Level (2,864). The only production in 1925 was New Dun (840 tons) and Old Ham (18 tons); and mining almost came to an end in that year. From 1842 the western district had produced 1,135,000 tons, and the eastern over 3,000,000 tons.[79]

Reasons for the output of iron ore dwindling to the trifling proportions of the 1920s, were the competition of imported Spanish ore, the exhaustion of the deposits above water level, and because the variable character of the ore and the small quantities won made it difficult to keep the consignments satisfactorily uniform in quality. Attempts in 1925 were made to resuscitate the industry:[80]

> Negotiations are in progress which, if they can be brought to a successful issue, will result in the iron ore mines of the eastern side of Dean being reopened and developed. Should the proposed syndicate be formed, the mines will be worked on a very extensive scale. Sidney Taylor, of Coombs Park, Coleford, who for the past few years has been connected with various coal-mining enterprises in the Forest, is interested in these matters, and G. Brocklehurst Taylor, of Coleford, is the solicitor acting for the vendors.

The requisite finance was not forthcoming, but in November 1926, Captain Pringle, a local coal mine-owner submitted a scheme to the deputy gaveller, W. Forster Brown, by which the iron ore gales on the eastern side might with Government aid be re-developed. He proposed the de-watering of the iron ore gales between Howbeach and Drybrook, a distance of some six miles from north to south, and comprising the Shakemantle, Perseverance, New Buckshaft, St Annal's, Fairplay and Westbury Brook mines, worked in the past by Crawshays for their Cinderford Iron Works. The deputy surveyor reported the scheme to the Forestry Commission 17 January 1927:

> The mines have been worked to varying depths below ordnance datum. The depth of Shakemantle shaft, which is sunk to the deepest point below ordnance datum, is 160 yards. Some of the other shafts

are sunk on higher ground and are deeper, but do not reach so deep in the measures as the Shakemantle shafts.

The relative depths of the several mines will be seen by reference to the section accompanying Captain Pringle's communication. Upon this section the several iron gales worked are also shown; and I have attached an ordnance map in which the position of the gales in plan will be seen.

It is proposed to unwater the mines from the Shakemantle shaft, and to deepen this shaft another 55 yards, to a total depth of 215 yards below surface level. The Shakemantle shaft is of large size and suitable for installing pumping machinery. All evidence available agrees that when the Shakemantle mine was abandoned there were large churns of iron ore left in the floor of the mine, and that the cause of abandonment was not due to lack of ore.

Taking the average production per acre which has been obtained from the gales worked down to the present depth at these several mines, I calculate that the resources of iron ore which would be won by the proposed development would amount to over 5 million tons.

The limonite iron ore which these mines produce varies in quality from a high grade ore, carrying up to 63 per cent of iron, with a low silica content, to one of less good quality where the proportion of iron is less and the silica content higher. The average of the run of the Shakemantle mine might be taken at probably 40 to 45 per cent iron content, with from 14 to 18 per cent of silica. No doubt a market could be found for this class of ore if it can be produced at a sufficiently low cost. It might require to be mixed with ore of a higher grade at the furnaces.

When these mines were worked it was necessary to pump considerable feeders of water; the quantity appears to have been somewhere about an average of 2,000 gallons per minute and this water was raised to a height approximately of 400 feet.

The actual cost of pumping this water in 1891 appears to have been £5,574 per annum. With present day costs and calculating the electrical power at ¾d per unit it will probably cost about £8,500 per annum. It would therefore be essential that in any scheme of development the output of the mine would be such as to reduce the cost per ton of ore for pumping to a resonable level.

I have gone into the question in some detail and am of opinion that if the Shakemantle, St Annal's and Westbury Brook shafts were fitted up with necessary winding machinery, etc, an annual output of 150,000 tons of iron ore could readily be obtained. The annual cost of pumping per ton of ore would be about 1s 2d per ton, a much less figure than that upon which the mines were working at the time they closed down.

Assuming the suggested adit level is driven, I estimate the cost of pumping up to the adit, with electrical power at ¾d per unit, at £3,500 per annum, equivalent to 6½d per ton of iron ore. If the adit was also used for the disposal of the ore a further saving of about £600 per annum could be anticipated in cost of winding the ore.

To unwater the mines within a period of six months, including dealing with the growth of water for that period and basing the amount of stock water at the assumed quantity of 337,551,895 gallons, given in my report of 9 June 1917, including all necessary plant, I estimate would cost £35,732, with electrical power at ¾d per unit. Possibly this figure might be reduced to £30,000 dependant on the actual cost of the plant necessary when tenders are called for. I therefore summarise the suggested scheme as follows, with electrical power at ¾d per unit:

	£
Estimated cost of plant required for unwatering	28,435
Estimated cost of unwatering including wages for six months	8,297
Estimated cost of equipping the mine to work 150,000 tons of ore per annum, including necessary rock drills, but excluding underground development	20,000
	£56,732
Less value of sinking pump plant, etc	3,000
	£53,732
Add underground development, say,	10,000
	£63,732

Say, £63,000, of which £53,732 would represent the cost of unwatering the mines.

An additional expenditure of £70,000 on driving the suggested adit would, I estimate, result in a saving of £5,627 per annum in pumping and winding at the mine, equivalent to a reduction of 9d per ton in the cost of producing ore.

The success of the scheme would depend upon the adventurers being in a position to provide a market for 150,000 tons per annum of this class of ore at a price per ton which would enable the mines to be carried on profitably.

Looking at it from the point of view of the Forestry Commission, if the scheme was to be successful it should result in an annual income of, say, no less than £2,500 per annum from the iron ore working at this group of mines for a long period of years. It is, however, evident that unless the people who had control of the mines were substantial people, who were in a position to provide the necessary market for the iron ore, the scheme would not be of any consideration from the point of view of providing any capital for the proving of the mines, but the scheme might be worth some consideration by the Forestry Commission or other Government department if it was developed something on the following lines:

That a substantial company, preferably a big iron making concern, with plenty of capital at its back, should take over the gales and guarantee in some form satisfactory to the Government that the necessary capital for the equipment of the mines for an output of 150,000 tons or some modification of this amount, in collaboration with the company, on the security of the mines in the form of debentures at interest, and this sum to be repayable in fixed instalments over a certain number of years. The question of the adit level to be one left entirely for the galees, because if once the mines are pumped out and the iron ore is proved to the satisfaction of the adventurers it may be to their interests, if it can be carried out, to drive the adit with a view to reducing their costs of production. The most essential feature, to my mind, is that before any serious consideration can be given to such a proposal, it is essential that the people who are to work the mine should be in the saddle and should be in a position to guarantee the market for this quantity of ore before any attempt is made to unwater the mine.

Captain Pringle has discussed the proposal with me, and before taking any steps on the lines of interesting iron companies in the proposition, is anxious to know, assuming he is able to get substantial people to consider the scheme, whether the Government would be prepared to advance £30,000 or any sum, to prove or help to prove that the ore exists in these gales in the quantity and of the quality estimated upon.

Three years later on 28 June 1930, the Free Miners submitted the following Resolution:

To the Rt Hon J. Ramsay MacDonald, Prime Minister; The Rt Hon Vernon Hartshorn, Lord Privy Seal; and to D. J. Vaughan, Esq, MP for the Forest of Dean.

At a meeting of Free Miners, representing upwards of three thousand men, duly convened and held at the ancient Speech House in the Forest of Dean and Hundred of St Briavels, 28 June 1930, it was unanimously resolved that the Prime Minister, Lord Privy Seal, and our local Member be humbly begged to take such prompt steps as might be necessary to give powers to the proper authority to send a Government Commissioner or Inspector to Coleford, Forest of Dean, to hold a local enquiry into, inter alia, the following:

1. That the Crown (Forestry Commissioners) as owners have valuable but dormant mineral assets (iron ore) in the Forest of Dean.

2. That the deep mines or gales are virgin below water level and that there are many millions of tons of ore on the East and West sides of the Forest, which could be at once worked from the deep of the old mines when once they are de-watered.

3. Whether or not it would be a sound commercial proposition for the Forestry Commission, as landlords, to dewater the mines, at the approximate cost of £45,000, as to £35,000 on the East side and £10,000 on the West side. (£15,000 was expended by a private company on the Western side some years ago and the major part of the work is done.)

4. In the year 1865, 2,240 men were employed in the iron industry of the Forest of Dean; whether the re-establishment of this industry would not absorb the whole of the unemployed in the district.

5. In the year 1893, the mines were finally forced to close down because Spanish ore was imported to South Wales at 10s per ton; the price today is around 22s per ton at South Wales ports. Spanish ores are becoming exhausted and more costly to mine, and there is no coal available there. Whether with modern methods and local electric power-supply now available, together with a scheme of nationalisation of the whole of the iron gales and certain coal gales, the Forest ores cannot be raised at a price and quality to compete with Spain both in South Wales and the Midlands.

6. That South Wales at the present time use 80,000 tons of Hematite per month, practically the whole of which is imported from Spain, mined by foreign miners, whilst 1,800 miners in the Forest are receiving unemployment benefit, at a cost of over £60,000 per annum.

7. Whether under a scheme of nationalisation of the iron mines and suitable collieries, modern blast furnaces might be advantageously erected locally by steel manufacturers of South Wales or the Midlands, and pig iron produced on the spot.

8. In support of this application we beg to enclose herewith facts and analyses, corroborated by authoritative reports and records.

9. We therefore humbly beg that you will put aside departmental difficulties and arrange for a local enquiry at Coleford in order that we and others in this district, with intimate knowledge of the

iron mines, may give and produce evidences outside the Crown Records, also that the Forestry Commission be asked to attend the enquiry, as landlords, to produce evidence from the Crown Office at Coleford, in order that this matter, which is of national importance, may be truly tried and decided.

10.   That an invitation be sent to the National Federation of Iron and Steel Manufacturers, Caxton House, London, for any of their members to attend such enquiry, if held.

> For and on behalf of the Free Miners of the Forest of Dean and Hundred of St Briavels, in the County of Gloucester,

(Signed) J. RILEY BROWN, JP, Chairman.
WILLIAM PAGE, Secretary.
40 Valley Road,
Cinderford,
Forest of Dean.

One of the prime movers in this matter was Henry E. Doughty, solicitor, of Staunton,[81] who in 1931 followed up the Resolution with proposals to raise finance sufficient to win ore in six gales (comprising seven mines—Dean's Meand, Westbury Brook, St Annal's, New Buckshaft, New Cinderford, Perseverance and Fairplay, all connected and drained by the Shakemantle mine) on the eastern side of Dean, with an area of 1,440 acres—241 acres of which had been worked over, producing on average 12,441 tons an acre. His chief assertions were: (*a*) there was a potential supply of 15 million tons of ore (the deputy gaveller had said 'over 5 million'), (*b*) no new shafts would be necessary, (*c*) the Crown had been asked to provide £25,000 on reasonable terms for de-watering, (*d*) the properties were freehold, subject to Crown Rents of £220 per annum, merging into a royalty of 4d a ton, and (*e*) the price of foreign ore at South Wales ports was 21s a ton compared with less than 10s in 1893. Doughty obtained a report from George Smith (formerly assistant manager and surveyor at Cinderford Iron Mines—his father Thomas having been manager) and published it, together with an estimate from E. Ivor David, consulting engineer, that the cost of de-watering would be about £25,000 (the deputy gaveller's estimate had been £53,232).

Finance was not forthcoming, consequently no new mining was begun on the east side of the Forest. On the west side the only mines which continued in production, thanks to Fred Watkins and his son, F. B. Watkins (Plate 30a), were those of Old Sling and New Dun (it had yielded 150,000 tons by 1925). In 1934, New Dun was employing 30 people. The Robin Hood, closed in 1927, was reopened in 1940 by the Ministry of Supply; Canadian soldiers for a while, assisted in its working, and the mine was abandoned in 1944. In 1942 the New Dun also was requisitioned by the government, who worked the mine from 5 August 1942 until 10 May 1945, having raised 2,689 tons.[82] This was virtually the end of ore-mining in Dean.

The history of the successive failures or abandonment of the highly speculative ore-mining is complicated by a variety of factors not immediately concerned with the question of ore reserves. Among these, poor demand for ore, foreign competition, and the fluctuating requirements of certain industrial processes with regard to special classes of ore, have at various times contributed to discourage extensive development. Serious consideration, and some application, has been given to the problem of dealing with water in the mining of deep ground, and exploration has been undertaken near and below water level, but most of the abandoned mines, especially those in the east, are deeply flooded, and de-watering would be uneconomic. The chief repository of ore has been in the Crease Limestone, but some workable deposits have been found in every division of the Dolomite or Limestone. Some people assert that huge reserves of many millions of tons exist;[83] however, F. B. Watkins has recently commented:

> Most miners are loath to acknowledge that ore in the Forest is practically exhausted. My father put in pumps to drain the lower measures in the New Dun Mine, and the Ministry of Supply went a stage further and explored the lower measures, but came to the conclusion that practically all of the ore is in the Crease Limestone. In all the mining experience of three generations of my family, no ore of any consequence was found in the Lower Dolomite, and I have no doubt that miners in the east of the Forest had the same experience and are well aware that there is no reserve of ore worth considering.

Millions of tons have been won from the outcrop of the Crease, and ancient mining of it probably removed from the Forest as much ore as all the mines and levels.[84] Consequently, Dean has probably yielded in excess of ten million tons.

Before they are forgotten, it is useful to put on record some of the names given to different types of the Forest ore: [85]

'Brush'—massive or stalactitic haematite with little or no gangue.
'Pipey brush'—a thoroughly stalactitic ore.

'Smith'—applied by some miners to a gravelly type brown haematite; and by others to powdery red haematite or brown haematite.

'Burler'—clean lump ore from the Lower Dolomite carrying about 58 per cent of metallic iron in the raw state.

'Fine'—ore from the Lower Dolomite carrying about 45 per cent of metallic iron in the raw state.

Extant surface evidence of the past mining eras in the 'Crease' comprises labyrinthine excavations ('scowles'), now rendered weirdly picturesque by irregular shapes, a profusion of ferns, and gnarled yews. Numerous shallow workings lie between Staunton mine and Crows Nest mine in the Coleford-Staunton area, and in the neighbourhood of the Delves in the Wigpool district. Others are evident in the Edge Hill and Collafield districts where, particularly at Edge Hill, 'old crop workings', in the form of open-cast trenches or of small bellpits on the crop of the vein, appear in the woods 100yd SSW of Westbury Brook shaft and trend in a southerly direction to St Annal's shaft. They can be traced from thence to a point 250yd SW of Abbotswood near Ruspidge, where they are lost on the outskirts of that village, but re-appear beyond and can be followed from the Soudley Valley for 450yd to the SSW. Many of the 'scowles' lie in West Dean at Noxon Park, in Perrygrove east of Clearwell, at The Scowles east of Newland, and at 'Devil's Chapel' south of Bream. In the Clements Tump to Bream area, the crop of the 'Crease' is marked by an almost continuous line of old surface workings. Other workings are found on the crop of the Lower Dolomite where the ore was won from irregular-shaped pockets and basins, and along the basins that trend SW and NNE, the pockets of ore having rarely exceeded 30ft in depth. South of Bream the 'Crease' is marked by a continuous line of workings and numerous shallow or 'land' pits.

As to cinders, in 1866 mounds of slag 'continued to be met with' and were 'numerous enough to catch the eye wherever the observer may direct his steps'.[86] Today they are rarely seen, many heaps having been buried, or removed for road-making, but deposits of them have been observed in recent times at Soudley, St Briavels, Aylburton, and High Nash near Coleford.

Other than the many 'scowles', a few mine-head remnants (Plates 28b and 29a) and disintegrating and constricting entrances to levels or adits, are the only surface evidences of an industry which had great economic importance in Dean. Underground, most if not all of the deeper mines are flooded; so too are many of the caverns and chambers of 'the old men's workings'—particularly in the east of Dean. Water, often of a green hue, made eerie by gloom and silence, is not the whole picture: the Royal Forest of Dean Caving Club after exploring the old workings, bring to light abandoned claypipes, 'nellies' (candle holders), lamps, ropes, ladders, trucks, and pumping equipment. The same club has taken photographs underground of bats, and of calcite straws of many shapes, sizes and colours festooned from roofs and draping the walls with curtain-like formations, as well as paving the floors. The straws developed after the workings were abandoned.

Some of the vast complex of caverns are far below the surface, for example, at Wigpool (c400ft); and a few caverns in Shakemantle are 140ft below sea-level. In some places it is possible to penetrate several miles through one mine system after another. Many of the old workings can be reached through almost unnoticed surface holes. Among the mines explored by the Caving Club on the east of the Forest are Wigpool ('Fox Hole'), Buckshaft, and Edge Hill ('Wych Elm', part of the Old Trow Ditch workings). Explorations in the west of Dean include Oakwood Mill Land and Deep Levels (Mushets), Old Bow and Old Ham near Clearwell. In all, an interesting pursuit by the club, but one fraught with danger and not to be undertaken without training, experience and proper equipment and, of course, the necessary permission. In recent years various barbecues and exhibitions have been held in the Old Ham, usually attended by some 300 people.

Water has been drawn from some of the mines: at Buckshaft and Beech Pit (Greenbottom) by East Dean RDC, and at Tufts Level by Lydney RDC who have a chlorination plant near the old Norchard colliery.

Mining of Ochre

Ochres and oxides in Dean occur in intimate association with the iron ores of the Crease Limestone, and have furnished valuable colouring materials. They are generally deposited in small quantities, but in a few places comparatively large masses have been found. Red and purple oxides predominate, but some yellow ochres have also been found as well as the inferior umber. Ochre is a yellow or brown hydrated oxide of iron. 'Colour' or 'oxide' is ferric oxide usually in an oily mass, while 'spurt' is an inferior oxide and is much more coarse in texture than 'colour'. Ochre has also been defined as 'a fine clay mostly pale yellow', and as 'kinds of native earth consisting of clay and hydrated oxide of iron, used as pigments varying from light yellow to brown'.

Oxide of iron (ochre and red), suitable for pigment, was found in limited areas only. For instance, none was ever found in the Sling mine or anywhere south of it, whereas quantities were won in the New Dun and Old Ham mines. Everyone working an ore mine in Dean hoped to find ochre or 'colour', but nearly all were doomed to disappointment. Many of the relevant records of output are unreliable, for ochre has been confused with oxide, 'colour', umber, and 'spurt'— the word ochre having been used loosely in the trade to denote an oxide of any colour. When a man worked in an iron-mine, even if he never saw ochre or oxide, his clothes always had a yellowish or brownish tinge.

Oxides and ochres have been mined in the Forest over many recent centuries, and possibly too by the Romans and earlier inhabitants. In the fifteenth century, Henry VI reserved the 'red and yellow ochre pits' in at least 500 acres of Dean Forest.[87] Ochre was ostensibly subject to the customs of the Dean Miners at least as early as the sixteenth century. In 1608 William Morse of English Bicknor, who traded as a 'Dyer', in all probability used Forest 'ochre'. However, persons other than the local inhabitants were interested in 'ochre', and in 1611 Robert Treswell, Surveyor of the Woods, submitted a petition to Sir Julius Caesar, for a licence to dig for yellow ochre in Dean and in Shotover (Oxon), paying £6 13s 4d per annum.[88] In 1634[89] Henry Hippon and Edward Lassells petitioned for a patent for 14 years for the exclusive right of digging yellow ochre in or about Littledean. In 1652 one of the Deputy Gavellers and five miners leased for 21 years their shares, and the King's share, in a 'Mine [ore] or Oker pitt', known as 'Yellow-shroft', subject to a covenant to supply certain London merchants with material which in all probability was 'colour'.[90] In 1667 the right to dig for ochre was saved to the miners by Section 11 of the Dean Forest (Reafforestation) Act. Henry Powle writing in 1678[91] records that in some places in the Forest, 'red and yellow oker' was found; and Dr Richard Parsons, who copied much of Powle's work, added: 'there is great plenty of red, blue and yellow ochre, the chiefest of which pits are at Yellow Craft in Little Dean'.[92]

There are no relevant records for the next century and a half, but

39 Charcoal burning in Dean c1909 (2): *(top)* the 'pit' ready to be ignited; *(centre)* the 'pit' smouldering; *(below)* charcoal being loaded for transport (See also plate 38)

40 *(above)* Tannery sheds at Collow, Newnham-on-Severn; *(below)* Rear of the Tannery house at Clearwell, showing slatted windows

on 29 September 1830 William Tingle and William Cooper received
a licence from the Crown 'to erect and continue a small water-wheel
upon the brook separating the Forest from Abbotswood under Staple-
ledge Enclosure, for the purpose of grinding ochre'.[93] The licence
was for 31 years and the charge £1 per annum. The works was south
of Ruspidge at a place now known as Cullamore (a corruption of
Colour Mill). Sopwith's Map of 1831 shows, opposite, 'Hales Ochre
Level'. *The Forester* of 1831 supplies a note of a 'colour works' at
Ayleford: [94]

> If the stranger pursues his walk or ride he will come to the Colour
> Works of Messrs Todd & Co in the romantic vale of Ayleaford. Here
> he will find that a considerable and costly enterprise has, with the aid
> of chemistry, transformed the native products of the Forest into all the
> varied colours which observation or fancy could suggest. The stiff
> and solid substances of earth have been rendered by fire sufficiently
> subtile for the brush or pencil, and made to retain a hue which, whilst
> it delights the eye, reflects on the mind the great powers and advan-
> tages of the noble science of chemistry.

The above was the 'paint work' noted in Chapter 2 as being run from
about 1828 to 1832 by Todd, Jeffries and Spirrins,[95] and sited somewhere below Camp Mill.

Writing in 1840, David Mushet records:[96] 'At a period, during the
late war, when there existed a considerable demand for the yellow
ochre of the iron mines of Dean Forest, and for a permanent black
colour for navy purposes', he tried experiments. Into an iron cylinder
2ft in diameter 8ft long built over a furnace grate 'about 2ft of small
coals were hard rammed into the lower end; above this were placed
about 5ft of yellow ochre in the state of an impalpable powder'. An
iron plate was fitted on top with holes; and the gas rising through the
holes was ignited. 'For several hours a good deal of inconveniency
was sustained by a violent agitation which took place in the ochre; but
which, from time to time, brought up traces of a perfect black colour,
denoting that a change from yellow to black had taken place in the
lower part of the cylinder. On examining its contents when cold a
variety of results were found: the yellow oxide of iron, for more than
a foot next to the cylinder bottom, was converted into grains of malleable iron slightly adhering together, and of a light greyish colour.
Above this the oxide was converted, for some distance, into a good
black colour, some of it very perfect; but towards the upper end of

S

the cylinder, the black became mixed with the original colour of the oxyde, which for lack of temperature or gas, had remained unchanged'. Other experiments were tried later, but there is no evidence as to their success or failure.

Nicholls[97] wrote in 1858: 'Red and yellow ochre of superior quality occur in the iron veins, and have at various times been in considerable request. They are now used in the neighbourhood for marking sheep, and tinting whitewash.' Writing in 1881, Insole and Bunning state:[98] 'Valuable deposits are found of yellow ochre [umber], red colour, and spurt. Yellow ochre is a Limonite in a finely divided state. Red Colour, or red earth as it is sometimes called, is probably Gothite and Turgite, also in a finely divided state. Spurt is the Crease in a disintegrated state highly impregnated with colour. The red earth varies in colour from bright red to purple. It and spurt are sold to paint manufacturers, who triturate and levigate them in the manufacture of oil paints.' Their statement regarding 'yellow ochre' should be treated with reserve, because very little has ever been found in Dean. F. B. Watkins' grandfather, his father and himself worked from 1860 to 1942 to find yellow ochre, but only a small quantity was found—at The Scowles. Other than one big churn of 'colour' at New Dun, red oxide was equally difficult to find—and it therefore commanded a high price. The Robin Hood mine was always regarded as a large producer of 'colour' but in all the years (from about 1870 to 1926) deposits were being worked there, they only produced three-fourths of the quantity obtained from the New Dun in 1912–14. Mr Watkins remembers the waggons hauling it through Coleford: on a wet day the streets were red. About one truck was railed each week; about two tons were hauled each day. The only true yellow ochre actually mined in the Forest since 1885 was at Crows Nest Mine (The Scowles) where Richard Watkins had about 50 tons which even in those days sold for £20 per ton.

In 1902[99] The Golden Valley Ochre & Oxide Co of Wick, near Bristol possessed 'some 500 acres of rich mineral deposits' in Dean. The West of England Ochre and Oxide Co also were seeking deposits. Both companies lost much money in their explorations. In 1906, 2,662 tons of ochre were mined in the Forest.[100]

On 18 October 1909[101] the 'White Gates Ochre Gale' was granted to William Wilce at a Certain Rent of £10 plus 2s 6d per ton for the first 50 tons, then 9d per ton for the remainder. On 19 September 1910[102] the 'Mirey Stock Ochre Gale' was granted to E. Bennett and

John Harper; the Certain Rent was £5, and the royalty one-fifteenth of the selling value, with a minimum of 6d per ton.

A quantity of red oxide ('colour') was won from the New Buckshaft, New Cinderford and St Annal's Mines, mainly from the last named.[103] The best quality, from the Buckshaft Mine owned by the Crawshay family, was world renowned and commanded a high price—indeed to the 1940s in America and elsewhere 'Crawshay Red' was the yardstick by which other natural red oxides were measured.[104] The New Dun oxide was of a very superior quality but it took second place to 'Crawshay Red', and that from the Robin Hood took third. The shades were also different. A cross-cut driven westwards in the Shakemantle Mine intersected 'yellow ochre 7ft thick'.[105]

The Robin Hood Mine (Highmeadow) was formerly worked principally for red oxide which found a ready market as a colouring material, but in later years its output of 'colour' diminished to negligible quantities and mining was carried on for iron-ore alone. 1,600 tons of 'colour' was won from the mine up to the end of 1925.[106] In 1927 a 'colour' lead was being followed.[107] The 'colour' and ore have been won from the upper beds of the Crease Limestone and the lowest beds of the Whitehead Limestone. F. B. Watkins worked this mine from 1926 until in 1932 he closed it. No ochre was found. He abandoned it after several years exploratory work, during which he won substantial quantities of umber, in favour of the New Dun Mine where far larger churns existed. The Ministry of Supply worked the Robin Hood Mine from 1940 to 1944 but found no oxide or ochre, and only raised a comparatively small quantity of iron ore. About 19 tons of 'spurt' was sold to The British Colour and Mining Co at Milkwall.

A good deal of 'colour' was won in Old Ham Mine, where the winning of ore in 1927 was only incidental to the development of 'colour'. At that time exploration of 'colour' leads was in progress, and 'colour' was being won from one churn. (F. B. Watkins 'remembers that churn very well; it was fairly good quality red oxide and produced about 300 tons—and enabled Mr Doughty to float a company to promote The British Colour and Mining Co at Milkwall'). 'Colour' won from Old Ham Mine was graded and mixed with inferior umber from a surface deposit worked in the Oakwood Valley. The British Colour and Mining Co were also working a small outcropgale at nearby Lambsquay for 'colour', where a bed was located in the Crease Limestone in ground missed by old workings.

F. B. Watkins from 1928 to 1931 mined from New Dun Mine some thousands of tons of yellowish ore, impregnated by yellow ochre. In about 1912–14 his father, Fred Watkins mined one of the largest churns of 'colour' ever discovered in the Forest; it was dug out with spades and was of the consistency of soft soap, the churn yielding about 2,000 tons of excellent quality 'colour' and about 5,000 tons of 'spurt'. This mine was worked by the Ministry of Supply from 5 August 1942 until 10 May 1945.

Relevant statistics of ochre are scarce, and those that are available are unreliable—ochre, as previously stated, has been confused with oxide, 'colour', umber and 'spurt'.[108] However, some outputs for the Robin Hood (Highmeadow) Iron Mine are given below: [109]

	Colour		Spurt	
	tons	cwt	tons	cwt
1917	212	14		
1918	404	17		
1919	482	11		
1920	859	16		
1921	383	18		
1922	35	3	96	0
1923	34	16		
1924	19	0		
1925	Nil			
1926	61	13	62	3
1927	Nil		23	5
1942	18	13		

The royalty paid to the Crown under the lease to 1927 was one-tenth of the selling price. Under the lease in 1942 it was 1s per ton. To conclude the available information on the mining of ochre in Dean, the following note left by Charles Jenkins is of interest: [110]

For many years the Robin Hood Mine was famous for the production of red oxide ('colour'), eagerly sought by paint manufacturers and dyers throughout this country and abroad, including the USA. £22 10s per ton at the mine was obtained in about 1919. (I understand that it was sold to Fred Watkins who resold it to the Golden Valley Ochre and Oxide Co Ltd, Warmsley, Nr Bristol.) The deposits varied in thickness from approximately one to four feet, and occurred in 'valleys' between two 'ribs' or 'side walls' of country rock.

Where deposits of red oxide ('colour') are found, water is invariably found percolating through the surrounding strata, and the workings are always very damp, which accounts for the miners using a wide board upon which to lie while under-holing (cutting) the 'colour'.

Ochre is generally found in the upper portion of the Crease Limestone, near the 'lid' or top rock stone of the ore-bearing strata, its presence being indicated by 'leads' or 'streaks' occurring in the rock through which the roadways are driven. In some instances the 'leads' have to be followed for long distances before striking the main deposit or 'churn'. The best quality has a high staining power, and is largely used in the manufacture of paint and colour-washes. Very little has been won from the Robin Hood Mine, and it was not of good quality.

Red Oxide ('colour') is found chiefly in the lower parts of the Crease Limestone, near the 'Underedge' rock or foot wall of the ore measures, and is generally overlain by large deposits of iron ore. Its presence is indicated by 'leads' in the same manner as ochre.

I am inclined to the opinion that 'colour' was formerly very tough marl ('clod') which has become entirely changed by the action of water percolating through the beds or layers of iron ore, and carrying with it various chemical properties which saturated the marl deposits and completely changed them to red oxide ('colour').

In the Robin Hood Mine I have seen marl ('clod') so closely resembling 'colour' that it was difficult at sight to distinguish between the two.

At Robin Hood there was a mill 'for grinding for paint'; much 'red paint' was made, particularly for the Midland Railway.

Processing of ochres and oxides took place at various places in Dean. At Milkwall (Plate 30b) the Colour and Mining Co used premises which were later used for the storage of waste paper. At Lydney (in 'The Basin', south-east of the church), William Jones and others had a colour works from c1887 wherefrom 'red ochre powder, was despatched in barrels; the premises later housed consecutively, a sawmill, wagon works, and engineering works. At Coleford (in Albert Road) a small colour works was owned by William Henry Fryer of Lydbrook. In the 1880s, a works named Cullamore stood south of Ruspidge, processing 'ochre (red, yellow and blue)' from the Buckshaft Iron Mine; the premises were later used by the Crawshays as a foundry. Another small 'paint works' was in the neighbourhood of the Flour Mill Colliery, near Bream.

References to Chapter 5

1 An old Free Miners' slogan. Cf Kipling, R's 'Cold Iron' from *Songs of Youth*, 1910:
    Gold is for the Mistress, Silver for the Maid,
       Copper for the Craftsman, cunning at his trade;
    'Good', said the Baron, sitting in his Hall,
       'But iron—cold iron, shall be Master of them all'.
2 Sibly, T. F. 'Iron ores: The Haematites of the Forest of Dean and South Wales', *Mem Geol Surv of Mineral Resources*, X, 1919.
3 Ibid, 2nd edn revised by Lloyd, W, 1927.
4 Trotter, F. M. *Geology of the Forest of Dean Coal and Iron ore Field*, HMSO, 1942 (reprinted 1964), chapters IV and X.
5 Dreghorn, W., *Geology explained in the Forest of Dean and the Wye Valley*, 1968. See also Piggot, R. J., *Bulletin HMG* 2(1), 1968.
6 Hart. *The Free Miners*, 26–9; *Archaeology in Dean*, 29.
7 Ibid, *The Free Miners*, 12, 13.
8 Ibid, 158.
9 Ibid, 13, 14, 15.
10 Ibid, 12.
11 Ibid, *passim*; *Royal Forest, passim*.
12 Ibid, *The Free Miners*, 43–9, 65, 59, 74, 78, 79, 82, 83.
13 In c1625 (Hart. *The Free Miners*, 169).
14 Ibid, 166 et seq.
15 Ibid, 169.
16 SP Jas I, 29 March 1606.
17 Hart. *The Free Miners*, 172
18 Ibid, 129.
19 Ibid, 43, 44.
20 Ibid, 34.
21 Cf the terms 'billies' and 'billy-boy', used in Dean mines in regard to hod-carriers.
22 Hart. *The Free Miners*, Chapter V.
23 Ibid, 206, 207.
24 SP. Chas II, 1666–7, vol 172, 153/135.
25 19 and 20 Chas II, c 8.
26 Hart. *Royal Forest*, chapters VI, VII, VIII.
27 Evelyn, John. *Sylva*, edn 1776, 56. In 1662, Evelyn wrote: 'Even in our renowned Forest of Dean itself, some goodly oaks have been noted to grow upon ground which has been as it were a rock of ancient cinders, buried there many ages since' (Ibid, 97).
28 Hart. *The Free Miners*, 79, 80, 103, 114.
29 Powle, Henry. Royal Society *Philosophical Transactions* 12, 1683, 931–5.
30 Hart. *The Free Miners*, 85, 19, 80, 81, 97.
31 Yarranton, Andrew. op cit, Nicholls. *Iron Making* . . . , 48, 49.
32 Hart. *The Free Miners*, 90, 114, 116.
33 Ibid, 103.
34 Ibid, 111.
35 Ibid, 112.
36 GRO D33; F138/251; Nicholls. *Iron Making* . . . , 53.

37 *Cal Treasury Books*, IX, 1682.
38 *BGAS*, 2, 1877–8, 231.
39 Nicholls. *Iron Making . . .* , 62.
40 Ibid.
41 Ibid.
42 Ibid, 64.
43 GRO D421/L20, T45, E44, T104.
44 Ibid, E44.
45 Ibid, D1677, GG 1473.
46 Ibid, D421/E44.
47 Hart. *The Free Miners*, 234.
48 Mushet, David. *Papers on Iron and Steel*, 1840, 389.
49 GRO D421/L20, T45, E44.
50 Ibid, E44.
51 *The Torrington Diaries*, ed C. B. Andrews, I, 1924, 18, 19.
52 Waters, Ivor. *About Chepstow*, 1952, 17.
53 *Third Report*, 1788, 91.
54 Ibid, 85.
55 Paar, H. W., op cit.
56 As to 'Devil's Chapel' and Clearwell Meend, see Bellows, John. *A Week's Holiday in the Forest of Dean*, 1880, 54, 56.
57 To 1866 by Nicholls (*Iron Making . . .* , 61–64); to 1919 by Sibly op cit; to 1927 by Lloyd op cit; and to their closure, by Trotter, op cit, 63–77.
58 Hart. *The Free Miners*, 257.
59 Ibid, 313.
60 Ibid, 319.
61 *The Award of the Dean Forest Mining Commissioners*, 1841, 177–201.
62 In many instances the boundaries of a particular mining property are those of a single 'gale'. In other instances the relationship of the mining areas and the 'gales' are less simple.
63 Wood, James G. *Laws of the Dean Forest*, 1878. A supplement to Wood's book is: Hart, C. E. *Laws of Dean*, 1952.
64 Paar, H. W., op cit.
65 Insole and Bunning, op cit, 82, give yields from 1873 to 1880.
66 Nicholls. *Iron Making . . .* , 64.
67 Cyfarthfa Papers, loc cit: letter 3 March 1858 from W. Crawshay to R. F. Mushet.
68 Memo c1859 to H. G. Nicholls, *penes me*.
69 Glam Record Office, Cardiff.
70 Insole and Bunning, op cit, 84, 85.
71 Ibid.
72 *Foresters ½d Newspaper* 24 June 1882.
73 Bellows, John, op cit, 67.
74 Insole and Bunning, op cit, 82.
75 Sibly, op cit, 21.
76 *Kelly's Directory* 1889.
77 *Forest Newspapers* 15 Dec 1893.
78 Sibly, op cit, 21.
79 Lloyd, op cit, 23.
80 *The Quarry & Surveyors & Contractors' Journal* 30 July 1925, 192.
81 *Forest Newspapers* 27 June 1930.

82 Ibid, 9 Aug 1935 wherein F. B. Watkins relates much of the history of the New Dun and other mines.
83 Lloyd, op cit, 27; Doughty Prospectus, 1931.
84 Sibly, op cit, 21.
85 Lloyd, op cit, 16, 20, 29.
86 Nicholls. *Iron Making* . . . , 8, 9.
87 BM Harl MSS 6839 f 332: Rpt of Commissioners in 1662.
88 SP Jas I, 67, 107/141.
89 Ibid, Chas I, 1634–5, 277, 301/77.
90 Hart. *The Free Miners.*
91 Powle, Henry, op cit, 931–5.
92 Bodl Liby, Rawl MSS, B323, 98, 99.
93 9th Rpt of the Commissioners of Woods . . . , 1831–2.
94 *The Forester* (newspaper), 3rd Issue, 9 June 1831, 22.
95 Nicholls. *History* . . . , 228.
96 Mushet, David, op cit, 789.
97 Nicholls. *History* . . . , 247. See also F231, 852.
98 Insole and Bunning, op cit, 72.
99 *The Quarry*, VII, 1902, 153.
100 *Vict C Hist Glos* II, 233.
101 88th Rpt of the Commissioners of Woods . . . , 1910, 61.
102 Ibid, 89th Rpt, 1911, 60.
103 Sibly and Lloyd, op cit, 1927, 34.
104 In 1941 it was stated that 'the reopening of iron mines in the Forest of Dean may enable supplies of Crawshay Red Ochre to be obtained once more from this area'. (*Trans* Oil & Colour Chemists' Assoc, Nov 1941, 24/281). This hope was not fulfilled.
105 Trotter, F. M., op cit, 70.
106 Sibly and Lloyd, op cit, 1927, 37. Analyses are included of raw ochres taken from Robin Hood Mine.
107 Ibid, 37.
108 Pocock, R. W., 'Ochres, Umbers and Other Natural Earth Pigments of England and Wales', Wartime-Pamphlet 21, issued in 1942 by the Geological Survey of Great Britain (20 pp), 4.
109 Information from the Gavellers Office, Coleford, 18 Jan 1952.
110 MS, *penes me.*

Six
Coal-mining

Oh, we're the Jovial Foresters, our trade is getting coal,
  Whoever knew a Forester but was a hearty soul?
The Parson prays, the coal to raise . . .
  We're Foresters in different ways.[1]

INTRODUCTION The geological structure of the coalfield (Figs 10 and 19) has been described by Trotter[2] and others.[3] The coal measures rest in a synclinal basin of older rocks, and fall into three main groups—Supra-Pennant, Pennant and Trenchard.

The lowest or Trenchard group consists of coals, shales, sandstones, grits and conglomerates; the group comprises the beds from the base of the coal measures to the base of the Coleford High Delf Seam.

Above the Trenchard is the Pennant group of massive sandstones with subordinate shales and a few coals; it includes the strata from the floor of the Coleford High Delf Seam to the floor of the Brazilly Seam. Within it are the Coleford High Delf, Whittington and Yorkley Seams.

The uppermost or Supra-Pennant consists of shales, sandstones and coal seams; it includes the Brazilly, No Coal, Churchway High Delf, Rocky, Starkey, Lowery, Twenty Inch and Woorgreen Seams. A major feature of the coalfield is the outcrops of seams around the edge of the basin—where the early mining took place. Another feature is the faults, 'wants' and 'washouts'.

Coal worked during the Roman occupation was found in the early 1930s at the site of the Chesters Villa in Woolaston, but coal could not adequately smelt iron ore, with the techniques then available—therefore mining of coal was not extensive. In Norman times, sea-coal, as it was called to differentiate it from 'cole' (charcoal), was sought in greater amounts, chiefly for domestic heating, and possibly for roasting ore preparatory to smelting. By 1244[4] the miners were allowed to win coal on their own account, subject to dues in cash or kind made either to the King, or to the forester-of-fee of the bailiwick. In 1246–7[5] receipts accrued to the King for coal sold and transported. By 1282[6] the foresters-of-fee of Abenhall, Bicknor, Staunton, The Lea and Blakeney claimed the coal in their bailiwicks, the King exacting nothing. The Earl of Warwick claimed it in his estate at Lydney, whereas the King held it in the bailiwicks of Bearse, Great Dene, Little Dene and Ruardean. The same year we read of *secolepyttes* (sea-coal pits) in Staunton bailiwick. Thus by the thirteenth century the miners were a somewhat 'free' and specially privileged class of operatives, encouraged and patronised by the King and the foresters-of-fee, in return for revenue in cash or kind. Many difficulties were subsequently encountered by the Free Miners in retaining their privileges.[7]

Weathered outcrops of the coal made its winning easy. However the tonnage won in Dean throughout the thirteenth to sixteenth centuries was small, and during 1551–60 Dean's annual output was perhaps not more than 3,000 tons[8]—probably used for domestic heating and for the burning of lime. Many years were to elapse before coal would largely replace wood as domestic fuel, and at least two centuries before it would be used to a great extent in smelting ore.

THE SEVENTEENTH CENTURY   Mining of coal became more prominent in the seventeenth century. Though the free miners' 'Laws and Privileges' (explained in Chapter 5) originally related chiefly to iron ore, clause 29 emphasised that 'the Sea Cole Mine is as free in all points as the Oare Mine'. The outcropping seams meant that the workings needed only to descend to a moderate and reasonably safe depth—a small pit, level, slope or adit with timbered sides and roofs, driven a short distance. Water, bad ventilation, and the difficulties of getting coal to the surface, were the chief limiting factors.

By 1612 there was a great demand for ore, and the owners of local blast furnaces soon challenged the miners' exclusive privileges in regard to that mineral. The ironmasters were granted by the King permission to take what ore they required, which with other matters led to clashes with the miners.[9] By 1628 the potential for coal-mining in Dean had reached some importance—Lord Howard of Naworth sent a coal-borer to his son-in-law, Sir John Winter, of Lydney, who was then engaged in an appraisal of coal in the Forest.[10] In 1635 Edward Terringham tried to obtain a monopoly of Dean's coal-mining, asserting:[11]

The farming of the coal will not in any way be prejudicial to His Majesty either in the farming of the woods or ironworks there, or in any way tend to the waste and consuming of His Majesty's woods in that Forest, which may appear as followeth:

It cannot be any prejudice to His Majesty in the farming of his woods and works, for the coalmines afford neither fuel nor any other materials to the making of iron, neither has there been any use made of them at any time heretofore by any of the farmers of His Majesty's woods and works there, being only of use to them the mines of iron ore which I seek not.

It cannot be any prejudice to His Majesty in any other ways in the waste or consuming of his woods and timber for the building of the coalpits, for whereas the colliers (which have taken the liberty to dig and dispose of these mines at their pleasure without rendering to the King any profit for it) have used and spent His Majesty's timber for the building and repairing of their coalpits (out of which His Majesty receives no benefit), I will save His Majesty that expense and waste of timber for I will not desire the allowance of any, but find it at my own charge.

The Surveyor-General, consulted on the matter, reported: [12]

I find that the coalmines have yielded small or no benefit to His Majesty or the Crown at any time, yet there has been some use made of them within His Majesty's soil, and that for the most part by the miners of the Forest. It will be inconvenient that any of the coalmines should be opened or used within any coppice or enclosure to be made within the Forest, or that any of His Majesty's wood or timber should be wasted or imployed therein.

Terringham had to wait until 1637 before he was granted 'all the mines of coal and quarries of grindstone' in the Forest for thirty-one years at a rent of £30.[13] The miners opposed the grant, and Terringham was soon complaining to the Privy Council that some of his workmen had been 'outrageously beaten and drawn out thence for dead, and their works smothered and fired'. He and others opened coalmines at Coleford, Snead, Yorkley, Norchard and Aywood, and three in the Stanck near Newland.[14] A 'surfe' (apparently a corruption of 'sough', an adit for carrying off water) had been driven to one of the mines—an early reference to de-watering. Over a hundred families had no other livelihood than mining of coal and ore. Terringham stopped his operations after six months, and in 1640 relinquished his lease to Sir John Winter. The miners continued to work their pits— three are mentioned in 1656: Crabtree, Hopewell, and Oake in Aywood, though the last was 'coaled and worked out . . . and their deep pit was sunk as deep as it could possibly be worked for water'.[15] Through their obstinacy and tenacity, and by litigation, the miners survived all the vicissitudes of leases, even of the Civil War, and by the Restoration were still asserting and exercising their rights.

Meanwhile coal in Dean was being subjected to experiments, chiefly to improve its suitability for domestic purposes, and also for smelting ore and forging iron. On 13 March 1628 the Crown granted to William Astell and others a licence for 14 years to smelt iron ore by 'pit-coal' on payment of £400 a year;[16] it is unknown whether their activities extended to Dean. During the Commonwealth, Captain Buck of Hampton Road (or Loade, in Shropshire) was granted a patent for 'the making of iron with coal', and in partnership with Cromwell, Major Wildman and 'many Doctors of Physick, and Merchants', he set up in Dean 'diverse and sundry works and furnaces at a vast charge'. Dud Dudley has recorded his connection with the experiments:[17]

> After they had spent much in their invention and experiments, which was done in spacious Wind-Furnaces, and also in Potts of Glass-House Clay; and failing, afterwards got unto them an ingenious Glass-Maker, Master Edward Dagney—an Italian then living in Bristow, who after he had made many Potts, for that purpose went with them into the Forest of Dean, and built for the said Captain Buck and his partners, a new furnace, and made therein many and sundry experiments and trials for the making of iron with Pit-Cole and Sea-Cole, etc. But he failing, and his Potts being all broken, he did return to Bristow frustrate of his expectation; but further promising to come again, and make more experiments; at which time Master John Williams, Master Dagney, Master of the Glass-House, was then drawn in to be a partner for £300 deposited, and most of it spent, the said Williams and Dagney, hearing that the Author had knowledge in the making Iron with Pit-Cole, Sea-Cole, etc, they from Captain Buck and the other partners importuned the Author, who was at that time in great danger by Parliament (being a Colonel of the King's Party) to go along with them into the Forest of Dean, which at that time durst not deny.
>
> Coming thither, I observed their manner of working, and found it impossible that the said Edward Dagney by his invention should make any iron with Pit-Cole or Sea-Cole, in Potts to profit: I continued with them till all their Potts and inventions failed . . . They desired me to come again a second time into the Forest to see it effected; but at that time, I saw their failings also.

A later report of the experiments says:[18]

> The partners erected large air furnaces, into which they introduced large clay pots, resembling those used at glass-houses, filled with

various proportions of the necessary mixture of ores and charcoal. The furnaces were heated by the flame of pit-coal, and it was expected that, by tapping the pots below, the separated materials would flow out. This rude process was found entirely impracticable; the heat was inadequate to perfect separation, the pots cracked, and in a short time the process was abandoned altogether.

Other experiments were conducted by Sir John Winter, of whom John Evelyn recorded in his Diary 11 July 1656:

> Came home by Greenwich Ferry, where I saw Sir John Winter's new project of charring sea-coal, to burne out the sulphure and render it sweete. He did it by burning coales in such earthen pots as the glassemen mealt their metal, so firing them without consuming them, using a barr of yron in each crucible or pot, which barr has a hook at one end, that so the coales being mealted in a furnace with other crude seacoles under them, may be drawn out of the potts sticking to the yron, whence they are beaten off in greate halfe-exhausted cinders, which being rekindled make a clear pleasant chamber fire, deprived of their sulphur and arsenic malignity. What success it may have, time will discover.

On 25 July 1661 Winter was granted a patent 'for the sole exercise of his invention of charring and calcining coal in pots, so as to make an excellent fuel without smoke'.[19] This and the other similar inventions may have increased the use of coal for domestic use, but success was not achieved in the adequate smelting of ore:[20]

> Several attempts have been made to bring in the use of Sea-Coal in these [Dean] Works, instead of Charcoal; but hitherto they have proved ineffectual, the workmen finding by experience that a sea-coal fire, how vehement soever, will not penetrate the most fixed parts of the ore, and so leaveth much of the metal unmelted.

Nevertheless, by 1677–8,[21] coal was extensively used in Dean for calcining, or ore-roasting, in the fineries, and for domestic heating and the burning of lime.

In February 1661 certain miners were accused that they had 'dug coal and sunk pits near unto His Majesty's surffe and coal works', apparently those re-possessed by Terringham and managed for him by John Witt,[22] whereupon a Commission reported the following April:[23]

> We viewed the several coal works and the surffe, and although the ordinary pits are liable to water and the miners could only dig in the summer, yet the surfe hath made such a passage for the water as they

dig the whole year and get a vast quantity of good coal, their presence being as inconsiderable as the former received the same judgement, and if any imposition were laid on this by degrees would raise a good yearly revenue. But it must be raised proportionable to the vent [sale] and not great at first, and by the best informations we could receive we compute that being well and directly managed might yield £500 per annum.

In 1675[24] a miner asserted that the value of coal obtained during the previous seven years was about £50 per annum 'above all charges'; he and the other miners 'had been at a very great charge, sometimes £2, sometimes £10 or £20, to drive or dig the pit or mine from the surface until they came to coal or iron ore'. The many coalmines in the Forest, if enjoyed without interruption, were worth £500 per annum 'besides all charges of managing the same'.

The Dean Forest (Reafforestation) Act, 1667,[25] saved 'unto the miners and persons using the trade of digging for iron ore, coal and ochre their lawful rights and privileges in all lands and grounds of the Forest, other than the inclosures for the time being they shall continue inclosed, as fully and absolutely as if this Act had not been had or made'. Yet the same Act, by section seventeen, gave power to the Crown to lease the coalmines, ostensibly to the Terringham family, a matter which led to inconclusive litigation with the Free Miners.[26]

By this time, improved methods of working had been developed. As early as 1637, a surfe had been driven to de-water a coalmine—a development which, as noted earlier, made possible mining throughout the year, instead of only in summer. The Mine Law Court in 1674[27] ordered that 'because the miners are at a very great charge to make surfes for the drainage of their coalpits, which when they have finished, others sink pits so near that they are deprived of the benefit, no miner shall come within 100 yards of another surfe to the prejudice of the undertakers without their consent'. An Order of 1682[28] went further: 'Whensoever any colliers have fully wrought out a coal pit through which goutwater must necessarily run for draining of the work, the colliers shall secure the pit by setting up strong and sufficient posts and rails round the pit.' The works were becoming larger and more dangerous: an Order of 1687[29] insisted that 'all coalpits and danger-ous minepits which are not working or which hereafter may not be wrought in for one whole month together, shall be sufficiently secured by a wall of stone, or by railing the same with posts and rails placed about 2ft distant from the mouth of such pit by the proprietors thereof; and likewise all pits left open for a goutway'. Protection to each working was extended to 300yd in 1693.[30] Donkeys, mules and horses had for long been used to transport minerals, and in 1687[31] there is a reference to horses used in levels for underground haulage. Coal was wound up by bucket or basket, rope, and hand-operated windlass. Later horse gins or whimseys were used.

Prices of coal were subject to fluctuation, usually at the decision of the Mine Law Court. In 1637[32] best grade coal sold at 4s a dozen of 12 barrels (3 Winchester bushels to a barrel), ie about 3s 10d a ton of 21cwt; the poorer grades fetched 1s 1d a dozen. Later, 'riddlers' were used for grading into fire-coal (the largest blocks), smith-coal for forging, and lime-coal for use in kilns for 'manuring land'. In 1656[33] coal was sold for shipping from the 'Slads at Wyeside' at 2s 8d a dozen 'in the mine and about the mine', ie at pit-head. In 1668[34] lime-coal to the 'Slad called Lyme Slad, in Maylescott' was priced at a minimum of 3s a dozen; lime-coal to the top of the Little Doward, west of the Wye, at 5s 6d a dozen and to other lime-kilns there at 5s 4d; the Blackstones 6s; the weir west of the Wye 4s; the weir east of the Wye 3s 6d; Coldwall 3s 6d; Monmouth 5s 6d; Redbrook 4s 4d; and Boxbush, near Lydbrook 3s. For transport, no more than four horses or mare foals were to be used by each miner. Six years later,[35] no fire-coal was to be sold under 4d a barrel. Minimum prices at the pit in 1676[36] were 6d a seam or barrel for fire-coal, and 1s 6d a dozen for lime-coal. Four years thereafter,[37] new minimum prices were fixed, delivered to the Wye between Monmouth Bridge and Huntsham Ferry: 8s a dozen for fire-coal and smith-coal, 4s 6d for lime-coal; and 3s 6d a dozen for all coal when delivered to the Wye between Huntsham and Wilton Bridge near Ross-on-Wye. For reasons best known to the miners, in 1687[38] all prices were cancelled, and the market made 'free'. Seven years later,[39] deliveries to the two Redbrook Copper Works were fixed at 8s a dozen for fire-coal and 'charking', and 6s for smith-coal. The ouput of coal for the years 1681–90 has been estimated at 25,000 tons per annum.[40]

THE EIGHTEENTH CENTURY Many new pits and levels were opened, necessitating revised regulations, particularly because of frequent hindrance, or even destruction of adjacent coal-works. The protection given by the Mine Law Court to each level (its effect was almost the extension of the gale) was increased in 1728[41] to 500 yards for those in the east of Dean. In 1754[42] the same court ruled that no 'water pit' should be sunk within 1,000yd of a level. Possession of a gale had become increasingly valuable, but the miners had already broken with custom by making many local influential people 'honorary free miners', and by subletting many gales with their mines to so-called 'foreigners'.

Prices of coal were rising: those fixed in 1701,[43] for a ton of 21cwt, collected, were a minimum of 5s to inhabitants of the Hundred of St Briavels, and a minimum of 6s to other people. In 1719[44] minimum prices delivered to Monmouth were: 9s a dozen barrels (36 bushels) for fire-coal, 8s for smith-coal and 5s 6d for lime-coal; and when delivered to the Wye between Lydbrook and Bishopswood, prices were 8s 6d, and 3s respectively.

There were many 'pitching' and loading places on the Wye,[45] from whence small barges plied down to Monmouth, Redbrook and Chepstow, or up river into Herefordshire. In 1741[46] new minimum prices at pit appear: 6d for 2¼cwt of coals (being 'a horse seam'), ten such seams to be taken as a ton; 4d a cwt for fire-coal; 5d for three bushels or a barrel of smith-coal; 1d a bushel for lime-coal; 13s a ton for fire-coal delivered to Hereford; 7s 6d a ton of 21cwt for fire-coal delivered to the pills on the Severn at Gatcombe, Purton and Lydney; and 7s a dozen for fire-coal and 'stone coal charks', and 5s 6d for smith coal, all delivered to the two Redbrook Copper Works.

On the Lydney Park Estate, particularly at the Tufts south of Whitecroft, the Bathursts were mining coal, unconnected with the Free Miners. A memorandum c1758–60[47] provides interesting information as to their costs and selling prices:

	s	d
12 seams or sacks of coal is reckoned one dozen.		
The colliers price for getting it by the dozen is	3	6
8 seams is generally reckoned one ton.		
By weight twenty hundred is one ton.		
Price of getting coal by the ton is	2	4
14 seams is reckoned one waggon load.		
Price for getting one waggon load is	4	3
Price for getting one load of lime coal is		6
Price for getting one dozen of smith coal is	3	6

Price for selling at the pit

	s	d
One waine load	6	0
Fire coal by the load	7	0
Smith coal by the dozen	3	0
Lime coal by the load	3	6
Fire coal by the sack or seam		7
Lime coal by the dozen	2	0

41 (left) E. A. Roberts, last of the charcoal-burners in Dean; (below) haulage of cord wood c1925: on the left an ex-WD 'Albion', 3-ton, solid tyred and chain driven. On the right a 'Sentinel' tipper

42 *(above)* Ash tent pegs being made at the works of Forest Products Ltd, Huntley, 1939; (below) turnery poles at H. V. Barnes' Turnery Mill, May Hill

Price for delivering

	s	d
Fire coal delivered at Lydney Pill, each ton	8	6
Fire coal each sack or seam	3	0
Smith coal each sack or seam		7
One load of fire coal and 4 seams of smith coal makes one load of charks.		
Price of one load of charks at the pit is	30	0
6 seams of fire coal makes 4 horse loads of charks.		
For getting it by the ton, viz 20 hundred weight:	2	4
One waine load is 12 seams, for getting which is	3	6

Coal works opened in Dean during the first half of the eighteenth century included: [48]

1706: Stay and Drink, under Serridge; Dark Pit, in Coverham.
1718: Hopewell, at Parkend; Speedwell, near Tresser Mill in Ruardean Hill.
1720: Sally Pit, Coleford.
1721: Broad Moore Grout; The Holly Pit.
1722: New Charity; The Nine Wells; Stand Fast; The Dry Tump.
1723: Go-on-and-Prosper; Monmouth Hill Work.
1724: The Old Colliery, near Coleford.
1725: Shute Castle Pit; The Oiling Quab, in Bromley.
1726: The Staple Pit; Short Standing.
1735: Gentlemen Colliers, or Harbourne Oake.
1736: The Little Suff,* in Serridge.
1737: Major Wade's Suff, near Aywood; The Bromley Knowle; Pluck Penny, in Nailbridge; Dowler's Chambers.
1739: Bushes Pit, in Berry Hill; The Society.
1740: Churchway, or Turnbrook.
1741: Cartway Pit; Harrow Hill Pit; Wyrrall Hill.
1743: Mendhall, in Yorkley; True Blue, in Ruardean; Littleworth; The Windmill, near Ruardean.
1744: Rain Proof.
1745: Church Hill, in Parkend.
1747: The Golden Pippin; Little Scare Pill.
1749: Long-looked-for, near Yorkley.

> * A corruption of 'sough'—a water outlet, for drainage.

Much skill and local experience had by now been applied to Dean's mining: appreciation of simple geological principles replaced more haphazard search. Success or failure, much depended on the diligence of the miner and on his technical skill and knowledge in meeting the

T

difficulties and the risks always attendant on mining. Despite regulations imposed by the Free Miners upon themselves, there were many
disputes. In 1748[49] the 'verns' (partners) of one 'company' complained
against those of another that they had 'sustained great damage at a
lime-coal work called Churchway, otherwise Turnbrook, because they
hindered the level and deep wall which they would not bring forward
to our new pit that was then just down; and likewise they hindered the
level in their new deep pit, and wilfully more they cut up to their land-
gutter, and took in the water by a single sticken-gutter in their backer
deep pit, and turned it across the bottom of our deep pit into our
air-gutter, which we prepared for ourselves and then, whereby our
lamping the charks was swelled down, and have destroyed the air,
and filled our gateway with water and sludge.' Five years later (1753)[50]
verns of a colliery named 'Gentlemen Colliers' complained of other
verns 'for forbidding us out of the colliery, that we should not get any
coal of the deep side of our former work, which coal our level drains,
and ours being the most ancient level; we have attended the place,
and burned our light, according to our laws and customs'.

Sometimes amicable agreement was achieved in regard to drainage—
as in 1754[51] between the verns of the 'Upper Rockey Coal Work' and
those of the 'Inging [Engine] Coal Work near Nailbridge'. The last
coalwork is probably 'The Water Wheel Ingine at the Orling Green
near Broadmoor' which the same year was accepted by the Mine Law
Court as 'a level to all intents and purposes, and liable to the same
laws as other levels brought up from the Grass Moor',[52] ie to ensure
to the works the 1,000 yards protection noted earlier. Its engine, driven
by water-wheel, to work the pumps, was claimed to be the first of its
kind in Dean;[53] it was replaced by a steam-engine c1777.[54] Among coalworks opened since 1750 were:[55]

1753: Prosper.
1755: The Bold Defiance; The Ginn.
1757: Now Found Out; Standfast.
1758: Pigg Pitt.
1772: Browns Green Colliery, near Lydbrook.
1773: Moorwood Coal Works.
1774: Arthurs Folly: 'begun in the Thirty Acre and brought up into
      Little Cross Hill'.

A survey made by A. & W. Driver in 1787[56] for the Commissioners
of Woods, listed the following coal works in existence:

Speech House Walk
Woorgreen Pits (3) (Thos Blunt, deputy surveyor, Thos Harvey, Christopher James & Co)
Twenty Inch Pits
Crowdelf Pit
Prosper Pit

Worcester Walk
Found Out Pits (2) (Thomas Bennett & Co)
Brown's Green Water Engine (Thos. Herbert)
Worrall Hill Pit (John Cook)
Farthing Well Pit (Wm Roberts & Co)
Moorwood Pit (Wm Evans & Co)
Mendall Work (Richard Blanch & Co)
Broomy Knoll (Richard Sladen & Co)
Bushes Pit (Richard Amperry & Co)
Young Men's Folly (Wm Evans & Co)
Prosper Work (John Delany & Co)
Nine Wells (Thos Worgan & Co)
Society Pit (John Wintle & Co)
Wimberry Pit (Dukes & Co).

Blakeney Walk
Slope Pit (Thos Cooper Jnr)
Venture Coal (Wm Williams)
Venture Coal (Evan Reynolds)
Rocky Pit (2) (Wm Knight & Co)
High Delph (3) (Keir & Co)
Meere Brook (2) (Thos Bracker & Co)

Parkend Walk: Coal mines belonging to:

Rich Heath (2)	Wm. Beach
Wm Robins	Thomas Beach
Peter James	Rich Beach
Rich Sloden	John Priest (2)
Isaac Kear (5)	Wm Davis
Wm Williams (2)	Jas Elsmore (2)
Wm Elway (2)	Geo Doward
Rich Hewlett	Rich Powell (2)
Edwd Elway	Thos Watkins
Edward James	Jas James
John James	Stephen Blanch
Jas Keer	Edwd Mouseall
Wm Cook	Lord Sherborne & Co
Rich James (2)	Benj Keer & Co
John Priest & Co (2)	

Ruardean Walk
Prosper-on-Time Pit (Jos Blanch)
Crow Delf (Jos Blanch)
Little Rocky (Jos Robins & Co)
Rock Roof (Wm Bennett & Co)
Twenty Inch (Emanuel Knight & Co)
Little Saff (Stephen Yearsley & Co)
Young Colliers (Rich Bennett & Co)
Old Vallett (2) (Thos Nicholls & Co)
Churchway (Thomas Territt & Co)
Homeford (John Bennett & Co)
Windmill (John Rudge)
Cross Knave (2) (Rich Marfell & Co)
Pluckpenny (Jos Blanch)
Cow Pits (2) (Robert Turner & Co)
Hopewell (Wm Buffin)
Little Suff (Stephen Yearsley & Co)

Littledean Walk: Coal mines belonging to:
Wm Moore
Chas Walden and Joseph Mountjoy (2)
Thos Hales and Wm Cooper
Thos Walden
Isaac Tingle & Co (7)

The gaveller in 1788 reported that in August of the previous year[57] within the Forest there were 121 coal-pits (31 idle), which pits produced 1,816 tons of coal a week. There were 662 Free Miners 'concerned and employed therein'; and the annual compositions or dues paid by them amounted to c£215 8s. The same year, the assistant to the deputy surveyor deposed:[58]

> The parts of the Forest in which the principal collieries are situate, are these: The Level of the Fire Engine Colliery, which is one of the principal works, is in the Bottom between Nailbridge and Cinderford Bridge, and there are pits all along the Bottom. There are several levels in the Bottom from Beechenhurst Hill along the Delves up to Nailbridge. Another large field of coal from Whitecroft Bridge (at the back of Whitemead Park) along the Delves to Great Moseley Green, and from thence through Old Valley Tuft and Aures Glow, almost up to Little Stapleage. These are the works which do the greatest harm to the Forest. There are some others on the Coleford side, from which a great deal of coal is raised. Very little timber is growing in any of these Delves; and inclosures might be made in the Forest, so as to exclude all the principal coal works.

Dean's coalworks at this time supplied 'the lower parts of Gloucestershire beyond Severn and some parts across the Severn about Berkeley, the greatest part of Herefordshire, the town of Monmouth, and part of the county of Monmouth'.[59] House coal was sold at 4s or 4s 6d a ton, smith coal at about 2s 6d, and lime coal for 'manure' at about 1s 6d, all at the pit. Coal delivered to Newnham-on-Severn to be shipped, sold at about 14s or 15s a ton.[60] Most of the coalmines were booming: a traveller in 1781 remarked:[61] 'The Forest of Dean is full of coal. The streams here run brown from the neighbouring coalpits, whence the happy inhabitants are supplied at one penny the bushel.'

Much coal continued to be delivered to various wharves on the Wye, particularly at Lydbrook, where it was loaded into small barges and carried either up the river to Herefordshire, or down to Monmouth, Redbrook and Chepstow. An observer wrote in 1770:[62]

At Lydbrook is a large wharf where coals are shipped for Hereford and other places. A road runs diagonally along the bank, and horses and carts appear passing to the small vessels which lie against the wharf to receive their burdens. The engines used in lading and unlading, together with the variety of the scene, produce altogether a picturesque assemblage.

Another author, commenting on excursions down the Wye, wrote 27 years later:[63]

We next approach Lydbrook colliery and a very large and extensive wharf, from whence commerce in coals is carried on to Ross, Hereford and other places. This productive mine is the property of Lord Gage. With all the dark and dingy attributes of this place, involved as it is in smoke and begirt with coal barges, it yet affords a very pleasant and interesting landscape. The high road that ascends the woody hill, screening the back-ground of this wharf, is perpetually enlivened by horses and carriages in this sooty sable commerce, while on the bank of the river beneath, the lading and unlading the vessels afford additional business and variety to the scene.

Throughout the first 75 years of the eighteenth century, levels were the principal means of winning coal, especially when a seam could be reached by driving a slightly ascending level—because this assisted in reducing the cost of removal of both soil and coal (no winding apparatus being necessary), and provided natural drainage. Nicholls records:[64]

The usages observed at the works entitled the proprietors of their respective levels to so much of the corresponding seam of coal as they could drain, extending right and left to the limits awarded by the gaveller. So far this mode of procedure was satisfactory enough, and would no doubt have long continued to go on amicably, had not the principle, highly judicious in itself, that no workings were ever to intersect one another, but always to stop when the mattocks met, been abused by driving 'narrow headings' up into different workings, whereby the rightful owner of the coal was stopped, and the other party enabled to come in and take it from him. Timber of considerable strength was required throughout the underground excavations to support the roof, hence proving a serious source of spoilation to the woods. Large slabs of it were also needed for the flooring, in order that the small coal-trams might be the more readily pushed forward over it, a space being left beneath for air to circulate, and for the water to run out.

If the vein of coal proposed to be worked did not admit of being reached by a level, then a pit was sunk to it, although rarely to a greater depth than 25 yards, the water being raised in buckets, or by a water-wheel engine, or else by a drain having its outlet in some distant but lower spot, such as is found to have led from the Broad Moor Collieries to Cinderford, a mile and upwards in length. The shaft of the pit was made of a square form, in order that its otherwise insecure sides might be the better supported by suitable woodwork, which being constructed in successive stages was occasionally used as a ladder, the chief difficulty being found in keeping the working free from water, which in wet seasons not unfrequently gained the mastery and drowned the men out. The skips appear to have been always rectangular in shape, similar to the shafts.

The Forest's collieries in 1779 'were not deep—because when the miners find themselves much incommoded with water, they sink a new one, rather than erect a fire engine [ie steam engine], which might answer the expense very well, yet there is not one of them; they have indeed two or three pumps worked by cranks, that in some measure answer the intention'.[65] Raising (winding) was a problem: the small enterprise of New Speedwell Colliery was worked by a 'horse-whim'; in other works, horses operated 'gins' as winding-gear. Oak was released to the miners 'for sinking the pits, and making what they called the gateway or gangway from the body of coal to the pit, and also for gutters in the levels for draining off the water'.[66]

From the mid-seventeenth century, coal had been used for roasting ore, and in finery forges, but attempts to use it for smelting at Redbrook in 1716–17 had not been repeated, and at Lydney in about 1773 had been unsuccessful. In 1761, Creed, steward to Lord Gage at Redbrook, observed to his master 'the new method of making iron in England with coal, a scheme that succeeds beyond expectation, and great numbers of furnaces are erected within these few years that blow with no other sort of coals, and the iron they make is little inferior to that which is by wood'.[67] However, not for two decades did the substitution of coal for charcoal in iron-smelting lead to new furnaces in Dean—at Cinderford in 1795, and Parkend in 1799. These and other subsequent furnaces gave an impetus to coal-mining.

The demand for coke, complemented by coal for steam-raising and domestic uses, made urgent the need for improved transport facilities. Transport in Dean had always been difficult and expensive, and roads used as mineral outlets to the rivers Severn and Wye were particularly poor. The Office of Woods deprecated expenditure on roads as encouraging the use of wheeled waggons with their large teams of horses, for transporting coal and ore, thus leading to the taking by the miners under custom of more timber. Such conditions kept the price of coal at a high level in markets outside Dean, with repercussions on the pits themselves—*vide* the small output in 1787, previously noted, of less than 2,000 tons a week.

THE NINETEENTH CENTURY 'Foreigners' holding gales through local Free Miners, had for many years been financially interested in the winning of the Forest's coal, and were anxious to expand, while the coke blast furnaces already noted were requiring large quantities of ore, coal and limestone. From 1799, pressure was brought by local and neighbouring industrialists for a tramroad network. Benjamin Outram reported in 1801 that his recommendations for tramroads throughout Dean to the rivers Severn and Wye were based chiefly on the potential of the coalmines:

A tolerably accurate estimate of the local coal trade may be readily formed by gentlemen acquainted with the country. But the extent of the coal trade to distant markets, must depend greatly on the price at which coals shall be sold at the pits on to the Forest: the lower they are rendered, the greater will be the extent of the sale, as they will be carried the farther in all directions, before the other coal can meet in competition with them; and, if they can be afforded cheap, this trade will be immense.

There followed in the period 1809–15 the establishment of three tramroads—noted in Chapter 5. These were laid upon the potential of

Dean's coal, ore and stone, and the need for effective transport. Much of the Forest was thereby connected with the Severn (at Lydney and Bullo) and with the Wye (at Redbrook, Lydbrook, Bishopswood and Monmouth).

The upsurge in industry led to widespread integration of coal, iron and transport interests.[68] Capitalists appeared as potential large-scale employers of labour and users of machinery. Subscribers to the Lydney and Lydbrook Railway Act 10 June 1809 included the Protheroes (John, Edward and Philip), David Mushet, and Samuel Hewlett. Two examples of the integration, those in connection with the enterprises of the Protheroe and Crawshay family, have been given in Chapter 5.

The Free Miners and those holding concessions through them, sunk deeper pits and drove more extensive levels, many of them requiring an ever increasing number of licences from the Office of Woods for land on which to erect steam-engines to pump and to wind.[69] Examples are:

1814: Thomas Phillips and Benjamin Morland	To erect a winding engine at Hopewell
1816: Bullo Pill Co	To make use of two fire or steam engines at Lower Bilson.
1818: John Trotter	To erect two small fire or steam engines at Vallets Level.
1820: Thomas Phillips	To erect a fire or steam engine at the Union.
1825: James Bennett and Thomas Meek	To erect a fire or steam engine at the Nelson.
1827: Edward Protheroe	To erect a pumping engine and a winding engine at Ivymoor Head; likewise at Parkend Main; a winding engine at Parkend Royal; and a pumping engine and a winding engine at Birches Well.
1829: Edward Protheroe	To erect a winding engine at Bilson Winning Pits, and to remove a winding and pumping engine from Protection and erect same at Crump Meadow.

1830: Meek, York and Dawe   To erect a pumping engine at Nailbridge.

1831: Edward Protheroe   To erect a pumping and a winding engine at New Fancy.

The increased activity led in 1825 to agitation for more 'protection' for the bounds of pits.[70] So great was the influx of financially large and small individuals claiming through the miners, and so many were the disputes in connection with limits and watering troubles, that in 1831 a Commission was appointed to investigate these and other relevant matters. The 'foreign capitalists' had great interests: for example, Edward Protheroe told the Commission: [71]

> The depth of my principal pits at Parkend and Bilson varies from about 150 to 200 yards; that of my new gales for which I have engine-licences, is estimated at from 250 to 300 yards. I have 12 steam-engines, varying from 12 to 140hp, nine or ten of which are at work, the whole amounting to 500hp; and I have licences for four more engines, two of which must be of very great power. My works have an additional importance as being connected with extensive iron-works dependent on them for coal. These iron furnaces and forges have recently been erected at the cost of about £100,000 and the whole property is held under the rights and titles of foreigners. I may add, too, that upon both iron and coal works so held, very large sums belonging to ladies, minors and others have been advanced and secured by mortgage, and the whole value of the railways, in which £200,000 have been invested, would be sunk and lost by the destruction of the trade depending on our capital.

Other evidence given to the Commission dealt with methods of working, and the need for new regulations. Their Fourth Report, of 1835,[72] resulted in the Dean Forest Mines Act, 1838,[73] by which the rights of the Free Miners were at last defined, and Mining Commissioners appointed[74] who, in 1841, made the Award of Coal Mines[75] whereby 104 gales were described and confirmed to claimants, and rules and regulations made for their working. Sets of plans of the coalfield were issued. The assignees of the coal gales, their rights assured, and regulations made to obviate much of the earlier chaos, began to develop their works, and with like Awards of ironmines and quarries, a profound change emerged in the organisation and scale of the Forest's industries, making even more urgent the need for improved transport.

In 1841[76] there were 69 individual or composite coalworks, detailed below: The capital letters in brackets indicate the seams worked viz:

HD (High Delph), LD (Low Delph)
NH (Nagshead), C (Churchway)
S (Starky), L (Lowry), R (Rocky)
PD (Parkend Delph)
B (Brazilly), H (Hill Delph)

		Depth (yd)	How raised	Tons raised annually
1.	Mile End Pit, Coleford (Trotter Thomas & Co)	67 (HD)	'High Pressure Engine 16in Cylinder'	6,000
2.	Near-the-last (Teague, Parry & Lewis)	60–70 (HD)	'One horse whim'	2,700
3.	Middle Pit (Peter Teague)	80 (HD)	'One horse whim'	4,800
4.	Upper Engine (Trotter Thomas & Co)	67 (HD)	'Engine winches steam cylinder'	4,500
5.	Prospect Pit (Peter Teague)	40–50 (HD)	'One horse whim'	3,300
6.	Darby Pit (Trotter Thomas & Co)	40–50 (HD)	'One horse whim'	3,300
7.	Bixhead Slade and Pit in Miles Level (late William Davies now Morrels)	25 (HD)	'Small high pressure steam engine on pit'	8,400
8.	Lower Bixhead Slade (David Mushet)	(HD)	'A level'	9,600
9.	Upper Bixhead Level (David Mushet)	(HD)	'A level'	21,000
10.	Whimberry Slade, Hopewell (Peter Teague)	(HD)	'A level'	7,500

C/f 71,100

		Depth (yd)	How raised	Tons raised annually
			B/f	71,100
11.	Speedwell Pit (Whitehouse): Their engine pit standing but worked out	30 (HD)	'One horse whim'	4,800
12.	Five Acres (Cross Knave Pit) (Elly and Nelmes)	30 (HD)	'One horse whim'	2,400
13.	Thatched Pit (John Lewis)	66 (HD)	'One horse whim'	2,400
14.	Newfoundland Pit (Johns Lewis— also owns Foundout, standing but intended to be worked again: Eastwards of no 14 are Thomas Bennett's two pits, Worrall Hill — stopped by the Commissioners)	66 (HD)	'One horse whim'	3,600
15.	Brickhill Bottom— The Folly Pit (Thomas Morgan)	(LD)	'Windlass pit'	1,200
16.	'A Level' (John Constant)	(HD)	'A level'	1,500
17.	Hopewell (late Thomas Miles, now Morrels)	46 (HD)	'Steam engine'	14,100
18.	Success Level (Trotter Thomas & Co)	(HD)	'A level'	7,200
				———
			C/f	108,300

		Depth (yd)	How raised	annually Tons raised
			B/f	108,300
19.	Fetteral Pit Level (Blanch & James)	(HD)	'A level'	13,125
20.	Winnels Level & Pit (Trotter Thomas & Co)	(HD)	'A level'	6,300
21.	Howlers Slade (Trotter Thomas & Co)	(HD)	'A level'	15,000
22.	Wirral Hill (William Lewis)	(HD)	'Deep level'	2,100
23.	Bream Chapel Quarry Pit—Nagg's Head	40 (NH)	'Windlass pit'	1,800
24.	Parkend Pits (Edward Protheroe & Co) One Pit	100/160	'Atmospheric engine pumping 11in box; 14 strokes to minute. One pit pumping and winding, 36in double Power condensing	
	Two Pits	180	21in double power drawing. The machinery is amply capable to land a much greater quantity'	90,000
25.	Birches old pumping engine draws the water from the Mosely Green South Independence Pit (no 26 below)		'An old atmospheric engine (no coal raised)'	Nil
26.	South Independence 1	100	'Engine and horse double power'	4,800
	South Independence 2	105	'Engine and horse and double power condensing'	8,400
			C/f	249,825

		Depth (yd)	How raised	Tons raised annually
			B/f	249,825
27.	James's Folly, Moseley Green (John Moss & Co) Two Pits and Engine Ditch Pit (same owners)	32	'Both windlass pits'	1,800
28.	Whitecroft Weavers Level (John James)	(H)	'A level'	1,200
29.	Lightmoor (Crawshay & Sons)	220 (will go 240)	'Pumping engine 18in cylinder on high pressure. Winding 15in high pressure. Both double power'	Nil
30.	Strip and at it (John Harris)	127(C) (R)	'Pumping 15in high pressure, and winds up Old pumping engine 10in double; 5in box; 27yd lift'	10,500
31.	Churchway Pit (James Bennett)	112 (C)	'20in cylinder atmospheric, and a 36in double condensing winding'	6,600
32.	Two Pits (James Bennett)	80 (S)	'Small steam engine'	4,800
33.	Protection (James Bennett)	(L) 75 (R)	'16in high pressure engine'	6,300
34.	Young Collier's Pit near no 33 (Nathaniel Smart)	50 (S)	'One horse whim'	750
35.	Pit near no 34 (Philip Jordan)	(S)	'One horse whim'	(Standing will work again)
36.	Collingwood (Reed, Doubley and Hall)	66 (S)	'One horse whim'	900
37.	Nelson (James Bennett) (Sinking)	50	'Sinking by a high pressure engine 15in cylinder'	Nil
			C/f	282,675

	Depth (yd)	How raised	Tons raised annually
		B/f	282,675
38. Gain all, Crump-meadow (Edward Protheroe & Co)	235 (C) (S)	'Condensing engine, 36in double: pumps and winds. Condensing 15in double, pumps. A new pit in sinking and powerful engine erecting to pump therefrom'	Nil
39 Brookhall Ditches (Edward Protheroe & Co)	153 (PD)	'Winch high pressure. The water discharged by level. Another pit sinking by a horse whim 40yd deep'	Nil
40. Burnt Log new Colliery (Edward Protheroe & Co)	(HD) (etc)	'Three pits will go down 100yd. One high pressure employed in sinking and two large engines building'	Nil
41 Old Bilson Colliery (Edward Protheroe & Co)	186 (HD) and (etc) 178	'Single condensing pumping engine 60in cylinder, and 20in ditto double winding. The large engine raises 96 gal of water a minute, 16 hours out of the 24'	15,000
42. Prospect Engine (Edward Protheroe & Co)	250 (R) and (L) 100	'36in cylinder double condensing engine'	13,800
43. Cannop Brook Oak Level (Mathewson & Co)		'A level'	3,150
44. The Winner Colliery above Bilson (Edward Protheroe & Co)	120(L) and (HD) 105 (R)	'30in cylinder condensing engine double power'	63,000
45 Hopewell Colliery near Nailbridge (James Bennett)	(2 pits)	'One horse whim (an old colliery reopening for deeper coals)'	(Standing)
		C/f	377,625

		Depth (yd)	How raised	Tons raised annually
			B/f	377,625
46.	(a) Luck-is-all (b) Victory (Timothy Bennett): Teague and Gould's colliery adjoining said to have been exhausted, having stopped 12 mths.	60(R) (L)	'14in double condensing engine'	18,000
47.	Broadmoor or Duck Colliery (Edward Protheroe & Co)	(2 pits) 65 (L) (HD)	'22in cylinder condensing double power'	10,500
48.	Regulator Colliery Pits no 1, 2, and 3 (James Bennett)	90 (S) (L)	'22in double condensing engine. A steam engine on no 3 not at work, will be sunk down to Hall delph'	9,000
49.	Watch Pit (Meek and Bolding)		'One horse whim'	1,800
50.	New Pit (Tipping and Brain)	Sinking	'One horse whim'	nil
51.	Old Engine Colliery (James Teague & Co)	Sinking (B)	'One horse whim'	nil
52.	Oak Pit (James Teague & Co)		'One horse whim'	(Standing)
53.	Trinity Pit (Nichols and Jones)	40 (S)	'One horse whim'	1,800
54	Fancy Pit (William Todd)			idle
55.	Folly Pit (James Bennett)	65 (HD)	'One horse whim'	3,000
56.	Ready Penny, late Whitsons (Elton, Meredith and Bryan)	30 (S)	'One horse whim'	900
			C/f	422,625

		Depth (yd)	*How raised*	*Tons raised annually*
			B/f	422,625
57.	Protector (Cheltenham Company)	100 (R)	'16in engine high pressure'	9,000
58.	Same Pit: Tormentor Pit ex-hausted (Cheltenham Company)	(L)	Same engine as no 57	3,000
59.	James Cowmeadow	100 (R) (2 pits)	'10in high pressure engine'	27,000
60.	True Blue (Cowmeadow and Cooper)	70 (R)	'One horse whim'	900
61.	Paraguay Two Pits (Edward Pro-theroe & Co)	} 'These 2 pits are close to Timothy Bennett's Foundry'	'10in high pressure'	idle
62.	Protector (Chel-tenham Co)		'One horse whim'	idle
63.	Mr James Bennett		'One horse whim'	idle
64.	Haywood Colliery Pit (Crawshay & Sons): The opening of this colliery is not complete.	70 (H)	'18in high pressure pump-ing engine' 10in high pressure wind-ing engine'	3,900
65.	Ruardean Hill: East Slade (Cheltenham & Forest of Dean Coal Company)	70 (H)	'High pressure engine in two pits'	idle (Extensive and offered for sale)
66.	Ruardean: Woodside (Proprietors as no 65)	60 (H)	'High pressure engine in two pits'	idle (Extensive and offered for sale)
			C/f	466,425

43 Stripping oak bark for the tanning industry: *(above)* stripping before felling; *(below)* stripping after felling

44 Wood chemical 'steweries' or 'distilleries' (1): *(above)* Broadmoor 1967; *(below)* Cannop 1966

	Depth (yd)	How raised	Tons raised annually
		B/f	466,425
67. Ruardean Hill: Two pits on Pluckpenny Level (William Todd)	100 (H)	'Two pits and single horse whims'	Standing for 18 mths intended to be worked again.
68. Newham Bottom level, Ruardean Hill (Robins and Evans)	53 (H)	'Pit and one horse whim'	2,400
69. Waterloo (James Butler) An extensive concern being in course of opening.	Sinking	'Two pits and two steam engines'	nil
		Total	468,825

It will have been noted that Edward Protheroe owned some ten coalworks, but he also held shares in about twenty others (*vide* the Coal Awards of 1841). William Crawshay had one only—Lightmoor; the iron-mines—these were not rateable—and furnaces, were the Crawshay's chief interests. Trotter Thomas & Co had seven coalworks (also a foundry—at Howlers Slade); Peter Teague had three, David Mushet two, and James Bennett eight. James Butler was sinking Waterloo—a colliery to become important (Plate 32a). Many other coalworks and their owners or lessees are given in the aforementioned Coal Awards.

The labour cost of winning coal, with wages at 3s a day, was about 1s a ton: four men hewed 15 tons daily. Coal was sold at the pithead at 7s to 9s per ton for best, and 2s for 'lime coal'. Sale prices of large coal at Bullo Pill, for shipping, was 10s 7d or 12s 6d a ton. Much of the coal went away by rail from Monmouth and Lydney. Large quantities were supplied to the Tinplate Works at Lydney and Redbrook, and to the furnaces at Parkend, Cinderford and Soudley. Immense quantities were sold locally for domestic fuel, the burning of lime, and the raising of steam.

U

In 1856[77] there were 221 coalworks, which yielded that year some 460,000 tons, chiefly won by the following ten largest collieries;

	Tons
	Tons
Parkend	86,973
Lightmoor	86,508
Crumpmeadow	41,507
Bixslade	26,792
Nelson	24,539
Hopewell, in Wimberry Slade	18,858
Valletts Level	17,918
Bilson	17,395
Arthur & Edward (Waterloo)	12,857
New Strip-and-at-it	11,502
	344,849*

* Exclusive of coal consumed by the engines.

A statement of all the coalworks in West Dean and their owners, for the years 1841 to 1856,[78] gives the annual tonnage raised by each coalwork.

Well before the 1850s, some coal shafts were being lined throughout with stone-walling, leaving a clear diameter of from 7 to 9ft. Many levels were also stone-lined, for example at Bixslade. Improvements had been made in drainage, pumping, winding and ventilation ('the air was carried around the face without a split, the power being a furnace at the upcast'). An increasing number of horses were used underground, to draw trams to the bottom of the shaft. 'Fire-damp' fortunately was absent, but stythe (carbonic acid gas) or black-damp termed 'blind' was occasionally met with in the vicinity of old un-ventilated workings.

Later, new methods of working the seams were devised: the 'long-wall' system was introduced about 1820,[79] but the 'pillar and stall' system was usually preferred in the Coleford High Delf seam, which generally ran thick, with scarcely any rubbish to 'gob' or 'goaf' the ground. The stalls were from 30 to 50 yards wide, with the road in the centre.[80] The main roads were about 110 yards apart, with stall-roads ranging that distance. Owing to the thinness of the seams it was neces-sary to be sparing in the driving of roads, and where the pitch or gradient of the seam was steep, say above 6°, hod-roads, or in rare cases jinney-roads (self-acting inclines) were 'driven to the rise, at right-angles to a main road, driven along the strike of a seam'.[81]

At the bottom of each hod-road stood a wooden stage upon which the coal was tipped and stacked ready for loading into 'tubs' which, when loaded 1ft 6in to 2ft above the sides, each held about one ton. The underground haulage system was of a primitive character, and in the steep measures coal was brought down to the loading stages in 'hods' (Fig 17), shallow wooden boxes about $2\frac{1}{2}$ft long $\times$ $1\frac{1}{2}$ft wide $\times$ 4in deep, mounted upon two slides or 'trotters' in the style of a

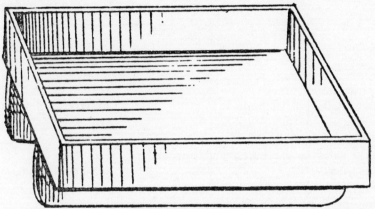

Fig 17. Hod used to convey coal underground (after J. J. Joynes, *Jnl British Soc of Mining Students*, XI, 6, 1889, 153).

sleigh. The hods were generally drawn by boys (paid about 6d a ton in 1889)[82] with a harness, called a girdle—a wide leather strap, split in the middle to slip over the head, so that a part rested on each shoulder; the two ends were brought together at the bottom, before and behind, and a chain with a hook was attached. The hod-roads were usually cut $4\frac{1}{2}$ to 5ft high by 5ft wide, but owing to the heaving-up or 'pucking-up' of the floor the height did not usually exceed $2\frac{1}{2}$ft.[83] Such exacting conditions in which young boys had to work (women up to about 1810 also did the same task) are difficult to imagine.[84] Fortunately this often cruel and always exhausting operation was abolished before the close of the nineteenth century.

Acts of Parliament passed in 1861[85] and 1871[86] made new regulations for gales and their working, while Select Committees, such as that of 1874,[87] enquired into and tried to propose ways of settling problems arising within the industry. In 1871, Commissioners reported details of 'coal worked, and how disposed of, in 1867 and 1868':[88]

Workings

	1867 Tons	1868 Tons	1869 Tons
Galees' returns of quantities worked exclusive of colliery consumption and that consumed by workmen	777,677	778,128	?
Estimated quantity consumed by engines	40,000	40,000	?
Estimated quantity consumed by workmen	30,000	30,000	?
	847,677	848,128	852,125

Disposals[89]

	1867 Tons	1868 Tons
By GWR from Lydney	7,760	7,617
From Bullo Pill Railway	300,000	306,000
By Water from Lydney	166,992	168,404
By Water from Bullo Pill (estimated)	59,380	61,220
Local sales in the Forest and surrounding districts	82,000	80,000
Consumed by engines	70,000	70,000
Consumed at iron works, tin works, and wire works in the Forest (estimated)	161,545	154,887
	847,677	848,128

An example of the means used in the mid-1870s to induce or invite capital with which to develop extensive mining concessions in Dean, is the prospectus of The Great Western (Forest of Dean) Coal Consumers' Co Ltd, which c1873 solicited applications for 6,000 shares of £20 each.[90] The directors were Edwin Crawshay, H. R. Luckes, F. Nash, G. W. Owen, A. J. Shinner, and W. Wylie. M. F. Carter was the solicitor, and F. A. Carter the secretary. The prospectus reads:

It is proposed to take over the Royal Forester and Cannop Level Collieries, in the Forest of Dean, with all the Plant, Machinery, Engines, Buildings, Stock, etc, and the land held therewith from the Crown, for the erection of all necessary Workshops, Cottages, etc, at £80,000.

The gales are held direct from the Crown, under the well-known Forest tenure, which vests the gales in the owners absolutely, subject to royalty, which in this instance is only 3d per ton; this royalty is subject to revision every twenty-one years, and the dead or certain rent is £120 per annum, merged into royalty: there is a sum of £2,700 standing to the credit of these collieries, which will be rebated in royalties, and be a source of profit to this Company to that amount.

The extent is over 400 acres superficial area, and quantity of coal in the different veins, estimated upon the established rules of calculation, over six million tons. Two shafts have been sunk and worked in the crop of these coals, which proved their excellent quality, and their value has been fully tested and proved by the workings of other well-known collieries on all sides of these properties.

Hitherto, the Forest of Dean coals from the Western side of the Forest have been mainly exported by shipping, there being a well-appointed port at Lydney (which has been enlarged and improved) for collier ships; but the Severn and Wye Railway Company have recently converted their Tramway into a Narrow Gauge Railway, forming a junction with the Great Western Railway at Lydney, these collieries having their own siding to the Severn and Wye Railway, coals may now be loaded into trucks at the pit's bank, and require no changes or transhipment for Paddington and the other London stations connected with it; and to all places on the Narrow Gauge System of the Great Western Railway a cheap, direct and expeditious transit is secured. The present prices of coal would show a very large profit, which it is not necessary to point out in a Prospectus, but taking the ordinary working profit it would not be less than 4s 6d per ton nett.

It is proposed to sink the present shaft down to the excellent Churchway High Delf Vein, a distance of only forty yards from the bottom of the present shaft, to put up the necessary additional Steam Power, and sink the second shaft required under the Mines' Regulation Bill, and so put the collieries in full working order up to an output of 400 tons per day: to do this the proposed capital will be ample to all requirements, and the time and cost to carry out and well execute this work will be most materially lessened by the shafts already sunk; and the engines, winding gear, etc, are of ample strength to carry out the sinking.

It is customary to make estimated calculations of future dividends, but the real value of good colliery property is now so well understood that it has been preferred to state the facts in connection with these collieries, their extent of acreage and quantity of coal; and as there is no anticipated difficulty of any kind to the promptly carrying out of the work, there can be no question of its proving an investment of a highly remunerative character, paying large and growing dividends as the output is increased by the opening up of the collieries.

It is proposed that all shareholders in the company shall have the privilege of buying coal (in trucks of 8 to 10 tons) direct from the collieries at the wholesale merchant prices. In itself, in present times, this would be a handsome dividend, whereas such an arrangement would not diminish the dividend of the non-buying shareholder, as the profit is estimated per ton on the basis of this arrangement, and the company would make arrangements for the delivery of the coal at the London and other stations.

This is worthy of special notice: there is no danger from fire damp; in the Forest of Dean all workings are carried on with open lights.

Mr Crawshay has agreed to accept, as remuneration for his services as managing director, in lieu of salary, £5 per cent on the nett profits.

The only Contract entered into is dated the nineteenth March, 1873, and is made between John Hooper of the one part, and Maurice Frederic Carter, on behalf of the Company, of the other part.

Although in 1880 some coal was still being won from the outcrop by means of levels and slopes, most mining was by shafts of from 8 to 10ft clearance, generally circular, and varying in depth from 50 to 300 yards.[91] These shafts were either carried down for some depth below the coal, or some distance above, from the bottom of which stone drifts, locally termed 'cut-outs', were driven to intersect the coal; in the former case these cut-outs were driven towards the 'dip' side of the coal, and in the latter towards the 'rise' side. The cut-outs were about 6ft high, and from 6 to 7ft wide, rising from the shaft at a slight inclination, allowing the water to gravitate to the pit sump. Where the cut-out intersected the coal, levels on both sides were driven in the seam in the direction of the strike, forming the main horse-roads; at the same time constituting (in many instances) the deep boundary of the gale in that particular seam. The cut-outs were frequently continued to win other seams.

Coal was wound in cages in a few of the larger collieries, but usually the earlier mode was accepted, of drawing up a tram or tub, locally termed a 'cart', by two or four single link chains, hooked to the sides or corners of the tubs and attached to the winding-rope (Fig 18). The tubs were guided in the shaft by two ropes by means of a 'rider', placed over a tub. In many instances, one winding-rope alone was used; and in a few instances a cage was attached in lieu of the tub when the workmen descended and ascended.

Machinery was in great demand for Dean's collieries. The follow-

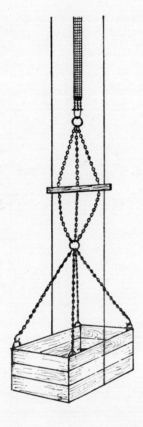

Fig. 18. Hauling-up box used at Crump-meadow Colliery (after H. R. Insole and C. Z. Bunning, *Jnl British Soc of Mining Students*, **VI**, 5, 1880).

ing list of extant drawings made by the Neath Abbey Ironworks[92] gives an idea of what machinery was required:

Foxes Bridge Colliery (Barrett and Crawshay)
1873: Sundries for a 30-inch, 6-foot stroke beam engine.
Lightmoor Colliery
1873: Sundries for a 15½-inch winding engine.
Littledean Woodside Coal Company (per J. Smith)
1873: Winding barrel.
Fairplay Pit, Mitcheldean (Osman Barrett)
1868: Winding apparatus for a 16-inch, 3-foot stroke, engine.
1868: Winding gear.
1868: Brake apparatus.
1868: Cylinder, piston and bottom for a 60-inch diameter, 9-foot stroke pumping engine.

For 1880, information is available on the principal pumping engines: [93]

	Diam of cylinder in	Stroke in cylinder ft	Stroke in pit ft
Lightmoor: Cornish Beam Condensing	78	9	8
Castle Main: Cornish Beam Condensing	78	9	9
New Fancy: Rotary Beam Condensing	36	7	$6\frac{1}{2}$
Hawkwell 1: Cornish Beam Condensing	50	10	9
Hawkwell 2: { Auxiliary underground Direct Acting Condensing	25	2	
Nailbridge: Rotary Beam High Pressure	$15\frac{1}{2}$	4	4
Bilson: Cornish Beam Condensing	60	7	7
Churchway: Cornish Beam Condensing	40	7	7
Haywood: Cornish Beam Rotary High Pressure	24	7	7
Foxes Bridge: Cornish Beam High Pressure	60	9	7
East Slade: Horizontal High Pressure	25	4	4
Strip-and-at-it: Cornish Beam Condensing	44	8	8
Trafalgar: Underground Direct Acting Manchester Pump	Two 15	$1\frac{1}{6}$	
Speculation: Horizontal High Pressure Rotary	24	4	4
Old Bobs (Cannop): High Pressure Bull	24	8	8
Arthur & Edward: Cornish Beam Condensing (not working)	60	10	10
Flour Mill 1: Bull Condensing (not working)	52	$8\frac{1}{2}$	$8\frac{1}{2}$
Flour Mill 2: Horizontal High Pressure Rotary (not working)	Two 14	$2\frac{2}{3}$	$3\frac{1}{2}$
New Bowson: Cornish Beam Condensing (not working)	85	10	10

Many other details of the above pumping engines and their boilers are available.[94] These engines (together with six in iron mines—see Chapter 5) represented practically the entire pumping force in the district. The quantity of water pumped varied considerably from season to season. The 19 engines representing the total draining power, in wet weather—when the pumps were going at their greatest speed—pumped each minute about 7,500 gallons of water, requiring 934 hp, and consuming 179 tons of coal in 24 hours. In dry weather, these figures were reduced by about one-half or two-thirds. The above quantity of water did not quite represent the feeders lifted, for at some 6 or 7 collieries water was wound up, not pumped. The coal consumed by the pumping engines appears in excess of what is actually totalled, because some of the boilers supplied steam to engines other than the pumping engines. Many of the engines were 'very old, having worked from 40 to 60 years.'

The output of coal in 1880[95] was 720,123 tons—about 1/204th of that of the whole of Great Britain. Lightmoor, Trafalgar, Foxes Bridge and Crump Meadow collieries were working the upper series of seams, raising about 500,000 tons annually, from an average depth of 250 yards.[96] The number of collieries and their respective outputs and drawing-shafts were: [97]

Output exceeding (tons per annum)	No of Collieries	No of Pits and Levels drawing coal	
		Pits	Levels and Slopes
125,000 to 200,000	2	3	—
100,000	2	3	—
50,000	2	2	—
25,000	2	2	—
10,000	3	1	3
1,000	20	15	10
500	6	6	—
100	5	3	2
Below 100	5	5	—
	47	40	15

The number of persons employed in Dean's coal industry for the individual years 1874 to 1880 were respectively 5,050, 4,694, 4,433, 4,148, 3,985, 4,291, 3,830,[98] while the number of lives lost in the same years were respectively 8, 6, 4, 3, 0, 6, 6;[99] previously, in 1871, 1872 and 1873, the death toll had been 11, 5 and 9.[100]

The industry was not only a dangerous one, but was also subject to fluctuations in fortunes. Collieries which at times flourished, at other times failed or became flooded, often with water from another colliery. Two reports in 1893, typical of many in the local press, will in précis suffice to indicate some of the vicissitudes: [101]

(1) Old Furnace (Wimberry) Colliery to be re-opened . . . Idle for some years . . . flooded . . . Wimberry Bottom . . . worked for some years by Trotter Thomas & Co . . . water burst in . . . carts, tram rails, tools and a large quantity of coal abandoned . . . Gale surrendered, and applied for by 163 Free Miners.

(2) Reopening of Flour Mill Colliery . . . Park Gutter as pumping station . . . originally intended to work from there. The recovery of the lost pumps was a feat of extraordinary difficulty . . . End of year before production will begin.

Coal at that time was extensively used by the neighbouring furnaces, tinplate works and wireworks. Coke was made in the open for the furnaces, while several towns, manufacturies and collieries made gas from coal.[102] The Forest's railways carried much traffic: they moved 652,592 tons in 1880—306,724 by the GWR Co, and 345,868 by the Severn & Wye and Severn Bridge Railway Companies.[103] From Lydney were shipped about 360,000 tons in 1884, and 240,000 tons in 1894.[104] House coal sold at the pits for 7s to 8s 6d a ton for block or large, 7s 3d for rubbles or nuts, and 1s 6d to 2s 3d for small.[105] The colliers' average wage was about 3s 8d a day of eight hours, with a coal-allowance at a reduced rate. About one ton was won per man per day. From 720,123 tons in 1880, and about 800,000 in 1890, output rose to 1,176,712 in 1898, and 1,067,000 in 1899.[106]

THE TWENTIETH CENTURY   Outputs in 1900, 1901, 1902 and 1903 were respectively 1,050,000 tons, 1,007,000, 987,000 and 847,000. (These tonnages, as usual, did not include coal won in the so-called 'excepted lands', ie the areas of private freehold which included Lydney Park Estate with its important Norchard and other collieries.) Some 28 million tons of coal had been mined from 1870 to 1903, and it was estimated in December 1903 that unworked coal in Dean totalled 306 million tons, of which it should be possible to win 258 millions.[107] Dean had its full share of disasters. They included floods in the Union Pit (4 September 1902) which claimed many lives, and in the Navigation and Waterloo collieries. Many acts of gallantry are on record. Fires from spontaneous combustion of coal occurred in Lydbrook Colliery in 1907 and 1908, and in Cannop Colliery in 1929. Extracts from reports made by HM Inspectors of Mines for 1902–9 are typical of those in many other years:

1902: Accidents: 5 fatal, 26 non-fatal (38 fatal accidents in the past 11 years).
Hopewell Drift Colliery: prosecuted for inadequate ventilation.
Navigation Colliery: failure to keep an accurate plan of workings: unexpected inrush of water from old workings—4 lives lost and 3 men entombed for nearly 120 hours.
1903: Accidents: 7 fatal, 7 non-fatal.
Princess Royal Colliery: prosecuted for inadequate ventilation.

1904: Accidents: none fatal. It has been suggested to me that some miners have gobbed up their work to hide the fact that they have trespassed outside their boundary for coal. Whether this is true or not I do not know, but a collier in Hopewell Engine Colliery remembers that 40 or 50 years ago, how in dry summers it was the practice to drive 'dipples' down on the lower side of the deep adit (which formed the body of the gale) as far as they could. This meant that coal was illegally obtained, a place was provided to put spoil, and a source of danger to adjoining gales resulted.

1905: Accidents: none fatal.
Wage rates: 20%–25% above the standard in 1879.

1906: Accidents: none fatal.
Mining slack in summer (not more than 3 or 4 days a week): even so, output had increased $9\frac{3}{4}$ per cent. Horses belonging to H. Crawshay & Co Ltd at Lightmoor would be difficult to surpass for cleanliness and attention: it is a pleasure to see the horses and to visit the stables.

1907: Accidents: 7 fatal, 12 non-fatal.

1908: Accidents: 3 fatal, 8 non-fatal.

1909: Accidents: 3 fatal, 2 non-fatal.

The Dean Forest (Mines) Act of 1904 (4 Edw VII, c 116) and of 1906 (6 Edw VII, c 119), made possible the working of the deeper measures. Thereunder, 44 undeveloped small gales were amalgamated into seven large groups or colliery-holdings—with the co-operation of the Free Miners, who were to receive a royalty of $\frac{1}{2}$d each ton raised (Plate 31a). All seven groups had a concession over about 2,000 acres, subsequently worked by six companies—Cannop Coal Co Ltd, Henry Crawshay & Co Ltd, Lydney and Crumpmeadow Collieries Co Ltd, Park Colliery Co Ltd, Parkend Deep Navigation Collieries Ltd, and Princess Royal Collieries Co Ltd.

In 1906[108] the collieries included Addishill, Bridewell, Crown, Crumpmeadow, Duck, Darkhill, East Slade, Forest Red Ash, Foxes Bridge, Gentlemen Colliers, Hopewell, Hulks, Lightmoor, Speech House Main, Little Brockhollands, Lydbrook Deep Level, New Fancy, Parkend Royal, New Mount Pleasant, Norchard, Princess Royal, Trafalgar, Wallsend, and Woorgreens. Of these, the Lightmoor, Parkend, Trafalgar, Crumpmeadow, and Foxes Bridge were the chief collieries working the 'Middle Series' of seams at varying depths, namely the Churchway High Delf, Rockey, Starkey, Lowrey and Twenty Inch. The Lightmoor Colliery, owned by Henry Crawshay and Co Ltd, was

by far the largest of these, having a depth of 300yd, and a daily output
of 800–900 tons. The Parkend and Fancy Collieries (240yd) owned
by the Parkend Deep Navigation Collieries Ltd, had a daily output of
about 500 tons; Trafalgar (200yd) 500 tons; Crumpmeadow (200yd)
500 tons; Foxes Bridge (300yd) 500 tons. These collieries working the
thinner seams produced first-rate house coal.

Among the principal collieries working the lower series, the Flour
Mill Colliery (Coleford High Delf seam) and the Park Gutter (York-

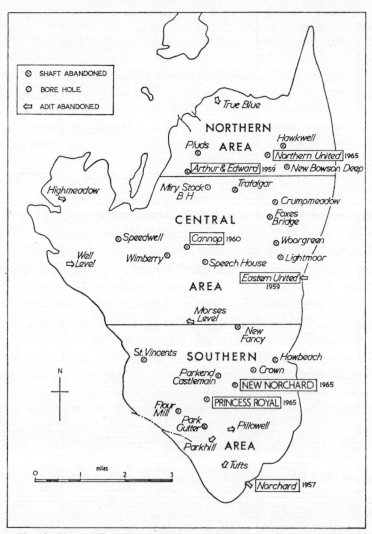

Fig 19. Plan of Dean's principal coal shafts and adits (after F. M.
Trotter, *Geology of the Forest of Dean Coal and Iron ore Field*,
fig 5).

ley seam), both owned by the Princess Royal Colliery Co Ltd, had an output of 600 tons a day. The Old Norchard Colliery (Coleford High and Trenchard seam), owned by the Park Iron Ore Co, was worked by a level, and had a daily output of about 350 tons. Lydbrook Colliery (Coleford High Delf seam), owned by Richard Thomas & Co Ltd, averaged 350 tons a day. Though fair house coal was obtained from the Yorkley seam, the principal output of the collieries working the lower seams was in steam and gas coal.

The advent of modern machinery and scientific practice brought the economic extraction of coal to a fine art. Yet after much expert investigation of the lie of the strata and the coal seams, and the location of 'faults', sinking of trial shafts and adits was first resorted to in order to 'prove' coal. Exploratory 'dipples' driven from the deep, were also tried, and not all were successful. The attractive features that the coalfield possessed, of freedom from fire-damp (enabling working by naked lights) and from too many major 'faults', were unfortunately spoiled by the varying thickness within seams, and the tremendous quantity of water encountered (particularly the accumulation of standing water in the older and upper workings, which could suddenly erupt) necessitating extensive pumping plant, especially in the deeper mines. As an example, Cannop Colliery, which began sinking in 1906, and during 1907 reached a depth of 87yd, had to contend with 3,000 gallons of water a minute. There were 2 pits each 14ft in diameter. They met the Coleford High Delf seam, 4ft 9in thick, at 205yd. By 1909, large feeders of water had been encountered varying from 2,000 to 3,400 gallons a minute. Evans' Steam Sinking Pumps were adequate down to 112yd where the feeders attained their maximum; electric turbine pumps were installed at this depth, and sinking with the Evans' pumps continued below it.[109]

Ventilation—another problem common to other coalfields—was overcome by 'fans' (with 'braddish' used to regulate the course of the air underground) and by surface fires in chimney-structures or fires hung in the upshaft, to induce draught and to extract foul air.

The number employed in the coalfield varied from 4,917 men and 561 youths in June 1914, to 4,407 and 709 respectively in November 1918.[110] In 1922, Cannop employed 685, New Fancy 694, Trafalgar 360, and Princess Royal 1,138.

Strikes and lockouts have harmed Dean's economy, particularly those from 16 November 1874 to February 1875, 24 February to 2 April 1883, and 8 July to 30 September 1893.[111] Subsequent strikes in

1921 and 1926 are vivid in many memories today: mounted police had to be called to Cannop to safeguard those persons whose will to work was paramount, or who had to remain at work to prevent flooding.

John Williams, miners' agent from 1922, has recorded that at the time of his appointment Dean was 'in the doldrums, economically speaking'. Poverty was everywhere. There were less than one-third of the 7,000 miners in the Union and it had a debt of £24,000. The house-coal collieries were working one and two shifts a week, and the minimum wage was 7s 9d a shift—sometimes only 5s on the surface. A buttyman would receive 5s to 10s a week more. Ably assisted by G. T. D. Jenkins, Williams saw the Union strengthened. He worked ceaselessly for the miners during the 7 months strike in 1926; by the end of it the miners were badly hit—'a book could be written about the events—a grim record of heroism and self-sacrifice on the part of that generation of miners'. The strike financially ruined many, and hundreds lost all their small savings: the strikers returned to work having gained nothing and lost nearly everything. The coal owners held the whip hand, and they used it liberally: the smallest fault or failing of a working miner meant either 'the sack' or the threat of it. Unemployment in the district was high, and dismissal meant destitution. The individual miner usually retained his thoughts to himself, and kept his mouth shut.

Trafalgar closed in 1925, Crumpmeadow in 1929, and Foxes Bridge in 1931. During 1929 the average numbers employed in Dean collieries were 4,646 below ground and 980 above, besides 87 clerks and salaried persons. In 1938 the figures were respectively 4,108, 800 and 82. In that year, coal mined in Dean amounted to 1,351,000 tons; during 1943 and 1944 the average was 945,000 tons—when about 4,340 were employed. The outputs thereafter were:

Year	Tons (thousands)	Year	Tons (thousands)
1947	753	1957	480
1948	777	1958	472
1949	768	1959	405
1950	723	1960	311
1951	751	1961	240
1952	731	1962	211
1953	696	1963	226
1954	613	1964	120
1955	521	1965	46
1956	509		

The Coal Act 1938 (1 & 2 Geo VI, c 52) had little effect on the coalfield, and the nationalisation of mines, with the formation of the National Coal Board, was received with dwindling enthusiasm by the miners. The labour force in 1947 was 3,812; in 1955 it was 2,575. Estimates and hints by the Ministry of Fuel and Power in 1946[112] had cast doubts on the future of the coalfield. Costs were rising, and supplies of house-coals were dwindling. Water was an ever present problem: after heavy rains, 40 tons of water had to be pumped for each ton of coal raised; in 1943, pumping for the six main collieries cost some £66,000, or 1s 8d per ton of coal. Distance underground was another problem: for example, the workings in Eastern United Colliery necessitated three miles of haulage roads. Geological disturbances, such as 'faults', 'jumps', and 'barren ground', added to the difficulties; so too did accidents and industrial diseases.

Lightmoor closed in 1940, and the New Fancy in 1944. The 'Revised Plan for Coal' (1959) asserted that it was unlikely that any collieries would be working in Dean after 1965. The Norchard closed in 1957, Eastern United and Arthur & Edward (Waterloo) 1959, Cannop 1960, and Princess Royal 1962. Much of the labour force had gradually been absorbed from one pit to another—until it too was closed. The last of the large collieries, Northern United, closed on Christmas Day 1965—an unhappy day for some 700 men and boys. The previous week, 1,120 tons had been raised. The closures gave rise to frustration and anxiety. Various officials, men inside the industry (eg G. T. D. Jenkins and other representatives of the miners), and outside it (eg F. Wickstead and colleagues on various committees), together with Charles H. Loughlin MP, accomplished sympathetic and successful work in connection with those made redundant. The chief driving force behind the whole was the Development Association (see Chapter 15).

During the 1960s, some opencast mining took place at Coleford, Edenwall, Yorkley and Steam Mills; and a proposal is mooted to do the same at Woorgreen, between the Dilke Memorial Hospital and the Speech House: local opinion is divided as to whether, even with many safeguards, this enterprise should be permitted.

There are many reserves of coal in Dean, but little of them will ever be won, except possibly by the opencast (controversial) methods, and certainly by the few remaining working Free Miners. Of the latter workings, there are about 18 small mines in production under licence of the National Coal Board, with an annual output in the region of 15,000 tons. Among them are the New Road level at Cannop (Hinton

Bros), and The Reddings and The Pludds (Eric Morris). At Heywood is a shaft-operated small mine, 38 yards deep (B. & R. Morgan). As long as there are Free Miners who continue to hold tenaciously to their rights, and who are willing to work hard and to risk their capital, a few small coal workings will survive.

Work in Dean's coal mines has brought to light many fossils of the 'Coal Forests' of millions of years ago. But, for the industrial archaeologist, coalmining is normally an unrewarding study. Once a colliery is closed, or a coalfield's life is ended, its shafts are covered or filled in, and almost invariably its surface plant and buildings are removed. Occasionally an engine house might be left standing, usually to be converted to another use. In Dean, despite coal being won throughout two millennia by means of innumerable pits and adits, the remnants of the workings, gear and machinery are few because the industry is now virtually at an end. Furthermore, any one mound or spoil-heap or any one disused shaft (now sealed for public safety with brick, stone, or timber) is little different from the numerous others to be seen throughout the district. Some land is to be seen which has been racked by subsidence due to coalmining, eg east of Poolway. A few colliery buildings are extant (eg at Cannop, used for education, at Northern United as warehouses, and at Lightmoor for a sawmill and wood preservation plant; at Eastern United the pit head baths have been used by a firm of paint manufacturers, and at Princess Royal the pit head baths have been used as a warehouse). The last remaining engine house is that of the old Cornish Pumping Engine at Lightmoor. Stone ventilation stacks survive at Stapledge and at Dodmore on the west of the Bream-Lydney roadside; and some pit head winding gear still stands at Bromley Pit and Prosper Pit. Most of the spoil-heaps have been removed, particularly to Llanwern, or planted with trees by the Forestry Commission. Some of the mounds have been levelled to provide recreation grounds, eg at Lydbrook and Steam Mills, and for camping sites, eg alongside Speech House Hill.

Material evidence of coalmining is chiefly below ground—lost to sight. Dean's workings, now flooded with gouty, chill water (but spared in 1954 from a proposal to dump atomic waste) lie silent and weird—the abode of bats, and often enveloped by poisonous air. Thousands of wooden pitprops (grown locally, or imported from Europe—the 'Narways' of the miners) lie broken, splayed or rotten, and covered with the fructifications and strands of various fungi (some so fragile as to be called 'nothings') including *armillaria mellea* (honey

45 Wood chemical 'steweries' or 'distilleries' (2): *(above)* Tufts c1945. From left to right: A. Bailey, J. M. Capel, J. H. Capel. Under each 'box' were four wheels; *(below)* Tufts c1961

46 Wood Distillation Works, Speech House Road: *(above)* 1914: in the foreground is a truck partly filled with wood for carbonisation, and immediately to the right is the charcoal cooling chamber. The distillation retort is to the left, while the rest of the plant is housed chiefly in the main brick building; *(left)* 1966: a 'charge' of wood entering the 'fire chamber'

fungus) whose luminosity was familiar to those who toiled among them. The now constricted roadways with their escape 'manholes', intertwine the gobbed-up workings; and many high roads have sunk to almost impenetrable passages, with dangerous falls creating chaos. Occasionally there is an instance of temporary stables, bringing a reminder of the gallant and useful part played by numerous ponies and horses—these animals, and comradeship, are among the few aspects of Dean's mining life which local miners recall with admiration and affection. The whole workings are sepulchres of industry—cities of flooded roads and byways, the large majority too dangerous and uninviting to again be seen by man. Only the few Free Miners who hopefully still pursue their trade, remind us of the long (some people might say, inglorious) past of the coalfield.

References to Chapter 6

1   Local song, 'The Jovial Colliers'.
2   Trotter, F. M. op cit, chapters V, VI, VII.
3   Regional Survey Report, *Forest of Dean Coalfield*, HMSO, 1946; Dredghorn, op cit; Piggott, R. J., *Bulletin HMG* 2(1) 1968.
4   Hart. *The Free Miners*, 12, 13.
5   Ibid, 15, 158.
6   Ibid, 14, 15.
7   Ibid, *passim*; *Royal Forest, passim*.
8   Nef, J. U. *The Rise of the British Coal Industry*, 1932, I, 20.
9   Hart. *The Free Miners*, 165–82.
10 Rees, op cit., I, 148, n 34.
11 Hart. *The Free Miners*, 184.
12 Ibid, 185.
13 Ibid, 187, 188.
14 Ibid, 189–94, 219.
15 Ibid, 78, 79.
16 SP16, Chas I, 1627.
17 Dudley, Dud. *Mettallum Martis*, 1665, 21–4; Scott's *Joint Stock Companies*, 1910, II, 460–61; Morton, G. R. and Wanklyn, M. D. G., *Dud Dudley—A New Appraisal*, Jnl West Mid Reg Studies, I/1, Dec 1967, 48–65.
18 Mushet, David, op cit, 45.
19 SP29, Chas II, 1661, 39/44.
20 Powle, Henry. Royal Society, *Philosophical Transactions*, 12, 1683, 931–5.
21 Ibid, 933.
22 Hart. *The Free Miners*, 208.
23 Ibid, 206.
24 Ibid, 220, 223.
15 19 and 20 Chas II, c 8, sec XI.

x

26 Hart. *The Free Miners*, 216–26.
27 Ibid, 85, 97.
28 Ibid, 107.
29 Ibid, 110.
30 Ibid, 112.
31 Ibid, 111.
32 E178, 13 Chas I, Mich 42.
33 Hart. *The Free Miners*, 80.
34 Ibid, 82.
35 Ibid, 85.
36 Ibid, 98.
37 Ibid, 105.
38 Ibid, 110, 112.
39 Ibid, 114.
40 Nef, op cit, 20.
41 Hart. *The Free Miners*, 125.
42 Ibid, 136.
43 Ibid, 117.
44 Ibid, 123.
45 Ibid, 129.
46 Ibid, 131, 132.
47 GRO D421/E23(1).
48 Nicholls. *History* . . . , 235.
49 Hart. *The Free Miners*, 134.
50 Ibid, 139.
51 Ibid.
52 Ibid, 136.
53 Nicholls. *History* . . . , 71, 235.
54 Ibid, 71; Hart. *The Free Miners*, 136, 236.
55 Nicholls. *History* . . . , 235, 236.
56 F16/31.
57 *Third Report*, 1788, 91.
58 Ibid, 108.
59 Ibid, 109.
60 Ibid, and App 26.
61 *The Torrington Diaries*, 1954 Edn, 37.
62 Anon. *Observations on the River Wye*, 1770.
63 Ireland, Samuel, op cit, 1797, 88, 89.
64 Nicholls. *History* . . . , 239, 240.
65 Rudder, S. *History of Gloucestershire*; Nicholls. *History* . . . , 237.
66 *Third Report*, 1788, 109.
67 GRO D1677, GG 1473.
68 Paar, H. W., op cit.
69 Reports of Commissioners of Woods etc; Third Schedule to the Coal Awards of 1841.
70 Hart. *The Free Miners*, 251, 310.
71 Ibid, 286.
72 Ibid, 257.
73 Ibid, 313.
74 Ibid, 319.
75 Ibid, 319 *et seq*. For 'gales' during 1842–77, see Wood, James G. op cit, App B.

76 GRO Q/Rum/175.
77 Nicholls. *History* . . . , 242.
78 F16/53.
79 Galloway, R. L. 2nd Series, 247; *Trans South Wales Institute*, II, 144–6.
80 Joynes, J. J. 'Description of Seams, and some of the methods of working Coal, in the Forest of Dean', *Jnl British Soc of Mining Students*, XI, 6, 1889, 152.
81 Ibid.
82 Ibid, 156.
83 Ibid, 152.
84 Mountjoy, Timothy. *The Life, Labours, and Deliverances of a Forest of Dean Collier*, c1887: records earlier tragedies at pits which included Heywood, Duck and Old Bilson.
85 Hart. *The Free Miners*, 358.
86 Ibid, 365.
87 Ibid, 369.
88 Rpt of Commissioners 'appointed to enquire . . . (re) . . . coal in the UK', 1871, III, 124.
89 Ibid, 124.
90 MS *penes me*.
91 Insole and Bunning, op cit, 75.
92 Glam Record Office, Cardiff.
93 Insole and Bunning, op cit, 84, 85.
94 Ibid.
95 Ibid, 61–94.
96 Ibid, 67.
97 Ibid, 76.
98 Ibid, 81.
99 Ibid, 83.
100 Hart. *The Free Miners*, 371.
101 *Dean Forest Guardian*, 13 Oct and 15 Dec 1893.
102 Insole and Bunning, op cit, 68.
103 Ibid, 87.
104 GRO Hockaday MSS.
105 Insole and Bunning, op cit, 80.
106 Final Rpt of Royal Com on Coal Supplies, II, 1905, 363.
107 Ibid.
108 *Vict C Hist Glos* II, 234, 235.
109 Rpt of HM Inspectors of Mines, 1907, 1908, 1910.
110 Rpt on the British Coal Mining Industry, 1919, I, 292–4; III, 106.
111 Final Rpt of Royal Com on Coal Supplies, op cit, 11.
112 'Forest of Dean Coalfield', HMSO 1946.

Seven
Stone, Clay and Lime

Dean's geological structure (Fig 10), to which reference has been made in Chapters 5 and 6, has yielded abundant supplies of stone, lime and clay. Thus the quarrying and working of stone, and the raising and utilising of lime and clay have been considerable industries, leading to others, eg, the making of cement and bricks.

Stone

Stone has been worked in Dean from time immemorial. The earliest known use was in the Bronze Age, c1800–450BC—the Tidenham Chase barrow cairn and ring were constructed of thousands of stones both from the Millstone Grit and the Lower Dolomitic Carboniferous Limestones.[1] All the capstones from both cists of the barrow were of Millstone Grit and there is considerable probability that these were not only quarried or levered from the strata but were also roughly shaped. All three of Dean's Megalithic standing stones also of this Age ie those at Huntsham, Staunton and the (now destroyed) St Briavels Longstone, were derived from the local Old Red Sandstone. The extant two stones show characteristic weathering grooves along the bedding planes. The Stroat 'Broadstone', which marked an ancient crossing of the Severn, came from a bed of Limestone which occurs in the Triassic strata at the nearby Pillhouse Rocks; and the 'Jubilee stone' on Tidenham Chase, erected in 1897, came from the same source. In the Iron Age, c450BC–AD43 the vallums of Dean's many camps had a core of stone excavated by the Celtic people from the accompanying fosses. The Welshbury dykes were built of Old Red Sandstone; other vallums and fosses are of the Carboniferous Limestone on which they stand.

The Romans quarried and used local stone for their buildings both at Lydney Park and at the Chesters Villa in Woolaston, where were found stone roofing tiles and Sandstone flags. They also fashioned their millstones from the pudding-stone strata of the Old Red Sandstone. This particular stone, on account of its toughness, has been utilised locally for millstones and cider presses up to the nineteenth century. Large roughly dressed discs of this strata occur in Dean's outcrops. These unfinished millstones may date from Roman times, but because they have not been milled they are impossible to date—Roman milling is distinct from that found on more modern millstones. Stone was also quarried for the many Roman roads in the Forest.

When Offa's Dyke was being built, the Saxon 'engineers' had the necessary stone quarried from the local strata. Several of their quarries lie on the eastern side of the Dyke in the stretches along the Tidenham Chase escarpment.

The ancient Cradockstone ('Gattle Cross') at Scar is of Forest Free Stone. The Norman castle of St Briavels was probably built with local stone, and when in 1362 its walls were badly in need of repair an estimated sum of £80 was required for 'hire of stone masons and stone cutters *(cementariis et latomis)* and other needful expenses'.[2] Lydney's Norman castle was also of local stone; and the Norman 'Castle of Dene' at Littledean is of the Old Red Sandstone. Dean's early preaching crosses, eg at Clearwell, Staunton, Lydney and Aylburton, are of local stone.

In 1435-6[3] Hugh Cromehall, 'Receiver of the Forest', accounted 'of 3s 4d of farm of stone mines in the quarry of Hanewye, within the bailiwick of Ruardean, so demised to John Mason of Mitcheldean'. He 'rendered nothing here of millstones acquired in Overebachehull this year because none were acquired; and he rendered nothing here of millstones acquired in the quarry of Hasseley during the time of this account for the same cause, nor for the quarries in the bailiwicks of Blakeney, Abenhall and Dean'. The following year, 1436-7,[4] Cromehall accounted for '3s 4d of farm of finding stone in the quarry of "Hanewaye" within the bailiwick of Ruardyn, thus demised to John Mason of Great Dean, his heirs and assigns'. In the same reign[5] John Hawtyne accounted for '4s of the farm of one quarry at Bykeshed formerly in the tenure of William Herdman now demised to William Smyth and William Kenet for the term of their lives and the longer liver of them for 4s a year as appears by the court roll of the 9th year; and in default of farm of the mine called Gryndstones above charged at 16s 4d and now at 10s and thus in decay 6s 4d'. The reference to 'Bykeshed' is of a particular interest because quarrying has been continued there to the present time—a period of over 500 years.

There is no evidence to show that the Free Miners' customary privileges extended to the working of stone—in fact the opposite seems to be the case. The earliest extant transcript (1610) of the miners' 'Laws and Privileges' makes no mention of stone or quarries, neither is there any reference to them in the extant records of the Mine Law Court. Furthermore, in 1683[6] it was asserted by one of the inhabitants that 'he had never heard that the quarrymen have or have had any power to make any laws, neither that they were governed by the laws and customs of the miners of coal and iron ore'. Another deposed that 'the quarryers are not concerned in the Mine Law Courts, neither have those courts jurisdiction over them as quarryers'. Nevertheless, the inhabitants, subject to certain qualifications, acquired a right by prescription to work the stone in the Forest, and this right was defined and confirmed by the Dean Forest (Mines) Act 1838.

By the beginning of the seventeenth century the working of stone was an important means of livelihood to some of the inhabitants. A muster taken in 1608[7] mentions six 'grindstone hewers', two 'millstone hewers' and two 'lime burners', but there must have been many more in these trades. In 1622[8] some of the inhabitants dug and claimed a right to dig grindstone on lands in the Forest farmed by Sir Richard Catchmay, whereupon the Attorney-General filed an Information in the Exchequer Court against some of them on Sir Richard's behalf. The Court, without decreeing the right, recommended to Sir Richard on account of their poverty not to oppress the inhabitants for such a 'trifling article', the stone not being worth more than the labour of raising it, and they each paid ten groats (= 3s 4d, a groat being 4d) as an acknowledgment—which remained the charge for opening and working quarries until 1859, when it was amended to £1 for each quarry of 20 yards in length, and 1s for each additional yard.[9] in 1612[10] William, Earl of Pembroke received a grant from the Crown which included the sand and stone of the Forest, while in 1636[11] the quarries were included in a grant to Sir Baynham Throckmorton and others. In 1637[12] 'the quarries of grindstone' were granted to Edward Terringham, to which the inhabitants took great exception, and they refused to forego their customary rights and privileges of coal-mining and quarrying. A lawsuit followed the same year,[13] wherein the legal arguments centred on the coal-mining customs, but neither in the coal mines nor in the quarries could Terringham deny the workers. In 1640[14] the stone quarries were included in a grant to Sir John Winter, but the local quarrymen were not interrupted. On 5 March 1661[15] Commissioners including Lord Herbert, constable and warden, appointed to enquire into the state and condition of Dean, were presented by the inhabitants with a 'Memorial'[16] claiming 'as enjoyed for divers hundred of years' *inter alia*, 'liberty to dig and get limestone, tilestone and other stones necessary to be imployed in and upon their ancient messuages, lands and tenements, and also to make and to get millstones and grindstones.' The Commissioners reported to the Exchequer 12 April 1662[17]:

> There are several quarries of stone and grindstone fit for the Navy, paving, tyle, slate, excellent for building and some millstone, but by reason that never as yet any yearly advantage accrued by it, we cannot set upon it any positive value.

The Dean Forest (Reafforestation) Act, 1667 contains two sections relevant to quarries. Section 6 enacted that 'in case any person or persons whatsoever shall presume to take, or shall obtain, any gift, grant, estate or interest . . . in any of the . . . quarries, of or within the inclosures, or any part thereof', such gift, grant, estate or interest shall be 'null and void'. Section 17 enacted 'that any lease or leases made or to be made by his Majesty, his heirs or successors, to any person or persons whatsoever for any term or terms of years not exceeding the term of thirty-one years in possession of the . . . quarries of grindstone in the Forest, or any part thereof, shall be of like force as if this Act had never been made'. Immediately after the Act, a grant was made to Francis Terringham of all 'the quarries of grindstone' for thirty-one years, at a charge, including coal mines, of £30 per annum. Once again the inhabitants would not relinquish their customary privileges, and in 1675[18] Terringham's widow commenced a lawsuit against some of the quarrymen. The interrogatories and depositions mention quarries at Bickshead, Ruardean Eaves, and Baddams Field. William Hawkins of Coleford, shoemaker age 77, deposed that the quarrying customs had been exercised for over sixty years. William Vicke of the same town had been 'bred up at the trade of cutting stone', and he and his father before him had used and enjoyed one quarry of stone at Bickshead and paid therefor 3s 4d yearly to the King's officer— the deputy gaveller. Vicke and many other families 'must perish if their liberty and calling be taken from them'. The stone in the Forest was 'hewn into grindstones, window stones, paving, and millstones'. No relevant judgement or decree has been traced.

In 1680[19] Commissioners made no comment on one of their duties—'to enquire who presume to dig or leave open any sort of pits and quarries of stone, and build lime kilns and burn lime, and by what pretence and right'. Three years later,[20] a lawsuit similar to that of 1675 was instituted by Thomas Becke against four quarrymen, wherein it was asserted that the laws and customs of the Free Miners did not apply to quarries, of which there were (old and new) about twenty at Bickshead, forty at Ruardean Eaves, and twenty dispersed elsewhere. Six were being worked at Bickshead and four at Ruardean. Two of the quarries were called Marefold and Hunters Beech; and the stone when first raised was not worth more than 12d a ton. Among the quarrymen were Richard Elly, Stephen Cowles, William Young, John Chapman, Walter Smart, John Wylse, Thomas Jenkins, and William Vicke. Elly had 'loaned' his quarry at Bickshead to Benedict Hall, Esquire, for £10—to enable him to raise sufficient stone to build his house. The lawsuit was not concluded—therefore the quarrymen's customs continued as hitherto.

There is a lack of relevant records for the following hundred years but a note dated 1761 reads: [21] 'Paid workmen to open a stone quarry in the Eastbach Mine and getting about 30 load of stone there, about one guinea; 7 days getting stone, 7s.' A document of c1775[22] mentions that the gaveller's powers did not extend to 'any stone quarry that is belonging to Lord Berkeley': Frederick Augustus, 5th Earl of Berkeley, was Constable and Warden about this time and it seems that he had rights in some if not all the quarries other than those in the Bailiwick of Blakeney.

With the growth of the iron ore industry and, later, of the coalmining industry, building and quarrying developments increased. At first the local structures were of the easily-worked Drybrook Sandstone, many of the neighbouring churches and oldest lodges in the Forest being of this material. Farm buildings used a large quantity of stone, and ground floors were of 'Forest Stone—an excellent freestone grit'.[23] In later years this stone was seldom used except for boundary walls and similar work—because the grey and blue Sandstones were discovered to be a more valuable material for building. In 1787 there were six quarries in Worcester Walk, 20 in Ruardean Walk, 13 in Blakeney Walk and 6 in Parkend Walk.[24]

Commissioners appointed in 1831 under the Dean Forest Commission Act (1 & 2 Will IV, c12) to enquire *inter alia* into the rights of Free Miners, heard much evidence regarding quarrying. On 24 December 1834, they were presented by 'the Free Miners in the occupation of quarries of stone' with a 'Memorial' to show:

1. That your memorialists claim, by custom existing from time immemorial, to have and exercise the privileges of Free Miners within the ancient perambulation of the Forest, being an exclusive right to open and work mines of iron and coal therein, and quarries of stone in the wastes of the Forest, and take the produce thereof for their own use or for sale, subject to the regulations of their own customs.

2. That to constitute a Free Miner, it is necessary that the person be born within the Hundred of St Briavels, the son of a Free Miner, and that he be resident therein. It is also understood to be necessary, that before a Free Miner can exercise his customary privileges on his own account, he should have worked a year and a day in an iron mine, coal work, or stone quarry of some other Free Miner within the aforesaid limits; though on this later point, as on some others, the usage has not been invariably uniform.

3. That with respect to quarries of stone, they claim that it is the duty of one of the King's gavellers in the Forest, on application by a Free Miner, to set out and deliver to him as a gale such convenient spot in the waste of the Forest for working a quarry as the Free Miner shall request, so as the same do not interfere with an older work of any other Free Miner, and be not in any garden or orchard belonging to any dwellinghouse; and that each gale should be 20 yards in breadth, if the situation of the ground will admit, and the work carried forward accordingly, in conformity with the Free Miners' custom.

4. That the custom as to working quarries is generally as follows: In the commencement of a quarry in a hill which approaches a circular form, the Free Miner takes a gale at its foot, and excavates in a right line towards the centre or most productive part of the hill, as far as the situation will allow. The Free Miner who takes the first gale has a right to determine the direction of his work to the centre. Any Free Miner who takes a gale adjoining the first must carry his work forwards in a direction parallel with the first, and so in like manner all successive gales must be worked in right lines parallel with the first, and with each other. Where the hill approaches a square, these parallel lines proceed at right angles from that side of the hill where the first work is commenced. Each Free Miner is precluded from making excavations laterally beyond the lines bounding his quarry on each side, but he may depart from the original horizontal line to suit the dip of the stone. The application of these rules is termed 'squaring the hill'. A gale may be taken on the directly opposite side of the hill, in which case the two opposite works would proceed until they met. A gale may not be taken otherwise ahead of a former one; but it may be taken beneath a former one, though in the same line, if the former is high up in the hill.

5.   That an entry of such gale should be written in the gaveller's book, on payment of a reasonable fee to him for his attendance, and signed by him; and thereupon the Free Miner to whom the gale has been delivered becomes entitled to hold the said quarry or gale to him and his heirs, and work the same, subject to a gale or rent of 3s 4d for the same to His Majesty on the Feast of St Michael the Archangel yearly, and subject to forfeiture of the gale in case the working thereof shall be wholly suspended for the space of a year and a day.

6.   That it is generally understood as the most ancient custom, that no other man than a Free Miner is entitled to work a quarry within the Forest; but if by descent, demise, or marriage any other person become seised of a quarry in his own or in his wife's right, he can only sell it to a Free Miner, or employ a Free Miner to work it, but that he can by no other means acquire any estate in a quarry in the Forest. But your memorialists admit, that occurrences have happened at variance with this ancient rule, to their detriment, through the default of the King's officers.

Signed:

Thomas Porter, Coleford.
Thomas Grindel, Coleford.
Richard Townsend, Coleford.
Richard James, Coleford.
William James, Coleford.
James Hawkins, Coleford.
William Simmons, Edge Hill.
Thomas Davies, Cleverend Green.
Thomas Williams, Ruardean Hill.
William Hawkins, Coleford.
Thomas Court, Herbert's Lodge.
Thomas Rosser, Coleford.
John Williams, Ruardean Hill.

Accompanying the 'Memorial' were:

1.   Copy presentment of the Jury of Survey, dated at St Briavel's 1684, 36 Chas II.
2.   An account of rents collected by Philip Elley up to 1788.
3.   An old gale-book, commencing September 1743, of Philip Elley, bailiff to Lord Berkeley.
4.   Various receipts for gale rent between September 1747 and 1804.
5.   Eleven accounts of Thomas James, steward of the Earl of Berkeley, from 1747 to 1762.

The Commissioners included the following in their 5th Report, dated 25 August 1835:

With regard to the quarries, it appears that persons born within the Hundred of St Briavels claim the right of opening stone quarries and digging stone in the waste lands of the Forest on payment of a fee to the gaveller of 3s, and an annual payment of 3s 4d. It is insisted upon by some of the witnesses that the further qualification of being born of free parents is necessary, and it is uncertain upon the evidence whether that sum would be payable for every person interested or by any number of persons in partnership. The ceremonies of taking a new work, the extent of it, and other particulars connected with it, are detailed in the evidence contained in the Appendix.

The practice appears to have prevailed either under the Crown or the lessees of the Crown since the time of James I. We do not, however, find any trace or evidence of it before the 19th year of that reign, in which year an 'Information' was filed in the Exchequer by the Attorney-General, on behalf of Sir Richard Catchmay, against certain persons for digging grindstone without his leave, upon which the court, without decreeing concerning the right, recommended, on account of the poverty of the defendants, that Sir Richard should not oppress them for so trifling an article, the stones not being worth more than the labour of rising them. What took place immediately after this recommendation does not appear, further than that some arrangement was made, by which each person who dug stones paid an acknowledgment of 3s 4d. But in 1721 and from thence from time to time payments appear to have been made to the Crown or its lessees with some variety of circumstances, in respect of the occupation of stone quarries in the Forest. Sometimes the payment of 3s 4d is made for a single quarry by an individual occupant, sometimes that sum covers several adjoining quarries and several partners, and sometimes a composition is made in respect of that sum considered as payable for every individual partner and for the occupation of each separate quarry.

In the Act of 20 Chas II, s 7 (1667), any grant, etc of or in any of the mines or quarries of or within the inclosures therein referred to, or any part thereof, is declared to be null and void; and by s 18, it is, among other things, provided that leases not exceeding thirty-one years to any persons in possession of the quarries of grindstone shall be of like force as if that Act had not been made.

Upon the whole it does not clearly appear to us that a good title can be established against the Crown, but we think it would not be right, after the long acquiescence in the usage, wholly to withdraw from those parties who now occupy quarries, or those who, according to their interpretation of the right, are now entitled to claim a gale, the advantages to be derived from the present system during their several lives, unless by giving them some compensation for their present interest.

We would recommend, therefore, as the best plan, that leases should be offered to all such parties born within the Hundred of St Briavels as shall apply for them within a certain specified time, on liberal and easy terms, or that an equivalent in money should be given in consideration of surrender to the Crown of the right claimed. And that all other persons occupying stone quarries for the future should be placed upon the footing of tenants to the Crown at fair conventional rents.

A claim [later refuted] has been made by Mr Ambrose, as lord of the manor of Blakeney, to grant gales and exact gale fees and rents within his bailiwick, founded upon a grant in the time of Edward III; but it does not appear to us that a good title can be established thereto against the Crown.

The Dean Forest Mines Act, 1838 (1 and 2 Vict, c 43) empowered a new Commission to ascertain what persons, whether as Free Miners or as claiming through or under them, were at the passing of the Act in possession of or entitled to stone quarries. The Commissioners were instructed to prepare schedules and plans of the quarries, to set forth rules and regulations for their working, and to set out the metes and bounds of each quarry and confirm its Award. They were only to award and define those quarries which had been *bona fide* in work within the five years next before the passing of the Act. Quarries awarded were to be held for 21 years from 29 September 1838, each at rents not exceeding 3s 4d per annum. If the owner was alive at the end of the 21-year period, he was to be allowed to continue in possession until his death, at the same rent; in other cases the rent was to be ascertained and fixed for 21-year periods by the gaveller. The qualifications of a Free Miner, so far as relevant to gales or leases of stone quarries within the open lands of the Forest, were to be similar to those for coal and iron ore, except that the statutory period of a year and a day should have been worked in a stone quarry within the Forest. The rights of quarrying were not to extend beyond the Forest perambulation. The Commissioners of Woods were empowered to grant leases of quarries to Free Miners for terms not exceeding 21 years.

Three years later, 24 July 1841, the Dean Forest Mining Commissioners made their 'Award of Quarries'. Gales totalling 313 were awarded, and the rent was 3s 4d per annum for each quarry not exceeding twenty yards in length 'and for every additional length, whenever the same shall extend to ten yards, a further rent calculated after the rate of 3s 4d per annum for every twenty yards'. The Awards were printed in 1841 (and reprinted in 1859) together with Rules and Regulations for the working of the quarries. The Annual Reports of the Commissioners of Woods include details of all leases of quarries subsequent to the Awards. Since Michaelmas 1859 the rent of quarries has been 20s for every quarry of 20 yards, and 1s for every additional yard of length.[25]

Among the duties of the Keepers of the Forest, at least during some parts of the nineteenth century, was reporting in connection with unlawful working and taking of stone and sand. The following are among the 'Presentments' of William Harvey, Keeper of Worcester Walk in 1838.[26]

May   2: Saw John Gwin filling a wagon with sand.
Oct   1: Saw James Fisher working at his quarry, not gavelled.
          Saw John Powell working at a new quarry.
Sept 27: Saw Mrs Aston digging sand.

Before the tramroad was laid to Lydney, stone for South Wales was hauled to Chepstow by road via St Briavels and Tidenham Chase. Four or more teams made up the convoy and helped each other up the 'pitches'. At Chepstow the stone was loaded into ketches and sloops which sailed to South Wales.

Nicholls, writing in 1858[27] of the Limestone beds of the district stated: 'the lower veins are locally called "blue stone", the middle "red stone", and the top vein the "white head", which is largely used as a flux in the smelting furnaces.' Referring to the Drybrook Sandstone, which he mistakenly calls Millstone Grit, Nicholls added:

This has been employed from very early times as a material for building . . . Most of the old buildings adjoining the parts where this grit crops out are formed of it, as several of the ancient neighbouring churches show, and likewise the oldest lodges in the Forest; now, however, this kind of stone is seldom used except for boundary walls, and such kind of rough work.

Of 'the Sandstone matrix of the coal-beds' he commented:

This constitutes the grey and buff-coloured rock so well known in the neighbourhood of the Forest as a valuable building material, as well as for ornamental stonework. Although for many years past it has been generally preferred to the gritstone of the district, and is commonly met with in the better specimens of stonework on this side of the Severn, of which Mr Telford's Over Bridge and Lord Somers' mansion at Eastnor are examples, yet originally such was not the case, since the earliest example of it being used for any considerable pieces of masonry occurs in the steeple of Ruardean Church, a work of the

15th century. Now, however, almost all the 320 stone quarries worked in the Forest are of this stone, which is very pleasing in tint and, if judiciously selected, very durable.

There had always been a fair market for Dean's stone, but towards the middle of the nineteenth century the trade was declining, partly because of adherence to old-fashioned methods of quarrying instead of the enterprising use of labour saving machinery which had come into use elsewhere. Among the quarrying enterprises were Porter Bros (established in 1820) with two quarries, and Trotter, Thomas & Co (established in 1836) with 20 quarries and, later, the Speech House Road Stoneworks. In 1850 Hall & Hall of London installed stone-sawing machinery at Parkend. The Mitcheldean Stone and Brick Works was begun by W. M. Colchester Wemyss in 1882, and at its peak employed some 70 men. Goodrich Court was built of its stone and bricks.

David & Co in 1889 owned Parkend Stone Works and 15 quarries. Three years later, an amalgamation was arranged—David & Sant Ltd—comprising David & Co, Trotter, Thomas & Co, and Porter Bros.[28] Other quarries were acquired, making a total of 41 by 1899. Between 300 and 350 workmen were employed. Wages for 'day-work' averaged 4s 4d a day; contract (or 'foot-work') enabled a higher wage to be obtained.[29] Knockley Quarries were being worked by George Smith, producing excellent 'Blue Forest Stone'. In 1900 the foregoing enterprises and the Wilderness Brick and Stone Co Ltd (Mitcheldean) were acquired by the Forest of Dean Stone Firms Ltd for £48,073.[30] Two independent firms operating in Dean were E. Turner & Sons (of Cardiff), with works at Bixslade Sidings and quarries at Fetterhill (Old Foggy), and Gorsty Knoll; and E. R. Payne & Son Ltd (of Newnham-on-Severn) with a stone works at Parkend and in Point Quarry, together with two quarries in the neighbourhood of Bixhead and Barnhill.

In 1899[31] the principal stone producing districts were the Fetterhill, Bixslade, Cannop Hill (Howlers Slade), Knockley and Wimberry Valleys (the local term for valley is 'slade'). The stone, pennant Sandstone from the coal measures, varied in texture and colour, usually in shades of blue and grey. The best Blue Stone beds are below the Grey, some 100–120ft below the surface according to the distance from the outcrop of Dean's geological basin-outcrop. There are usually four layers of Blue Stone varying from 2ft 6in to 5ft 6in in thickness; it is much superior to the Grey, in colour and texture, and commands a higher price as monumental and better class building stone. The

Grey variety is used for engineering work, such as for engine beds, docks, ashlar, coping and girder beds; also for steps, landings, and cills. Another shade of 'Forest Stone' was known as 'Mine Train Stone' (after the old iron ore mine once worked through David & Sant's quarry in Bixslade); it was very hard and durable, and varied in colour from grey to several shades of red: a large quantity was supplied in 1899 for tooled ashlar to the Marquis of Bute for some of his rooms in Cardiff Castle. Other quantities were used for docks and engineering purposes.

The method employed of splitting the rock was by cutting, with the quarry axe, main and cross V-shaped channels about 7in deep, and from $3\frac{1}{2}$ to 4in wide. Into these were inserted broad wedges, driven with a sledge-hammer, splitting the stone in a straight line down to its lower bed. Then with the aid of crow-bars and steam-crane, the blocks were torn from their beds and hoisted to the top of the quarry, where they were 'scrappled' to shape by the quarrymen, or sent in the rough to the works at Speech House Road and Parkend. Among the plant used to raise the stone from the quarries were 10- to 15-ton steam Guy Cranes, 10-ton Scotch Steam Derrick Cranes with 60ft jibs, similar 3-ton cranes, and hand cranes.

The stone was conveyed down the slades to the loading sidings by means of 'trams' drawn by horses—over tramways from $\frac{1}{2}$ a mile to $1\frac{1}{2}$ miles in length. The gradients were very steep, and because a team of horses took from 25 to 30 tons on each journey, great care and experience became a necessary qualification of the brake-men ('spraggers') in charge.

There were two main stone works. The machinery at Speech House Road (Plate 35b) in 1889 comprised three horizontal saw frames, one large machine to plane landings, steps, cills and pavings, and one exceptionally large circular saw. The machinery at Parkend comprised six horizontal sand and water saw frames, three planing and moulding machines, one circular rubbing table, several lathes, and an overhead gantry. Some 60 masons were employed, and the machinery was kept working night and day.

Until about 1900 the markets for Dean's stone were chiefly in the West of England and in South Wales (where it was valued because of its property of resisting impure atmosphere). Demands now came from London, Birmingham, Sheffield and Belfast. The piers and abutments of the Severn Railway Bridge (since demolished) were of Forest Stone. Other quantities were used in the Severn Tunnel.

Red (Wilderness) Stone, of the Old Red Sandstone formation, quarried exclusively near Mitcheldean, is of bright colour, fine texture and great hardness. It was used for carving in most classes of monumental work and in buildings, for example in Abenhall Lodge (J. W. Probyn), Mitcheldean House (Francis Wintle), Barnwood House (Gloucester), Flaxley Vicarage, part of Harrow College, and in buildings at Bristol, Birmingham, Barry, Cheltenham, Newport, Port Talbot and elsewhere.

In 1910 The United Stone Firms Co Ltd was formed, and acquired the chief stone enterprises in Dean. Three years later the Company published 'A treatise of Forest of Dean Stone' which included photographs of Speech House Road Stone Works, Point Quarries and Works, and Coffee Pit Quarries. The following year, their catalogue included photographs of stone works at Speech House Road, Bixslade, Cannop and Fetterhill; and of the quarries of Point, Coffee Pit, Oak (Plate 35a), Spion Kop, Bixhead, Wilderness, Birch Hill, Howlers Slade, and Knockley. In 1917 the Company went into liquidation, at a time when the industry suffered from suspension and cancellation of orders for general supplies of sawn monumental and building stone. The company continued under a receiver until it was reorganised and taken out of liquidation in 1926 by Walter Bryant, a native of Coleford, and later a Lord Mayor of Bristol. The company was incorporated as United Stone Firms (1926) Ltd. Thereafter there was foreign competition (eg Italian marble and granite).

Some of the quarries were independent. In 1925 the Whitecliff lime kilns and stone quarries were sold to a group of London financiers, the sale being negotiated by Sidney Taylor of Coombs Park, Coleford (later of Old Dean Hall near the Speech House).[32] Two years later, Taylor negotiated a sale of Drybrook Limestone Quarries (which had been idle for several years) the chief financiers being Joseph Ward and C. E. Parker of Sheffield.[33]

The United Stone Firms (1926) Ltd overcame many difficulties and gave welcome employment until in 1932 it went into liquidation and was run for about seven years by a receiver. In 1939 the enterprise was acquired by Frank Scott-Russell and others, and was renamed as the Forest of Dean Stone Firms Ltd. Mr Scott-Russell died in 1943, and subsequently his son Peter has been managing director, with Jack James (who had been manager from 1932 to 1939) as general manager.

After the 1939–45 war, the Whitecliff quarries were acquired by

47 Waterloo Corn Mill, Upper Lydbrook: *(above)* from a painting c1913; *(below)* a photograph c1930

48 *(above)* Corn Mill in Lower Lydbrook. Note the two grindstones; *(below)* Corn Mill at Longhope

Fred Watkins (Whitecliff Quarries) Ltd (who also made bricks there). The quarries were sold in the mid-1960s to Man-Abell (Whitecliff Quarry) Ltd. The Forest of Dean Stone Firms Ltd, operating from Bixslade Stone Works between Cannop and Parkend and employing in their works and quarries about 60 men, continued to market 'Bixhead Blue' and 'Barnhill Grey' Sandstone. Large quantities were supplied to the University College of Wales (Aberystwyth), the Nuclear Power Station at Berkeley, University College (London), the Shire Hall at Gloucester, and to many large bank buildings. In more recent years their stone was used for the Motor Port of the Severn Road Bridge and for the Long Bridge in Bideford. Their quarries at Bixhead and Barnhill are still in operation. So too is another quarry nearby which supplies the independent Pullen's (now Simpson's) Stone Works at Fetterhill (Plate 36c).

Many quarries other than those noted above have been worked throughout the Forest for roadstone ('road metal'), particularly in the Lower Dolomite at Hawthorns, Blackpool Bridge, Edge Hill, The Plump, Littledean Hill, Shakemantle (a huge quarry owned by Foster, Yeoman & Co Ltd), Bream, Staunton and Drybrook. Limestone for the same purpose has been quarried at Bearse and Stowe. The seven chief road-stone quarrying enterprises are now at Shakemantle (*supra*), Drybrook (Drybrook Quarries Ltd), Cherry Orchard (Hoveringham Stone Ltd, previously R. D. Sims), The Scowles (Rogers Quarries Ltd), Tidenham (T. S. Thomas & Son Ltd), and at Stowe and Whitecliff (Man-Abell, Ltd).

Many of the waste mounds of the derelict abandoned quarries, for example on Cannop Hill, are partly overgrown with gorse, while the crevices within them form a habitat for large colonies of jackdaws. Some quarries (again at Cannop Hill and at Bixhead) are awesome, and (although fenced) dangerous, and should be avoided.

Clay

Darkhill Brickworks near Fetterhill were owned by David Mushet in 1841, when they included 'sheds, stove and kiln, with a Horse Clay Mill for making firebricks'.[34] By his will dated 15 April 1847 he demised to three trustees 'bricks and belongings to the Darkhill Brickworks and an old clay level near thereto, and a dwellinghouse there occupied by Thomas Davis'.[35] The trustees on 12 July paid £2 'for

Y

mending the Clay Mill'. The premises were advertised for sale 13 July, and an inventory of the brickyard in that month reads: [36]

	£	s	d
1—7ft grinding stone with cast iron hoop 13in wide 1½in thick cast iron pan and fitted up for one horse	5	5	0
4 new clay carts 3ft 7in × 2ft 8in × 1ft 6in	5	0	0
4 old clay carts 3ft 7in × 2ft 8in × 1ft 6in	3	0	0
1 flat carriage, with 4 cast iron wheels, 12ft long × 4ft 2in wide		10	0
5 new shovels		11	3
1 spare cast iron roller for clay mill: 4cwt	1	4	0
3 spare cog wheels: 2cwt		12	0
1 Clay Rolling Mill with cog wheels, brass fittings etc complete, calculated for 2 horses	40	0	0
3 wheelbarrows		12	0
1 One-horse-power tempering mill	2	0	0
1 Bucket			6
Sundry old brick moulds		5	0
An old sheet iron pump 8ft long, 4in diameter, very inferior		2	6
11 empty casks		11	0
9 full casks of cement (iron)	2	5	0
324 12-inch squares at 6d	8	2	0
33,435 firebricks of various kinds at £3 15s a 1,000	125	12	0
3½ tons of tram plates, wide	14	0	0
12 tons of tram plates, narrow	48	0	0
At Lydney Wharf: 6,650 firebricks at 8s 100	26	0	0

A sale notice 17 April 1857[37] described them as 'containing less than ¼ acre, with Grinding Mill, Kilns, and Buildings for making firebricks and capable, when in repair, of producing 300,000 bricks per annum'. About this period J. Moore and J. Harper were raising clay at Darkhill under a Crown licence. The Darkhill Brickworks and others built on the old 'Titanic' site were later run by the Milkwall Brick Co.

James Grindell was raising clay near Darkhill in 1855, 'under the St Vincent Colliery Gale'.[38] His brickworks, situated at Fetterhill, a few hundred yards south-east of Darkhill, were run thereafter in conjunction with Philip Edell Wanklyn (trading as Wanklyn & Grindell). In 1875 and 1887 they were making 'firebricks and pottery'.[39] As late as 1907,[40] their 'pottery' was still in operation:

At a small factory [near] Coleford, which has been in existence for nearly 50 years, brown ware, both glazed and unglazed, is produced, besides chimney pots, tiles, crests, firebricks, and building bricks.

On 9 June 1932 the plant and equipment of the Milkwall Company's brickworks were scheduled to be auctioned 'under Distress for Rent [to the Crown] and by order of the Receiver:'

A brick manufacturing plant complete, comprising 7ft Pan by John Jones & Co Ltd, Loughborough, Pug-Mill no 6 with 20in Rollers by J. Whitehouse & Co, Preston, and Wire Cut Machine with cutting off table, the whole in working order. A quantity of 6in and 8in Balata Belting. A new Milan and Smith's Westing-House Dynamo, 50hp, 400–440 volts, and a 3-Phase Self Starter. A large quantity of Fire Arching and Square Bricks, Rails and Sleepers, 2 Winding Drums, Iron and Rubber Steam Piping, Brick Barrows, Planks, Stamping Machine, Iron Beds, 8 Iron Trams, Wood Benches, and Vices, Anvil, Grindstone, Erection of Lean-to Galvanised Office with window and door 10ft × 9ft, Old Iron, etc.

However, the auction was cancelled because the rent was eventually paid, and thereafter the enterprise was run by Milkwall Brickworks (1933) Ltd, until the works closed in 1937.

Another brickworks—Marions, between Coleford and Staunton—was owned in the 1840s and 1850s by James Hall of Redbrook ('spirit merchant, maltster and brickmaker') who manufactured 'firebricks of every description' for sale at 63s a thousand.[41] He was adjudged bankrupt in 1860—*vide* a Sale Notice, Valuation and Title in that year.[42] By 1902[43] D. Thomas owned the works, to be followed by the Coleford Brick & Tile Co. A small steam engine pulled clay to the works, and at a later date an overhead ropeway was erected above the Five Acres to Staunton road— at a time when the crop of the argillaneous measures associated with the Trenchard coal seams were being dug intermittently nearby. The works were closed c1940, and the premises are now used for the sawmills and fence manufactory of Dean Woodlands Ltd.

The Mitcheldean Stone and Brick Works (M W. Colchester Wemyss with J. Miller Carr as manager) were opened in 1882. At its peak, the works employed some 70 people who, besides producing building-stone and bricks (facing and moulded), made urns, bowls, tiles, drain-pipes, flower pots, garden vases, rustic stumps, pitchers, and architectural and fine art terra-cotta. There were three kilns, each capable of holding 65,000 bricks. The works closed c1907.

Fireclay raised in 1879 totalled 210 tons, and in the following year 886 tons,[44] while the surface clay raised in the same years were respectively 9,000 tons and 6,000 tons. Three tons of clay made about 1,000 bricks. In 1880 the local brickworks comprised:

	Kilns	*Men employed*
Nailbridge	7 (5 at work)	14
Darkhill*	4 (3 at work)	14
Coleford	2 (1 at work)	7
Cinderford	3 (1 at work)	3

* Darkhill was also making 'common red ware'.

Other places in Dean where bricks were made were Parkend (Christopher Morris, 1840),[45] near Coleford (J. Watts, 1856),[46] New Hulks Colliery (Soilwell), Stapledge,[47] Bilston,[48] Steam Mills, Ellwood (Ellwood Green Brick Co in the 1870s), Broadwell, and near Phipps Bottom. The Coleford Brick & Tile Co began a brickworks at Hawkwell (on the site of the tinplate works) using maiden clay from above 'the Spider Delph' nearby. The works still makes bricks by hand. The near-by Broadmoor Brick Company was founded in 1923 by the Lydney and Crumpmeadow Colliery Co. Now employing about two dozen men, it uses shale from the spoil heaps of the old Duck Pit and the Winning and Crumpmeadow collieries. Bricks were made at Whitecliff in the 1960s by Fred Watkins (Whitecliff Quarries) Ltd. Other bricks are still being made at Shakemantle Quarry by the Doura Brick Co.

Lime

Limestone in Dean was quarried and burnt for lime ('to manure lands' and for mortar) from at least Roman times, but records of it date from the thirteenth century. In 1252 the Constable of St Briavels Castle was ordered by the King to make in a kiln (*rogum*) '1,000 quarters of lime', and to deliver it to the Severn for the keepers of the works at Gloucester Castle.[49] Six months later, the Constable was instructed to make an additional 400 quarters and deliver the lime to the Severn with the 1,000 quarters 'lately made there'.[50] In May of the following year, the Constable was instructed to deliver to his castle, for the King's use there, one-half of the 1,400 quarters he had made, and to deliver the other half to the Severn for the sheriff of Gloucester.[51]

Many records are available thereafter of lime-burning, and the industry has continued until this century. Some was illegal: in 1691[52] a few inhabitants were accused of digging and burning lime. In 1787 there were 21 lime kilns in the Forest.[53] In 1880[54] much lime was 'burnt from the Limestone and utilised by the neighbouring farmers and others, as manure and for making mortar'. At Bream, for example, Hatheway & Wilden were lime-burners in 1887, and R. Shingles, Fred Watkins and G. H. Wildin in 1902; Timothy Moore was burning lime at Mitcheldean in 1858, and James White at the Plump in 1887.[55] Much lime-burning was done around St Briavels and Stowe (the families of Miles, Price, Dorrington, Russell and Burley).[56]

Thus lime kilns were a common feature, and many, now abandoned, are still to be seen within the Forest: a few which come readily to mind are at Whitecliff, Highmeadow (near Whitecliff), Bream, Blakeney Straits (Plate 37a), below Symonds Yat Rock, Oakwood, and Staunton. As late as 1942, Drybrook limestone for lime-burning was being worked at Milkwall (H. A. Smith) and Tidenham Chase (P. H. Ingledew).

Miscellaneous

Sandstone has been worked on a small scale for building-sand at several places including Drybrook, Lydbrook, Edge Hills, Crabtree Hill, Broadwell Lane End, and Dean's Meand. Concrete products are being made at Broadwell Lane End by Concrete Utilities Ltd of Ware.

A factory working marble was in operation at Bullo Pill on the Severn in 1823, and is believed to have stood north of the basin. An advertisement in 1825 records 'Bullo Pill Patent Marble Works'.[57] By April 1830, Sir James Jelf, of Bristol, had sold the works to a man from Camberwell, who intended to continue the business.[58] Samuel Hewlett supplied a boiler for the works. A visitor in the summer of 1831 observed there 'marble of Italy, England and Ireland wrought by British skill into the most useful and ornamental objects';[59] and the works were 'extensive and ingenious'. By April 1834 the proprietor, Mr Wrench, wanted to give up the works; the railway company agreed to terminate the tenancy on 24 June next, and the 'engines and old machinery' were to be sold in the following October.[60] In that month, the Protheroes unsuccessfully sought a lease of the works for a tinplate or other factory.[61]

Cement was made near the 'Wilderness', west of Mitcheldean (Plate 36a) from c1894 to c1919 by The Forest Portland Cement Co. The chief source of material was the 'Cementstone Quarry' one-third of a mile SW of Mitcheldean, working the Lower Limestone Shales. In 1894, William Fennell was the 'analytic-chemist' there.[62] A photograph of c1910 (Plate 36a) shows the premises. In 1912, about 60 tons of cement were sent daily by rail, and some 200 men were employed. The works closed during the First World War—partly because the German-made gas engine which powered some of the machinery had failed.

References to Chapter 7

1   Hart, C. E. *Archaeology in Dean*, 1967, 9.
2   C145: *Cal Misc Inquisitions*, III, 20 Aug 1362.
3   E101/141/1.
4   SC6/858/15.
5   Ibid, 850/20.
6   E134 35 Chas II, Mich 40.
7   Smith, John. *Men and Armour for Gloucestershire in 1608*, 31–76.
8   Fosbrooke. *History of the County of Gloucester*, 1807, III, 112.
9   39th Rpt of the Commissioners of Woods . . . , 28 June 1861.
10   Hart. *The Free Miners*.
11   Ibid.
12   Nicholls. *History* . . . , 27.
13   E134 13 Chas I, Mich 42 and 13–14 Chas I, Hil 16.
14   SP16/468/560.
15   *Third Report*, 1788, 14.
16   Nineteenth-century copy, *penes me*.
17   BM Harl. MSS 6839, fol 335.
18   E134 27 Chas II, Mich 28 and Hil 21.
19   GRO Probyn Papers, 457.
20   E134 35 Chas II, Mich 40.
21   GRO, Machen MSS.
22   Nicholls. *History* . . . , 286.
23   Marshall. *Rural Economy of Gloucestershire*, 1796, I, 37.
24   Drivers' Survey in 1787.
25   39th Rpt of the Commissioners of Woods . . . , 1861.
26   MS book of William Harvey, *penes me*.
27   Nicholls. *History* . . . , 247.
28   *The Quarry and Builders' Merchant*, IV, (37) Jan 1899, 3–11.
29   *The Quarry*, II, Feb 1897, 37. See also Smith, William. 'The Forest of Dean Stone Quarries', ibid, I, Oct 1896, 191–2.
30   *Forest Newspapers*, 18 May 1900.
31   *The Quarry and Builders' Merchant*, IV (37) Jan 1889, 3–11.
32   *The Quarry & Surveyors' & Contractors' Jnl*, 30, 1922.
33   Ibid, 32, 40.
34   GRO Q/Rum/175.
35   Ibid, D637/II/7/B7, B9.
36   Ibid.
37   Ibid, D192/4.
38   34th Rpt of the Commissioners of Woods . . . , 1856, 133.

39 *Harris's Directory*, 1887.
40 *Vict C Hist Glos*, II, 1907, 215; F16/50 (MR 417).
41 GRO D637/II/5/L2, B1.
42 Ibid, B3.
43 *Harris's Directory*, 1902.
44 Insole and Bunning, op cit, 69, 90.
45 Duncan Committee Rpt, 1840, App B7.
46 Ibid.
47 F16/50 (MR 417).
48 Ibid.
49 *Cal Liberate Rolls*, IV, 38.
50 Ibid, 77.
51 Ibid, 125.
52 E134/6080.
53 Drivers' Survey, 1787.
54 Insole and Bunning, op cit, 70.
55 *Harris's Directory*, 1887, 1902; *Slater's Directory*, 1858.
56 Creswick, W. J. *Where I was Bred*.
57 *Gloucester Journal*, 28 March 1825.
58 F of D Rly Min Bk, 13 April 1830.
59 *The Forester*, 2 and 9 June 1931, 12, 22.
60 F of D Rly Min Bk, April 1834.
61 Ibid, Oct 1834.
62 *Kelly's Directory*, 1894.

Eight
Gold-mining

In Dean, near the top of the Old Red Sandstone, are conglomerates of sedimentary origin, largely made up of quartz-pebbles embedded in a red sandy matrix composed of quartz grains of various sizes. The conglomerate bed is exposed at many places on the edge of the coal-basin. The Buckstone near Staunton is part of the continuation of the same bed which completely encircles the basin and is continuous beneath it. The formation presents a resemblance to the 'Banket' or gold-bearing conglomerates of the Transvaal, Rhodesia and West Africa, but in the case of Dean the proportion of gold is much smaller. Throughout the centuries attempts have been made to test the suitability of the deposits for working on profitable lines.

Until 1680 there are no direct references to the Forest of Dean in connection with gold. However, there is reason to believe that when grants were made in previous centuries in connection with Gloucestershire, Dean was one of the districts particularly involved.

On 22 October 1370[1] 'an indenture was made between Edward III of the one part, and Robert Rous of Bristowe and William de Notyngham of Bissheie of the other part, being a lease for seven years from this date of all the king's mines of gold, silver, lead and tin found in Gloucestershire in hills, fields, waste places, etc.[2] The king was to have for his seignorage the ninth pound of all plate of gold and silver arising from the mines, and 'where lead ore shall be found the lord of the soil shall have the thirteenth part of the ore, and where tin shall be found the tenth part of the tin ore, and the lessees the residue of the profit'.

The following year, on 12 July,[3] the same two lessees were 'appointed to take twelve miners, stampers (boliarios) and smelters (meltarios) in the county of Somerset and put them to work in the king's mines of gold, silver, tin and lead in the county of Gloucester, which the king has demised to them at farm, to stay there as long as shall be necessary, at their wages'.

In the previous year,[4] Edward III had granted William de Notyngham all his mines of gold, silver, lead and tin in Gloucestershire for seven years and later he obtained like grants for other counties. A similar grant was made to Henry Burton in 1378; other grants were made in 1382 and 1388.[5] In 1427 the gold rights within Gloucestershire passed in the general grant to John, Duke of Bedford. On 30 July 1462[6] the king granted a five-year licence 'to Galias de Lune, William Marynere and Simon Spert to mine within the counties of Somerset and Gloucestershire for lead, tin or copper ore in which silver or gold may be had, yielding to the king every eighth bolle[7] of ore, and to make mills and take workmen as they require'.

There was another grant in 1465. In 1485 the Gloucestershire gold rights were included with other counties in the general mining commission granted to Jasper, Duke of Bedford and others.[8] In 1564 Gloucestershire was included in a patent or monopoly granted by Queen Elizabeth to William Humphreys, Cornelius Devos, Daniel Hochstetter (or Houghsetter) and Thomas Thurland, to seek for gold, silver and quicksilver in certain counties (including Gloucestershire) in England, Wales and Ireland within the Pale.[9] The company formed to work this grant was incorporated by charter in 1568 as 'The Society for the Mines Royal'. Another grant in 1565 to William Humphreys and Christopher Schutz was worked by 'The Society of the Mineral and Battery Works'. The Societies were later amalgamated and held their monopolies until after the middle of the nineteenth century.[10] It does not appear that their operations at any time met with any degree of success. The above patents were confirmed and amplified by James I and became the charter of the Mines Royal Company.

In c1680, a gold mine was discovered at 'Little Taunton' [Taynton] in Gloucestershire. 'The Society of Mines Royal seized them [this and another] and granted two leases of them to some refiners, who extracted some gold; but they did not go on with the work, as the gold sometimes would not repay or requite the charge of separation though often it did.'[11]

On 9 July 1685, Henry Guy (presumably on behalf of the Treasury) wrote to Sir Robert Howard (Auditor of the Receipt) and William Harbord (Surveyor-General) enclosing a petition[12] from Abraham Shapton regarding the Taynton mines. They were instructed 'to deliver to him [Shapton] the lease about the mines royal in Great Taunton, co. Gloucester'.[13]

On 4 October of the same year Howard and Harbord were instructed 'to report on the Petition of Abraham Shapton showing that he has received back the lease and assignment of the mines royal holding (as he believes) gold and quicksilver, assigned to Sir Robert Howard and the Surveyor-General which they are ready to assign back to the petitioner: but being unable to pay the five years now due by his covenants to the Company on the £10 per annum rent or to set the mine on work, the petitioner prays to be paid said £50 or for the Lord Treasurer to purchase the estate'.[14] The three 'old quarries' marked on the six-inch Ordnance Map in the neighbourhood of 'Black House' may have been near Shapton's workings.

There are no further records to assist, except that Calvert[15] mentions 'On the discovery of gold in Gloucestershire and Bedfordshire in the last century [ie the eighteenth] the Crown grantees seized the mines and worked them', while Fosbrooke[16] referring in 1807 to Taynton wrote: 'It has been asserted that in about 1700 gold was extracted from an ore found here, but not in sufficient quantity to repay expense.' Again, the sale particulars of an estate at Taynton, 1844, refer to the matter and add: 'Mining and refining is now a much more simple and less expensive operation than it was a century ago. A spirited individual may find this "a Mine of Wealth".'

In 1906 gold was reported to have been discovered in the auriferous conglomerates near Micheldean, and operations of an exploratory kind were carried out. In this connexion an adit[17] was driven into the Lea Bailey hill side about $1\frac{1}{2}$ miles south-west by south of Micheldean Road station.[18] Samples from the eastern outcrop were collected by C. G. Cullis and L. Richardson, and were assayed by E. A. Wright in the Metallurgical Laboratories of the Royal School of Mines, who reported that the samples contained a small amount of both gold and silver. According to J. M. Maclaren[19] the siliceous pebbly conglomerates were found to carry about 6 grains of gold to the ton.[20] It was found that gold did not occur in sufficient quantity to be workable with profit.

In 1963, Gerald Rudge[21] interviewed some of the residents in the neighbourhood of the Lea Bailey and Mitcheldean, but their recollections were hazy, and sometimes quite contradictory.

In the Lea Bailey enclosure on the western slopes of Wigpool there are many shallow trenches in the wood around the outcrop of the conglomerate which are understood to have been used for sluicing, although it is difficult to see where the water came from. It has been suggested that they were merely trenches of an exploratory nature, possibly dug in an endeavour to make the work of the syndicates dealing with the operation look alive.[22] Trial digs were also carried out at

Staple Edge, near Soudley, but without success. Some of the holes may be seen close to the quarry worked in the 1950s by Forest Concrete Products Ltd.

The syndicate formed to seek for gold was the Chastan Syndicate Ltd, of which the following particulars are given in the 1908 volume of the Stock Exchange Official Intelligence:

Chastan Syndicate Ltd. Registered 20 November 1906. 13/14 Abchurch Lane, EC. Directors: Sir H. F. Nicholson, K.C.B. (Chairman), Dr J. H. Crowley, F. G. Jones, C. F. Kennedy. Secretary, H. H. Thompson. Mining rights have been acquired in the Forest of Dean, Gloucestershire, over about 1,814 acres of gold-bearing property, and an adjoining property of about 109 acres has been purchased. Development is in progress. Authorised and Issued Capital—£49,000 in £1 shares fully paid. No accounts have been issued and no dividend has been paid. Transfer form—Common; fee 2/6d. Telegraphic address: 'Perpetuity' London. Telephone No. 5132 Bank.

In 1907 a Take Note was granted to the syndicate by the Commissioners of Woods to work the gold, gold ore, silver and silver ore in about 3,677 acres of land in or adjacent to Dean. The land in question ran in a belt north-east from Cockshoot inclosure. The Take Note terminated by effluxion of time in 1908 and was not renewed.[23] From a report[24] of an Ordinary General Meeting of the syndicate held on 25 July 1908 it is learnt that there were 700 shareholders. The venture had been a failure, and, although there were 'assets worth about £7,000', there were no funds in hand. An auctioneer's catalogue 3 July 1907 of some effects of the Chastan Syndicate Ltd includes equipment at Fairplay Iron Mine and Inkerman colliery; however the sale particulars do not mention gold mining. The syndicate was wound up in September 1908, the Liquidator being G. C. Harrower, College Hill Chambers, Cannon Street, London, E.C.4. The only reference to the syndicate found since that time is the following note written in 1913 by A. O. Cooke in his book, *The Forest of Dean*:

Has any reader cause to rue the once much talked of Chastan Syndicate, formed to discover English gold? We are within hail of one at least of the imagined seams [Staple Edge]; digging was for some time carried on within our woodman's 'beat' on Staple Edge—much to his wonder and amusement, his local knowledge not disposing him to sink his savings in the enterprise. But he understands that 'many ladies in London put a heap of money into it'—a statement doubtless true.

At one time there were hopes that gold would be workable in another part of the Forest, and the 86th Report of the Commissioners of Woods[25] contains the following records: '28 Oct 1907: Sale of Mines Royal in parts of the Clearwell Court Estate'. When the estate was offered for sale in 1908, the sale particulars stated:

> It is believed that the conglomerate rock, in which gold has lately been discovered in the Forest of Dean, lies under a great portion of the Estate. By a Deed of Conveyance dated 28 October 1907 the gold and gold ore, and silver ore, and all other Mines Royal under Ord. Nos. . . . were granted by the Crown to the predecessors in title of the present Vendors' Testator and are comprised in the sale.

Subsequently, during 1907 to 1921, the Office of Woods received several applications to prospect for, and to win, gold and silver in Dean;[26] however, no work was undertaken.

It is of interest to record the attempts at gold mining in the district, although there does not appear any prospect, even with modern processes, of the conglomerate being worked as an economic proposition for gold. Therefore it is unlikely that in Dean one will ever meet a goldminer . . . 'in a cavern, in a canyon, excavating for a mine'! And, of course, any gold found belongs to the Crown.

References to Chapter 8

1   Close Rolls 44 Edw III, m 7d.
2   For some additional details of a similar grant in Devon and Somerset, see *Close Rolls*, 43 Edw III, m 9d.
3   Pat Rolls, 45 Edw III, m 31.
4   Calvert, John. *The Gold Rocks of Great Britain and Ireland*, 1853, 98.
5   Ibid.
6   Pat Rolls, 2 Edw IV, m 7.
7   Perhaps 'barrow', or 'billy'—a load carried on the back.
8   Calvert, op cit, 99.
9   *Opera Mineralia Explicata*, 26; Pettus, John. *Fodinae Regales*, 46; Calvert, op cit, 120–1.
10 Lewis. *The Stannaries*, 41–2.
11 Abbot's *Essay on Metallic Works*, 1833, 203; Watson's *Compendium of British Mining*, 1843, 60.
12 Now missing.
13 Out Letters (General) IX, 101; Cal Treasury Bks, VIII, 252 (T27/9).
14 Ibid, 152; ibid, 354 (T27/9).
15 Calvert, op cit, 40.
16 Fosbrooke. *History of the County of Gloucester*, 1807.

17 Later known as the Bailey Level which was worked for iron ore. An article on the Chastan Syndicate Ltd appeared in the *Dean Forest Guardian*, 26 April 1907.

18 Cullis, C. G. and Richardson, L., 'Some remarks on the Old Red Sandstone Conglomerate of the Forest of Dean and the Auriferous Deposits of Africa', *CNFC*, XVI, 1907, 81–5.

19 Maclaren, J. M. *Gold: its geological occurrence and geographical distribution*, 1908, 122–3.

20 There are 480 grains to the troy ounce.

21 The Gloucester *Citizen*, 28 Aug 1963.

22 One local resident suggested that some gold had been placed in the conglomerate!

23 Information from The Forestry Commission, 16 March 1945.

24 *The Times*, 27 July 1908, 17, col 6.

25 86th Rpt of the Commissioners of Woods . . . , 29 June 1908, 64 App 7.

26 F3/1029, 1033, 1246, 1249, 1472. Applicants included J. Godbott and J. Dolman.

Nine
Silviculture
and Woodland Produce

The history of Dean so far as it concerns silviculture and woodland produce has been related and documented in *Royal Forest*.[1] From being a region conserved chiefly for hunting 'beasts of the chase', by the sixteenth century Dean became a forest renowned especially for its ship-timber. Despite the conservation practised from at least the twelfth century, whole trees, or their timber and wood, were given away by the King to noblemen, monasteries and churches, or used for his castles, or sold on his behalf. Numerous smaller trees, usually coppice and other underwood, were sold (or illegally taken) to smelt iron ore. Of such sales, references have been found to over £3,000 expected or received in the twelfth and thirteenth centuries. Burning of charcoal, for bloomeries and forges, was widespread. Many other trees provided timber to shore up small mines. Oaks were used for the King's galleys, and for shingles to roof castles and churches, while their bark sustained small tanneries. Another use of wood was in quarrels for crossbows—from 1223 to 1293, at least half a million were despatched from St Briavels; the total output may have been much greater, because the annual output was often 25,000.

Similar utilisation continued throughout subsequent centuries, but in Elizabeth I's reign, trees suitable for ship-timber were conserved (sometimes beyond their prime). Thereafter, the iron industry expanded, necessitating increased supplies of charcoal. Up to the Civil War, only a little ship-timber had been used, and the first ship to be built in Dean sailed in 1633 (see Chapter 14).

During the Commonwealth (1649–60) and after the Restoration, some silviculture was practised, much ship-timber was sent to naval dockyards, and several ships were built on the Severn (see Chapter 14). Many trees were used for various purposes—house and bridge-building, laths, staves, 'cardboard', saddle trees, and trenchers. The charcoal iron blast furnaces in Dean virtually ended in 1674, but much charcoal and cordwood sustained neighbouring ironworks to c1800.

Throughout the eighteenth and nineteenth centuries, silviculture progressed, and increased supplies of timber went to the Navy, to the miners, and to contractors. From the 1850s, when iron replaced timber in the building of ships, the rôle of Dean's woodlands changed to that of pure silviculture in order to grow trees for multifarious purposes, which later enabled the Forest to play an invaluable part in supplying some of the necessities of the two World Wars. Credit is due, first to the Office of Woods, and from 1919 to the Forestry Commission. Uses of the trees have been touched upon in Chapters 1 and 2 (The Charcoal Iron Industry); and the uses of the cordwood are emphasised in Chapter 10 (Wood Chemical Works). In this chapter some of the other usages are discussed.

Charcoal-burning

Wood consists largely of carbohydrates (compounds of carbon and water) which burn at relatively low temperatures, and for this reason, no matter how dry, cannot be used as an industrial fuel where very high temperatures are required. If, however, wood is subjected to a process

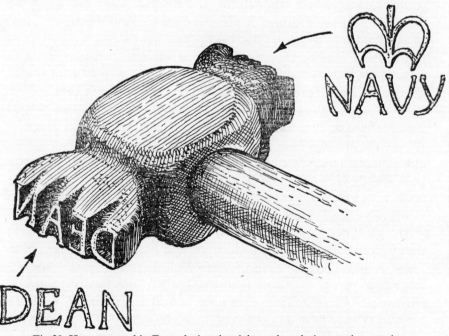

Fig 20. Hammer used in Dean during the eighteenth and nineteenth centuries.

of distillation in the absence of air, the carbohydrates break down and volatile compounds are driven off, leaving carbon in the form of charcoal, and a small quantity of ash. Because the ash and impurity content of well 'made' charcoal is low, it can be considered essentially as available carbon. Thus wood can be turned into an ideal high-temperature fuel for smelting of iron ore, forging of iron, and domestic heating and cooking.

Charcoal-burning is one of the oldest industries in the world. From the days when early man first conjured metals from their ores and forged them, until the invention of the coke oven in the eighteenth century, charcoal was essential to every smith and ironworker, and part of the foundation of British industrial wealth was laid by the grimy charcoal-burners of the woods. All the bronze, iron, glass, and precious metals of the ancient and medieval craftsmen were refined by its use. Early man and his successors produced charcoal by firing wood in simple open-air 'stacks'. To limit the supply of air, thus obviating the wooden billets bursting into flame, earth or turf was used as covering. The charcoal was recovered, but all the by-products were wasted.

In Dean, charcoal was almost wholly used to smelt iron ore. Its production was the chief reason for the impoverishment of the woods, yet its burning was a rational use, and natural replenishment of the cover would have followed if animals, both wild and domestic, had been fenced out. From at least the thirteenth century the trade maintained many people. Thus their presence was tolerated by those who administered the Forest, and though it is evident that their occupations disregarded much forest law (beasts of the forest and their habitat were more important than trees, and almost more important than people) usually charcoal-burners were a necessary and welcome class of operatives. Grantees of woods within the Forest found the trade lucrative, although often unlicensed.[2] In 1237[3] the king ordered his forest officers to 'diligently view and enquire' in what places his eight movable forges could with least damage be set up to use maple, thorn, hazel, and dead wood; oaks, beeches, ash and chestnuts were not to be used.

The great destruction committed by charcoal-burners is recorded in the eye-roll of 1270; they 'bought wood and timber of the foresters-of-fee and made charcoal both of that which they thus bought and the other large part of wood and timber which they took furtively throughout various places'.[4] They were fined and 'it is ordered that no one henceforth may have any charcoal-pit in the Forest'. The small effect produced by this order is evidenced by 2,290 hearths, old and new,

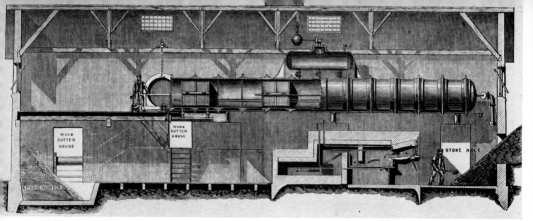

49 Cone Paper Mill: the wood paper-making machinery, 1869: *(top)* front elevation; *(centre)* front view of the timber slicer; *(bottom)* end view of the timber slicer. The boiler exploded in June 1873 and destroyed the mill

50 *(above)* Cone Paper Mill: buildings which had been converted to a laundry, 1967; *(below)* Guns Mill Paper Mill and dwelling house

found by the Forest regarders in 1282, who drew attention to the stools obliterated by the hearths and their ill-effect of preventing re-coppicing.[5] For the year 1279–80 the constable of the Forest accounted for £7 7s 'for old branches and underwood sold divers times to make charcoal, which is called in these parts old charcoal-pits'.[6] The value of the wood used for making charcoal to maintain a forge for a whole year seems to have been anything from £12 to £70 according to estimates of that time.[7] Occasionally charcoal was brought in from outside the Forest.[8]

At times wood for charcoal was obtained at the king's expense,[9] at others it was carefully assessed by 'the hearth', 'the pit', or 'the week'.[10] Two documents, probably the earliest of their kind, give specific details for Dean under the heading *vendico fossarum* (sale of charcoal-pits). The first, of 1278,[11] names 52 people who had been making charcoal; the charges against them varied, eg 2 pits for a total of 9 weeks at 5s, ie £2 5s, and the total charges came to £58 7s. The second document, of 1279,[12] names some 48 burners; the charge against them was usually 5s for 4 or 5 weeks, and the total £43 1s. Both documents give the number of weeks each person operated, and name the places in the Forest.

In 1325[13] charcoal was sold at 9s a dozen of 12 seams (probably 12 bushels). In the following year[14] some underwood was sold 'for the sole reason that, by an unfortunate fire from a certain charcoal pit setting light to the bracken, the wood was accidently burned; and so that it might grow again the order was made for the cutting and selling'. In 1333,[15] 9 acres of underwood were sold for 40s 6d, and cost 20s 3d to cut and burn into charcoal. Thus underwood fetched 4s 6d an acre, cutting and charcoaling cost 2s 3d an acre, and it took 9 man-days to cut and convert one acre. Wages at that time were 3d a day. An interesting reference in 1435–6[16] is to charcoal used for domestic heating—for 'Speeches Day'[17] at Kensley. This was obviously to heat the court-room when inhabitants appeared before the verderers to speak of their privileges and requirements, particularly in respect of common and estovers (botes).

By Henry VIII's reign trees were still relatively plentiful but scattered and neglected, and did not warrant too much concern. Game was no longer ultra important; there were only remnants of the herds of earlier centuries. The woods by now were reduced to between 15,000 and 20,000 acres, chiefly of the silvicultural system known as high forest, with only a little coppice-with-standards which came more to the

z

fore following the Statute of Woods of 1543. The widely-spaced stand-ards, chiefly of oak, were reserved for timber for ships and other build-ing, and when felled their bark was used for the tanning of leather. The coppice, chiefly of hazel, field maple, thorn, holly and other inferior species, served a variety of purposes besides that of fuel for smelting, among them fences, hurdles, domestic fuel, and for use in 'wattle and daub'. 'Standards' (termed 'stadelles' or 'storers') had to be conserved on each acre of coppice, and the new growth had to be protected by fencing or hedging. But contemporary with Dean's conserved areas must have been thinly stocked woods with 'scrub, brushwood, and thicket, where the trees were being thinned out by the action of man and beast'. No full silvicultural policy had as yet evolved, and the need for ship-timber was potential rather than current.

By Elizabeth I's reign the need to conserve ship-timber was import-ant. Charcoal-burning, though ostensibly it took only the smaller, in-ferior trees and the lop and top, was in opposition to a policy of conservation. However, three important Acts in the first, twenty-third and twenty-seventh years of the reign (though they did not apply to Dean) prohibited the felling of timber-trees of oak, beech and ash to make charcoal, if the trees were within 14 miles of the sea or of any navigable river. Coppice and underwood, of any species below medium timber-size, were the best material for charcoal and where accessible to bloomeries and forges, were needed in uninterrupted supply. Regular customers of wood for smelting relied on the leasing or purchasing of coppice-woods 15 to 30 years old, enclosed against animals; four to eight rotations of crops could be raised instead of about 12 timber-trees an acre which might decay before felling was permitted. Owners and lessees of coppices disliked leaving standards which limited the useful wood in a coppice; they were tempted to cut down the 12 reserved on each acre under the Statute of Woods, and to leave younger ones in their stead. Elizabeth's Act of 1559 defined timber-trees as at least 'one foot at the stubble'. The provision for 12 standards on each acre gave room for oaks to develop big boles and crowns with large branches, ideal for ship-building; any heavier stocking would have drawn up the oaks and re-duced the amounts and quality of the more saleable under-storey, the cop-pice; and wood for fuel was in more demand than timber. Taverner's survey of Dean's woods in 1565 shows chiefly neglect and secondly the effect of the iron industry. Some of its woods were pure coppice, some were coppice-with-standards but the large majority were still the silvi-cultural system called 'high forest'—like many of its hardwood areas to-

day, but with one major difference: the larger trees were mostly debranched, some 'well-nigh unto the top'. The effect on a tree of this
debranching, termed shredding, sometimes done when the underwood
was cut, would depend on the care used in such 'pruning'. As growth in
girth is proportionate to crown, excessive shredding reduced the annual
increment. But shredding gave some benefits: it obviated the taking
of timber-trees; the tree itself had less adverse effect on the coppice
under or near it; and when felled the debranched tree did less damage
to the underwood. Shredding was condoned, as shown by a warrant
issued by Taverner 3 November 1572:[18]

> The underwood together with the lopping and shredding of all those
> trees which heretofore have been used to be lopped and shred, grow-
> ing in the Forest of Dean, are meet to be sold this year to the ore-
> smiths in the same Forest. No timber-trees nor saplings of oak likely
> to be a timber, to be fallen by colour hereof. And the spring [ie the
> seedlings and re-growth] reserved.[19]

The voracious blast furnaces came to Dean's borders by 1575. Iron
works at Lydbrook, Whitchurch, and Bishopswood made the chief
demands. In 1610, coppices totalling 520 acres on the east of the Forest
were leased for Winter's Lydney furnace; surveyors said that 30 cords
an acre, or 15,600 in all, could be raised, reserving sufficient standards
for the State; Winter asserted that no revenue had been received from
the coppices for 27 years and no more than £7 yearly at any time. The
price paid by Winter for his 21-year lease was £800, ie about 30s an
acre, or 1s a cord. By 1611 ironmasters connected with the above and
other works obtained concessions of Dean's trees and permission to
erect blast furnaces within the woods. These and later concessions
led to large-scale depletion of Dean's woods despite prohibitions, committees, commissioners, and a host of forest officials high and low—all
detailed elsewhere.[20] During the Commonwealth, to supplement
enclosure the first sowing of seed and planting took place; this was
commendable but inadequate.[21] At the time, 45s a load was paid for
producing large charcoal and 22s 6d for small, termed 'brazes'.[22]
In 1660, 'of all bad and good wood generally there went 5½ short cords
of wood to make a load of charcoal'; and 'there went to make a ton of
sow iron, two loads or sacks of charcoal or thereabouts'.[23]

Soon a more enlightened policy was to be projected in Dean. During
the century, the Forest had contributed towards the support of government by way of iron and ship-timber, and had been the great recourse

for gratifying the favourites of the monarchs, but the improvident and often ill-defined grants of concessions as to timber and ironworks, with the confused mixture of rights and privileges created by them, and coupled with rights of common, pannage, and estovers, had the worst possible effect on the woods. The whole was 'a perpetual struggle of jarring interests, in which no party could improve his share without hurting that of another'.[24] Dean's need of protection, rehabilitation and conservation was urgent, and legislation to effect this came by way of the Dean Forest (Reafforestation) Act 1667. Seven years later the King's Ironworks were demolished—the end of 64 years sporadic activity.[25] Since 1610 these and other works in the neighbourhood had used immense quantities of wood—a ton of charcoal requiring about 8 tons of wood, or a load of charcoal needing $2\frac{1}{2}$ to 3 long cords or $4\frac{1}{2}$ short cords. After 1674, only ironworks outside Dean's woods, at Flaxley, Lydney and Redbrook, and those in Monmouthshire and Herefordshire, were sustained by her cordwood. Unsuccessful attempts were made to induce the Crown to enter the iron industry, because ample supplies of cordwood were still available. In this connection it was stated that to make a ton of raw iron $4\frac{1}{2}$ cords at 8s = 36s were required, cutting and cording would cost 12s, charcoaling 6s 8d and carriage to works 8s. To make a ton of bar iron £3 12s 6d worth of charcoal would be needed, plus carriage of 8s.[26] Following the Act of 1667, sowing, planting, and enclosure were effected, but little of this commendable work came to fruition (beyond producing some invaluable ship-timber) due to the opposition of commoners and the laxity of officials. Natural growth of inferior species produced much wood which was sold for charcoal to supply the works at Flaxley, Lydney and Redbrook and others further afield. Thus the trade of charcoal-burning on a fairly large scale continued in Dean much longer than elsewhere—indeed to at least 1795, when coke (much later than in most parts of the country) began to be used for smelting

Charcoal-burning did not die out. After the last local blast furnace closed, and even after supplies were no longer needed by the more modern forges at Lydney and Lydbrook, there was always a market (despite the local near-monopoly of the 'steweries'—see Chapter 10) for comparatively small quantities of differing grades for numerous purposes in London and elsewhere. Burning in the woods was done before, during and after the First World War by families (usually father and son) of which the more prominent were those of Faulkes (see Chapter 10), Hardwick, and Roberts. A comprehensive set of photographs (1909–12) of the activities of the Hardwicks is extant (Plates 38 and 39).[27] From these and other contemporary records it is clear that in general the method of making charcoal (little changed from time immemorial) was as follows. A dome-shaped stack was made of billets of wood from small trees or branchwood of hardwoods (not conifers). It was covered with sods and earth, and a few inlet flues (mere holes) were left at ground level, with one outlet flue at the top. Skill was needed to build a stack which would char well and evenly without collapsing, and to start the fire down in the heart of it. After the fire had got under way, and the wood near the core had been burned and to some extent destroyed, the inlet flues were gradually closed. The remaining wood then received insufficient air for its complete combustion, but sufficient heat remained to force out the volatile matter as gases, leaving the carbon content behind. The charcoal-burners lived a lonely life, because they could not leave their work by day or night. The process took several days to complete and continually the charcoal-burner had to stay beside his stack, watching it every few hours in fear that a sudden collapse of its earthen covering might admit too much air and so cause the whole stack to be destroyed, or to have to be laboriously rebuilt. Stopping the process was even more tricky than starting it off. Any sudden inrush of air before the stack was quite cold would cause the whole to catch fire. First the slow fire had to be extinguished by closing all the flues, which was done soon after a change in the colour of the smoke from white to blue indicated to the charcoal burner that the right stage had been reached. The stack was allowed to cool off for two or three days, being watched the while, whilst the burner filled in the time by building his next stack. Then it was opened, somewhat hopefully, and if it had cooled sufficiently, it was unpiled. As a rule, water was added to ensure safe cooling. Thereafter it was a question of separating the 'brunts' (partly burned ends of billets) from the charcoal, and grading and bagging the latter.

The last charcoal-burner in Dean was E. A. Roberts (Plate 41a) who lived near Guns Mill. Two short accounts of his life and techniques are available.[28] He began his activities during the First World War, and in the 1939–45 war, despite the five-year blackout, he made charcoal in the open for the first three years. During the Second World War batteries of charcoal-burning portable metal kilns (like a huge stove with a removable lid and chimney) were worked in Dean, as elsewhere. This is an unskilled method whereby wood is thrown into a large 'drum'. Roberts was put in charge of these charcoal 'cookers'. He temporarily returned to normal burning for a few years after the war. Since his death, Dean has not witnessed a sight which had hitherto been characteristic of her woods for at least two millennia. Now only the Speech House Road Works (see Chapter 10) continues to produce charcoal.

Oak bark and the Tanning Industry

The craft of converting animal-skins into leather is one of great antiquity, and a tannery was a necessity under the conditions of economic self-sufficiency existing in Britain well into the nineteenth century, when each community produced many of its requirements. The leather industry was composed of two fairly distinct branches: tanners, curriers and the users of heavy leather, principally shoe-makers and saddlers; and the light leather works, particularly leather dressers, glovers and the makers of leather clothing. In Dean, tanners and curriers were in evidence as early as the thirteenth century, when a record of 1276[29] states that at Stears, Reginald de Wodeham 'fore-stalled the market at Newnham for leather, and held the tannery there'. In 1599,[30] Elizabeth I granted to Sir William Winter of Lydney 'a tan-house in Newerne called the Marlong House with the yard, pits and gardens, and two closes of pasture land called the Tanhouse Leaze, and Tanhouse Mead adjoining, containing 3 acres'. In 1579[31] Winter received from Sir Thomas Porter land in Lydney called Tanhouse Croft. William Trestyd was a tanner in Newland in 1598.[32] In 1614,[33] it was alleged that timber-oaks had been felled at Cannop, and planks from them hauled to Newnham-on-Severn to make tanners' vats. Richard Gardiner was a tanner at Lydbrook in 1628,[34] Thomas Wor-gan carried on the same trade at Whitecliff in 1629,[35] and in 1635 John Sadler of Monmouth leased to Thomas Probyn, tanner, his tanhouse and outbuildings at Newland for a term of 21 years at £6 13s 4d per annum.[36] Thus by the seventeenth century tanneries were being operated at Newnham-on-Severn, Newland, Whitecliff (the Tanhouse is again mentioned in 1670),[37] Lydney, and Lydbrook. In later centuries there were tanneries in or near all the foregoing and other villages, as will be noted below.

Newnham-on-Severn: There were two tanneries and barkyards, one at Broadoak (near today's 'Silver Fox Café') and the other at Collow on the south-west of the town (in sheds now part of Underhill Farm—

Plate 40a), where in the nineteenth century 'many women workers in cotton sunbonnets carried the bark to the leather-aproned men in the odorous tannery'. Bark was brought from Dean by packhorses. John Swayne Taylor was a tanner in the district in 1858,[38] and A. J. Shiles in 1902.[39] The tanneries closed c1918. Near Station Road in the town is 'Curriers Lane'.

Newland: In 1778[40] Samuel Simmons, tanner, demised to his son William his dwellinghouse (today's Tanhouse) and farm in Newland held on lease from Edmund Probyn, with his 'tanyard and all stock in the tannery trade'. William, junior is mentioned as a tanner there in 1792.[41] James Rogers was a tanner in the district in 1801, when he purchased bark from Ann Bathurst of Lydney.[42]

Whitecliff: Thomas Worgan, tanner, lived in Coleford in 1710, and probably ran the Whitecliff tannery.[43]

Lydney: Little is known of the tannery at Newerne in Lydney except that it was in operation in the late seventeenth century.[44]

Littledean: G. Nelmes and Onesiphorus Purnell were curriers at Littledean in 1858.[45]

Longhope: A tannery stood south of the village of Longhope, where Fred Coleman was the tanner in 1858.[46]

Mitcheldean: A tanhouse and tanyard owned by the Colchester-Wemyss family operated at Mitcheldean in the nineteenth century.[47] Ann Bannister was the currier there in 1858.[48]

Woolaston: John Barrow, a tanner, of Woolaston in 1750 purchased oak bark from Rowland Pitt, ironmaster, who himself had bought cordwood from the Bathursts at Lydney.[49] Four years later, Barrow (of Woolaston Grange) contracted to purchase bark from Lord Gage in Hangerbury.[50] In 1791 John Probyn, tanner, of Broadend near Woolaston purchased bark from Thomas Bathurst of Lydney Park.[51] William Packer and his son William were tanners at Woolaston in 1883.[52] The Tan House at Brookend is extant.

Clearwell: Early in the nineteenth century, William Stephens and his sons Josiah and Benjamin had a tannery in Clearwell towards the bottom of the village,[53] comprising drying-sheds, stacking yards, cleaning-pits, and a bark-grinding mill. They obtained hides from nearby farms and slaughterhouses, and after tanning and curing, they sold the leather to local bootmakers and saddlers. The Tannery House (Plate 40b), the early home of the Stephens, still stands; the pits have long since been filled in and the deteriorating sheds were demolished in 1964.

In addition to the foregoing tanneries there were others further afield, at Chepstow, Monmouth and Ross-on-Wye. Tanning was an exacting industry. After the oak bark had been hauled into the yard it was cleaned of moss and lichen, and then ground into a near-powdery state. It was then transferred to the leaching pits where the tanning-liquor was made by pouring cold water on to the powdery bark. The skins were scraped and cleaned in a stream or in a cleaning-pit, and the hair was removed by steeping in lime-pits for up to six weeks. The next process was the removal of flesh and lime, followed by immersion in a series of tanning-pits. The skins were afterwards washed and hung in drying-sheds with slatted windows. The whole process took from fifteen months to three years. The stench in the tanneries was 'something which had to be lived with'.

The industry used vast quantities of bark from oaks felled in Dean and on neighbouring estates for ship-building and other constructional work. The trees were felled in April or May, at which time the tanning content was richest and the rising sap made the bark easy to strip (Plates 43a, b). After drying in the open, the bark was sold. Estate owners, particularly the Wemyss, the Bathursts and the Gages found the sale of bark remunerative. The Wemyss family of The Wilderness near Mitcheldean c1770 sold large quantities of bark to John Boughton of Gawlett near Flaxley.[54] Sometimes the purchaser had to undertake the stripping. In 1791,[55] Thomas Bathurst sold to John Probyn of Brookend 'the oak coppice bark growing in the Old Park', computed as 50 to 60 tons, also 'the oak stock bark growing on trees marked for felling nearby', computed as about 5 tons, with permission to 'strip, rank, dry, harvest, cure, weigh, take and carry away . . . and to cut and make lights [clearings] in all convenient places in the Coppice Wood necessary for curing, drying and harvesting the bark'. On other occasions the stacked bark was sold by auction, as in 1781 : [56]

19 June 1781: For Sale by Auction at the Plume of Feathers [today's Feathers Hotel] in the town of Lydney: Between 80 and 100 tons of prime Coppice Bark free from tithe and all other outgoings. The chief Condition of Sale is that the Bark shall be sold by the ton, the same to be weighed in the woods at 21cwt to each ton, and put up at £2 19s per ton, no person to advance by less than 1s per ton at each bidding.

The auctioneer was Robert Carr, and the purchaser (at a sum not stated) was William Lewis, timber merchant, of Woolaston. In 1793 the Bathursts sold bark on 93½ acres, at £5 7s 6d an acre, to Joseph Swayne of Newnham-on-Severn and William Clarkson of Alvington. They purchased other bark from the Bathursts in 1804; and James Rogers, tanner, of Newland had done likewise in 1801.[57] From the Crown woods in Dean, 1,510 tons of bark were sold during 1761–8; during 1809–17 the price ranged from £12 2s 6d to £14 a ton. In 1831, small oaks were stripped while standing (before felling) and their bark (termed 'flittern bark') was sold at prices ranging from £4 7s 6d to £7 10s a ton.[58] During 1838–47, 7,399 tons were sold by the Office of Woods at prices of £3 15s to £5 5s a ton;[59] and the cost of stripping (at a time when workers were paid 1s $2\frac{1}{2}$d to 2s $\frac{3}{4}$d a day) was 20s $9\frac{1}{2}$d a ton when stripped off timber-trees, and 30s when removed from thinnings.[60] Much bark was shipped from Gatcombe and Newnham-on-Severn to Chepstow,[61] and large quantities were also supplied to Monmouth, Ross-on-Wye, Gloucester, Bristol, and Ireland. Today, oak bark is little used for tanning, and therefore only occasionally are supplies sent from Dean.[62]

Wood Turning

Individual wood-turners in Dean plied their trade in early times, but the first large-scale industry was established in 1788[63] by James Constance & Sons at Longhope. The firm gradually absorbed other turners, in particular those of the Baldwin family in the same village, and the Barnes family of Soudley. Wood-turnery was carried on at 'Camp Mill', Soudley during c1870–90 in premises which had once been a flour mill and from c1825 to 1870 had been Samuel Hewlett's second foundry. By 1904[64] Constance's works at Longhope 'covered a large area, one-fourth roofed', and employed 40 people. Immense stocks were held of seasoning poles, chiefly birch, sycamore, ash, and alder. The equipment comprised circular and band saws, drills, and turning lathes of many sizes, the largest being capable of turning handles 12 feet in length.

The products manufactured comprised a great variety of turned wood, including handles for brushes, brooms, mops, hoes, rakes, hammers, sledges, spades, shovels and picks. Other products were washing dollies and peggies, wood shives, cider bungs, spreaders, skittles and balls, and ladder rounds (rungs). Among the firm's specialities were hoe, prong, and hay-rake handles, of which Constances made many thousands each year; and scythe sneads, chiefly for Sheffield, where the blades were added.

The processes were varied. Each article before it was completed went through a number of hands, and frequently on to several machines. Much of the work required accurate judgement and considerable skill. Thus in splitting a log from which to make a prong stem, rake, hoe, or other handle, advantage had to be taken of the shape and grain of the log to secure the best result and to obviate waste. When bending or straightening, shaping or turning, the greatest care had to be exercised. All the turnery poles were felled during October to March and were peeled in strips on three sides, and stacked in yards to thoroughly season before use; and in many cases, after being sawn into lengths, they were again seasoned for several months.

In 1904[65] the members of the Longhope company were Stephen W. Constance, and his sons W. J. and John. The business was sold in the 1940s to L. O. Roberts of Mitcheldean, whose son-in-law, Keith Allan, is now the principal member of the company, which still thrives. Although several modern conceptions and up-to-date machinery are used, many of the old skills remain, and about 40 men and women are employed.

In 1932, H. V. Barnes, one of the executives at Constances, began a separate turnery at May Hill, near Dursley Cross; and by 1950 he was employing 45 workers (Plate 42b). The works were closed in 1961. Meanwhile in 1948 he, with his son Colin, formed a second company, at Valley Road in Lower Cinderford, at first employing 5 men. For some time the proprietors of the new works traded under the name of Valley Brush Company Ltd; subsequently the name was changed to H. V. Barnes & Son Ltd, and the company now employs about 70 men and women.

Miscellaneous

Among the most interesting enterprises within the Forest have been those connected with 'rural woodland industries'. By the seventeenth century, many woodland skills were evident (beyond those of felling, stripping and charcoal-burning): hurdles were made for fencing and to carry charcoal; and wood was cleft to produce cooper's timbers, lathes, staves, speakes, spokes and helves.[66] However, compared with some regions of southern England, little 'underwood working' has taken place in Dean. Other than a few underwood workers around Mitcheldean, Longhope and Dursley Cross (where 'old Mr Daw' made numerous hoops), most of such workers have been in and near Huntley. In that village during the 1920s and 1930s, Major Charles Ackers, OBE of Huntley Manor introduced the skills of cleaving pales (from sweet chestnut and Douglas fir), stakes, tent pegs (ash) and other products, and those of weaving wattle hurdles (from hazel), making bar-hurdles (ash), and of tying birch for besoms (adding lime handles) and for horse-jumps, as well as for use in processes connected with vinegar and iron industries. His company, Forest Products Ltd, has through these and other enterprises provided much employment. One particularly interesting product has been oak shingles, cleft by hand, with which to clad the spire of the church at Westbury-on-Severn. Nearby, on the Lea-Huntley road, a firm until recently made numerous wooden ladders of all types (the earliest reference to ladder-making in Dean is in 1246).[67]

Sawmills have had a place in Dean during many centuries. As early as 1612,[68] there were many 'saw-pits' in the Forest, and the timber sawn in them was 'a great quantity'. By 1614, there were at least eleven in use;[69] and many others were operated in later years. The advent in the nineteenth century of larger sawmills, eased the task of sawing, and in Dean they became increasingly efficient; three were operated by the army during the Second World War at Whimsey, Brierley and Cannop, and several of the collieries also had small sawmills. Today there are modern mills at Parkend (L. Rivers, previously Parkend Sawmills Ltd, and, much earlier, Bartlett & Bayliss), Huntley (Forest Products Ltd) Coleford (Dean Woodlands Ltd), Walford (Herbert Smith), and Lightmoor (James Joiner & Sons Ltd), where there is also a pressure impregnation plant. Other sawmills are operating at Saunders Green (Cooper Bros), Ruardean Hill (F. F. Coleman & Son; H. G. Coleman; and D. and F. Coleman), Bream (Edmonds & Son Ltd), Longhope (A. G. Lane Ltd), Mile End (A. P. Humphries), Nailbridge (S. T. Smart Ltd), Hollyhill (W. Mills & Sons Ltd), and Lower Cinderford (A Mills & Sons). Throughout Dean there are about ten small mills and some eight 'Log merchants'. Dean Woodlands Ltd, and the associated A. G. Lane Ltd, both noted above, make a speciality of panel fences. At Tufthorn near Coleford, is the interesting factory of Formwood Ltd, 'Melamine surfaced wood particle moulders', who use large quantities of Dean's spruces; and a few miles away at Monmouth is the factory of Flakeboard Ltd.

All the foregoing industries aid Dean's economy, not least in providing a market for many thousands of trees. The Forest, ably managed by the Forestry Commission, with a chief forester (S. J. Betterton) co-ordinating harvesting and marketing, annually supplies thousands of tons of saw-logs, pulpwood (for the mill at Sudbrook) chipboard and fibreboard wood (chiefly for St Anne's boardmill at Bristol), turnery poles, and many other items. Each year, the increment of (ie the wood 'put on') Dean's trees is over 30,000 tons; and a conservative estimate of the volume (the present standing tonnage) of the woodland crops is ¾ million.

References to Chapter 9

1 Hart. *Royal Forest, passim.*
2 Ibid, 43.
3 E32/29.
4 C66, 21 Hen III, m 11.
5 E32/30.
6 SC6/850/19.
7 E146/1/26.
8 Ibid, 25.
9 E32/29, 30, 332, 334.
10 Ibid, 332.
11 Ibid, quoted in Hart's *Royal Forest*, 44, 45.
12 Ibid, 334, quoted in Hart's *Royal Forest*, 44, 46.
13 E101/140/17, 18.
14 Ibid, 19.
15 Ibid, 20.
16 SC6/858/15.
17 'Speeches Day' is important as explaining 'Speech House', a derived designation.
18 E101/141/3.
19 'Spring' is the young growth from germination (natural regeneration from self-sown seed, or from root suckers), and sometimes that from stools after coppicing.
20 Hart. *Royal Forest*, Chapters, 5, 6, 7.
21 Ibid, 148.
22 Ibid.
23 Ibid, 150.
24 Ibid, 168.
25 Ibid, 175.
26 Ibid, 181.
27 The photographs are held by the Forestry Commission Research Station, at Alice Holt Lodge, Farnham, Surrey.
28 *Everybody's Magazine*, 1940; Waters, Brian. *The Forest of Dean*, 1951. 136–40.
29 SC5: *Rot Hund*, I, 4 Edw I, f 182.
30 GRO D421/T22.
31 Ibid.
32 Ibid, D1677, GG562.
33 E178/3837, m 12–18.

34 GRO D1677, GG732.
35 Ibid, D33/E227/199.
36 Ibid, D1677, GG811.
37 Ibid, GG952.
38 *Slater's Directory*, 1858.
39 *Harris's Directory*, 1902.
40 GRO D637/IV/8.
41 *British Universal Directory*, 1792.
42 GRO D421/E56.
43 National Liby of Wales, Mynde Documents, P207/46.
44 Information from R. A. J. Bell.
45 *Slater's Directory*, 1858.
46 Ibid.
47 GRO D36/731, 40.
48 *Slaters Directory*, 1858.
49 GRO D421/E52.
50 Ibid, D1677, GG1301.
51 Ibid, D421/E52.
52 Ibid, D637/1/99.
53 Hart, C. E. *Watts of Lydney: 1851–1965*, 1965, 8, 9.
54 GRO D36/E7.
55 Ibid, D421/E52.
56 Ibid, E55.
57 Ibid.
58 Hart. *Royal Forest*, 215.
59 Ibid, 216, 220.
60 F16/53.
61 Waters, Ivor. *Leather and Oak Bark at Chepstow*, 1970.
62 For contemporary information on tanbark, see Aaron, J. R. *The Utilisation of Bark*, Forestry Commission, 1960; Clarkson, L. A., 'The Case of the Leather Industry', *Bull Inst of Hist Res*, 38(98) Nov 1965.
63 *Industrial Gloucestershire, 1904*, 40, 41.
64 Ibid.
65 Ibid.
66 GRO D1677, GG1557; Hart. *Royal Forest*, 147, 186.
67 *Mem Rot*, 30 Hen III, r 18, m 5.
68 E178/3837, m 23.
69 Ibid, m 12–18.

Ten

Wood Chemical Works and Distillation Works

Wood Chemical Works ('Steweries' or 'Distilleries')

Until early in the seventeenth century, Dean's charcoal fed its bloomeries and primitive forges. Thereafter, for almost two centuries charcoal fed voracious blast furnaces, forges and slitting mills. However, during the second half of the eighteenth century—in most parts of Britain, coke replaced charcoal as fuel for smelting, and charcoal-burning became a dying industry, though a few continued to eke out a livelihood from this ancient and fascinating trade. Fortunately for the economy of Dean (where two furnaces continued to use charcoal in preference to coke into the early years of the nineteenth century), action was taken to make charcoal in retorts or cylinders at depots within or near the Forest, with the complementary aims of producing pyroligneous acid and tar, and of processing some of the charcoal.

The process of distillation of wood originated on the Continent, perhaps in France or in Sweden—where wood- or Stockholm-tar, one of the products, has long been an article of commerce. Towards the end of the eighteenth century the industry came under the observation of Richard Watson (1737–1816) DD, FRS, Bishop of Llandaff, well-known for his chemical researches.[1] His lordship says of the matter:[2]

In about 1786, application was made to me by the government, to know whether I could give any advice relative to the improvement of the strength of gunpowder; and I suggested to them the making of charcoal by distilling wood in close vessels. The suggestion was put into execution at Hythe in 1787, and the improvement has exceeded my utmost expectations. Major-General Congreve delivered to me a paper containing an account of the experiments which have been made with cylinder powder (so called from the wood being distilled in iron

338

cylinders), in all of which its superiority over every other species of powder was sufficiently established.

Another account, by Congreve, Comptroller of the Royal Powder Mills at Waltham Abbey,[3] says that the type of retort was first recommended by Dr George Fordyce, and that the cost of the 'cylinder charcoal, in March 1801 was 22s 9d a cwt. As well as at Hythe and Waltham Abbey, plants were established at North Chapel near Fernhurst, and at Faversham, Kent.[4] For North Chapel there is available a detailed description of the plant and process:[5]

The 'cylinder room' was 60ft long. There were three sets of cast-iron cylinders or retorts 2ft in diameter by 6ft long, three to each set, placed in a brickwork setting along the centre of the 'room'. Each cylinder was closed by an 'iron stop' 18in long, filled with sand, besides which a 'sand door' was made to project obliquely from the front of the cylinder. At the back were copper pipes 7ft long connecting the cylinders to half-hogshead barrels to draw off the steam or liquid which flows in large quantities into the tar barrels during the process of charring. The cylinders were heated by coal fires. The charge consisted of 5cwt of cordwood 18in long, to each set. The fires were lit at 6.30 am and kept up for 8 hours, about 8 bushels of coal being required for each set. The retorts were drawn during the following morning into sheet-iron coolers, shut up close to prevent the charcoal smouldering. The output was 3 to 4cwt of charcoal (ie 60 to 80 per cent of the charge) and about 100 gallons of liquid [ie from 15cwt in 3 sets of 3 cylinders]. The tar-acid, they daily draw from the barrels, put into a large tub, and preserved in hogsheads; but at present it cannot be used because a patent is out for the monopoly of the sale. It is worth 6d a gallon. The charcoal goes to Waltham and Faversham.

The above description tallies closely with the two sketches (Figs 21a and b) of the plant used at Faversham in 1798.[6] The wood was cut into 3ft lengths and packed into iron cylindrical cases known as 'slips':[7]

An opening into the rear of the slip, corresponding with another in the retort, permitted inflammable gases, generated by the charring, to be carried into the furnace, where they were consumed, while other pipes removed the tar and pyroligneous acid. When the blue colour of the gas flame, indicating carbonic oxide, showed the wood to be sufficiently charred, the 'slip' was withdrawn and placed in a cooler, provided with a close-fitting lid, for several hours. When cool, the charcoal was stored for about a fortnight before grinding, to avoid the danger of spontaneous combustion. Properly made gunpowder-char-

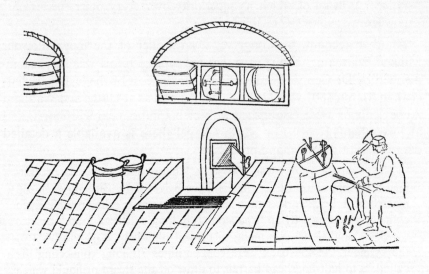

Fig 21. Wood chemical 'steweries' or 'distilleries' (after H. W. Dickinson and E. Straker, *Trans Newcomen Society*, XVIII, 1937–8, 61–6).

51 *(above)* Camp Mill leatherboard factory, Soudley c1905; *(below)* Rowley Paper Mill on the Cone

52 *(above)* The Roman road at Blackpool bridge; *(below)* omnibuses used for transporting workmen, Cannop Colliery c1933

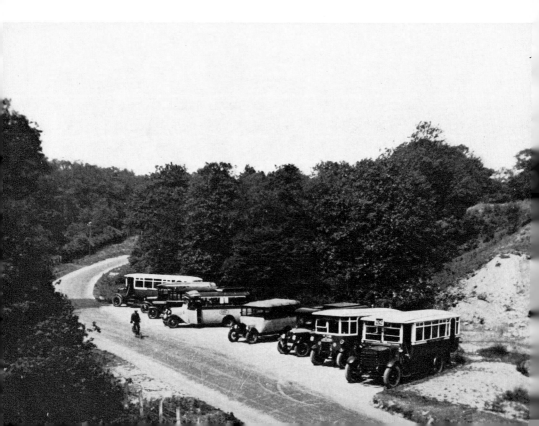

coal was jet black in hue; when broken, it showed a clear velvety surface. The grinding mill generally resembled a huge coffee mill, from which the pulverised charcoal passed into a 'reel' or cylindrical frame, covered with copper wire cloth, of about 32 meshes to an inch. The material sufficiently fine to pass through this fell into a bin, while the coarser particles were collected for regrinding.

Pyroligneous acid was a by-product in these State-owned gunpowder manufactories, and from Waltham Abbey, on 8 November 1791, John Finlay secretary to the Duke of Richmond, sent to Charles Macintosh in Scotland a sample for investigation: [8]

> I have some of the acid of wood (pyroligneous acid), and shall send you a couple of bottles that you may see its strength. I shall at the same time send you a bottle of the acid which has been once distilled from the coarse kind, and shall beg of you to let me know what you would give per gallon for each kind, or what they would be sold for at Glasgow. I must endeavour to dispose of it for the Board of Ordnance to the best advantage which I can.

Macintosh eventually began his own manufacture of the acid, producing it at a cost of about 4d a gallon.[9] At the State's plants the by-products—crude alcohol, acetic acid and tar—were a nuisance: 'the tar has been a great burden on the hands of those who have been largely concerned in this trade'.[10] A record of 1814,[11] shows that wood distillation was well known in Scotland:

> Pyroligneous, or wood acid, is produced by the distillation of wood in a cast-iron retort. The gas passing through a 'worm' contained in a refrigeratory, is condensed in the same manner as common spirits. The wood is left in a charred state in the retort, and may be used for any purpose to which charcoal is applicable. This acid is a powerful solvent of iron; and being only 4d a gallon, is now almost universally used for making acetate of iron, or iron liquor; and acetate of alumine, a red liquor, for calico printers and dyers. There are seven works for making pyroligneous acid in Scotland—four, at Camlachie, Tradestown, Brownfield, and Lanark, in Lanarkshire; one near Torryburn in Fifeshire; and two at Millburn and Cordale in Dumbartonshire. One ton of wood affords about 90 gallons of acid and 10 gallons of tar. The latter comes over with the acid; but being heavier, readily subsides, and is separated.

The distillery at Millburn, in the Vale of Leven, established by Turnbull and Company towards the end of the eighteenth century,

2A

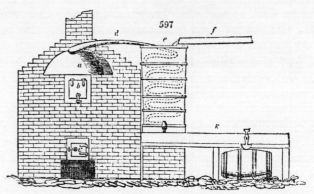

Fig 22. Wood chemical 'steweries' or 'distilleries' (after J. C. Loudon, *An Encyclopedia of Agriculture*, 1831, 657).

employed about seven hands, and consumed daily a ton of small wood, chiefly oak, 'from which the liquor, a kind of coarse vinegar', was extracted: [12]

The process is beautifully simple. A number of iron ovens or retorts are placed in a row, and filled with the timber cut into small pieces. A fire of coal or charcoal is kindled in a furnace attached to each and, by its heat, forces the acid to fly off in the form of vapour. This is conducted by a small tube proceeding from each retort into a refrigeratory or long metal pipe, on which a jet of cold water from above is continually falling. Here the acid is condensed, and runs from the end of the pipe in a considerable stream of reddish brown colour. Besides the liquor thus procured, which is employed in making colours for the calico printers, there is a considerable quantity of tar and charcoal produced during the process, the value of which is esteemed equal to the expense of fuel.

Turnbulls subsequently established works in other parts of Scotland, the principal one being at Camlachie, Glasgow, which was opened in 1808. The foregoing technical information was later supplemented: [13]

The spray of all trees not resinous may be used in the distillation of pyroligneous acid. This acid is much used in calico printing works; and, according to Monteith, sold in 1819 in the neighbourhood of Glasgow at from £1 2s to £1 10s a ton. The distillation is carried on in a cast or malleable iron boiler (Fig 22): (*a*) which should be from 5 to 7 feet long, 3 feet wide, and say 4 feet deep from the top of the arch, built with fire-brick. The wood is split or round, not more than three inches square in thickness, and of any length, so as to go into the boiler at the door. When full, the boiler door (*b*) is properly secured, to keep in the steam; then the fire is put to it in the furnace below, and the liquid comes off in the pipe above (*d*), which is condensed in a worm, in a stand (*e*) filled with cold water, by a spirit (*f*), and empties itself first in a gutter below (*g*) and from that it is led into barrels or any other vessel; and thus the liquid is prepared. One English ton weight of any wood, or refuse of oak, will make upwards of eighty gallons of the liquid. There is also a quantity of tar extracted, which may be useful in ship-building (*Gard Mag* vol ii).

The advent of peace in 1815 doubtless rendered several of the isolated plants superfluous in regard to charcoal for gunpowder, and at that time the by-products scarcely commanded any market.

By 1814, some or all of the above processes were known in Dean. In that year Bevington Gibbins, 'chymist' of Lydney, leased from the Rt Hon Charles Bathurst of that town three parcels of land near the canal for a 'chymical factory', and agreed to purchase 1,000 cords a year at 9s 6d each.[14] Gibbins installed machinery and equipment, but the process which he carried out is obscure. He paid his rent until 29 September 1816 and was released of his agreement on the following 16 October,[15] whereafter Bathurst in a letter 15 November[16] bemoaned 'the Chymical Work, upon which I reckoned, having been abandoned with very little compensation to me, and the cordwood left on my hands at the depreciation which at present, I suppose, is general'. Perhaps Gibbins' operations had comprised simply the production, grinding and treatment of charcoal, and the processing of wood-tar— increasingly in demand for the building and repair of ships. However, he may have also been engaged in the manufacture of pyroligneous acid, which contains acetic and formic acid (and a small quantity of propionic and butyric acid), methyl alcohol, methyl acetate and acetone (allyl alcohol, methyl ethyl ketone—in very small quantities—and traces of ethyl alcohol); in addition there are substances called 'disolved tar'—because when the acid is distilled these remain in the residue—and insoluble tar. The water content of pyroligneous acid is about 80–85 per cent.

Though the enterprise at Lydney had failed, other chemical works (known locally as 'steweries' or 'distilleries') were later established in Dean—at Cannop (1835), Oakwood (c1844), Lydbrook (1857), Whitecroft (c1876), Broadmoor (c1844), and Tufts (1887).[17] In 1881 the works employed about 130 men,[18] and all provided outlets for immense quantities of otherwise unsaleable wood: mules and donkeys

bearing iron cradles holding cordwood were amongst the characteristics of the Forest.[19] Each of the establishments is described below.
CANNOP The Cannop Chemical Company was established about
1835[20] in works which were situated on Crown land near the north-
east corner of the present crossroads at Speech House Road, the locality being known in early times as 'Cannop Bridge'. In March 1841 the
owner, George Skip,[21] had 'eight retorts distilling wood for pyroligneous acid; also steam engines, buildings in an extensive yard, and two
workmen's houses'; and the annual value of the property was £40.
He was making 'sugar of lead', ie lead acetate. The charcoal was
burnt in the yard in iron boxes, ovens or cylinders. The acid and
tar were collected in vats, the wood-tar at the bottom, and were
allowed to settle. The acid was then transferred to another vessels
where yellow oxide of lead (Pb O) was added; this dissolved in the
acid and neutralised it. The solution was then boiled down until the
lead acetate ('sugar of lead') crystallised out. The wood-tar was run
off to another vessel, thickened by boiling down, and then sold for
preservative purposes—for example, for ships' bottoms. If the wood-
tar was boiled down sufficiently, it became wood-pitch, used for caulk-
ing ships' hulls. Probably many other products were dealt with, as was
the case, noted later, at Lydbrook.

In 1858 the lessees under the Crown were The Forest of Dean Chemical Co, designated 'Manufacturing Chemists'.[22] They relinquished the
lease by 13 January 1865, on which date a lease was given by the Office
of Woods to Crawshay Bailey, Thomas Gatrex, Philip Williams,
Charles Nicholson, Henry Salisbury Milman, and Crawshay Bailey
junior.[23] The name of the company was retained, and their under-
tenants were Major James Pearce King, of the Elms, Monmouth, and
William Henry Jackson. On 22 September 1869 a horse of the company was leader in a team employed in drawing empty tram wagons
down the tramroad (which ran parallel to the broad gauge railway
which had recently come into use between Lydney and Cannop) when
at a point between Parkend and Cannop, the horse, having no driver
in attendance, crossed over onto the broad gauge line and was killed
by the engine. At an enquiry of the hauliers and enginemen at the chemical company's offices, Jackson claimed £40, the value of the horse.
The Severn & Wye Railway Company declined, but 'much regret the
loss he has sustained'.[24] In May 1870, two GWR trucks were set on
fire on the S&W; they had been loaded with charcoal which was still
'in a state of ignition'.

In 1870 a patent was licensed to be used at Cannop, being 'an invention of improved means of and appartus for reducing charcoal and other friable substances to a fine or impalpable powder, particularly applicable to the manufacture of a substance for lamp black'. The invention was that of Johan Emphrain Lundgren of Sweden, for which a patent (no 1774) was taken out in the United Kingdom in 1863 by R. A. Brooman, patent agent, and assigned to H. A. Preeston & Co Ltd, 31 Fenchurch Street, London[25]—who extended the licence to Cannop. In January 1871, Major King sent to Preeston's 40 barrels of 'Vegetable Black in 1lb and ½lb packets'.[26] The patented apparatus to use the process was:[27]

> One, two or more cylindrical vessels, each divided into two compartments; the cylindrical vessels are arranged on the same shaft, or independently; they are mounted on trunnions, and rotary motion is imparted to them in any convenient manner. Each compartment is separated from the adjoining compartment by a partition, and is furnished with an aperture through which the balls of spheres of iron, glass, stone, marble or other suitable material, and the material to be reduced, are inserted; these apertures are at first closed by screw or other stoppers. When the material has been sufficiently reduced, the stoppers are replaced by wire gauze or perforated plate which, during the rotation, affords passage to the powder or reduced material into a receptacle provided for the purpose.

The inventor claimed that 'charcoal or carbon of every kind, pulverised as before stated, may be employed in all cases where ordinary lamp black is now used; for instance, in the manufacture of printing and other inks, in paints, in dyeing leather, in wood varnishes, and sealing wax—and it is especially adapted for the manufacture of printing ink, and is free from the empyreumatic odour inherent to ordinary lampblack'.

King, on 5 April 1871,[28] sold to Thomas Leach Nicholas, of Monmouth, for £2,250 one-half of the Cannop lease (dated 13 January 1865) which included four messuages with erections, buildings and yards, total 2 roods and 18 perches, 'used for manufacturing chemical goods or products or in connection therewith', together with 'the plant, machinery and effects of and in a licence to use the invention'. By 22 September 1874 the proprietors were Nicholas and his partner David Fry, who together on that date obtained a new lease, having overcome the Office of Woods' attempt to raise the rent by 300 per cent![29] Two years later, their company had the designation 'Naphtha manufacturers, Cannop Works',[30] and in 1880 they were still making pyroligneous acid, as well as 'brimstone from Mount Etna, turned into oil of vitriol', ie sulphuric acid.[31] The manufacture 'was on a large scale', and the vapours were 'decidedly pungent'. The following year, the works were recorded as making sulphuric acid using sulphur from Sicily,[32] which they supplied to the local tinplate works for the removal of ferric oxide and other impurities on the iron plates, before they were tinned. The naphtha was used principally for varnish, and the acetic acid was made into sugar of lead, for use in paints and in calico-dyeing.

In May 1889, Nicholas was trying to sell the business, which had yielded only £200 profit a year, to S. M. Thomas who had a similar business at Lydbrook.[33] By 1892, the Cannop Chemical Company was obtaining coke (for fuelling) by rail from Whitecroft.[34]

In 1893, Thomas Newcomen (born 8 May 1859 at Warwick, where he was educated at the King's School) came to reside in Coleford, and in the following year he purchased the Lydbrook Chemical Co from S. M. Thomas & Co, together with the associated Cannop Chemical Co.[35] Around the turn of the century, the industry was not prosperous, and although Lydbrook survived, Cannop became idle. A tramroad to the Cannop works was removed by 1901,[36] and on 24 March 1902 Newcomen gave to the Office of Woods a year's notice of his intention to relinquish the premises[37] which thereafter fell into disrepair. Some of the abandoned buildings were used to house sheep and horses; and a small office was used occasionally as a chapel. Although the old processing at Cannop had ended, in 1913–14 a large wood distillation plant (discussed *infra*) was built about 50 yards away to the south, and is still making immense quantities of charcoal. The deteriorated buildings of the old works and its dwellinghouses (for long occupied by the families of Capel and Baldwin) were demolished in 1966 (Plate 44b).

LYDBROOK   The Lydbrook Chemical Co was established in 1857 by Messrs Russell & Powell[38] in buildings and a yard in central Lydbrook now occupied by Webb's Garage. S. M. Thomas of Wynols Hill near Coleford took over the business c1884;[39] he owned also the Oakwood Chemical Works (*infra*). Thomas, trading as The Lydbrook Chemical Co, had an 'accommodation office at 89a, Bow Common Lane, London, E,— now the premises of Messrs Thomas Hill-Jones Co, Ltd, chemical manufacturers. This London company or its predecessors had some connection with the Lydbrook and Oakwood works. Thomas's business-card shows that his company, as 'Charcoal Manufacturers', offered the following products: [40]

Wood Naphtha Solvent	Charcoal Blacking
Wood Naphtha Miscible	Plumbago
Forest Lamp Black	Charcoal Lump
Coal and Coke Dust	Charcoal, Turf Burned
Powdered Charcoal	Charcoal Fuel
Filtering Charcoal	Acetate of Lime

Most of the products were despatched by rail from Upper Lydbrook station. The manufacture was still in process in 1880.[41] In 1894 Thomas Newcomen[42] purchased from S. M. Thomas & Co the Lydbrook Chemical Company together with 'the connection of the Cannop Chemical Co and the Oakwood Chemical Works.' The manager in that year was John Samuel Priest.[43] Thereafter the Lydbrook works developed, 'the plant being operated night and day'. In October 1900 a serious fire occurred from spontaneous combustion of charcoal.[44] John M. Capel, late of Oakwood, became foreman that year. The premises were repaired, and by 1904 Lydbrook was the only survivor of the Forest's chemical works, though one of the others (Tufts) was resuscitated in later years. In 1907,[45] 'besides a large charcoal manufacture carried on both in the Forest and in the factory', the Lydbrook works manufactured 'the closely allied products of naphtha, tar, acetate of lime, blacking, etc'. Another record, for 1904, reads: [46]

In addition to the charcoal made in the works, a number of men are employed in burning charcoal in the Forest, an old method revived. In the works and in the Forest from 30 to 40 hands are given constant employment. The plant at Lydbrook is complete and equipped with all necessary machinery and appliances. It comprises retorts for carbonising wood, distilling apparatus and grinding machinery.[47] Almost every particle of wood which is brought to the works is manufactured into some useful product. A considerable portion is transformed into charcoal (about 30 per cent of the weight of wood used) and from 65 per cent to 70 per cent is recovered as vapour, this being condensed in iron and copper pipes laid in a stream, which flows alongside and through the works, into a thick liquid from which is distilled the wood naphtha,[48] crude acetic acid,[49] and tar. The crude acid is further manufactured into acetate of lime.[50]

The only waste is a small percentage of gas which, being useless is burnt. The processes of manufacture are exceedingly interesting. One of the specialities of the firm is powdered charcoal, largely used in the metal trade for facing moulds.[51] This is ground by a process which gives it the fineness and evenness so much desired. It is also prepared for paint making, for chemists' use, etc. By reason of its fineness of texture, 'Lydbrook Charcoal' has gained a high reputation wherever it is known. The various products manufactured by these works are sent to all parts of England and Wales, and are also exported.

The plant included steam boilers fired by coal which drove the machinery. One product not mentioned above, made by Thomas Newcomen, with his son Arthur in charge, was 'charcoal biscuits', sent off in packets. Blacking was despatched in casks, and naphtha in iron drums. The Newcomens also patented a flat-iron heated by charcoal. John M. Capel, the foreman, moved to Tufts c1907. The works closed about 1919, whereupon Newcomen sold the premises to Mr Flewellin, who resold to Mr Webb for a garage. Some of the old retaining walls are still visible; and a boundary wall at one time reached out to the kerb of the road. The name 'Lydbrook Chemical Co Ltd' still survives because it is associated with the Shirley Aldred Group of Companies which includes Wood Distillation Ltd at Speech House Road; and the Group's trading includes the same work as that which was done at Lydbrook.

OAKWOOD   By 1844, George Skip of Bream Lodge (who held the chemical works at Cannop) 'had erected at Oakwood a chemical works for the distillation of wood'.[52] The following January he was in trouble with the Office of Woods after polluting the Oakwood Brook which ran through his works and passed near Whitemead Park, the residence of Edward Machen, the deputy surveyor—a singularly tactless thing to do! On 11 February 1854, Isaiah Trotter of Coleford purchased the works as from 25 March that year;[53] and he was still running them in 1858,[54] and in 1887[55]—with Joseph Merry as his foreman. The S&W PD Plan of 1872 includes the outline of the buildings, and of a large pond called 'The Stewery Pool'. Horses and pack-mules hauled the cordwood and the charcoal. By 1891, the proprietors were S. M. Thomas & Co who had as their foreman, John M. Capel.[56] In 1894 Thomas Newcomen purchased the works;[57] and in that year, Capel having moved to Somerset, (he returned in 1900) the manager was John Priest of Bream.[58] The manufactory closed in June 1900,[59] and in due course the buildings were absorbed into the premises of the Flour Mill Colliery.

TUFTS   On 5 August 1887[60] Isaac Jacobs of Lydney, 'Chemical Manufacturer and Outfitter', obtained from the Office of Woods (through Sir James Campbell Bt, deputy surveyor) a 99-year lease at £10 per annum of about one acre at the Tufts, south of Whitecroft, on which to build a chemical works. Jacobs covenanted to erect, within two years 'all such buildings and erections as in the neighbourhood are usual and proper for the purpose of manufacturing chemicals . . . and one substantial dwelling house for the foreman or manager of the works'. Building began, but a house was not completed, probably because Jacobs (it is said) became a bankrupt. On 19 November 1890 Henry Merry, then lessee, demised the lease to Samuel Wilkinson Woods, bank manager, of Newnham-on-Severn. In 1891 'The Crown Chemical Works' was in the hands of H. Merry, Bristol Villa, The Caves, Bream.[61] On 31 August 1895, the Crown sold the land and buildings to the Bathurst family of Lydney (who still own them) and who 12 December 1895 released Woods on payment of £70 from the covenant to erect a dwellinghouse. Woods agreed to expend £80 within three months in 'providing and fixing a new wash boiler [for the raising of steam] and two ovens [retorts for the charcoal processes] in addition to the ovens now erected thereon, and upon any other general improvements required in the buildings of the said Chemical Works'. The lessee was given permission to sublet, if he requested, to James Hughes & Son of Parkend. It is uncertain from the above information what processes were employed in the works, nor how long the works were running, nor indeed whether Woods put them into operation. In March 1905[62] Wood's executors surrendered the lease to the Bathursts who on the following day assigned it for $81\frac{1}{2}$ years at £5 per annum to Thomas Newcomen, 'Chemical Manufacturer, of Sunny Bank, Coleford, and of the Lydbrook Chemical Works'. Newcomen covenanted 'to proceed to expend upon the premises £40 in providing and fixing a new wash boiler and two ovens in addition to the ovens now erected thereon, and upon any other general improvements required to the buildings for the purposes of the Chemical Works carried on therein.' Some of the improvements carried out are evident from correspondence between Newcomen and James Lauder, land agent to the Bathursts.[63] Newcomen, whose foreman from about that time was John M. Capel, late of the Oakwood and Lydbrook Chemical Works, submitted the following invoice from Llewellins & James, engineers, of Castle Green, Bristol:

13 January 1906: Repairing Copper Still sent, cutting it apart, cleaning and annealing sides, fitting and rivetting on new copper dome 6in higher than before, new copper ring and cover 16in dia. One new 2 coil steam worm

made from 2in and 1in copper pipe with wrot copper
stays and gunmetal inlet and outlet connections and
screw down 2in for 1in iron pipe and jointed in middle   £   s   d
by gunmetal flanges and bolts and nuts   35 18   3

	cwt			
Credit: By Old Copper	0	1	22	
By Copper pipes etc.	0	2	1	
	0	3	23 at 6½d	2 18 0

Forwarded by GWR to the Tufts, Whitecroft   £33   0   3

Newcomen also paid £20 for 'overhauling, fixing and building' a
weighing machine, and £27 10s for a boiler. He wrote 30 May 1910:

> Nothing has been laid out in ovens; as a matter of fact £240 would
> hardly provide another pair, and the verbal arrangement was that the
> sum of £40 should be laid out in plant extra to what was there, and
> such has been done. The weighing machine is extra; the large Copper
> Still is also for a new process and product, and the boiler had to be
> provided to get a sufficient pressure of steam to work the Still—the
> old boiler was only passed for 15lb pressure, this for 50lb.

Newcomen and Capel closed Tufts (but not Lydbrook) c1913 and
joined the Wood Distillation Works at Speech House Road. They
remained until 1917, when they reopened Tufts, and 20 January 1919
Newcomen, still trading as the Lydbrook Chemical Co, was authorised
by the s&w to extend his loading bank. Capel's son John H. (with
experience gained in a chemical works in Dundee) joined him at Tufts,
but he was replaced by his brother Ternly Capel in 1928.

The process at Tufts was as follows. Charcoal was made in four
cast-iron ovens (kilns). Cordwood in iron boxes with wheels (Plate 45a)
were pushed in on rails, and 'coked' by coal fires set below the ovens.
The gases were led through two square vats (condensing tanks) filled
with water. The resultant products, pyroligneous acid and tar, were
fed by gravitation into round tanks fixed into the ground. The tar,
which lay at the bottom, was pumped to wooden barrels. The acid
was pumped through two flask-shaped stills containing copper coils,
and fed by steam from a boiler; from them naphtha emerged, which
was drawn into two more vats, whereafter lime was added, the whole
left for 12 hours, and then placed in a large pan fixed into the ground
with a coal fire beneath it. Boiling took place until solidified, and
when cooled the resultant acetate of lime was dug out and placed on

the top of the four ovens, and later bagged for sale. The tar was railed in barrels, the naphtha in steel drums, and the acetate in sacks. The charcoal was sent to Lydbrook to be ground. The works were noted as a place to obtain a cure for whooping cough—inhaling of the fumes was recommended by the local doctors!

Thomas Newcomen died 27 July 1937.[64] He was 'almost the last of the old type of wood distillers'. John M. Capel retired c1940 (he died in 1943) whereupon his son Ternly became foreman. The Tufts works were continued by Arthur Newcomen until 1948, when the equipment was sold by auction and dismantled. Two large vats went to the Wood Distillation Works. Ternly, the last of the Capel family to work in the old 'steweries', stayed only to clear the site after the auction. Tufts was the last of the old-process chemical works. Thereafter the premises were left empty and unkempt, but within the site Alfred Faulks made charcoal in the open until 1949, selling it to Newcomen. Today only a few dilapidated buildings (with one barrel set into a floor) and a chimney stack remain (Plate 45b).

WHITECROFT   About a hundred yards to the NNE of Tufts stood the Whitecroft Chemical Works, sometimes known as Morgan's Chemical Works, and listed in 1876 as 'Messrs Chapman & Morgan, Chemical Works Proprietors'.[65] The date of the commencement of the business is unknown, but the layout of the premises is shown on the S&W Plan of 1877, when the proprietors were still Chapman & Morgan.[66] The history of the enterprise is the most obscure of all those of the local works. Joseph Worlick, one-time signalman at Tufts Junction, worked there as a clerk. On 8 August 1883, David Harries of the works reported that they were closed,[67] but in 1887[68] and 1891[69] 'M. Morgan & Co' were still listed as in occupation. By 1906 the siding to the works had not been used for some years and required renewal, whereupon it was decided to remove the rails;[70] but the Midland Railway's distance-diagram no 51A dated 1917 still showed 'Chemical Company's Siding'. Today only some nearby derelict cottages remain.

BROADMOOR   The chemical works at Broadmoor in Lower Cinderford was built c1864 by John and Thomas Powell, 'manufacturing chemists', of the Plump Hill near Mitcheldean. In April of that year they requested from the Office of Woods water rights in the 'Old Engine Brook' for the use of the 'Chemical Works',[71] and in June 1865 they received a licence for 31 years at £1 per annum.[72] By 1881[73] the company were making acetic acid into sugar of lead. A local esteemed gentleman, the late C. A. J. Hale (d 1968), remembered the enterprise working in 1884, 'but it was not very active, judging from the very thin smoke coming from the chimney'. By October 1886 the business was owned by George Frederick Church, butcher, Stephen Wallace Hadingham, and William Spence (manager), all of Cinderford, trading as The Broadmoor Chemical Co,[74] whose letter-head describes them as 'manufacturers of charcoal, sugar of lead, acetate of lime, naphtha, etc'. The late Alderman J. L. Jones, who did much good work for Cinderford and its neighbourhood, remembered the works in progress from about 1889, when they were known locally as 'the Distillery'. As a railway official at Cinderford GWR, Whimsey Branch, he accepted large casks each containing 5cwt of sugar of lead, to be consigned chiefly to Bristol. Incoming traffic was mainly sulphuric acid contained in large carboys. Rumour had it that the manager, a Scot, succeeded in distilling some whisky there, and that following a call by an excise officer he was dismissed! The enterprise was closed by about the turn of the century.[75] The premises were sold in November 1902, and the plant was dismantled and removed, the particulars of sale[76] comprising:

Premises known as 'Broadmoor Chemical Works', comprising 1 acre and 5 perches, together with a stone-built Boiler Shed, Egg-end Boiler 30ft long × 6ft diameter, pipes and fitting; three cast iron Receiving Pans, 5ft diameter, and cast iron Boiler at rear of shed; brick-built Chimney Stack with stone base; cast iron Still, set in brickwork; brick Still House with 4 copper Stills and pipe connections; copper Pump, eleven Acid Tubs, stone-built Lime House with cast iron Boiler and pipe connections; two cast iron Retorts set in masonry; small Shed, stone-built Sugar of Lead House and Staging, together with two lead Pans 14ft × 3ft × 1ft, one ditto 5ft × 3ft × 2ft, one ditto 7ft × 3ft 3in × 1ft, one ditto 8ft 6in × 3ft 3in × 9in, one ditto 7ft × 4ft 3in × 1ft, one ditto 6ft × 4ft × 1ft 6in, one ditto 6ft 6in × 4ft × 1ft 9in; copper Boiler 4ft diameter, ditto 5ft 6in diameter, and pipe connections; Sugar of Lead House, with 2 lead Pans and Staging, galvanised iron Shed; stone-built Acetic Acid Shed with stone Still, 3 large Tubs, 2 large Tubs sunk in the ground, and small Engine Bed, 3 cast iron Pans 5ft diameter; Shed with galvanised iron roof, with Cornish Boiler and fittings, 12ft long × 5ft 6in diameter; also Receiving Tank; 9 cast iron Retorts set in masonry with corrugated iron roof; cast iron Piping; lead Pump and 2 Tubs; large Shed; Smith's Shop; Store Room and Shed with Lofts over; Office; Stabling for 9 horses. Also Stone-built Dwelling House adjoining Lot 1., now in the occupation of Louis John Cartwright.

The site for the last few years has been occupied by J. W. Hynd-man's sawmills. Some of the dilapidated buildings, including stables and smith's shop (with its old bellows and hearth) still stand; a pipe projecting from the ground is believed to lead to an underground tank which contained acetic acid (Plate 44a).

Some indication of the type of plant used and of the kind of pro-cess in Dean's chemical works is obtained by noting those in a similar enterprise which until 1966 was in existence for about 150 years in Glasgow—owned by Stuart Turnbull & Co (Camlachie) Ltd. There was a set of 12 retorts (termed 'a setting') each consisting of a cylin-drical tank about 5ft 6in in diameter and 6ft deep, holding 12–13cwt of cut pieces of dried cord-wood, or rather less weight when carefully stacked thin waste planks or boards were used. There were two lugs on opposite sides near the top of each retort, for lifting them in and out of the set. When full of wood, each retort was lifted and placed in the set by means of an overhead gantry with an electric hoist; in earlier times the retorts were man-handled. A lid was then placed on top of each retort, and jointed by a few bolts, and luted with clay. A vapour-pipe like an inverted V was placed to lead from the lid to an acid-and-tar main pipe, luted with clay.

Heating of the retorts was by wood-gas and an under-led flue to a stack. When carbonisation was complete, the supply of burning gas under the retorts was blanked off by dampers. Each charge took 18 hours, but a 24-hour cycle was worked. Each vapour-pipe and lid was removed, and each retort lifted by the hoist out of the set, and its charcoal tipped through a hole in the floor at one end of the set. The hole was in the roof of a brick-built chamber with a door. A man sprayed water to quench the charcoal as it was being emptied through the hole. After 24 hours' cooling, the door was opened and the char-coal was raked out and bagged ready for further processing. Mean-while the emptied retort was returned by the hoist to the refilling point, and the cycle was then continued.

The vapour-pipes, during the carbonisation, led the acid-and-tar vapours to vats, where the tar liquid was allowed to settle. The upper layer of pyroligneous acid was pumped to a vat containing iron fil-ings and turnings. The acid was neutralised and formed iron acetate. The crude liquor containing the acetate was pumped to a pan for 'boiling down' in order to concentrate the solution to the required density: this was then run into barrels for sale as 'iron liquor', which was principally used as a mordant in dyeing cotton and linen. The lower layer in the vats consisted of wood-tar. This was also pumped out to other boiling down pans, in order to remove acid, water, and spirit, and to somewhat thicken the tar; it was then put in drums for sale. No attempt was made to recover wood-spirit.

Another indication of the fascinating chemical processes in Dean is provided by A. H. Churchouse, chemical engineer, of Worksop:[77]

The 'cylinders' described in the *Transactions of the Newcomen Society*, vol XVIII 1937–8 appear to have been the forerunners of retorts used at Worksop in the first 10 to 15 years of this century. A description of the retorts was given to me by an old man who worked with them when a boy. The details below may not be exactly accurate, but are sufficient to indicate the main features. The retorts were cylindrical, but had a flat bottom; they were about 8–9ft long and 5–6ft at maximum diameter and made of wrought iron sheet about $\frac{1}{2}$in thick, rolled to shape and rivetted. The door, in one piece, was an angle frame covered by a $\frac{1}{4}$in sheet. The angle was shaped to the retort and formed an inner flange which located the door in place. The retorts were fastened in by an iron bar dropped into lugs in the brickwork and then wedged in. Any leaks which showed were luted with clay. With the door removed, 8ft lengths of wood were stacked in; and shorter lengths were thrown in: each retort held approximately one cord of wood (25–30cwt). When loaded, the door was lifted into place and held in position by the iron bar. Each retort had its own fire hole, with a cast iron trough below containing water. This practice was continued in the larger modern retorts—but the function is obscure: it was supposed to give off a little steam to keep the underside of the firebars cool! The retorts were fired with coal and the moisture that was driven off at first was allowed to escape through the top of the copper 'down take'. When the steam changed to a more light-blue gas, the 'lids' were put on—causing the vapours to pass along the 'down takes'—through a seal and along a 9in copper pipe. The initial lengths of this pipe were cooled in an underground iron trough—and then further on—at a lower ground level in a brick tank called a 'bosh'. This bosh is still in use as a trough for settling suspended mud and silt from the canal water which is used for cooling. Where the pipe emerged from the 'bosh' an upriser allowed the gas to escape into an underground tank called 'the well'—and this too is still in use. No attempt was made to utilise the gas for heating. The acid and tar were pumped from the well by a single pump with a double suction. The longer limb went to the bottom of the well and pumped tar, to a tar 'still' or pitch 'still'. The other limb, some $2\frac{1}{2}$ft shorter, pumped acid to a neutralising tank where lime was added. After boiling off the spirit portion from the neutralised liquor in a lime lyes still—the remainder was evaporated to dryness to give 'brown acetate of lime'. After 24 hours' heating, the retort door was removed, using two 'handles', and the charge was raked out using a rake made of a piece of sheet iron fixed to a length of pipe. For some reason the rake had a straight side and a round side: this may be a 'carry over' from the time when earlier retorts were cylindrical and the rake was shaped to the contour of them. In part of the retorts were iron plates onto which the charcoal was raked—and then thoroughly quenched. When sufficiently cool, the charcoal was bagged and removed to a store. A fresh charge of wood was loaded while the charcoal was cooling off, and then the cycle was repeated.

Apparently two or three experimental retorts were constructed—in which the fire was not directly under the retort—because it was found that the retorts tended to burn through where the flames impinged on to them. Also tried was the idea of raking the charcoal into boxes, putting a sheet of iron over the box as a lid, luting round with clay, and allowing to stand until cool. The long copper pipe which acted as a 'condenser' gave much trouble by blocking up with tar: it was a filthy and smelly daily job 'rodding it through'—and my old informant remembers vividly the ever black and smelly hands that were his lot for several years while working on this job. And so there was developed a rectangular box retort—with internal rails of 2ft gauge. They were long enough to take four boxes each holding about 8–10cwt of wood. (There is a difference of opinion here: my informant says that the retorts only held two boxes, but the son of the old foreman is certain he remembers four to a retort). The boxes had solid sides, ie no perforations, and when charged with wood were pushed into the retort. When carbonised, the boxes were withdrawn, and a lid put in place: this was supported on an angle bracket running round the top of the box. They were pushed along the rail and coupled together, and a horse drew the 'train' to the cooling shed. When cool, the charcoal was bagged and stacked—with the result that many fires occurred! It was not realised that freshly made charcoal absorbed oxygen from the air—which combined with the carbon in the charcoal: in fact a form of combustion! If the heat which was generated did not disperse, the mass heated up and soon reached ignition point.

A further improvement was incorporated. To avoid the fire flames impinging on the retort bottom, an arch was introduced—with side ports—so that the hot gases from the fire could pass up the sides of the retort and over the top, thus preventing flame impingement. Then, in addition, internal side dampers were introduced to deflect the flue gases down to a flame at the rear of the retort, below ground level.

Since the 2ft track was on ground level, the bottom of the retort was also at the same level—hence the 'fire hole' had to be below ground level, and the first firing pit was cooled. The products of decomposition of the wood no longer relied on the long copper pipe for cooling, because tubular condensers were introduced. There was an upriser from the top of the retort to the top of the condenser. The vapours and gas passed down through the tubes of the condenser and the liquid which formed, together with the gas, passed through a seal port. The liquor (pyroligneous acid and wood tar) passed through a 2in copper pipe to a large barrel-shaped vat. In order to keep the liquor flowing, the tubular condensers on the top of the retorts were run warm, because maximum cooling was not desired; even then, the 2in copper line had to be steamed through every day. In the barrel vat was a central 12in pipe, into which the liquor ran at the top and out at the bottom—so that tar separated. The pyroligneous acid overflowed from the top of the barrel vat, through a tubular condenser and into the well—thus completing the cooling of the 'pyro' and reducing the loss of 'wood spirit'.

It is obvious that the processes in the wood chemical works were both skilful and interesting. Few people in Dean now remember them in operation.

The Wood Distillation Works at Speech House Road

The earlier processes of charcoal-burning in 'pit' and kiln have been described in Chapter 9. A modern process—carried out in large retorts has been used for over fifty years at Speech House Road, some 50 yards south of the earlier 'chemical works' which closed in 1902.

By 1911[78] the Office of Woods were considering the utilisation of Dean's large amount of waste wood, particularly branches ('lop and top') of oak and other hardwoods, which accumulates during the felling of trees and has to be cut into lengths of about 4ft and stacked in cords. Charcoal was in great demand for various industrial purposes, as also were by-products of wood—chiefly wood-spirit, and acetic acid which could be turned int acetate of lime. Wood-spirit was the main source of methylalcohol, for which there was an increasing demand in the dye-stuff industry, and for making formaldehyde for the control of anthrax. Acetate acid of lime was the source of acetone,

53 Lydney Docks: *(above)* c1900; *(below)* c1930

54 (above) 'The Big Six' of passenger road transport in West Gloucestershire and South Wales. From left to right: Arthur J. Watts, Howell Davies, John H. Watts, Ralph Williams, Guy Bown and T. John Jones. In 1937 these gentlemen formed Red & White Transport Company Limited which in 1948, following nationalisation of the passenger transport, became United Transport Company Limited, now a leading public company with large overseas interests; (below) Inauguration of the Gloucester-Newport direct service of 'Red & White', 7 November 1927. (Photograph taken outside the Lydney Town Hall)

urgently needed for the manufacture of cordite—a plasticised mixture of nitroglycerine and nitrocellulose.

It is evident that in those critical years just before the First World War, the Government were concerned to utilise the indigenous resources for which there would be great demand in an emergency. Probably it was thought that Britain, dependent on imported foodstuffs and many raw materials, would in a war find its imports restricted by enemy submarines; hence shipping would need to be conserved wherever possible. The Office of Woods were able to obtain the financial support which they required to further their plans for utilising cordwood. Approval was given for the erection of a Wood Distillation Works at Speech House Road. The cost, trivial by present standards, is given in a Government report dated 1914:

Buildings	£8,000
Machinery	£6,500
Fillings, architects' commission, fencing etc	£1,000
	£15,500

The plant and buildings of 1913–14 would today, even with modern methods of construction, cost £150,000 to £170,000. The plant, including a single retort, was constructed in Germany by the firm of F. H. Meyer of Hanover-Hainbolz; many of their patents were incorporated, and their original drawings are dated October-December 1913. E. Maples Lanton, architect, of Newport, Monmouthshire, was responsible for the erection of the buildings; and German technicians supervised the installation of the retort and its ancillary equipment together with the distillation plant, steam engine, and the boiler in the main buildings. Only the production of charcoal, grey acetate of lime, wood-spirit and wood-tar was contemplated. Meyers estimated that the following products would be obtained from the plant by carbonising 420,000 cubic feet (some 12,000 tons) of wood annually. (The yields quoted are low according to present technical knowledge): [79]

Grey acetate of lime	384	tons
Wood-tar	270	tons
Charcoal	1,380	tons
Wood-spirit	90	tons
(equal to 23,400 gallons of 8·61lb each)		

2B

The production of acetone from the acetate of lime was planned for a later date; but Britain was at war before this could be done, and it was not till 1915 that the acetate retorts were installed. The wood-distillation and refinery plants were started up by the Office of Woods in October 1913.[80] The works were ideally situated at Speech House Road where four roads meet, and were adjacent to the single track railway line at Speech House Road Station, from where a siding was run to the works. This location, with the woodlands all around, was also ideal because all the wood had to be brought in by horse-teams: long hauls would not be economic. Teams of noble Shire horses strained to haul the three or four huge oak trunks on the drays, clear of the ruts and mud in the woods, but the teams of smaller horses or mules, struggling just as hard to get cordwood out of the woods, were little known and unsung. Some 1,500 to 2,000 cords were stacked in the works yard, partly to dry out but mainly to provide a supply on hand throughout the year and when dragging out from the Forest was impossible during inclement weather.

A cord is the traditional measurement of cordwood. The billets, 4ft 3in in length, are stacked to give a rectangular heap about 4ft 3in high. Each 8 feet along the length of the stack represents a cord, ie about 128 cubic feet. A properly stacked cord weighs up to 40cwt, but 25–30cwt is usual, and the cordwood is weighed on arrival at the factory's weigh-bridge. About 5 tons of cordwood produces one ton of charcoal.

Rail-tracks of standard gauge were laid on the stacking yard to enable bogies or cradles on wheels to be pushed to the stacks of cord-wood for loading. The bogies were about 10ft long and were cylindrical, about 6ft in diameter, with bottoms of sheet iron supported on small-wheel carriages, and sides of rails or angle iron, all forming a skeleton structure. The billets were picked up by hand and laid in lengthways, in two bays. Each bogie held about two cords, and five bogies made a charge to the retort. They were pushed, or where possible hauled with steel cables by an electric winch, to a traverser (a pit about 3½ft deep with brick sides) along the bottom of which was a rail-track. On this track a flat-platformed bogie was run, the platform being level with the bogie-rails in the yard. Rails on the platform were lined up with the yard rails, and a filled bogie was pushed on. The traverser-bogie with its wood bogie was then pushed along until they were opposite the retort, when the wood-bogie was pushed on to rails out-side the retort and then into the retort along the rails therein. The operation was continued until the full charge was loaded, each bogie pushing that in front of it further into the retort. The short lengths of rail bridging the space between the outer rails and the rails of the retort were removed. The retort-door was lowered into position and tightly clamped.

The retort was a cylindrical box of iron plate about 56ft in length and 7½ft in diameter, and supported by brickwork on each side along the length. It was heated by a coal-fire in a furnace below ground-level to the left side of the retort. The hot flue-gases from this furnace passed under an arch, running underneath the whole length of the retort, passing from the arch through port-holes at various distances along its length. Dampers between the retort and the outside brickwork enabled the heat to be regulated and directed to the outer parts of the retort to maintain a uniform temperature. Two pyrometers were placed in the flues, one near the furnace, and the other near the outlet-flue to the chimney. The retort was hot from the previous working, but once the retort was charged and the door was closed, the fire was stoked. It took about 2–3 hours to reach the desired temperature in the flues as indicated by the pyrometers, ie 380°C, and heating continued for another period of 18–20 hours, when gassing of the charge practically ceased. Hence a 24-hour cycle was worked. The next day, when the firing was complete, the entire charge of five bogies, after the raising of a door similar to that at the charging end, was withdrawn at the far end of the retort. Often it was so hot that it would burst into flames when it reached the open air; it was therefore sprayed with water. The bogies were drawn by a steel cable and an electric winch into a cooler, a cylindrical box of similar dimensions to those of the retort. When inside, the outer door of the box was closed, and water was sprayed over the outside; this together with the lack of air within the closed box extinguished any fires. When the retort was discharged five more bogies of cordwood were again charged, and the cycle was repeated. After a further cooling for 24 hours, the bogies were withdrawn to the unloading point, where the charcoal was bagged and stacked for 'conditioning'.

As heating proceeded in the retort, moisture was first driven off; then the wood started to break down, to be converted into charcoal. The so-called by-products became vapour and gas: they left the retort through the roof by way of two openings, each of about 12in diameter, connected to two 12-inch copper pipes. These led to Meyer's patent 'tar-separator', a large cylindrical copper vessel about 4ft in diameter and 7½ft high, supported on cast-iron legs some 6ft above the top of the retort; its function was to condense the tar-vapours to tar, while permitting the vapours of acid, spirit and water, together with the wood-gas, to pass on. The tar, with some 'liquor', ran through a seal to a tar-pit, while the vapours passed through a tubular condenser consisting of 120 1in copper tubes surrounded by a water-jacket, where all the products except the wood-gas were condensed and collected in three large wooden vats each of about 1,600 gallons. The gas passed on through scrubbers to remove the last traces of spirit and vapour before being conducted to the furnace under the retort where the gases were burned; they thus helped to supply heat for the carbonisation process. The tar-separator caused much trouble through blockage by tar; by putting about 3in water-gauge back-pressure on to the retort, it caused gas 'blow outs' around the doors. Besides loss of by-products in this way, the constant maintenance of the separator was an unwanted expense.

The wood-tar in the tar-pit was pumped to a tar-still, a copper vessel fitted with a steam coil and a tubular condenser, in which the water, acid, and spirit in the tar, together with some wood-tar oils, were removed by heating and passing the resulting vapours through the condenser. The liquid so formed was run into the by-product vats. The residual tar was tapped into barrels or drums and allowed to cool before being sold.

The by-product liquid, pyroligneous acid, in the wooden vats, was pumped across the yard to a vat in the acid-room, where milk of lime (then lime slurry) was added until the acid neutralised, when the liquor was pumped for settling to vats at the top of the building. The following day it was run to another settling-vat on the first floor, and after settlement for another period of 24 hours it was pumped to the top of the building. This settling was considered necessary to remove solid impurities, which were difficult to remove by filtration. Finally, to remove the wood-spirit, the liquor was run to an iron column, mounted over a pot-still in which was a steam-coil, where it was boiled, and the vapours were passed up through the column in contact with the descending liquid. Eventually a state of equilibrium was reached in which the low-boiling spirit passed out of the column to the condenser, while the hot liquid in the pot-still overflowed to a tank to be pumped (still hot) to an evaporating-pan where it was boiled down to a specific gravity of about 10 degrees Baumé. The concentrated liquor then passed to the pan of a rotary drier, in which there was a large drum internally heated by steam. As the drum revolved in the pan of hot acetate liquor, it picked up a thin coating of it; this dried on to the drum while it revolved. A scraper placed lengthways along the drum removed the almost dry acetate of lime, which was then spread on a drying-floor for final drying to about 3 per cent moisture before being bagged.

The spirit which left the top of the iron column as vapour was passed through two further columns. In the first it came into contact with dilute sulphuric acid, and in the second with a dilute solution of caustic soda. The vapours issuing from the second column were condensed to yield 'purified' methylalcohol (sweet-smelling and 'water-white' in colour) but still containing acetone, esters and aldehydes. In these columns the greatest loss of spirit occurred, and the expected yield of some three gallons per ton of wood was never realised.

Electricity power-lines did not reach the works until they were run to Cannop Colliery after the Second World War, therefore the factory made its own DC power. That for driving the electric winches was made by running a small engine as required. Lighting at 100 volts came from a battery of accumulators kept charged by a dynamo. Steam was raised in a Dank's Lancashire boiler 27ft × 7ft 6in diameter, working at a pressure of 100lb per square inch. This supplied steam for the process work, and also that required to run a large 35hp single-cylinder non-condensing steam-engine made by Marshall, Sons & Co Ltd of Gainsborough. This engine drove everything—the fan engine, the electrical dynamo, the rotary drier, and the odds and ends that were eventually attached to the shaft which ran from the engine-house to the other end of the building for the rotary drier.

Charcoal and acetate of lime were munitions of war, therefore shortly after hostilities began, the factory passed from the Office of Woods to the control of the Ministry of Munitions. R. L. (later Sir Roy, and then Lord) Robinson took part in the management. The Ministry also took over other charcoal-factories, including that of Shirley Aldred & Co Ltd at Worksop, Notts, who had been making charcoal at various places around Sheffield since 1796. Dr C. Scott-Garrett, MBE was the chemist in charge of the manufacture of acetone in Dean; working with him at the time were Thomas Newcomen (manager) and his son Arthur, also John Capel (chief stillman) and his sons.

Captain Ryecroft Aldred was seconded from the Army in 1916 to supervise the production of acetate of lime, not only in 'His Majesty's

Wood Distillation Factory, Worksop', but also in Dean and in other works erected by the Ministry at Bideford, Andover, Chichester and Ludlow. He, with W. F. Walker, then superintendent at Worksop, and Dr W. G. Young, had during December 1914–January 1915 visited Dean and made a comprehensive report on the working of the plant. The tar-separator received some adverse criticism, but the experience gained at the plant had been utilised in establishing the new works noted above, and in making alterations in the Worksop plant to produce grey acetate of lime instead of the brown acetate; the rotary drier was not adopted because it was too expensive to run.

The loss of merchant ships through the actions of enemy submarines soon reached serious proportions; the saving of shipping-space and internal rail-traffic became imperative. Every gallon of acetone that could be made was required, and the newer wood-distillation plants set up by the Ministry of Munitions were doing their utmost. The Weizman fermentation process using grain, installed at the Cordite Factory at Holton Heath near Poole in Dorset, never got into full production, but the process was installed in Canada. Meanwhile, all wood-distillation factories were used to make acetate and supply it for conversion into acetone, including the Dean factory where, in 1915, acetone retorts and acetone distilling plant were installed. At the same time there were two shorter rectangular retorts (instead of cylindrical as was the German retort). These held two wood bogies each, thereby doubling the output of the plant.

In the process for making acetone the dry acetate of lime was spread on shallow trays, stacked in frames on short bogies. These, like the bogies containing wood to charge the charcoal retort, were pushed into specially designed smaller retorts, and heated to 450°–500°C, causing the acetate to break down and yield acetone, which was driven off as a vapour through tubular condensers, leaving on the trays a residue of calcium carbonate. When the charge was finished the bogies were withdrawn and other fully charged bogies were pushed into the retorts. When cool the trays were emptied and the carbonate discarded. After reloading, the bogies were ready for the next charge.

The crude acetone was distilled to separate the 'acetone oils' (higher ketones), and treated with permanganate of potash, to yield the purer acetone required for making cordite. The 'acetone oils' were used as a high-boiling solvent in spray painting, and for 'dope' to camouflage early aeroplanes, etc. The production of charcoal was immense. Thomas Newcomen and his associates left the works in 1917 and reopened the comparatively small Tufts works; they had kept their Lydbrook enterprise in work.

POST FIRST WORLD WAR   After the war production continued at Speech House Road until May 1919;[81] then for four years there was no production because following the Government practice, all wood distillation plants were put up for sale. While other plants were broken up and sold piecemeal, the Dean works were taken over in 1924 by a private company (financed in particular by a Mr Richardson, a north-east coast shipbuilder), Wood Distillation (England) Ltd. Two of the directors were a Mr Edwards (Richardson's son-in-law), and Captain Wigney, who had run the Ludlow Factory. They were assisted by Dr Scott-Garrett (with experience at Speech House Road, Bideford and Chichester) and F. T. Goldsworthy, who had been engineer at Bideford and Chichester, and, after the war went to Burma to install a plant for making charcoal in the jungle of Mandalay. Few men would have come through that experience unscathed, but such was Goldsworthy's sterling worth that he returned with a full knowledge of the problems of a wood-distillation plant, a knack of doing carpentry with a pocket knife, and nothing worse than a taste for strong cheroots!

The early twenties were not good times for industry, because after the short initial boom in trade the inevitable slump set in. With steel-output declining and shipyards closing, business was difficult, especially for the smaller companies. Many charcoal-producers closed down, and matters were not going too well in the Dean works. The Worksop plant kept running, but was closed completely during the 1926 coal-strike. However, the firm of Shirley Aldred, who had modernised their plant after it was relinquished by the Ministry, was able to get off the mark quicker than most of their competitors, and had in fact started work at Warminster, installing two wood-distillation retorts from the wartime plants at Chichester in the early part of the 1920s. In 1927–8 the Dean company went into liquidation and the plant was for sale, but Captain Aldred and W. F. Walker again made an inspection, with the result that Wood Distillation (England) Ltd was purchased by the shareholders of Shirley Aldred. While retaining its individuality the Dean company had the benefit of more than a century of 'know-how,' and Goldsworthy remained as manager.

With the works completely shut down, the period of reorganisation started. Walker took up temporary residence at Cannop, and with Goldsworthy and a hard-working band of men led by the late Henry Wilson, a redoubtable blacksmith, set to work to modernise the plant.

The old German cylindrical retort with all its trappings, including the tar-separator were removed, and two American-type rectangular retorts were installed, from the war-time plant at Bideford. These held only four bogies but about the same amount of wood. A new off-take for the vapours rising from the retorts, devised by Walker and developed by Goldsworthy, were completely successful and overcame the difficulties of blockage by tar. The effect was to condense out part of the tar, which then ran through a seal to the acid-vats. The remainder of the vapours were passed through tubular condensers similar to the German ones, in which the vapours were condensed to pyroligneous acid, while the incondensable wood-gas passed straight to the furnace, each to its own retort. The condensed pyroligneous acid was collected in the same vats as the tar. Tar and acid were distilled together, the tar preventing fouling of the steam coils (a trade secret for many years!). The distilled acid was neutralised with milk of lime as before, but no period for settling was required. Instead, the neutralised liquor was run into lees-stills in batches; these were 3,000–4,000 gallon vessels, heated with steam coils, with a vapour-pipe on top leading to a large tubular water-cooled condenser. About 40 per cent of the liquid was distilled off, and this contained all the wood-spirit. The remainder of the liquor was run, still boiling, to large evaporating pans placed alongside and near to the top of the long retorts. After boiling down to some 50–60 per cent moisture, ie to a wet crumbly solid, the acetate of lime was shovelled on to the top of the retorts, and the drying was completed.

The 40 per cent of liquor containing the wood-spirit was run, in batches again, to the pot-stills. Continuous working was abandoned, and likewise were the acid and soda washing columns. The iron columns were retained, and served as fractionising columns, that is, they permitted the wood-spirit to be removed, with a little water, while retaining the bulk of water in the pot. After stripping, this water was discarded.

The crude spirit was subjected to more purification, in separate distillations over lime and then over sulphuric acid; the latter was subsequently discontinued. With the simplified working and better yields of by-products the company was set for profitable working. The alterations were carried out during the second slump, 1929–32, so disastrous in America and on the Continent. As the country's economy improved, so did Wood Distillation (England) Ltd, who were ready to take an increasing share of business. By 1935, 600 tons of wood was 'retorted' each month, using 300 tons of coal in that period. Work went on twenty-four hours a day, seven days a week, and twenty-two men were employed.

More changes took place in the works. Methylalcohol was no longer readily saleable at economic prices, following the synthesis of methanol, ie 99–100 per cent methylalcohol, from hydrogen and carbon monoxide. Methyl acetate, an ester formed from methylalcohol and acetate acid, was in demand as a solvent of many uses. Therefore a method was developed to make this ester from the wood-spirit and the relatively strong distilled pyroligneous acid; the remainder of the acid was still converted to grey acetate of lime. The resultant solvent, sold under the trade name of 'Esterul', was in increasing demand for many years, and especially during the Second World War. It contained 50–55 per cent of ester, the remainder being acetone and methylalcohol. More acetone was required for this, therefore some of the acetate of lime was placed on trays on top of the wood-bogies and converted to acetone in the charcoal-retorts. The acetone was evolved towards the end of the process when the highest temperature was reached in the retorts, and passed over with the pyroligneous acid. At this stage the evolution of pyroligneous acid was falling off, so that acetone vapour was not diluted; much was carried off by the wood-gas, and burned. It became necessary to install gas-scrubbers to recover this. Remembering the blockages on the early German scrubbers, a different type was used enabling the blocked packing to be removed periodically at the base of the column, while topping up with clean packing. In addition, spent acetic acid from a works in North Wales became available in reasonable quantities, and this was used to increase the ester production, without using too much acid and thereby lowering the production of acetate of lime. 'Esterul' output was thus increased to about three times the pre-war level. Acetone is widely used in the storage of acetylene, the cylinders being filled with Kieselguhr or granular activated charcoal, then with acetone, into which the acetylene is dissolved under a pressure of some 120lb per square inch. Compressed acetylene is explosive, but by dissolving it in acetone—which is absorbed in the Kieselguhr or activated carbon— this risk is eliminated.

AFTER THE SECOND WORLD WAR   During the 1939–45 War the Speech House Road plant had been run with the minimum of repairs. Consequently after the war much was required to be done, and the opportunity was taken under the Government's Deferred Repairs tax regulations to effect major repairs or renewals of condensers, pumps, and vats. Alfred Baldwin, the present foreman, and his colleagues, gave every support to the executives. The whole plant was reconditioned by 1950. In that year Captain Aldred, managing director, died. His son, Commander J. B. Aldred, retired from the Navy, became managing director of Shirley Aldred & Co Ltd, and the Captain's other son, Philip S. C. Aldred, became managing director of Wood Distillation (England) Ltd. The production of charcoal was fully maintained. A new process, solvent recovery, begun at the Worksop plant of Shirley Aldred, was transferred to Speech House Road under P. S. C. Aldred, in 1955. A contemporary enterprise, started in the late 1950s, was the making of 'iron liquor', for which plant was installed. This liquor is a solution of iron acetate used in the dyeing industry as a mordant for fixing the dye to the material. A large tonnage was used, particularly in Ireland. Crude pyroligneous acid was converted into iron acetate; and the solution was then boiled down to a strength of about 40–45 per cent.

In 1960, recovery of by-products from wood was discontinued: tar, acetate, wood-spirit, and 'Esterul' were no longer saved; and the making of 'iron liquor' also ceased. Some of the redundant plant was sent to Worksop. In place of the discontinued processes steps were taken the same year to install a rotary furnace for the manufacture of activated charcoal, which is used in the sugar industry, in the manufacture of pharmaceuticals, glycerine, and various anti-biotics, in the treatment of drinking-water and (in a slightly different form) in gas masks, air-conditioning plants, and solvent-vapour recovery plants.

F. T. Goldsworthy retired from his post as manager of the Speech House Road plant in 1957 (he died in 1960). His son, Frank, continued in local charge until October 1957. In 1964 P. S. C. Aldred resigned from active participation in the running of the plant, still known locally as the 'Chemical Works', leaving W. Stephen as manager. The production of charcoal continues, as well as the manufacture of steam activated charcoal. Work on solvent recovery has expanded by the installation of more plant to deal with a wider range.

Charcoal produced at the works is of many qualities, and of nine grades from 1in down to 20in mesh. Other specifications include 150, 200 and 300 mesh powder; polishing blocks, barbecue charcoal; and a special grade for slow combustion stoves. A general classification of the charcoal is: stick, granulated, powdered, ovoid, and block. Uses, as well as for storage heaters, include mixtures for case-hardening, metal smelting, and foundry and horticultural work, for artificial silk, and for 'black powder'. Other uses range from fireworks and for polishing copper printing rolls, to exhumations and finger-printing.

Over the years, the large-scale uses for charcoal have declined. Many factories in countries throughout the world have closed. Those that remain have modernised their production methods, and new uses are coming along which should keep them in production for many years to come. The industry that is reputed to be dead refuses to lie down! The Wood Distillation Works, though no longer 'distilling', survives—producing large quantities of charcoal, and providing a market for inferior hardwoods as it has done since 1914.

References to Chapter 10

1　Dickinson, H. W., and Straker, E. 'Charcoal and Pyroligneous Acid Making in Sussex', *Trans Newcomen Society*, XVIII, 1937–8, 61–6.
2　*Anecdotes of the Life of Richard Watson, Bishop of Llandaff*, 2nd edn 1818, I, 240–2.
3　Congreve, 'A statement of facts relative to the savings which have arisen from manufacturing gunpowder at the Royal Powder Mills; and of the improvements which have been made in its strength and durability since the year 1783', 1811, 26.
4　Dickinson and Straker, op cit, 63, 65.
5　Young, Arthur. *Agriculture of Sussex*, 2nd edn 1808, 432.
6　Dickinson and Straker, op cit, 64. The two sketches (by John Ticking, 'Master worker at the Royal Mills') appeared in 1909 in *The Rise and Progress of the British Explosives Industry*, 20, 21. See also *Jnl of Industrial Archaeology*, Feb 1968.
7　Dowsett, J. Morewood. 'Charcoal Burning', *Geog Mag*, XVIII (9), Jan 1946, 387–92.
8　Clow, A. and N. *The Chemical Revolution*, 1952, 249.
9　Ibid.
10　Parkes. *Chemical Essays*, 1815, II, 272.
11　Sinclair, Sir John. *The General Report of the Agricultural State and Political Circumstances of Scotland*, App vol III, 1814, 308.
12　Clow, op cit, 250.
13　Loudon, J. C. *An Encyclopaedia of Agriculture*, 1831, 657.
14　GRO D421/T79.
15　Ibid.
16　GRO D421/E47: letter to John Pidcock, ironmaster, 15 Nov 1816. It is uncertain whether this works had any connection with the 'Tar works' at Lydney, which is reputed to have stood by the canal; the buildings were converted to cottages by Richard Thomas & Co but were demolished c1958.
17　For general information on wood-distillation, but not mentioning Dean, see Klar, M. *The Technology of Wood Distillation*, 1903.
18　Insole and Bunning, op cit, 89.

19 Bellows, John, op cit, 1880, 61.
20 The layout of the Cannop works is shown in Sopwith's plan of 1835.
21 GRO Q/Rum, 1841.
22 *Slater's Directory*, 1858.
23 F3/330.
24 Paar. *The Severn & Wye Railway*, op cit, 53.
25 GRO D637/I/60; D638/6.
26 Ibid.
27 Ibid.
28 Ibid.
29 F3/330.
30 *Kelly's Directory*, 1876.
31 Bellows, John, op cit, 14, 24.
32 Insole and Bunning, op cit, 88, 89.
33 F3/330.
34 S&W Min Bk, 19 April 1892.
35 F3/330.
36 Paar. *The Severn & Wye Railway*, op cit, 53.
37 F3/330.
38 *Industrial Gloucestershire, 1904* (Chance & Bland, Printers, Gloucester).
39 Ibid.
40 Specimen, *penes me.*
41 Bellows, John, op cit, 50.
42 *Trans Newcomen Society*, XVII, 1936–7, 241.
43 *Kelly's Directory*, 1893.
44 *Dean Forest Guardian*, 26 Oct 1900.
45 *Vict C Hist Glos*, II, 1907, 211.
46 *Industrial Gloucestershire 1904*, op cit.
47 Probably two kinds: (*a*) some type of 'cracking mill' (? roller with spikes), and (*b*) a horizontal 'pebble mill' (a cylinder in which pebbles revolve).
48 Wood naphtha—a mixture of Methylalcohol, Acetone, Methyl acetate, Aldehyde, Allyl alcohol, and traces of others.
49 Crude acetic acid—the principal acid in Pyroligneous acid.
50 The crude Pyroligneous acid was neutralised with a lime slurry (ie lime slaked), and the resultant solution was evaporated to dryness: this gave the crude acetate of lime.
51 The mould was made with damp sand, the pattern removed, and the mould dusted with powdered charcoal.
52 F3/229.
53 Ibid.
54 *Slater's Directory*, 1858.
55 *Harris's Directory*, 1887. Both Isaiah Trotter and J. Trotter are shown as connected with the works.
56 Ibid, 1891, 25.
57 *Industrial Gloucestershire 1904*, op cit.
58 *Kelly's Directory*, 1894, 436.
59 F3/230.
60 Lease in Lydney Park Estate Office.
61 *Harris's Directory*, 1891, 24.
62 Lease in Lydney Park Estate Office.

63 Letters in Lydney Park Estate Office.
64 *Trans Newcomen Society*, XVII, 1936–7, 241.
65 *Kelly's Directory*, 1876.
66 Ibid, 1878.
67 S&W Min Bk, 8 Aug 1883.
68 *Harris's Directory*, 1887.
69 Ibid, 1891.
70 Officers' Mins S&W Jnt Rly, 31 Jan 1906 and 11 April 1906.
71 F3/776.
72 43rd Rpt of the Commissioners of Woods . . . , 1865, 99.
73 Insole and Bunning, op cit, 89.
74 F3/776.
75 Shown in 1901 as disused (2nd edn 6in OS Map).
76 *Dean Forest Mercury*, 31 Oct 1902. Premises sold by A. E. Dykins, Auctioneer, 12 Nov 1902.
77 A. H. Churchouse besides being connected with the Worksop works, took a great interest during 1930–70 in the Speech House Road Wood Distillation Works. He and the present manager, W. Stephen, have been most generous in providing information.
78 The Office of Woods asked the S&W Rly Co, 11 April 1911 for a siding-connection at Speech House Road to a proposed chemical works.
79 A government report in 1914 says: 'As production commenced only a few months ago, sufficient time has not yet elapsed for the purpose of enabling the results and estimates to be fully compared, but the experience already gained leads to the conclusion that the above output will scarcely be obtained.' See also *WNFC* 1946–8, 31.
80 92nd Rpt of the Commissioners of Woods . . . , 1914, 35.
81 F3/1248 (Correspondence 1912–19); F3/1428, 1429.

Eleven

Fulling Mills, Corn Mills and Agriculture

From at least the eleventh century, Dean's streams had an important bearing on the introduction and siting of mills for fulling and for corn. All played a useful part in the local economy.

Fulling Mills

Water-driven fulling mills for cleansing and thickening cloth were introduced into England in the last quarter of the twelfth century. In Dean, clear, swift streams flowing down towards the Severn and the Wye, together with local and Herefordshire wool, were the foundation of a small woollen industry requiring fulling mills. Lanthony Priory had such a mill at Aylburton in 1291,[1] and still held it in 1531–2.[2] Another fulling mill stood at Flaxley in 1291,[3] and another at English Bicknor in 1301 (owned by Celia de Muchgros).[4] In 1334 Hugh le Hornare of Rodley leased to Christiana de la Hulle a fulling mill at Newland with a watercourse 'running from King's Mill to the way leading to St Briavels',[5] and it was still in use in 1490—when at the Court of St Briavels William Wyrehale admitted to holding 'Kyngsmyll' in Newland with all streams and springs except the water running to the fulling mill.[6] The 'Kyngsmyll' ('a water-mill newly built in Ashridge') is referred to in 1434–5 as being owned or tenanted by John Wyrehale, 'and next to two fulling mills' owned or tenanted by John Yevan and partners, and another by John Waller.[7] In 1438 John Walker of Churchend in Newland, fuller, had a mill there.[8] In 1583 Christopher Monmouth conveyed a fulling mill and water mill at Lydbrook to Thomas Smalman and William Hill.[9]

It is interesting to compare the foregoing information, and information hereunder on corn mills, with the statement about the Elizabethan adventurers searching for a suitable wire-works site in 1566—

' . . . we were forced to search the country by Severn side more than 40 miles; and finding all the pleasant rivers set full of grist and tucking mills, we crossed the Severn to view the rivers of Usk and Wye . . .'—and in due course arrived at their 'promised land' of Tintern!

Four little centres of the woollen industry may be discerned in 1608.[10] The most considerable was around Mitcheldean, where there were 3 clothiers, 14 broad weavers and 4 weavers, as well as 3 tuckers, which suggests that there may have been a fulling mill.[11] Another clothier lived nearby at Abenhall, with a few weavers and 2 tuckers.[12] Altogether some three dozen weavers lived in the district, which meant an annual output of about 700 pieces of cloth. Westbury-on-Severn was another centre for the industry: nearby at Rodley, lived William North, clothier and his servant, whilst there was a fuller at Northwood to deal with the output of the 23 weavers of the area.[13] A little to the south, William Gough, clothier, lived at Purton—the centre of a Severnside area through which were distributed 15 weavers, with fullers on the small streams at Alvington and Aylburton.[14] In 1701–2, Guns Mill between Abenhall and Flaxley, previously a blast furnace, comprised a fulling mill and two grist mills—mortgaged to Thomas Foley for £100.[15]

Corn Mills

The streams in Dean helped to give rise to numerous corn or grist mills from the eleventh to the twentieth centuries. *Domesday* (1086) gives several indications of mills along the tributaries of the lower Severn, and of one near St Briavels. The mills soon increased in number and size, and there arose throughout the region dozens of manorial and other corn mills.

In the thirteenth and fourteenth centuries, 'water mills' stood at Awre (1278 and 1344), Abenhall (one in 1301 and 1317, and two—'in a bad state and ruinous'—in 1341), Purton (1285), Ruardean (1293, 1306, 1317 and 1376), Lydbrook (1306), Blaisdon (1301), and Mitcheldean (two in 1319).[16] In Newland in 1434–5[17] John Wyrehale owned or was the tenant of the 'Kyngsmyll' in Ashridge; by 1490, William Wyrehall held the mill.[18] Nearby, in 1434–35, John Watkins and his wife Joan had a mill on the brook called Redbrook, for making 'instruments'.[19] In the same district, a mill (Burchore or Birchore) was in use in the thirteenth century, and again in 1380, 1396 and 1407;[20] a mill in Highmeadow was held by Thomas Ball in 1428, and by another in 1501;[21] and a mill stood nearby at Staunton in 1484.[22] In 1435–36[23] mills stood at Lydbrook, Mitcheldean, Mork, Brockweir (Walter Chalner), 'Horwalhulle' (Richard Lawrence of Bream), and 'Alvyston' (Thomas Payne); and a mill was being built at 'Lowkyneslond' (Ralph Greyndour) and at Mitcheldean (John Coune). It is impossible to say whether all the above were corn mills. The same uncertainty applies to a few of the mills noted below.

'Okewods Mill', a corn mill near Bream, was owned by John Lawrence in 1520; another corn mill at Redbrook was sold in 1598 by William Trestyd of Newland (tanner) to Thomas Dixton of Pennalt. In 1618[24] Sir William Winter and William Bell owned corn 'water mills' at Oakwood, Joyford, Whitecliff and Lower Clearwell (two being on Thurston's Brook). Two corn mills (one being 'Gabb's Grist Mill') operated in Lower Lydbrook in 1622–3; and in 1636–7 William Carpenter sold to Benedict Hall a corn mill in Poolway Green, Coleford.[25]

Some research has been undertaken into the corn mills of the region, but many more years of investigation would be necessary in order to provide a chronological record of their history and the names of their owners and tenants. To assist the student who may wish to pursue the investigation, the following tentative information is placed on record.[26]

ON THE CINDERFORD-RUSPIDGE BROOK

Bright's Corn Mill, Ruspidge   Dating from c1818, when Thomas Brace received a licence from the Office of Woods to convert to a corn mill an old water-wheel used for drying coal. In 1856 it was let to S. Allaway and H. Crawshay, and later to Samuel Bright, miller. Went out of use when drainage by a colliery upstream reduced the water supply: the owner refused the offer of a steam engine.[27] Now converted into a house, and the pond filled in. The remnants of the iron wheel on its massive axle were removed in 1953, and at the same time the wheel-pit was filled in.

ON THE BLACKPOOL BROOK

Nibley Mill   On Studd's Farm, below Furnace Bottom. Now a gabled house partly half-timbered and with a stone mill adjoining. The iron framework of the overshot wheel was still visible in 1951, but the pool is now dry, and overgrown. The miller there in 1858 was James Powell.

55 Dean's turnpikes[1]: *(top)* Whitecliff; *(centre)* Berry-Hill *(below)* Coalway. (Photographed on 31 October 1888)

56 Dean's turnpikes (2): *(top)* Poolway; *(centre)* Parkend; *(below)* Crossways. (Photographed on 31 October 1888)

Blakeney Upper Mill Converted into two semi-detached houses, named 'Sunnydale'. Ceased to work c1900. Inside the working part of the mill (an overshot one) are iron pillars and archways made at Soudley Forge. The miller there in 1858 was Richard W. White.

Blakeney Lower Mill On the lane leading to Etloe. An overshot mill, now represented by a row of cottages. The remnants of the iron wheel were visible in 1951. Stephen A. White was the miller there in 1887.

Awre Mill On the Bideford Brook, being the lower length of the Blackpool Brook.

ON THE LEY BROOK

Upper Ley Mill In 1940 the iron framework of the wheel was still in position. A brick building, now ruinous, set amongst coppice and marsh.

ON THE HOPE (or WESTBURY) BROOK

Abenhall (or Over) Mill In 1951 traces were to be seen of the overshot wheel, fed on the crown through an iron pipe.[28]

Hart's Barn, Longhope The site of a corn mill c1702–82.[29]

Parish Mill, Longhope A long stone building, partly stuccoed, with a well kept pool, and with parts of the iron wheel still in position c1950.

Furnace Mill An old stone building now converted into cottages (Plate 48b). Once part of, or near, a blast furnace, and thereafter a tannery, grist mill, sawmill and maltings. At the rear of the mill is a silted up pool together with dilapidated stone and weatherboard out-buildings. A cottage (not the oldest) is dated 1799.

Blaisdon Mill A large stone building, once a corn mill, but according to local information last used as a sawmill.

Westbury Mill Built of local stone. Now dilapidated, and the pool was filled in c1933. The tail race forms a roadside ditch and joins the main stream opposite the gardens of Westbury Court. In 1858 the millers there were Anselm Bailey, Tom Hooper and James Watson.

Severn Mill At the outfall into the Severn. Brick-built, and now with rotting wooden sluice-gates and footbridge.

ON THE FLAXLEY BROOK

Guns Mill A corn mill prior to being a blast furnace and paper

2c

mill. Now a picturesque half-timbered building, fast falling into decay, with a complex of other buildings and ponds. Many remnants of buildings lie on the Brook between Guns Mill and Flaxley. They may have been connected with forges or corn mills.

Flaxley Mill A plain stone building, fast falling into decay, adjacent to a half-timbered farmhouse. A board setting out grinding charges at the mill is to be seen in the Gloucester Folk Museum. A. R. Ebborn was the miller there in 1902.

Bosley (or Cutt's) Mill Now demolished. Site still traceable before the Flaxley Brook joins the Hope Brook.

ON THE CONE STREAM

Rodmore Mill Disused by c1881. Subsequent owners or tenants were George Lewis (1887) and J. Nicholls (1902).

Cone (Upper) Mill This site was chiefly used as a paper mill, but may previously have been a corn mill (see Chapter 12).

Cone (Lower) Mill A corn mill from the Middle Ages, and in use today. In 1912 'three good pairs of ancient mill-stones were rumbing within', and a drawing made in that year is extant.[30]

ON THE BROCKWEIR BROOK

Brockweir Mill and Abbots (Hudnalls) Mill One was leased in the nineteenth century as a grist mill. A 'grist mill and pond' owned by Henry Smith appears on the Hewelsfield Tithe Map, no 208.

ON THE OAKWOOD BROOK

Oakwood Mill The site of a corn mill from c1520 until the eighteenth century. One of the buildings is standing.

ON THE NEWERNE STREAM

Whitecroft A corn mill from the eighteenth century, owned by the Morse family (1858 and 1902),[31] and now owned by Lydney Farmers Ltd. It is uncertain whether this was the same mill as Kidnells Mill, where in 1808 Richard Morgan was the miller.

ON THE LYD BROOK

Upper Lydbrook Mill and Lower Lydbrook Mill Both corn mills were undershot types. The Lower Mill is shown in Plate 48a (note the two grindstones). Millers in Lydbrook have included: Alfred and Thomas Cooper, Edwin and William Wintle, Thomas

Burdock (1858); Thomas Burdock, O. Oldland and the Little family (1902). There are a few remnants of buildings, embankments and races.

ON THE HOW (HOUGH) BROOK

In the nineteenth century a corn mill stood near the junction of the How and Lyd brooks (Plates 47a and b), a short distance below the Waterloo colliery.

ON THE MORK BROOK

Mork Mill No 610 on the St Briavels Tithe Map, when Jane Wells was the owner and Charles Keedwell was the tenant. Disused by 1881.

ON THURSTAN'S BROOK

On this brook, which ran from Poolway in Coleford to Newland, there were several small mills, some of which may have been for the grinding of corn. Thurstan's Brook is the source of the Valley Brook which flows to Redbrook (see *infra*).

ON THE REDBROOK VALLEY BROOK

One or more corn mills are reputed to have stood on this brook, which flows from Newland to Redbrook.

ON THE SWAN BROOK

From at least 1608, three corn mills stood on this brook, which flows from Newland to Redbrook. They were the Upper Mill (Hall's), the Lower Mill (Bun's), and King's (Quick's). In 1836 the first two mills (successors to the earlier mills) were described as: [32] 'two good and well constructed grist mills each working two pairs of large French Bur Stones; Butling and Dressing Machines; Pot and Pearl Barley Machine; Corn and Flour Lofts, Kilns, etc.' The King's (Quick's) Mill became in the nineteenth century the site of the Wye Valley Corn Mills. Among the millers at Redbrook were Henry Courteen (1828), Thomas Courteen, Edwin Morse and Thomas Davies (1858).

During parts of the nineteenth century, and in some instances into the present century, corn mills stood at Woolaston Grange (where the wheel is extant); Alvington (Wood Mill) and on the Ferneyley Brook (Daniel A. White was the miller there in 1858); Aylburton (at Mill Brook and Lower Common, and on the Plane Tree Brook— first noted in 1832;[33] and T. Godwin was a miller in the district in 1881 and 1902); Joyford (pre-1800); Littledean (above the Greyhound Inn, where a whitewashed cottage and a former mill pond and leat indicate the site); Mitcheldean (at Millend, the site being marked by Tusculum House where there are an embanked pond and sluices);[34] Newnham-on-Severn (a corn mill, with a mill house called Brook House);[35] Soudley (Camp Mill c1868–88); Ayleford (see Chapter 2); Purton (Woodfields Water Mill);[36] Lower Soilwell (on Plumers Brook); and at Bishopswood.

The Wye Valley Corn Mill, noted above, was enlarged as a flour mill following the opening of the Wye Valley Railway in 1876. Another flour mill, at Steam Mills in Lower Cinderford, was owned c1840–5 by Timothy Bennett, 'miller, corn and flour factor, maltster and coal merchant'. From c1887 it was owned by Thomas and Francis Wintle, and in the 1900s it was equipped with 'the Elite system, invented by William Gardner & Sons, milling engineers of Gloucester'. The premises were subsequently used as part of a machine tool factory and, still later, as a storeroom for plastics.

The history of the mills for corn, flour and fulling in the region indicates the wide usage of Dean's streams; and the adaptability of some of their premises for subsequent industries has been noted in other chapters.

Agriculture

Primitive agriculture was practised in Dean from the Early Iron Age. Subsequently, easily worked land was gained by clearing and burning patches of woodland, and thereby the soil became enriched with wood ash. After a few rotations of crops, low in content and quality by to-day's standards, and subsequent decrease in fertility, the inhabitants moved to other stretches. Animals were grazed on the pastures, in particular the alluvial 'tack lands' alongside the Severn, and were frequently moved to higher ground or to Dean's fertile, stream-fed valleys. Wild boar and deer were abundant. In Roman and Saxon times, sheep and cattle grazed in the clearings, and swine thrived on the acorns and beech mast. During the Norman period the inhabitants enjoyed recognised privileges of commoning and pannage. Manorial and monastic agriculture came to the fore, in particular in the Tidenham and Woolaston districts, and were later continued by squires and other local landowners or their tenants.

In more recent years, sometimes to the detriment of silviculture, commoners (including miners and colliers ekeing out an extra few shillings each week) continued to graze sheep and run pigs. Orthodox agriculture has been practised in fields, meadows and 'plecks' scattered throughout the Forest and its neighbourhood. The land is of medium quality; there is little arable and orchard, but beef and dairy herds are raised on some farms. Though an 'unspectacular' and relatively small part of Dean's industrial history, agriculture as elsewhere has played a useful rôle in the economy of the region.

References to Chapter 11

1   *Taxatio Ecclesiastus Nicholai*, IV, 172.
2   *Valor Ecclesiastus*, II, 425.
3   *Taxatio Ecclesiastus Nicholai*, IV, 171.
4   *Glos IPM*, IV, 231.
5   Gloucester City Liby, 214(3).
6   GRO D33/B/227/124.
7   SC 858/14: Mins A/cs 13–14 Hen VI.
8   GRO D33/B227/103.
9   GRO D33/138/267. Lydbrook is the only mill in Dean noted by Tann, Jennifer. *Gloucestershire Woollen Mills*, 1967.
10 Smyth, John. *Names and Surnames*, 31; Perry, R. 'The Gloucestershire Woollen Industry, 1100–1690', *BGAS* 66, 1945, 99, 100.
11 Ibid.
12 Ibid, 35.
13 Ibid, 45, 73.
14 Ibid, 54, 58.
15 Gloucester City Liby, Deeds I(1).
16 *Glos IPM*, IV, 106, 128, 161, 234, 238; V, 47, 163, 164, 173, 285, 302; VI, 100.
17 SC 858/14: Mins A/cs 13–14 Hen VI.
18 GRO D38/B227/124.
19 SC 858/14.
20 GRO D1677, GG3, 16, 44, 70, 106, 138 and 151.
21 Ibid, GG187, 229.
22 Ibid, GG285.
23 SC 858/15, 20.
24 Deed of 1618 in Hereford Cathedral Records Room; a copy in GRO
25 GRO D1677, GG331, 562, 676, 688, 826.
26 Some of the information on corn mills has been provided by Miss G. M. Davies, 'Mills of the Dean Forest Borders', *Glos Soc for Ind Arch, Newsletter* 14, Feb 1970, 21–5.
27 F3/778: correspondence 1861–1919.
28 GRO D36/T1, E84.
29 Ibid, D49/T1155 and D1202.
30 Cooke, A. O. *The Forest of Dean*, 1912, 222.

31 F3/778: correspondence in 1860–1919.
32 GRO D637/VII/31.
33 Ibid, D421/T46.
34 Ibid, D36/T59.
35 Ibid, D265/T6: 1717–1851.
36 Ibid, D637/II/8T1, 2.

Twelve
Paper and Leatherboard

Paper

In the early days of the paper-making industry, manufacturers sought mill sites where there was an ample supply of water for power (preferably having been dammed to serve earlier industries, such as fulling, corn and iron); the water had to be pure and clear for the paper-making process. Quite small streams sometimes sufficed, especially for the early mills. In and around Dean, several blast furnaces or forges, with their streams,[1] dams and water-wheels, were converted to paper mills, operating one or two vats or small machines. All of these went out of existence before the present century, chiefly because of effective competition from bigger and better situated mills, using improved machines. Time also brought excise duties on paper, changes in transport, and new kinds and sources of raw materials.[2]

GUNS MILL The first of the Guns Mill paper-mills was converted from an iron furnace[3] some time between 1732 and 1743,[4] when 'any Paper Man who is capable of undertaking a White Vat' might have heard of a master by applying to Joseph Lloyd at Guns Mill and where he would 'meet with all suitable encouragement'. Joseph, son of Joseph Lloyd of Guns Mill, is recorded in 1739 in the Parish Register of Flaxley.[5] One of the workmen in 1745 was Stephen Hill, age 34.[6] In 1746[7] Joseph Lloyd, senior, took an apprentice named William Bayham of Newland. On Lloyd's death in 1761[8] the paper-making was carried on by his widow (Hannah) and Joseph Lloyd, junior. A watermark, 'LLOYD', of c1770 is extant.[9] Further fragments of information[10] show that the industry was carried on there throughout the second half of the eighteenth century. In 1762 and 1766[11] apprentices absconded from Hannah and Joseph Lloyd respectively. Lloyd in 1771[12] married Miss Robinson of Littledean, 'an amiable young lady with a genteel fortune'. The partnership between Joseph Lloyd junior and his son, 'paper-manufacturers of Guns Mill', was dissolved in 1816.[13]

The Excise Letter[14] of 1816 records Joseph Lloyd at three mills, nos

143 (Guns), 144 (Middle Mill) and 145 (Upper Mill). The Middle and Upper were washing mills. In 1819 and 1827 Joseph Lloyd & Sons were producing a wide range of papers as well as blotting-paper.[15] Greenwood's Map of Gloucestershire, 1824, shows three mill symbols at Guns Mill, and the Tithe Map and Apportionment of Abenhall parish, 1840, refer to the paper-mill as the lowest of a group of mills there, some of the others upstream being 'washing mills'; both these and the paper-mill were still in the occupation of Joseph Lloyd. Guns Middle and Upper Mills were close together, but after 1832 no reference has been found to the two mills.

By 1847 Mill no 143 (Guns) had passed to George Lunnon; by 1860[16] to Aaron Goold, making printing papers; and by 1864[17] to the 'Guns Mill Paper Company', producing coloured and cartridge papers, and 'printings, brown, grocery papers etc'. By 1871 the company was making 'white and coloured printings and cartridges', using one machine 53in in width. Four years later[18] the owner was Joseph Skipp Lloyd, a Cheltenham barrister; his manager or lessee was Henry Affleck, and the products were brown papers, made on one machine 46in in width; the following year the machine was stated to be 48in in width. Affleck was still owner or lessee in 1880, making 'browns and cartridges' on a 48in machine. As late as 1900, rolls of paper were seen being conveyed by horse and cart to Grange Court Station, four miles away. No later reference has been found. In 1964 the Gloucester Society for Industrial Archaeology made a building survey of the site. The lower building (Plates 7a and 50b) is now part of a farmstead. Above is the old pond, now levelled and cultivated, and beyond stand the shells of the two washing mills.

RODMORE MILL This paper-mill—previously a furnace and then a forge, stood on the Aylesmore stream which helps to form the Cone nearby to St Anne's spring which is marked by a stone structure, with an arch dated 1887. The Cone from the thirteenth century was the boundary of the Marchership of Striguil (later, Chepstow) and the Forest of Dean. The mill was advertised to let in 1774[19]—there was 'a constant supply of fine spring water to serve the engine and great plenty of water to work the mill'. It was again advertised in 1789[20] as 'on a modern construction' and adapted for the making of white and brown paper. On 20 October of that year the premises were leased to James Hoffenden Stephens, paper-maker; by 5 August 1805 William Stephens was in charge;[21] in 1795 he had taken an apprentice, Thomas Davis. William, son of William Stevens, paper-maker, was baptised at St Briavels in 1815. In the Excise Letter of 1816, the mill is numbered 140 in the Hereford Collection, and it was in the occupation of William Stevens. In 1832 the paper-maker was James Stevens.[22] Elizabeth Stevens of Rodmore Paper Mill, aged 86, was buried in 1841. No later reference has been found. The premises had been converted to a corn mill in 1887, when George Lewis and a Mrs Smith resided there.[23] In 1902 the occupier was J. Nicholls.[24] The pond, sluice and some buildings are extant.

ROWLEY MILL   Rowley Iron Forge on the Cone stream, advertised for sale in 1797,[25] was converted to a paper-mill. In 1809[26] a partnership was dissolved which had been between Joseph and Thomas Morris of Chepstow, paper-makers at Rowley Forge, and at Pandy Mill, Monmouthshire. The Excise Letter of 1816 designates Rowley Mill as no 141 in the Hereford Collection, and it was in the occupation of Thomas Morris. In 1820 the paper-maker there was Joseph Morris, to whose name that of Richard Morris is added in the Excise Letters of 1829 and 1832. By 1841, John Lavender was the occupier. One beating-engine was at work in 1851.[27] By 1875[28] Rowley had become a card-board board-mill wherein Henry Williams was making 'milled and engine boards'. In 1878 the mill is described as 'Aylesmore Mill, Alvington, having one 72in machine and 8 vats', while in 1879 the mill was owned and advertised by Frank J. Noble & Co (together with Clanna Weir Mill no 144), having 4 vats and making 'machine and hand-made milled boards'. The advertisement reads:

Mill nos 141 and 144
Frank J. Noble & Co
Aylesmore Mills and Clanna Weir Mills,
Alvington, near Lydney, Glos.
Milled, Engine, Portmanteau, and other boards
both machine and hand made:
Browns, Grocery and other Papers.

Rowley Mill had a 72in machine and 8 vats in 1880, but was not working. From 1884 to 1890 Robert McNeil owned the mill—a 74in machine and 2 vats, with 'water and steam'. He was making millboard. A Scot, James Russell, was the owner in 1902,[29] and described as 'patent board manufacturer': Wilfred Kingston of Woolaston, who worked for him for one year (1918), remembers the machinery driven by water-power. The raw material was pressed-bales of used paper, which was later chopped or shredded, and then steamed, stirred, and beaten into a pulp which ran around rollers into 'felt'; it was then pegged-out on wire to dry, and unless care was taken it was easily broken. It was then dipped in 'a red liquid' and 'rolled through steam', before being pressed into cardboard and trimmed by a cutting machine. The Mill closed about 1930. The pond, sluice, wheel-pit and some buildings (now used as a residence) are extant (Plate 51b).

CONE MILL   This mill stood above the main road near Woolaston, where Richard Barrow, paper-maker is recorded in 1774.[30] He died in 1777, and the Cone Paper Mill, lately in his possession, was advertised to be let[31]—'a large commodious paper-mill, with convenient drying houses'. Barrow had for some years past used the mill to manufacture different kinds of writing and other papers. The next proprietor was probably John Ward of Woolaston, paper-maker, dealer and chapman, who went bankrupt in 1793.[32] By 1795, Samuel Jenkins, malster, paper-maker and farmer, insured the stock and utensils in the Cone millhouse,[33] and in 1801 he, described as a maltster, miller and paper-maker, again insured the stock and utensils.[34] Evidence that the mill was idle for some years is that it does not appear in the Excise Letters until 1820, hence its high number, 519. It was then occupied by John Reece.[35] The firm of Reece and Sandford, who also had paper mills in Monmouthshire, worked the mill to c1860 making 'white and pottery tissue, double crown, and cap papers'. In 1841 there were ten paper-makers and one engineer at Woolaston.[36] James Birt, paper manufacturer at nearby Alvington is recorded in 1858.[37]

In 1869 the Cone mill became the property of the Gloucester Paper Company, whose chairman was a Mr Palmer of Reading, and whose secretary was a Mr Goulding of London. In 1871 they had one machine 44in in width making 'cartridges and fine small heads'. Thereafter an entirely new process was used, resulting in probably the first mill in Britain to make paper from wood; indeed, it is believed to be the first Natron-cellulose pulp-mill in Europe. Details of the process and machinery are available in two contemporary descriptions: [38]

> The wood mostly used was off-cuts of pine deals, in rectangular slab form, about 14in square. The original wood-cutting machine consisted of a cast-iron frame in which the slabs were clamped and then fed up to a steam-driven cutter, but this proved to be too slow, and difficult to adapt to differing sizes of wood. This machine was superseded by one designed by Mr Leigh of the adjacent Severn Ironworks. The cutter was a 4-ton cast-iron disc carrying two knives, rotating at 200–250rpm and fed by rollers with timber from an inclined hopper.

The $\frac{1}{2}$in thick slices fell from the knives between a pair of horizontal crushing rollers rotating at different speeds (to avoid simply compressing the wood) which reduced the bulk to about $\frac{1}{2}$in square $\times$ $\frac{1}{8}$in thick. The feed roller journals were sprung, enabling them to adjust themselves to varying timber thicknesses, while some of the driving shafts had conical sections, so that they slipped if over-loaded.

The chips were loaded into wire cages and rolled into a boiler 3ft 9in in diameter by 32ft long, made of $\frac{9}{16}$in thick Lowmoor iron and heated by high-pressure hot-water pipes. After charging, the boiler was closed by a bolted end-cover with a lead seal, caustic soda was pumped in, and a temperature of about 220°F was maintained for 5–6 hours. The wood was thus converted into chyle, and the subsequent processes were conventional, consisting of washing (and, if necessary, bleaching) in the potching engines, and thence to the beaters, which reduced the fibres to pulp (Plate 49).

The lye (spent caustic) was originally used to boil a charge of straw or esparto, but because a cleaner and better paper could be made from all wood, this practice ceased when an efficient means of recovering the soda was evolved, by pumping the lye into evaporating pans heated by pipes. The treacle-like residue was transferred to shallow iron pans heated over furnaces. The dried mass, rich in resinous matter, was converted to soda ash in a furnace, the gases which evolved (about 2cu ft per lb of wood boiled) were passed back to the evaporating furnaces. By treating the soda ash with lime, to reduce it to a caustic state, 80 per cent of the original caustic soda was recovered.

The boilers and evaporators were to Houghton's patent, the English rights of which were acquired by the Gloucestershire Paper Co. The paper made from wood, although dearer than that from straw or esparto, was very strong, much being used for glass- and emery-paper, packing paper and envelope manufacture.

From the two accounts summarised above, it is noteworthy that whereas the cutter is stated to have produced 6 to 10 tons of chippings per hour, the boilers (there were two) which could only be charged with 28–30cwt, were used alternately (one boiling, one re-charging) and the boiling process took 5–6 hours. It thus appears that the cutter must have been idle for long periods, which suggests that the high efficiency of the caustic recovery process was not matched by an appreciation of the poor economics of under-used capital equipment; but of course there may well have been unrecorded local conditions, eg a market for surplus chippings; or unreliable raw material supplies.

The adjacent Severn Ironworks mentioned in the foregoing account was in 1872[39] called the 'Severn Engineering Works', at which 'boilers and apparatus for the making of paper from wood, straw, etc, and of patent evaporating apparatus, are manufactured'. The Cone Paper Mill had 'the apparatus in active operation'. All the draughtsmen were foreigners; most of them 'of considerable linguistic attainments'. Unfortunately the plant came to a sad end, a serious explosion occurring in June 1873: [40]

A boiler explosion occurred at the Gloucestershire Paper Mills at Woolaston on Friday, whereby a great part of the works, which are of an extensive character, are now a ruin. These mills were re-opened some six years ago by a limited company, whose energies have been directed to carrying on some scientific experiments in the manufacture of paper by the exclusive employment of wood. In these operations powerful plant was supplied by Messrs Houghton, engineers, of London. The principal part of the process consists in the boiling of wood until it becomes pulp; but, in order to effect this, steam power of extraordinary pressure is necessary. Having cut the timber into the required lengths it is packed in perforated cages, and then again packed in the boilers, of which there are two, each 30ft in length, surmounted with expansion domes for relieving the pressure. The pressure was capable of employment up to 500lb the square inch. The boilers were built of powerful wrought-iron girders and strong masonry, being situated at the side of the mills. They were alternately employed, the one being packed during the boiling of the wood in the other. In order to convey the required heat, intricate piping charged with boiling water was employed, so that, unlike ordinary boilers, these were not in proximity to fire, and being constructed of five-eighth iron and excellent workmanship they were considered capable of resisting any degree of pressure. Fortunately, the boilers and other parts of the machinery occupied the south side of the works, and in a parallel line with a stream of water. At the time of the accident the persons employed were on the opposite side of the works, and owing to the noise of the machinery on that part the explosion was scarcely heard. The principal indication was by the flooding of the mills from several large tanks, the dismantling of the building, and breakage through the floors by the falling débris, although, fortunately, the bulk of this was confined to that part of the works occupied by the boilers and pulp vats, all of which is now a conglomerated mass of ruins. The boiler literally flew from its seat through the roof, thence over the pond, uprooting two large oak trees and several other trees, then knocked down a stable, and eventually entombed itself in an enbankment two hundred yards or more from the works, whilst part of the iron roof was dashed a quarter of a mile distant. The widest confusion among the workpeople prevailed, and the place was besieged by their wives and relatives, who feared that the accident was attended with fatal results; and it was not until some time had elapsed that it was ascertained that no lives were lost, or serious injuries inflicted. Mr Mackay, the manager, at once telegraphed to the secretary, Mr Goulding, at the London office, Threadneedle Street. Meanwhile the chairman of the company, Mr Palmer, of Reading, happened to be on his way to Woolaston, and arrived soon after the explosion. The extent of the damage is estimated at upwards of £6,000. On Saturday a staff of men were engaged in digging out the entombed boiler, which gave way at the riveting on the dome end. At present it is difficult to say whether the works will be refitted to extend the experiments in this system of paper-making, several works on the same plant being now in process in Sweden. Should, however, the company decide to do so, increased strength will be necessary to resist the required pressure. Had the explosion taken place five minutes earlier, upwards of a dozen men must have been killed on the spot.

The mill using esparto grass was reopened in 1874[41] by James Edwin Randle, and news, printings and coloured printing-papers were made on a machine 48in in width. In 1876 Randle's trustees were G. & J. A. Noble, 8 Lombard Street, London, and they ran the works until 1879 making 'news, and white and coloured printings'. From 1880 to 1883 John McPherson was making there 'news, white and coloured printings on a 54in machine'. From 1885 to 1891, Thomas Patterson Gillespie, who lived at Cone House, was making 'blottings, printings, news, E.S. writings, envelope papers, square and angular, and tinted papers', on a machine 80in in width.[42] The output in 1886 was 26 tons a week. W. Matthews was his clerk in 1887,[43] and George Thomas (or Thompson) was his manager from 1887 to 1891.[44] Mrs Kingston of Woolaston, aged 88 in 1970, remembered the mill at work. It used esparto grass, hauled from Woolaston Station or from the small wharf at Cone Pill. The works closed in February 1895.[45] Subsequently the lower buildings and stables were used as a steam laundry. Despite a fire c1945, some of the ruined buildings are extant, as well as a dry mill-race, mill-pond, sluices, and reservoir, together with the former mill manager's house (Plate 50).

CLANNA WEIR MILL This paper mill on the Cone had been a forge, leased consecutively to the Tanners, the Daniels and the Pidcocks from 1775 to 1790. In 1878, Frank J. Noble held the mill (no 144)—making machine and hand-made mill boards, with 4 vats. The following year the premises were advertised for sale by Noble (see *supra*). In 1887[46] it had two vats, and was being run by Moses John Mason, making 2 to 4 tons of millboard each week. On 31 July 1888 Mason took a lease of the leatherboard mill at Camp Mill in Soudley. The present Clanna Weir house, occupied by Mrs Dolly Simmonds, was formerly the main cardboard mill building; nearby, another building formerly part of the works, was later used as a sawmill powered by a turbine driven by water taken via a 'canal' from the ponds above. Mrs Simmonds' father used to take the 'cardboard' by pack-horse to the Woolaston district.

LONGHOPE MILL   The only reference to this paper-mill, which stood about $\frac{1}{4}$ mile south of the bridge over the railway at Longhope, is in an Excise Letter of 1821,[47] when Benjamin Constance was the paper-maker at Mill no 244. Previously on the site was a blast furnace and later a tannery.

HALL MILL (AWRE)   Hall Farm, on the Breme stream about a mile west-south-west of Awre, appears to be the site of the paper-mill shown on Greenwood's Map of Gloucestershire, 1824. In the Excise Letter of 1816 this mill is designated no 142 (Hall) in the Hereford Collection. Joseph Lloyd was the paper-maker, and also in 1829, followed by Thomas Newell in 1832 and Benjamin Small in 1834—the date of the last Excise reference.[48]

REDBROOK   A paper-mill stood at Lower Redbrook before 1680, and another at Upper Redbrook before 1710, as evidenced by the sale on 3 June that year to Benedict Hall from the Committee of Management, 'of the present stock of the copper works at Upper Redbrook Mill, formerly used as a paper mill, and now converted into a copper works'.[49]

Leatherboard

On 31 July 1888 Edwin and William Crawshay, coal and iron magnates, leased to Moses John Mason, late of Clanna Weir Mill, millboard manufacturer, at £28 per annum, Camp Mill in Soudley with mill, buildings and water-wheel, for many years used as a foundry by the Hewletts, then as a mill for wood turning by Peter Constance, later as a flour mill, occupant unknown, 'but now for making of millboard'.[50] There were 2 vats, and the output in 1889 and 1890 was 2 to 3 tons each week. The Customs and Excise records of 1890 confirm a board-mill there,[51] and in 1894 it was making 'milled, engine, portmanteau and other hand-made boards', using two vats. By 1901 Miss Jane Mason (probably sister of M. J. Mason) and G. Smith were the manufacturers, using paper and rags as raw material;[52] there were two water-wheels for power, and a hand-mill. Water was plentiful, coming from the Sutton Ponds and from the Cinderford-Soudley stream, which received much water from Shakemantle Iron Mine.

On 18 October 1901, James Joiner of Dulcote in Somerset, bought the premises from Henry Crawshay & Co Ltd[53] and negotiated water rights with the Office of Woods.[54] The following year, 19 July[55] he sold the works to the Dulcote Leather Board Co Ltd,[56] a firm in which he was a partner with a Mr Sheldon. The works at Dulcote were destroyed by fire 30 September 1904,[57] and Joiner with some workmen (Mr Snooks, Henry Williams, and William Burrows) moved to Soudley about the turn of the year, and for his company he improved the cottages and installed machinery including a two-flued Lancashire Boiler with a high circular steel chimney. He used the Dulcote process-making leatherboard, principally for stiffeners in the boot and shoe industry.

Frederick Drew (aged 77 in 1970), of Ayleford House, remembers some of the process when he worked there in 1905. Paper, rags, string, and old pattern books were ground by beaters, and the pulp travelled on rollers through a presser, emerging as wet sheets of mill-board which were pegged up in racks in a drying room heated by hot water pipes, whereafter the boards were trimmed, and the heel-like shapes were pressed out by a foot-operated stamper. R. C. Bloxsome, of Ayleford, who worked at the mill in about 1907,[58] recollects the two overshot water-wheels, only one in use, developing 8hp, and assisting a steam engine. The boards (the best included bits of chamois leather), were pressed into shape for inner soles, and heel stiffeners. In 1908 about 20 hands were employed, but the company faced difficulty in obtaining raw material, and on 25 May it ceased operating.[59] The premises, having a floor space of about 18,000sq ft, were auctioned 20 November 1911, when they comprised:[60]

Mill (80ft × 25ft 6in), stone with slated roof.
Mill (49ft × 26ft) stone with tiled roof.
Foundry Shop (97ft × 34ft).
Drying Room (96ft × 16ft 6in).
Smith's Shop (18ft × 18ft).
Boiler House (78ft × 24ft).
Offices (28ft 6in × 16ft).
Overshot water-wheel (4ft wide, 12ft diameter), wrought-iron floats, and timber arms, capable of developing up to 15hp.

The only 'bid' was one of £100 by James Joiner; the premises (Plate 51a) were finally sold to him for that sum on 11 April 1912, but remained idle for some ten years. In 1922 Joiner began there a sawmill. Within three years, the two old 12ft water-wheels were replaced by a turbine and steam engine and later by two diesel stationary engines of about 150hp. Sawmilling ceased about 1952, and after an idle period the premises were leased to a dealer in scrap cars, much to the dismay of those who value the aesthetics of the nearby Lower Sutton Pond.

References to Chapter 12

1   GRO D1677, GG1010.
2   Shorter, A. H. 'Paper Mills in Gloucestershire', *BGAS* 71, 1952, 145–61; Ibid, *Paper Mills and Paper Makers in England 1495–1800*, 1957.
3   Bigland, R. *Collections relative to the County of Gloucester*, 1786, I, 1.
4   *Gloucester Journal*, 19 July 1743.
5   Information from L. S. Lloyd.
6   GRO Bond MSS D2026.
7   *The Apprentices of Great Britain*, Book 50.
8   *Gloucester Journal*, 24 Feb and 22 Dec 1761.
9   Shorter, op cit, 1957, 391.
10 Rudder, S. *New History of Gloucestershire*, 1779, 63, 209.
11 *Gloucester Journal*, 23 March 1762 and 1 Sept 1776.
12 Ibid, 5 Aug 1771.
13 *London Gazette*, 2 Nov 1816.
14 Excise Letter: used to refer to General Letters or Orders of the Commissioners of Customs and Excise.
15 GRO (1) 548: invoice of Joseph Lloyd & Sons 28 Sept 1819 (with an 1818 watermark, and another dated 27 March 1827.
16 *The Paper Mills Directory*, 1860.
17 Ibid, 1864. The owner was probably John Birt (Waters, Ivor. *Chepstow Miscellany*).
18 Ibid, 1876.
19 *Gloucester Journal*, 12 Dec 1774.
20 GRO D637/11/9/E2, including plan.
21 *Gloucester Journal*, 15 June 1789.
22 Confirmed by St Briavels Tithe Map (1838) no 76.
23 *Harris's Directory*, 1887.
24 Ibid, 1902.
25 *Gloucester Journal*, 26 June 1797.
26 *London Gazette*, 6 March 1809.
27 *House of Commons Papers*, 1852, LI, 128.
28 *The Paper Mills Directory*, 1872.
29 *Harris's Directory*, 1902.
30 *The Bristol Poll Book*, 1774.
31 *Gloucester Journal*, 26 May 1777.
32 *London Gazette*, 30 March 1793.

57 *(left)* W. J. Smith and Frank (later Sir Francis) Brain—partners in the making of fuses; *(below)* Sir Francis Brain, 1913, who lived at Trafalgar House and who was typical of the coal owners of Dean

58 *(right)* John H. Watts, M Inst T, a pioneer of passenger road transport in Gloucestershire and South Wales and co-founder in 1937 of Red & White United Transport Co Ltd. He is now President of United Transport Limited. A gentleman whose life has been in passenger road transport. His businesses and many benefactions have greatly aided Dean and many other areas; *(below)* Watts of Lydney Ltd, an aerial view of garage and workshops built up in conjunction with many other business interests by John H. Watts and his brother Arthur J. Watts

33 SFIP 648376, 4 Nov 1795.
34 Ibid, 717358, 17 April 1801.
35 Confirmed by Woolaston Tithe Map (1838) no 647.
36 Smith, Brian S. Glos Soc for Ind Arch Newsletter, 14 Feb 70; quoting HO107/369.
37 *Slater's Directory*, 1858.
38 *The Engineer*, 24 Sept 1869, 210, 214; *Murray's Handbook* (Glos, Hereford & Worcs) 1872, 53, 54, quoting the *Iron Trade Advertiser*.
39 *Murray's Handbook*, op cit.
40 *Gloucester Journal*, 28 June 1873.
41 *The Paper Mills Directory*, 1876.
42 *Directory of Paper Makers*, 1885 and 1890.
43 *Harris's Directory*, 1887.
44 Ibid., 1887 and 1891.
45 *Forest Newspapers*, 28 Feb 1895.
46 *Harris's Directory*, 1887.
47 Excise General Orders, Printed, I, 1819–23: General Letter 1 Sept 1821.
48 Shorter, op cit, 157.
49 GRO D1677, GG1010, 1092.
50 Information from Stanley Joiner.
51 Shorter, op cit, 158.
52 *Harris's Directory*, 1902.
53 Information from Stanley Joiner.
54 F/3/790.
55 Information from Stanley Joiner.
56 Atthill, Robin. *Old Mendip*.
57 *Wells Journal*, 6 Oct 1904.
58 R. C. Bloxsome also worked at Woorgreen Colliery 'at a time when the main roof fell in'.
59 Information from Stanley Joiner.
60 Ibid.

Thirteen
Communications and Transport

Rivers, Roads and Transport

Entrance to Dean in early times was chiefly from the Severn, up track-ways worn away by the feet of men, horses, cattle and sheep, by the dragging of timber, and by rain and frost. Some of the tracks are the 'hollow-ways'[1] of which many are to be seen today; others were used by the Romans after they had placed on them a hard surface. Dean has four reputed Roman main roads (Fig 23).[2] The first runs east to west from *Glevum* (Gloucester) to *Blestium* (Monmouth); the second from north-east to south-west from Gloucester to *Venta Silurum* (Caerwent) and *Isca* (Caerleon); the third, known as the Dean Road (Plate 52a), from north to south, connecting the district south of *Ariconium* with Lydney; and the fourth east to west from Newnham-on-Severn via Cannop Bridge to Monmouth. The first two roads met military requirements; the other two met economic needs, chiefly traffic in iron ore and charcoal. The road from Newnham-on-Severn to Monmouth is in part that referred to in 1255[3] when the King authorised the felling of a 'trench' or 'ridding' alongside the road 'for the use and safety of adjoining parts, 12 perches in width and 6 perches on each side'. Similar 'trenches' elsewhere had been authorised in 1248. Because the Severn could not be crossed below Gloucester except by ferry (eg at Newham-on-Severn) or by individual boats, there was no direct communication with the relatively fast-growing Bristol area.

During subsequent centuries the tracks and roads within the Forest were ill-kept and inadequate. Even in the eighteenth century, men, mules, donkeys and horses found difficult the numerous small roads, a few kept in tolerable repair by the parish road surveyor elected annually by the Vestry! From 1745, Turnpike Trusts were established, and their roads were introduced. The maintenance of the 'through roads' was met by the tolls collected at gates which closed across them, and which were operated by keepers who lived alongside in small cottages (Plates 55 and 56). The two main roads through the Forest were from

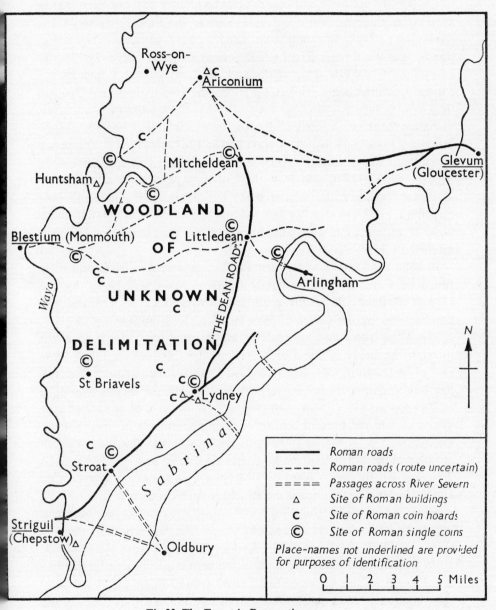

Fig 23. The Forest in Roman times.

Mitcheldean to Coleford and from Littledean to Coleford, whence other roads led to St Briavels, Newland and Monmouth. During 1761–86, the Crown expended £11,631 on roads 'yet it appears from the evidence of the deputy surveyor and others that the greater parts of these roads are not only useless, but disadvantageous to the Forest',[4] ie to the interests of timber! The only road used in 1788 for conveying naval timber was the Purton Road which served all parts of the woodlands except the Chestnuts, Edge Hills and the Lea Bailey.[5] Witnesses informed commissioners in that year that the two main roads harmed the Crown's interests because they 'afforded the readier means to convey away coal in waggons and carts, in which timber has sometimes been concealed'.[6] However, a traveller in 1781 observed:[7] 'for seven miles from Mitcheldean, a very good road leads through this noble Forest'. During 1796 and 1800 the Crown expended, or advanced to Turnpike Trusts, £10,654 on roads.[8] Throughout the nineteenth century the roads were slowly extended and improved, and by 1856 there were 41 miles of Crown roads, for which the tolls collected that year totalled £1,331.

In 1888 the Dean Forest Turnpike Trusts were abolished and their functions were taken over partly by the Crown and partly by the County Council. A useful road from Mierystock to Lydney was handed over by the Office of Woods to the local authorities in 1903. It ran along the Lyd-Cannop-Newerne valleys, from north to south through the heart of the Forest. (From the thirteenth century these valleys had been the line which divided Dean for the purposes of gavelling, and incidentally helped to keep East and West Dean at variance and somewhat aloof from each other.) Development of roads has continued during the present century, and improvements are being made and planned in particular to provide better access to the M50 at Monmouth and the M5 at Ross-on-Wye, and via Chepstow to the M4 and the Severn Road Bridge (opened by HM Queen Elizabeth on 8 September 1966) which made redundant the Beachley-Aust car ferry.

Improved roads brought improved transport. Prior to the outbreak of war in 1914, John H. Watts of Lydney (Plate 58a) was in partnership with H. T. Letheren in the Lydney Posting Company. By 1919, when Mr Watts returned from the war, the company owned 17 horses and 14 vehicles, chiefly operating in and around Dean. Later the company operated larger motor-buses from Lydney to Gloucester via the Forest. Other operators in the region included Daniel Walkley and W. T. Edwards, as well as many small 'bus firms' (Plate 52b). Mr Watts expanded his transport interests into South Wales and, after encountering and overcoming much competition, in 1925 he and his brother Arthur joined with several of their competitors and other contemporaries to form Western Services Ltd (Plate 54b). Following the acquisition of other transport companies, the co-partners (affectionately known locally as 'The Big Six'—Plate 54a) formed Red & White Services Ltd, with headquarters at Bulwark, Chepstow. The subsequent history of this rapidly expanded company, which later led to the formation of the large Red & White United Transport Company Limited (1937) and the world-wide interests of United Transport Company Limited (1948), have been recorded elsewhere.[9] Other local passenger transport enterprises, including those of the families of Bevan, Cottrell and Edwards, have achieved success. The same can be said of local goods transport firms such as those of Reads, and Rossiter & James.

Navigation and shipping on the Severn have been discussed by Brian Waters[10] and F. W. Rowbotham;[11] and on the Wye by B. J. Stevens.[12] The small harbours or 'pills' of Gatcombe, Purton, Newnham-on-Severn, Lydney and Cone have been mentioned in earlier chapters. Gatcombe and Newnham-on-Severn, though never possessing an enclosed dock, were busy little ports, particularly the latter, where the chief exports were timber, bark, coal and iron. Lydney harbour was at first a little port, with a long history (see Chapter 14, boat and ship building). The dock was built by the Severn & Wye Rly & Canal Co, with a canal along the mouth of the Newerne stream. The main exports have been coal and timber (Plates 53a and b). (Today, Lydney's chief imports are foreign logs for the plywood factory at Pine End—Plate 61a). Bullo Pill was a busy little port throughout the middle of the nineteenth century, its basin often being crowded with Severn trows trading between Gloucester and Bristol, and with barques and brigantines sailing with coal, iron and limestone to the Bristol Channel ports and beyond them to Cornwall, South Wales and Ireland.[13] Occasionally a steam ship entered the harbour and, as these ships increased, more of them arrived at Bullo rather than at the more restricted Lydney Harbour. Chiefly because of the contraction in Dean's coal industry, the railway shed at the dock was closed in March 1931, there being insufficient trade to keep it in operation.

The (still useful) canal to Lydney Docks is one of three which have been built in Dean. Of the other two (both now dry), the first was a small one for coke at Broadmoor (see Chapter 4) and the other for

Pidcock's ironworks along the west side of the Newerne valley from Lydney northwards (see Chapter 2). Lack of water, and awkward topography, were the chief reasons against the provision of canals in the region—although a proposal for an extensive canal was made in 1784.[14]

Tramroads and Railways

The history of rail transport in the Forest and its neighbourhood is well documented, and has been augmented by the thorough research undertaken by H. W. Paar[15] who has written with clarity and interest on this subject. Reference has been made in Chapters 5 and 6 to Dean's tramroads and railways (Fig 24). Horse-worked cast-iron tramroads were first proposed in about 1800, to improve transport facilities for industrial products, about 90 per cent of which was coal, with a little iron ore and stone, and 10 per cent iron and other merchandise. The fact that the land was owned by the Crown and that extensive lines were envisaged, led to opposition from the Office of Woods. However, in the period 1809–12 three tramroads were established, whereon the plodding willing horses hauled crude wooden waggons with flangeless wheels.

The first tramroad (by the Severn & Wye Railway & Canal Company), was a line with branches, which linked the two rivers, and served Dean's western valley, although it did not reach two important towns—Coleford and Cinderford. Locomotives were introduced in 1864, a temporary broad-gauge railway was laid up to Mierystock in 1868, and in 1869 extensions were begun on standard gauge. In 1879 the company amalgamated with the Severn Bridge Rly Company, and the s&w & sbr was taken over jointly by the Great Western Midland Railway Companies in 1894. The second tramroad, on the eastern side of Dean, linking the valley of the Cinderford-Soudley Brook with the Severn, was built by the Bullo Pill Railway Company, partly under its Act of 1809 and partly privately. Renamed the Forest of Dean Railway in 1826, it was replaced by a broad-gauge railway in 1854. The third tramroad, opened in 1812 by the Monmouth Railway Company, linked Coleford and the Forest with Monmouth. The Coleford, Monmouth, Usk & Pontypool Railway Company purchased most of it in 1853, but failed to convert it into a railway, this being done by the Coleford Railway Co in 1883; the line, however, was closed in 1916. The Forest of Dean Central Railway was built from New Fancy Col-

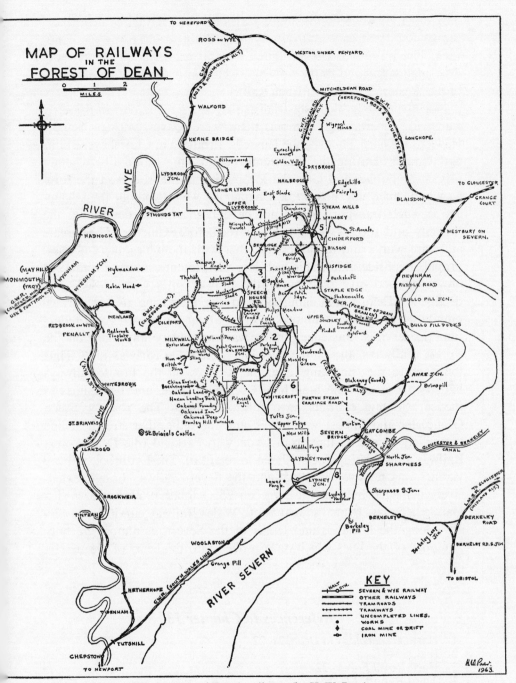

Fig 24. Map of Dean's railways (by H. W. Paar).

liery down to Awre on the South Wales line, but it was ill-fated. Many branch-line tramroads and railways were built to serve various industries. The tramroads carried much mineral traffic, but their capacity was small compared to the railways, which in due course became part of the Western Region of British Rail.

Not surprisingly, the industrialists played a leading part in the early transport undertakings. Among them were David Mushet, Samuel Hewlett, Richard Thomas, the Russells, Protheroes, Crawshays, Brains and Goulds. During the nineteenth century the tramroads, whether private or public, and later the locomotive railways, served the furnaces and other enterprises (see Chapter 4), which without the advantage of such transport would not have been able to develop to the capacity and success which they achieved before extinction. The tinplate and wire works and foundries, together with the mines and collieries, provided considerable traffic well into the present century. From 1949 onwards, successive sections of the railway lines were closed. The decline of Dean's coal industry, and the increasing use of lorries, omnibuses and cars, combined to bring about the closures and reductions in services. Passenger traffic was never very important on the Forest's railways, and on the s&w line it ceased as early as 1929. Thus long before the 'Beeching' axe, the services on the Forest railways had been pruned. The branch services have gone, and other lines in the surrounding districts have followed them. The route between Gloucester and Chepstow survives; and the only other stretch of line tentatively in use, is that from Lydney to Parkend (the Dean Forest Railway Preservation Society hope to retain it). The Lydbrook railway viaduct was removed in 1965, and the Severn railway bridge, extensively damaged by a petrol barge on 25 October 1960, has been dismantled. Today, Brunel's great South Wales Railway curving majestically along the lowlands and banks of the Severn, is almost the only reminder of the lines which once probed into the heart of Dean.

References to Chapter 13

1 Hart. *Archaeology in Dean*, 21, 22.
2 Ibid, 33–41.
3 Hart. *Royal Forest*, 22.
4 Third Report, 1788, 31.
5 Ibid, App 39.
6 Ibid.

7   *The Torrington Diaries*, Edn 1954, 37.
8   30th Rpt of the Commissioners of Woods . . . , 1852.
9   Hart, C. E. *Watts of Lydney Ltd: 1851–1965*, 1965; ibid, *Forest Newspapers*, 25 Sept 1965.
10 Waters, Brian. *Severn Tide*, 1947.
11 Rowbotham, F. W. *The Severn Bore*, 1965.
12 Stevens, B. J. 'Navigation on the Wye', *Memorials of Monmouth*, no 5, 1965.
13 *Jnl of Industrial Archaeology*, 5(1) Feb 1968, 98–100.
14 Stroud Navigation Min Bk, 13 April 1748; *The Forester*, 16 Dec 1875, reminiscenses of William Teague, aged 81, on the occasion of the opening of the S&W Rly to Coleford.
15 Paar, H. W. op cit.

Fourteen
Miscellaneous Industries
of the Past

Dean has had many industries which do not fall readily into those categories discussed in other chapters. These additional industries (Fig 25) are discussed herein.

GLASS   In the mid-seventeenth century, Lorraine glassmakers came to Sussex, where there was an abundance of beech for billets to fuel furnaces, and suitable other raw materials, particularly sand.[1] When the local woods became denuded by their process, the glassmakers moved to Hampshire (Buckholt), Herefordshire,[2] and Gloucestershire.

In Gloucestershire, their glass furnace at Woodchester has been excavated and described.[3] In the same county, other glassmakers settled at a place now known as 'The Glasshouse', at the eastern foot of May Hill, adjacent to 'Newent Wood'. Three of their kin, John Pilney (a Frenchman), Abraham Tyzack and Anthony Voydyn, described as 'glass founders of the glasshouse', appear in the Newent Parish Registers of 1599–1601.[4] The site was discovered in 1949 and cursorily examined, fragments of drinking glass being found.[5] Sand for the works was probably obtained from the Upper Drybrook Sandstone, exposed at Hangerberry Hill near Lydbrook, 10 miles away. Beech billets came from the adjacent Newent Wood and from Dean. The works are not mentioned in a list of 1696[6]—this is not surprising, because the glassmakers appear to have thoroughly demolished their furnaces and buildings before they moved to Staffordshire. The site needs excavating and reporting upon.

In 1620, Sir Edward Mansell erected at Newnham-on-Severn 'the first glasshouse in England to use coal'.[7] He may have experimented there with 'the new type furnace, fired by coal from Dean'.[8] Houghton[9] in 1696 lists the works as 'two bottle houses'; they were in ruin by 1712.[10] The Wilcox family were the most noted glassmakers in the town. The site was approximately that where stood the old Anchor Inn, ie in the north part of the town. The foundations were extant in 1780, 'but there is lately a very considerable verdigris-work set up in its room and carried on with a laudable spirit'.[11] Verdigris is a green crystallised substance formed on copper by action of acetic acid, and used in medicine, and as a pigment. Specimens of glass are dug up from time to time in the adjacent gardens. Two whole wine bottles were recovered when part of the site was excavated while laying pipes for Newnham Waterworks.[12] John Boevey of nearby Flaxley Abbey had wine bottles stamped with his seal, and these may have been made locally. Tangible relics of the glassworks are the extremely hard black building-blocks made of the 'dross', to be seen in the walls of several nearby houses. They were formed in moulds, and measure approximately 16in × 9in × 9in.

Dean does not appear to have had any subsequent connection with

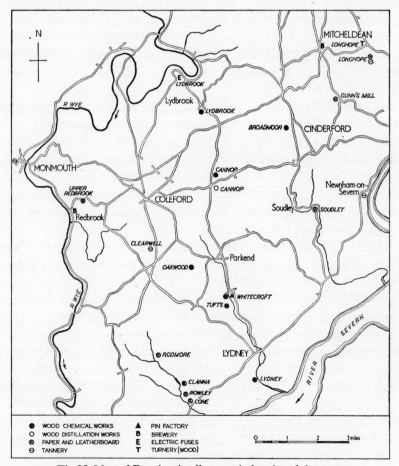

Fig 25. Map of Dean's miscellaneous industries of the past.

glass-making, other than to supply to the industry at Bristol crushed 'cinders', particularly the 'scruff' or 'scoria' derived from smelting iron ore, for the making of glass bottles. This industry, known locally as 'stamping', has been discussed in Chapter 4.

NAILS   Making nails was an industry which brought a livelihood to many villagers, particularly in Littledean and Mitcheldean. At Abenall, sheds near the Congregational Chapel were first used in nailmaking c1700, where as late as the nineteenth century the trade was followed by John the Pillar and later by his grandson Tom the Nailer.[13] They bought metal strips, from which they made 4in pit-spikes, delivered to the Dean mines by donkeys laden with panniers. James Mathews and John Griffiths with his son were nailers in Mitcheldean in 1858.[14]

At Littledean in 1745 there were six nailers of ages from 19 to 28, namely Edward Hale, John Hale, John Pearce, William Pearce, Joseph Wheeler, and William Aberell.[15] As late as 1835 'manufacture of nails affords the chief employment to the labouring classes'.[16] In the same year John Jones had a nailer's shop at the north end of nearby Blaize Bailey.[17] There were four nailers in Littledean in 1858,[18] and one (William George) in 1902.[19]

In 1858[20] nailers were to be found at Coleford (John Roberts), Clearwell—where there is still the 'Nailer's Arms'—(Richard Goodes, William Jenkins and Esther Williams), and at Aylburton (George Brinkworth). Other small nailworks were at Stroat, and at Newnham-on-Severn (where the place-name 'Nail Yard' survives).

CANDLES   In the nineteenth century, Newnham-on-Severn had a candle factory, reputed to have been situated on 'The Green'.[21] Tradition has it that colliers from Dean paid frequent visits to purchase their requirements. In the early 1960s, excavations for an extension to the 'Aldrex' premises disclosed a large cauldron which may have been used in the process.

ROPES   Ropes were made in the nineteenth century at Westbury, Newnham-on-Severn, Mitcheldean, and Lydney. Northwood Green near Westbury had a flourishing rope-making business, using as the raw material the inner bark of 'witrod', a local name for the lime-tree.[22] Waggon-ropes comprised five cords joined together, and halter-ropes three. Daniel Jones was the chief rope-maker there. An almost allied trade at Westbury was the making of baskets and putts (in which to catch salmon) by the Jackson and Wyman families.[23] Another industry (in 1880) in nearby Ley Park, at a place called 'Vans', was the growing of teazles for raising the nap on cloth.[24]

At Newnham-on-Severn, Mrs Elizabeth Clifford had a rope-works in at least 1858,[25] 1887[26] and 1902.[27] John Stephens was a rope-maker at Lydney Basin in 1858.[28] Another rope-works was at The Warren near Priors Mesne at Bream—where there is a traditional 'Rope Walk'.

POTTERY It has been said that 'the only pottery kiln recorded for Gloucestershire was at Tidenham, but no details are known'.[29] However, a pottery at Whitecliff near Coleford was noted in 1803—'where casting pots are made'.[30] This stood opposite the old 'Nagshead' inn; and around 1830[31] the potter was John Watts. In 1852 his 'Whitecliff Pottery' charged the following prices: [32]

Pans and Jugs—13d a dozen.   Cream pan—3d each.
Bottles—2d, 2½d, 3½d each.   Chambers—7d each.
Bowls—3½d each.

John Watts was still the potter there in 1858, when his advertisement read: [33]

Manufacturer of Red and Black Ware—Chimney, Garden, Rhubarb and Seakale Pots, Socket Pipes, Draining Pipes, Glazed Ridge and Angle Tiles. Garden Pots of every description. Tobacco Pipes, Marbles, Yellow Ware etc.

Another 'pottery' and brickworks (see Chapter 7), owned by Wanklyn & Grindell,[34] was situated at Fetterhill, a few hundred yards south-east of Darkhill.[35]

SILK From c1816, some 80 people were employed at Coleford in the silk-throwing industry—evident from the following draft of a petition addressed to the House of Commons by Robert Jackman, silkthrower, of Coleford 'and other inhabitants of the same town employed and otherwise interested in the trade': [36]

Your petitioner, Robert Jackman, relying on the protection hitherto afforded to the British Silkthrower by the prohibition of the importation of foreign wrought silks has expended considerable capital in the erection of a Silk Mill and Machinery for throwing silk in the town of Coleford and has employed for 5 years past upwards of 80 persons in the trade.

That the employment of so many persons in a part of the county where there exists an excessive population has been increased in consequence of the erection of this mill who would otherwise have been dependant on an uncertain mode of subsistence is of material importance to the inhabitants of the town with regard to the partial relief thereby afforded of the burden of the poor rate and to the expenditure of their wages in the town.

That it is the decided opinion of your petitioners that should the prohibiting Statute of the Importation of Foreign-wrought silks be repealed and the free admission thereof be allowed, it would materially injure the interests of the whole of your petitioners inasmuch that it would tend not only to the serious loss of this Robert Jackman but also to the throwing of so many persons out of employment who would consequently become a serious burden upon the other inhabitants of the town and parish.

Your petitioners therefore humbly request that the question of remitting the Duty on Silk, which remission would be of considerable advantage to the trade, may stand entirely unconnected with any alteration in the prohibition as the Trade now enjoys of foreign-wrought silks as such remission coupled with an infringement on the prohibiting system would prove a grievous calamity to all classes of the Trade and affecting almost utter ruin to those persons who have embarked their capital therein.

The works stood near the present Baptist Chapel and the original Chapel of 1799 (whose founders may have been interested in the industry). The premises were demolished late in the nineteenth century. RAILWAY WAGONS Railway rolling stock was repaired, and sometimes built, at Bullo Pill and Lydney. The proprietor of Bullo Pill Wagon Works in 1874[37] was Joseph Boucher who lived at Newnham-on-Severn where he was described as 'a railway carriage and wagon builder and brass and iron founder'. He advertised as such, adding—'Wagons built for cash, or Redemption terms for 3, 5 or 7 years'. He also manufactured railway wheels, and offered to carry out repairs at Gloucester, Swindon, Reading, Lydney, Chepstow and intermediate stations. Three hours increased working time per week is noted in September 1876[38] at both Bullo and Newnham-on-Severn. In 1889 at Lydney Junction land was let to the Forest of Dean Wagon Co.[39] This company, owned by Joseph Boucher,[40] including the Bullo Pill Works, was acquired in 1890 by the Forest of Dean Wagon Co Ltd—registered 21 February 1890 with a capital of £5,000 in £5 shares.[41] The 25in OS maps of 1876 and 1901 show the works, but their subsequent history is unknown.

At Lydney Junction in 1889[42] the Gloucester Wagon Co was leased land for a workshop. Two years later[43] the North Central Wagon Co was leased 100 sq yd of land there for an office and a repair-hut. In 1897 The Standard Wagon Co and the Gloucester Wagon Co were operating at Lydney Junction;[44] each had a siding, and that of the latter company was new.

In 1920 the West of England Wagon Co was formed at Lydney by a Mr Wentworth and Percy Moore (managing director of Princess Royal Colliery and, later, of the Norchard).[45] They used premises, below the Church, which had been part of a colour works. The wagon works continued under the managership of Percy Sanson until it went into voluntary liquidation c1962. Thereafter the premises were used by the Watts interests as a tyre depot, and in 1966 released to Albany Engineering Co Ltd.

In April 1922, Wagon Repairs Ltd acquired at Lydney Junction the repair shops and siding formerly occupied by Gloucester Railway, Carriage & Wagon Co Ltd and the British Wagon Co Ltd. The same company about this time also acquired the siding of Wellington, Jones & Co. The works at the Junction closed c1964, and the premises remained empty until used by Berry Wiggins & Co Ltd, tar distillers.

GAS WORKS   Much of Dean's coal in the nineteenth century was coked in the open to provide fuel for her blast furnaces.[46] Larger quantities were used to manufacture coal-gas, particularly for lighting. By 1881, 'the several towns in the district, and the manufacturies and collieries, made gas from coal'.[47] Works stood at Coleford (until the 1940s), Cinderford, Lydney, Newnham-on-Severn, and Mitcheldean. Most, if not all, were originally run by privately owned companies of local people, until they were taken over by the South Western Gas Board.

Records of the Newnham Gas Light & Coke Co Ltd are extant for the years 1888 to 1918.[48] At Cinderford, in 1887, the company was 'Bilson Gas Light Co';[49] and the premises, vacated in the 1940s, now house a foundry. Lydney Gas Works, which had been rebuilt in 1947, following nationalisation, was closed in 1957. In accordance with 'the planned economy' of the Gas Board, Lydney became a holder station, obtaining its supply from the national grid with which it is now connected. The Forest's supply of gas from the grid was cut off when the Severn railway bridge was severed in 1960, and an emergency supply had to be slung across the gap until a new 'over-land' pipeline was completed.

PATENT FUEL WORKS, WHITECROFT   Possibly by 1866, and certainly by 1876, 'patent fuel' was being manufactured from coal at Whitecroft by the Compressed Coal Co.[50] The buildings and sidings are shown on the 25in OS Edition c1878. Coal for the process came from Pillowell. The prime mover in the enterprise was Simeon O. Holmes, born in 1864 at Leigh, Lancashire, and educated as a mining and mechanical engineer.[51] He was the grandson of Simeon Holmes, a colliery proprietor in South Wales and Dean. In his early life, S. O. Holmes had considerable experience as a marine engineer, and later became managing partner for the Dean Forest Fuel & Coal Company,[52] where he applied his abilities to the draining and working of a colliery that had been flooded for many years. In 1893 the company was one of the most prosperous in the coalfield.

Later (not at Whitecroft), Holmes invented an improved briquette-making machine, claimed to be 'a machine *par excellence*' for producing small fuel blocks, and capable of an output of 25,000 to 150,000 blocks a day.[53] In 1893 it was being worked in London, where Holmes was the owner of the long-established coal business of W. Hardman and Sons, of Earls Court. In 1893[54] he was a member of the firm of S. Holmes & Co, St James' Wharf, Caledonian Road, London, N, and in that year his machine was described thus: [55]

It may be prefatorily explained that the novelty in the machine at issue is entirely confined to the peculiar construction and operation of the rotary cylindrical table with its moulds and rams in which the fuel-blocks are formed and pressed. The vertical cylinder at the top of the machine is a pugging and mixing mill of any approved construction, and the same remarks apply to the mould-filling contrivance situated below the mill. The essence of Mr Holmes' ingenious invention relates to the table for making the block-fuels, and consists in the construction and arrangement of a rotary metal drum carrying the moulds and stamps which are brought in turn into positions for filling, compressing and discharging the same.

The moulds, each containing a ram, which practically may be of any convenient number, are arranged at the extremities of the radical parallel arms forming the table, which is caused to rotate about a transverse horizontal shaft by appropriate gearing. These arms are so located that when two of the same are in a vertical plane two others are in a horizontal line or, in other words, the series of moulds are arranged at right angles to each other. The table receives an intermittent angular motion by the gearing so far as to bring the moulds opposite the filling, pressing and discharging mechanism respectively. Two reciprocating links work on either side of the table, actuated by a crank eccentric on the main shaft, and are provided with projections on their inner sides which engage with and operate the plungers or rams in the moulds. These rams, fitted to each mould, are of any approved section and are carried by a plate having projecting lugs to engage with the reciprocating links mentioned and arranged to slide within the arms of the rotating table to and fro in the moulds, when actuated by the devices explained.

The solid peripheral portions of the table close the opening in the

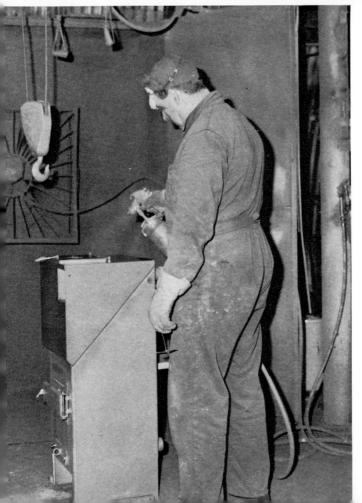

59 (above) Arthur J. Watts, an engineer and industrialist of many talents who has done much to further industries and employment in Lydney and district; (left) a 'Watts boiler', invented at Lydney by A. J. Watts and W. H. Franklin. In 1960 Watts Metal Industries Ltd sold the rights in the boiler to Allied Ironfounders Ltd of Lydney, who in 1966 transferred their business to Manchester and now operate as Glynwed Foundries Ltd

60 *(above)* F. Wickstead OBE, JP, a leading local industrialist, in front of an etching of the Mitcheldean 'Forest Brewery' premises, which from the 1940s he helped to transform into an important factory for photographic equipment. Thereafter he played a leading part in building up the great Rank Xerox factory, which is now so important in Dean's and the nation's economy, employing some 3,000 people; *(below)* Rank Xerox premises, Mitcheldean, 1970

charging apparatus except when the mouths of one series are under the aperture. A stationary curved shield is fixed between this charging orifice and the fixed block against which the contents of the moulds are pressed, so as to prevent the loss of any of the contents as they travel from the vertical to the horizontal position or from the charging to the compressing apparatus. One series of moulds on coming perpendicular under the charging opening is filled with the fuel composition and then travels through an arc of 90° to the horizontal position. The reciprocating links are then drawn forward and carry with them the stamps which compress the composition against the fixed block. The moulds are then caused to move through half a circle, or 180°, to the opposite point where the pressing motion of the links give the rams a further movement to eject the blocks from the table. While travelling through the next quarter of a circle to the refilling position the stamps fall back by their own weight so as to allow space for the recharging of the moulds.

It will be now understood that the cycle of operations described proceed as before so long as the machine is at work. In the illustration [not reproduced] it will be seen that a series of fuel-blocks, which may be of any reasonable size, are in the process of being discharged from the moulds provided in the circumference of the rotary table, but it will be apparent that the number might be conveniently multiplied according to requirements, eg 1 to 24. The discharging mechanism is viable. The main and countershafts are driven by spur gearing at suitable relative velocities. The star motion on the opposite side of the machine is for intermittently turning the table a quarter of a revolution as and for the purposes already explained. In practice, the slack or pulverised coal, admixed with a suitable proportion of pitch, is automatically fed into the mixing mill by means of a mechanical elevator of any known construction. Steam is admitted into the interior of the mill for heating the pitch, so as to cause the conglomerate to unite into a solid block when compressed in the moulds described. The machine is patented in all countries, and the chief claims made for the press are: (1) unique simplicity of construction and action; (2) a minimum cost of operation and maintenance; (3) it produces any number of blocks at one operation; (4) the entire manufacture is automatically performed; whilst (5) the machine is self-contained, therefore no foundations are required. In conclusion, it may be pointed out that great advantage is claimed for the self-contained character of the moulds and pressing rams within the table, which removes all risk of damage or breakage from the plungers not mathematically coinciding with the position of the moulds—a weakness said to be present in all other machines on the market.

2E

It is not known by what year the Patent Fuel Works closed at White-croft, but in 1882 The Pyramid Electric Light Co (*infra*) was using premises, believed to have been those used by Holmes, and which in 1910 became the Pin Works (*infra*).

ELECTRIC LIGHT WORKS, WHITECROFT   These works were established in 1882 by The Pyramid Electric Light Co,[56] probably in premises which previously housed a Patent Fuel Works (*supra*). A report 8 July 1882[57] reads: 'on Monday evening, as an indication of progress made at these newly opened works, the electric light was tried, and interested a number of inhabitants who had not before witnessed the effect of turning night into day! It is the intention of the Company to provide for public and private lighting by electricity.' The premises, from 1910, were used as a pin manufactory (*infra*).

PINS   In the eighteenth century pins were made in The Red House at Littledean.[58] They were of a peculiar type $1\frac{1}{4}$in long, sharply pointed, and had a cross bar about $\frac{3}{8}$in long instead of the usual round head. The premises in the nineteenth century became a Workhouse. Mitcheldean also had a pin industry in the early nineteenth century, chiefly operated in the Workhouse at Millend.

Whitecroft became the venue of a widely renowned pin manu-factory—begun in 1910 by Maurice and Stanley Jarrett in premises which previously had housed a Patent Fuel Works and an Electric Light Works (*supra*). The Jarretts (whose grandfather had been man-ager of the Great Western iron furnaces at Soudley, and whose father, Edgar, had mined iron ore) began the works, with six girls as employees. For some fifty years the enterprise was known locally as the 'Pin Co' because safety pins were the chief product of an increasingly diversi-fied manufactory, which gave welcome employment to the district. In 1947 the Whitecroft Pin Manufactury Company became a subsidiary of United Transport Company Ltd. In 1964 the well established company was acquired by the Scovill Manufacturing Company of the USA, and renamed Whitecroft-Scovill Ltd (see Chapter 15).[59]

ELECTRIC FUSES   Members of the family of Brain, with substantial in-terests in Dean's collieries and iron mines, brought to the Forest some renown through their inventions, patents and enterprises in connection with electric fuses. Cornelius Brain opened Trafalgar Colliery, east of Brierley, in 1860 and he and his brother Charles, and later W. B. Brain, had a lengthy private tramway, and held an interest in the Golden Valley and Drybrook iron mines.

Francis William Thomas Brain. AMICE (born 28 October 1855) was consulting engineer to, and later managing partner of, the Electric Blasting Apparatus Co, near Cinderford, who in 1875 with their electric fuses helped to sink a coal shaft by simultaneous blasting of dynamite.[60] The company continued making these fuses, with periodic improvements.

Frank (later Sir Francis) Brain was associated with the use of electric light on the Severn railway bridge in 1879. He provided illumination 'by means of a couple of powerful lamps, supplied by a Gramone machine'.[61] That apparatus was soon afterwards re-erected near Trafalgar, and a football match was played at night under its light. In 1882 he installed electrically-driven underground pumps at Trafalgar—the first in England:[62]

> This commenced working in December 1882, and attained such success that three additional plants were erected in May 1887, and are now doing the larger part of the underground pumping. The last installation consists of a double-throw 9in Plunger, by 10in stroke, situated 2,220yd from the Generator, and 1,650yd from the bottom of the shaft; the pipe main is 7in in diameter, and at a maximum speed of 25 strokes the pump lifts 120 gallons per minute, 300 feet high. The Electric Motive Force is 320 volts, and the current required is 43 amperes. The cost of the engine and the electrical plant was £644.

In 1893 Frank Brain (Plate 57a), then residing at Trafalgar House, and in charge of the colliery, applied for, and was granted in 1894, a patent relating to his electric fuses.[63] The following year he applied for, and was granted in 1895, a patent for further improvements in electric fuses.[64] The Electric Blasting Apparatus Co acquired the sole right to Brain's patent system of shot-firing—'an ingenious and very simple method by which any number of shots can be fired simultaneously, all the men, however, being out of the pits at the time'.[65] Their 'Electric Fuse Factory' stood on the west of Trafalgar Colliery. The manufacture of the detonators in particular was extremely hazardous, resulting in the explosive stores and filling-huts being widely distributed throughout the woods. In 1909 Brain was described as 'manufacturer of electric detonators, fuses, and electric fuses'.[66] He was knighted about this time, when president of the Colliery Owners' Association (Plate 57b).

The Trafalgar Colliery had on its management from 1878 William J. Smith (Plate 57a), who was equally keen as Brain and other colleagues in pioneering in particular the use of electricity and electric shot-firing for blasting. In 1885 Brain took Smith into partnership; he (Smith) actually fired the first detonator underground, and also supervised some of the blasting of the Severn railway tunnel. He died in 1895 at the age of 42, and his son, Harold, then 16 years old, took over the preparation of the mixing of the explosives used in the detonators. Harold W. Smith (Plate 24b), in his early twenties, did much of the development around the turn of the century, and continued with the fuse factory until Brain sold it in 1913; thereafter there is no evidence of it working. Meanwhile, young Smith, having considered that there was a market for one of the principal materials he was using, electric wire, decided that the cheapest way to insulate wires for the long fuse-leads was by extrusion. In 1906 he made his first tentative approach to cable-making (see Chapter 4). By c1912 he was trading under the name of The Electric Detonator Co, when he built detonator huts and explosive stores at the 'Fuse Factory' at Stowfield alongside the Wye near Lydbrook. Contemporaneously in 1912 he erected nearer the river a cable factory, discussed in Chapter 4. The Electric Detonator Co at Stowfield was acquired in 1920 by Nobel Industries.

BREWING, CIDER AND MINERALS   As early as 1616,[67] cottagers in Dean 'baked and brewed' with the King's wood, and brewing of ale on a small scale continued in the locality well into the twentieth century. Brewing on a larger scale was carried out in the nineteenth century at Redbrook (*infra*) and Mitcheldean (where the Wemyss family owned a 'Brewhouse').[68] Smaller establishments were in operation at Ruardean (a 'Brewery House' stood near the 'Malt Shovel' inn where, as late as 1910, the maltster and brewer was Edward Thompson),[69] Etloe (where in 1887 Wilkinson & Co owned a 'Steam Brewery'),[70] Aylburton (a malthouse stood west of the George Inn), and Lydney (opposite the Feathers Hotel).

At Redbrook there were two breweries. One, owned by the Burgham family, was situated south of the incline, between the tramroad and the road. It is shown on the 6in OS maps of 1880–1 and 1900. Many donkeys and ponies with their carts were sent to Redbrook from Dean to collect 'wet grains' to feed swine. The other brewery, shown adjacent to the Turnpike Gate House in Upper Redbrook on the CMU & P PD Plans of 1852, was owned by James Hall and described as 'house, offices, brewhouse, malthouse and sheds'. The two breweries were demolished after the Second World War.

The brewery industry in Dean followed the pattern in other parts of the country.[71] Small establishments were acquired by larger firms, and other companies entered the ever enlarging trade—in 1912, for instance, the Anglo-Bavarian Brewery Co Ltd had a lease from the s&w of land at Lydney Town station, with permission to erect a storehouse thereon.[72]

A brewery at Mitcheldean in the second half of the nineteenth century was the largest establishment of its type in Dean. It was established in 1868 by Thomas Wintle.[73] The site was exceptionally favourable, because it was several miles from any works—an important factor because only in a pure atmosphere could fermentation be brought to perfection. Another advantage was the supply of suitable water, obtained from the hills a short distance away. In 1870, a new malthouse (Plate 60a) was erected of local red sandstone. Subsequently other additions were made, increasing the capacity several times. About the turn of the century there were added a new boiler and copper house, cask washing sheds, dray sheds, and a motor house. In the boiler and copper house and in some other departments, the walls were of white glazed brick. The woodwork everywhere was painted and frequently washed; and the floors were of concrete. The dust arising from the screening of the malt was converted into mud by a special apparatus and then discharged into a drain. The plant also included a cooperage and carpentry shop, a fitting and repair shop, extensive stables, and buildings for vans and the large motor used for delivering. The premises were lighted throughout by gas, but later replaced by electricity.

Practically all of the barley used in the brewing was obtained from Herefordshire, and the hops from Worcestershire. Before malting, the barley was put through a cleaning apparatus which rejected all the small, broken and imperfect grains. No adulterant was used in the process. Frequent laboratory tests were made to ensure uniformity of product. The plant brewed mild and bitter ales and stout, all despatched in casks.

Wintle's son Francis continued the business from about 1893. By 1904[74] he employed some 60 men, and had throughout the district 60 to 70 public houses at which his products were sold exclusively, and also agents in all the neighbouring towns. In March 1923, owing to ill health, Francis Wintle had the business put up for auction, when the sale particulars were:[75]

The Forest Steam Brewery
Mitcheldean, Glos.
Together with 72 Licensed Properties,
also Shops, Cottages etc

Brewing Side

Boiler House: Two 28ft by 7ft 6in Lancashire Boilers by Danks & Co, complete with fittings to work at 80lb pressure.

At the rear of the Boiler House, a Patent Water Softening Plant by Lassen–H. J. Ort, with 40–barrel Cast Iron Cold Liquor Tank supplying softened water to boilers.

Brick-built Coal Bunker to serve Boilers and Copper.

Copper: 100–barrel Fire Copper fitted with powerful Auxiliary Steam Coil returning exhaust steam to Boiler through Pratt's Patent Trap.

Hop Back Room: Containing 90–barrel Circular Cast Iron Hop Back by Ramsden, fitted with Gunmetal False Bottom and Hop Spargers. Copper Wort Circulator.

Set of Fine Three-throw Wort Pumps by Ramsdens.

Engine Room: Marshall's Patent Steam Engine of about 16hp.

8hp Steam Engine by Adlams.

Paul's Patent Heater for Heating Brewing Liquor with exhaust steam from Engines.

Donkey Pump by Adlams for Pumping Brewing Liquor.

Bore Hole and working Scott's Yeast.

Press: Dynamo for working Electric Rousing Pump.

Fan for cooling Casks in Washing Shed.

Pump Room: Set of Two-throw Deep Well pumps.

Air Compressor, Tank, etc.

Copper Floor: 12-barrel Cast Iron Underback fitted with Silent Heater.

Copper Wort Safe with four draw-off Cocks from Mash Tun.

Mash Tun Room: 18-Quarter Cast Iron Mash Tun with Internal Rakes and Gunmetal False Bottom by Adlams, with Wood Cover in two parts with Counterpoise Weights.

Steele's Mashing Machine by Adlams.

Gauges for Tanks, etc.

Enclosure forming Brewer's Office and Laboratory.

Enclosure forming Sugar Store no 1.

Tank Room no 2: 60-barrel Hot Liquor Back by Ramsdens.

40-barrel Hot Liquor Back by Adlams. Both lagged and fitted with Silent Heaters.

40-barrel Liquor Tank.

Enclosure of Circular Iron Grist Case with Mixer.

Mill Room: Nalder Separating Malt Screen, with Dust Destructor.

Pair of Double Malt Rolls by Ramsden.

Malt Elevator.

(Malt is brought by Worm direct from Malt House and elevated to Mill Room. Screened and ground at one operation. Capacity about $12\frac{1}{2}$ quarters per hour).

Tank Room no 1: 12-barrel Hot Liquor Tank with Silent Heater.
40-barrel Liquor Tank.
Circular Copper Dissolving Vessel, jacketed, capacity about four
Barrels, by Adlams.
25-barrel Cast Iron Dissolving Vessel fitted with Silent Heaters.
Sack Hoist commanding all floors.

Fermenting Side of Brewery

Tank Room: Fitted with Cast Iron Cold Liquor Tank by Adlams,
about 200 barrels.
Cooling Room: Cast Iron Cooler by Adlams, about 90 barrels, with
Copper Straining Sieve and Aerator.
The room is fitted with Louvre Windows.
Refrigerator Room: Fitted with 35-barrel Refrigerator by Adlams.
Round Room: Fitted with Four 100-barrel Kauri Pine Fermenting
Rounds with Attemperators, etc and one 10-barrel Copper-lined
Fermenting Round.
Steam Heating Grids are fitted under each of the 100-barrel Rounds.
Square Room: Fitted with one Cedar Wood and three Red Deal 100-
barrel Fermenting Squares with Attemperators, fitted for Hot and
Cold Liquor with Copper Parachutes, Skimmers and Gear. Steam.
Heating Coils are fitted under Squares.
Outside this Room is a 60-barrel Cast Iron Cold Liquor Tank for
overflow from Attemperators.
(The Squares and Rounds are of recent erection).
Ground Floor: Yeast Room fitted with Scott's Patent Yeast Skim-
ming Plant with Press sufficiently large to deal with the whole of
the Skimmings at one setting up.
Two slate Yeast Backs on Piers.
Racking Room: Morton's Patent Three-cock Portable Racker.
Finings Room: Partitioned off from Racking Cellar.
Large Beer Cellar partly underground.
Smaller Cellar adjoining, both fitted with Iron Rolling Vats.
Two Hop Stores over Cellar. Large and Roomy Carpenter's Shop.
Cork and Shive Store, and Paper Room.
The Vat Room contains:
One about 165-barrel Vat.
Three about 150-barrel Vat.
One about 48-barrel Vat.
One about 40-barrel Vat.
One about 32-barrel Vat.
One about 28-barrel Vat.
Some of these Vats have not been in recent use.

N.B. The Brewery obtains from a Deep Bore Well a Supply of Water for Boiler and other general purposes. Also a Supply from a Spring in Mill Meadow (other property of the Vendor), by means of a Hydraulic Ram and Pipes, a right to continue which will be granted to the Purchaser. In addition to this, Brewing Liquor will be supplied through a meter into a Concrete Tank in Cannocks Malt House at 6d per 1,000 gallons. The purchaser is to pay the annual sum of £25 for the right to take water from the Spring in Mill Meadow and for the right of drainage and maintaining sewage pipes as now existing on the Court Farm, other property of the Vendor.

The Brewery Premises are subject to a Tithe Rent Charge of £3 2s 9d per annum.

The Maltings

Ground Floor: Furnace with King's Patent Heat Regulator.

Storage for Coal round Kiln.

Working Floor, fitted with Overhead Runway for Malt Baskets, and Doorway giving access to Barley Sweating Plant Furnace.

First Floor: Two 25-Quarter Cast Iron Conical Self-emptying Barley Steeping Cisterns.

8hp Steam Engine by Adlams worked with steam from Brewery Boiler.

Nalder Rotary Barley Screen with Fan, Half Corn Separators, etc, with set of Elevators delivering into Cisterns.

Small Power-driven Malt Mill for Country Trade.

Barley Bin, capacity about 400 bushels, feeding Boby's Patent Sweating Machine, steam or fire heated, capacity about 32 to 40 bushels per hour, fitted with Large Fan.

Collecting Bin, about 200 bushel capacity, feeding Elevators with barley sprouts, delivering to First and Top Barley Floors.

There is good accommodation for Storage of Barley on this Floor.

(This Floor is connected to the Brewery by an enclosed Bridge).

Second Floor: Working Floor fitted with Overhead Runway and Baskets.

Hoist for lifting Grain from Ground Floor.

Bottom Kiln fitted with Boby's Patent Malt turners.

(The Malt Bins lie on either side of Kiln and have a total capacity of about 2,000 Quarters).

Third Floor: Working Floor fitted with Overhead Runway and Baskets. Hoist for lifting Grain from Second Floor. Top Kiln fitted with Boby's Patent Malt turners.

Fourth Floor: Barley Store and Bins.

Hoist for unloading from Wagons in Yard.

Yard

Loading-out Area paved with Granite Setts.

Cast Iron Grains Tank with Automatic Measurer delivering direct to carts.

Large Garage with two Inspection Pits enclosed by two pairs of Folding Doors, with Engineer's Shop adjacent.

Raised Cask Washing Area with MacCardle's 6-nozzle Cask Washing Plant and 24 Drying Nozzles.

40-barrel Cast Iron Cold Liquor Tank (lagged) to supply Malt House.

40-barrel Cast Iron Hot Liquor Tank to supply Wash House.

Wood Enclosure of Sugar Room, no 2 with door.

1,000-Gallon Bulk Storage Petrol Tank fitted with Gilbert & Bartness Measuring Pump.

All this part of the Yard is covered with Corrugated Iron on Steel and Iron Supports, and paved with Granite Setts or Blue Brick on edge.

Weighbridge to weigh 5 tons.

Trap Shed.

Cannocks Maltings now containing Large Concrete Cold Liquor Tank supplying Brewing Liquor to Brewery.

Beer Store with Grain and General Stores over.

Stabling comprising Seven Stalls with Coach House or Motor Garage with Lofts over.

Open Cart Shed with Tiled Roof.

Cask Shed covered with Corrugated Iron Roof.

Brick-built Erection of Three W.C's and Urinal.

Corrugated Iron and Timber-built Blacksmith's Shop.

The modern red brick-built Range of Offices comprising Private Office, General Office, Grains Office, approached by flight of stone steps from Brewery Yard. Stores under Offices.

Newly-built Stabling in Meadow comprising Three Stalls, Loose Box, Lister's 6hp Petrol Engine for driving Chaff Cutter, Chaff Cutter by Lister, Chaff Store, Large Loft over, and lean-to addition.

In rear of the Brewery is a small Meadow with Entrance Gates from Side Road with Sheds and Stores.

N.B. The Purchaser will be required to take by valuation in the usual way all the Loose Plant and the whole of the Casks, Jars, Bottles, Cases, Motor Lorries and Cars, Horses, Carts, Drays and other Rolling Stock, Harness, Office Furniture and Miscellaneous Effects belonging to the Vendor either upon the premises or at any of the tied or free houses or elsewhere, together with the stock of Malt, Barley, Hops, Beer, Stores, etc. Also all Book Debts, Rents and Outstanding Loans.

> The Purchaser will in addition have the benefit of the trading of Three Licensed Clubs, Two Fully-Licensed Houses and One Beer House, of which the Vendor is Mortgagee of the premises, and will be required to pay on completion the amounts due on such mortagages the Total Principal of which is £6,950.

The result of the auction is not known, but by 1930 the business was in the hands of the Cheltenham & Hereford Breweries Ltd. The malthouse (which had been badly damaged by fire in 1926[76]) was leased to Colletts of Gloucester, who finished malting there c1945.

During the 1939–45 war most of the premises (Plate 60a) were used under lease by British Acoustic Films (later Rank Precision Industries Ltd), for the manufacture of cameras, projectors, and associated equipment. The whole now forms a small part of the huge premises of Rank Xerox Ltd, whose chief manufacture is Xerox copying equipment (see Chapter 15).

Apart from the brewing industry, cider-making was carried on in many farm premises (eg at Joyford), and on a larger scale at such places as Deep Filling in Huntley (by the Knight family) and at Tibberton (Daniel Phelps). Furthermore, mineral-drinks were made, eg at Lydney (by one of the Watts family), and at Lydbrook—where the 'Valley Springs Co' still operates.

ELECTRIC POWER Lydney Power Station, belonging to The West Gloucestershire Power Co Ltd, was built in 1922–3 in the Newerne Valley about half a mile north of Lydney. Coal was brought direct from the adjacent Norchard Colliery, and from the railway sidings, by means of an electrically-driven belt conveyor delivering direct into storage bunkers above the boiler furnaces, without the intervention of manual labour. The coal was fed by gravity to the furnaces. There were four water-tube boilers in the Boiler House, each pair provided with a separate chimney and an induced-draught fan.

The Turbine House was extended in 1928 to accommodate three generating sets, the largest having a capacity of 7,500kW, the others each of 5,000 kW, making a total plant capacity of 17,500 kW. The electrical energy, generated on the 3-phase alternating current system at 6,600 volts, and at the national frequency of 50 cycles, was controlled in the adjacent switch-room which contained the main control switches, together with the switchboards for the Station auxiliary plant and outside supply. At the Main Transforming Station, situated about 300yd from the Switch-Room, the pressure was transformed from 6,600 volts to 33,000 volts, to enable the electrical energy to be transmitted long distances. The total capacity of the transforming plant in 1929 was 12,000 kVA.[77]

From the Main Transforming Station the transmission lines were spread around the coalfield, to supply the large collieries for a variety of purposes and in particular for pumping water. The power was also used for other industrial and domestic purposes in the neighbouring towns and villages. A transmission line to Chepstow provided a supply to the undertaking of the Chepstow Electric Lighting and Power Co Ltd. Another line ran to the Stroud district, crossing the Severn by means of two submarine cables; and another line between Lydney, Gloucester and Stroud, provided supplies in duplicate to those centres. Sub-stations were established in the various districts where the pressure was reduced from 33,000 volts to a pressure suitable for use in the factory or house. A notable feature of the company's transmission lines in the long span of overhead wires across a valley towards Blakeney: in 1929 it was the longest span in Britain—1,043yd. Subsequently, the equipment was enlarged and improved, and run first by the Electricity Generating Board, and later by the Midland Electricity Board. After serving the region so ably, the station, with its imposing 85ft tall water cooling tower—a local landmark for some 40 years—was demolished during the winter of 1968-9.[78]

BOAT AND SHIP BUILDING No explicit reference to the local building of ships from Dean's timber has been found up to and during the thirteenth century, but many small boats which plied along the Severn and the Wye were built on or near their banks.[79] Timber was sent to Bristol for the King's galleys. There are no records of boat-building on the rivers during the fourteenth and fifteenth centuries: a few small boats may have been built,[80] but no timber for boat-building elsewhere is known to have been carried from the Forest.

The first authenticated record of a large ship built on Dean's riverside is in 1633, when Thomas Dean and William Jones built one of 70 tons, using the King's timber without leave.[81] John Purnell was building a ship in like manner: 'for her keel he took a beech 80 feet long, which was sealed with His Majesty's mark'.[82] The Lords of the Admiralty ordered the deputy surveyor, John Broughton, 'to seize and stay all barks built or building in the Forest of His Majesty's timber'. During the 1640s a small quantity of timber was supplied to build a few local boats.[83] In the 1650s the Admiralty began to build frigates at Dean. Daniel Furzer, one of their hired master shipwrights, built the *Forester*, a fifth-rate frigate, at Lydney Pill, where it was launched 5 September 1657.[84] It was a ship of 306 tons gross, with 22 guns, carrying about 100 men. Furzer also built a 20-ton trow to carry timber, as well as the 620-ton *Princess*—a frigate with a keel 104ft long, a breadth of 32ft 8in, and a depth in the hold of 14ft 4in; it was launched 29 August 1660[85] with about 54 guns and a complement of about 120 men. Furzer also repaired the *Grantham*. He informed the Admiralty in October 1664 that Lydney 'is not so fit a place now for building a ship as formerly, on account of the growing of the sands, not known in man's memory before',[86] and recommended 'Conpill, 3 miles below, because it is clear of sand'. Conpill lay at the mouth of the Cone stream on the Severn, and here Furzer 3 April 1667 launched the *St David*, 'a most complete new ship of 64 guns', of similar size to the *Princess*. Thereafter, dissatisfied with conditions in Dean, Furzer moved to the Portsmouth Navy yard. Such was his progress that from 1699 to 1706 he was Surveyor of the Navy.

During the 1650s, immense quantities of ship-timber were sent to Bristol and other naval dockyards (Fig 20). Thereafter until the 1860s, when iron replaced wood for ship-building, Dean was the most important source of such timber. Understandably, Samuel Pepys and Lord Nelson took a personal interest in Dean's trees. Professor Albion has said:[87] 'From the days when Cromwell ruled England till the Battle of Hampton Roads sounded the knell of wooden ships of war, the heads of the English Navy worried over its timber shortage'. He avers that Dean was 'the most famous of the nurseries of naval timber'[88] and that 'the name Dean was more closely associated with naval timber than that of any other woodland in England, and it furnished a more constant supply of oak than any other of the Crown forests'.[89]

There was a small amount of local boat-building in the eighteenth century alongside the Severn at Awre, Gatcombe, Purton Pill, Newnham-on-Severn,[90] and Broadoak; and on the Wye at Lydbrook,[91] Brockweir, Chepstow,[92] and Redbrook. Newnham-on-Severn was very busy in the 1780s and 1790s, building the *Fanny* (1783), the *Galley* (1785), the *John* (1786), the *Recovery* (1792), and the *Endeavour* (1794).

During the first few decades of the nineteenth century, John Hunt built the *Sally* (1801) at Broadoak, and at Newnham-on-Severn the *Glory* (1802). Thomas and James Shaw built at Gatcombe the *Ann and Betsey* (1802), the *Union* (1803), the *Ann* (1831), and the *Thomas* (1834). Thomas Hudson built the *Aliza* (1806) at Redbrook; and George Morse the *Eliza* (1807) at Lydbrook, where Charles Woore built the *Prudence* (1820) and the *Betsy* (1826). At Brockweir, the *Swift* (no 1) was built by Thomas Swift & Co in 1835, the *Swift* (no 2) in 1838, and the *Swallow* in 1843.

Thereafter, there was little building, except at Lydney where in 1834 James Ward of Bishopswood applied to the s&w for land near Lydney Basin on which to instal a smith's shop and saw-pit in order to build boats and barges. However, the land (which was 'below David Mushet's wharf at the Basin') was let that year to a prior applicant, David Davies, at £10 per annum.[93] In the same year, the s&w leased land on the east side of the outer harbour for ship-building to Thomas and James Shaw of Gatcombe.[94] Davies relinquished his barge-building yard in October 1835, 'because it was a great impediment to the trade upon the canal'.[95] Some boats and ships were repaired there up to 1878,[96] and in 1880 the 'Lydney shipyard' was leased to T. R. Egelstaff for 21 years.[97] Ten years later, Walter Gardiner held the shipyard, which he relinquished in June 1892, when it was relet to Mr Dodgin of Bristol.[98]

The foregoing summary of industries does not include several small trades hitherto practised in Dean or in its neighbouring villages. For example, at Littledean small sails were made, and several 'sailors' are mentioned in the parish register. In Coleford Workhouse late in the eighteenth century, occupants were employed in spinning flax and hurd, and Samuel Franklin was paid to weave it into cloth—$2\frac{1}{2}$d a yard for hurden cloth and 3d for linen and linsey. Among other trades which come readily to mind are: carpentry (in a wide range); building of carts and waggons (T. Clark of Brookend near Woolaston was an outstanding craftsman in this trade); wheelwright work (to give one example, at St Briavels there were three wheelwright's 'shops'—those of Henry Hulin, Matthew James and Edward Grey); and the salmon-netting trade on the Severn. Furthermore, there were the skills of the blacksmiths, locksmiths and tinsmiths—many of whom, including those working for collieries, were called 'general sheet-metal' or 'mechanical' workers—experienced craftsmen of a type rarely found today, who in the early part of the present century quickly acquired the skill to repair pumping equipment, cycles, and early motor-cycles, cars and omnibuses, which gave some of these men their first introduction to mechanics and elementary engineering.

References to Chapter 14

1 Kenyon, G. H. *The Glass Industry of the Weald*, 1967.
2 Bridgewater, N. P. 'Glasshouse Farm, St Weonards: A small Glass-working Site', *WNFC* 37, 1963, 300–15.
3 Daniels, J. S. *The Woodchester Glass House*, 1950.
4 Ibid, 5, 19; Kenyon, op cit, 217.
5 Daniels, op cit, Plate XVII.
6 Houghton, John. *Letters for the improvement of trade and husbandry:* List of glasshouses, etc 15 May 1696 quoted in Hartshorne A. *Old English Glasses, 457.*
7 Woods, M. K. *Newnham-on-Severn, a Retrospect*, 1912, 5, 19, 46, 47; Davies, G. M. *Jnl of Glass Technology*, Dec 1970.
8 Kenyon, op cit, 218.
9 Houghton, op cit. See also Petition to the House of Commons in 1696–7 by glassmakers of Newnham-on-Severn and Gloucester (*Jnl of the House of Commons*, XII, 93, 282), mentioned by Powell, H. J. *Glassmakers of England.*
10 Atkyns, R. *History of Gloucestershire*, 1712.
11 Rudder, S., op cit.
12 *Forest Newspapers*, 12 Nov 1954.
13 Smith Brian, S. *Memories of Mitcheldean since about 1890.*
14 *Slater's Directory*, 1858.
15 GRO Bond MSS.
16 *Curiosities of Great Britain, Alphabetically Arranged*, 1835.
17 *Report on Dean*, 1835, 24.
18 *Slater's Directory*, 1858.
19 *Harris's Directory*, 1902.
20 *Slater's Directory*, 1858.
21 Information from Canon R. J. Mansfield.
22 Women's Institute Records, Westbury, 68.
23 Ibid.
24 Ibid.
25 *Slater's Directory*, 1858.
26 *Harris's Directory*, 1887.
27 Ibid, 1902.
28 *Slater's Directory*, 1858.
29 *BGAS*, 55, 336.
30 Rudge, op cit, 1803, II, 104.
31 *P. G. Harris's Directory*, 1830.
32 MSS, *penes me.*
33 *Slater's Directory*, 1858.
34 *Vict C Hist Glos*, II, 215.
35 F16/50 (MR417).
36 *Forest Newspapers*, 18 Jan 1952.
37 *Kelly's Directory*, 1874.
38 *Engineering*, Sept 1876.
39 S&W Min Bk, 1 Jan 1889.
40 *Harris's Directory*, 1887; *Post Office Guide*, 1879.
41 *Iron*, 7 March 1890.
42 S&W Min Bk, 2 April 1889.

43 Ibid, 17 Nov 1891.
44 Ibid, 22 Oct 1897.
45 Information from R. A. J. Bell.
46 Insole and Bunning, op cit, 68.
47 Ibid, 22B.
48 GRO D2211.
49 *Harris's Directory*, 1887.
50 *Kelly's Directory*, 1876.
51 *Invention*, 25 March 1893, 237.
52 Ibid.
53 Ibid.
54 Ibid.
55 Ibid.
56 *Foresters ½d Newspaper*, 2 Sept 1882.
57 Ibid, 8 July 1882.
58 *Forest Newspapers*, 7 March 1952.
59 Ibid, 24 Feb 1967.
60 *Invention*, 25 March 1893.
61 *Gloucester Journal*, 18 Oct 1879, 'Opening of the Severn Bridge Railway'.
62 Hughes, H. W. *A Text-Book of Coal Mining*, 1893.
63 Patent no 14,091, 1893: 'To make firing more certain, more sensitive, and less liable to moisture and other effects.'
64 Ibid, no 9,368, 1894: Similar objectives to those of Patent no 14,091.
65 *Invention*, 25 March 1893.
66 Anon. *The Rise and Progress of the British Explosives Industry*, 1909, 338.
67 Hart. *Royal Forest*, 96, 138.
68 GRO D36/T26, 39.
69 *Kelly's Directory*, 1910.
70 *Harris's Directory*, 1887.
71 Mathias, P. *The Brewery Industry in England 1700–1830*, 1959.
72 S&W Officers' Mins, 23 April 1912.
73 *Industrial Gloucestershire, 1904*, op cit, 56, 57.
74 Ibid.
75 GRO D2242 III/2/1, 1923.
76 GRO PH 66/9, 10 (two photographs).
77 West Gloucestershire Power Co Ltd publicity booklet, 'A record of 5 years progress: 1925–9'; 'An Engineering Record', 1923 (The Foundation Co Ltd).
78 *Forest Newspapers*, 27 Sept 1968 and 24 Jan 1969.
79 See, eg, *Cal Close Rolls*, C62, VI, 30.
80 E32/33.
81 *Cal* SP16/250/292;/302/23.
82 Ibid.
83 Hart. *Royal Forest*, 138.
84 Ibid, 144, 145; Harris, Frank H. 'Lydney Ships', *BGAS* 66, 1945, 238–45.
85 Ibid, 145, 146.
86 Ibid, 163.
87 Albion, R. G. *Forests and Sea Power*, 1926, vii.
88 Ibid, 107.

89 Ibid, 108.
90 *BGAS* 18, 13.
91 Farr, G. E. *Chepstow Ships*, 1954.
92 Ibid, and Waters, Ivor. *About Chepstow*, 1952, 25.
93 S&W Min Bk, 14 Jan 1834 and 14 April 1835.
94 Ibid, 14 April 1835.
95 Ibid, 13 Oct 1835.
96 Ibid, 22 Aug 1878.
97 Ibid, 3 Jan 1881.
98 Ibid, Dec 1891; and April and May 1892.

61 (above) Pine End plywood factory, Lydney; (below) Royal Forest factory, Coleford, of the Beecham Group and previously H. W. Carter & Co Ltd

62 *(above)* R. A. Lister & Co Ltd, Cinderford; *(below)* aerial view north of Parkend. The Remploy factory is on the left, and the stoneworks are at the bottom centre

Fifteen
The Changed Industrial Scene

For over one thousand years, man in Dean mined iron ore and coal, and therewith sustained bloomeries, blast furnaces and manufactories for steel, tinplate, wire, and cable. Now the mining has virtually ceased. Tramroads and railways have come and gone; and mostly new industries are providing the employment. In spite of the Forest's vast mineral wealth, the conservatism of most of those responsible for industrial developments in the eighteenth and nineteenth centuries kept the scale of most enterprises small or fragmented, and sometimes behind in technical progress compared with other districts, and hence Dean was vulnerable to competition. As examples may be cited the longevity of smelting with charcoal (when competitors had gone over to coke), the late introduction of both tramroads and railways, the tardy use of waste gas utilisation plant, and the failure to adapt ironworks to steel production (often talked about but never done). Expansion could have taken place if large-scale investment, beyond that of the Crawshays, had been available for developments. There is a time for prudence and a time for risk, in industry as in other spheres of life, and in Dean failure to suit the mood to the moment exacted a price in gradual stagnation, and collapse in the face of competition. Unfortunately, too, the necessary hard-coking coal was not present in the Forest, as at Blaenavon and Merthyr, otherwise Dean might have been pre-eminent in the coke iron blast furnace industry at least so long as the meagre reserves of local ore lasted. Furthermore, there was the conservation of the Free Miners, with their numerous small enterprises, frequently changing hands: not until 1904 was there any semblance of the region being worked as a unified coalfield.

The changed and changing industrial scenes in Dean have been described in part in *Royal Forest* and in part in other books;[1] and the descriptions have been amplified herein. This chapter particularly takes up the survey after the industrial strikes of 1921 and 1926, and the depressions in the early 1930s. By the mid-1930s various organisations and individuals (chiefly enlightened industrialists, planners and officials) were keenly aware that new industries would be vital for Dean's economy. In 1938 the Forest of Dean Industrial Development Committee was formed from a small beginning, the Coleford Trade & Improvement Society. The new voluntary Association (later renamed the Development Association of the Royal Forest of Dean) comprised representatives of the Lydney, East Dean, and West Dean Rural District Councils and the County Council, employers, trade unions, landowners, Chambers of Commerce and Trade, the Forestry Commission, the local Member of Parliament, and the authorities for Planning, Rivers, Electricity, Gas, Water, Highways and Transport. Its single purpose was, individually and collectively, to facilitate the introduction of new industries, and to further the expansion and development of all local industries old and new wherever it was possible to do so.

The outbreak of war in 1939 gave a renewed impetus to the mining of coal and iron ore in Dean, and made demands on the woodlands, which not only supplied an immense volume of produce but also sheltered from the enemy untold quantities of munitions of war—a usage which incidentally bequeathed to the Forest many invaluable woodland roads. In 1940 building began of Pine End Works as a 'shadow factory' alongside Lydney canal, in order to make plywood for the building of aircraft. This was the first major industry to come to Dean—a result of planning by the Development Association. The venture was conceived by private sponsors at the outbreak of the war, and instructions to proceed were given by the government after the fall of France (1940). Production was started in April 1941 before the completion of the whole factory, and the output was confined to plywood (using chiefly Canadian birch and some home-grown beech) more particularly for the world famous 'Mosquito', but also to a large extent for gliders such as the 'Horsa' and the 'Hamilcar' used for the invasion of Europe. At the end of the war, the production changed to commercial applications, such as for railway rolling stock, ship-building, house-building, decorative veneers, furniture, road transport, hoardings, concrete shuttering, and a variety of other uses to which plywood is put today. In 1946 the control of the factory (Plate 61a) passed from the government to Factories Direction Limited (see *infra*) who had previously acted for the Ministry of Supply under the name of Aeronautical & Panel Plywood Co Ltd.

Another industry came to Dean in 1940—British Acoustic Films, a company within the Rank Organisation, housed in the empty Mitcheldean Brewery (see Chapter 14 and Plate 60a). The factory produced bomb sights, fire direction tables, and other precision equipment necessary for the war. Thereafter many types of photographic equipment were manufactured—from 8mm home movie cameras and projectors to 16mm equipment for use in industry and education, as well as professional film equipment based on the designs of Bell & Howell of Chicago. The industrial activity was highly technical and precise in nature, involving some 30,000 operations through numerous intricate processes in which over 3,000 different parts were almost constantly on the move, and necessitating almost one thousand different raw materials. Cameras used in the Everest Expedition were made at Mitcheldean. The company increased its premises and its labour force. The future was bright . . . but no one expected that the factory would one day expand to the immense proportions which it later achieved.

In 1944 R. A. Lister & Co Ltd opened in Cinderford a branch factory (Plate 62a) for engineering including diesel engine manufacture. The company, which later extended its operations and its premises, has been a great asset to the town.

In 1947 H. W. Carter & Co Ltd (formed by the Armstrong family and with the technical assistance of Dr V. L. S. Charley), manufacturers of blackcurrant juice and soft drinks, moved from Bristol into a fine modern factory (Plate 61b) at Coleford. The company, welcomed because of the receding employment in mining and some other trades, was soon processing blackcurrant, apple, lemon, citrus and other juices (for 'Ribena', 'Quosh', 'Rosena', and allied products) under the most hygenic conditions.

Pine End, British Acoustic Films, Lister's, and Carters, Dean's pioneer new industries, gave (and continue to give) invaluable employment to men and women who were unaccustomed to factory work and who at first were not eager to learn new trades. Men from tinplate, mining and other industries found the clean light jobs strange and unnatural, but they welcomed the newcomers and soon adapted themselves to the tasks. Special provisions were made by the employers or by independent bus operators to provide transport for distances up to ten miles. The new industries fitted in well with the two comparatively older (but modernised) factories making cable and wire at Lydbrook, and there was not undue competition for labour. Among other industries which came to Dean, usually with encouragement from the Development Association, were World's Wear Ltd (manufacturers of light clothing) to Coleford in 1950; and Meredith & Drew (biscuit manufacturers) to Cinderford in 1951, employing about 550. From the 1950s planned industrial buildings (previously a war-time depot) on the Lydney Industrial Trading Estate (with which the Watts family in particular have played a leading rôle) attracted many welcome industries: among them were Duramin Engineering Company Ltd (1950), Watts Automatic Boilers, J. Allen Rubber Co Ltd, and Typrod Ltd (1952). The well-deserved success of the endeavours of the Development Association was chiefly due to the members being linked by a common interest in social service allied to commonsense, a combination which resulted in a generous increase in prosperity for all concerned. The Honorary Public Relations Officer and Planning Consultant, Gordon Payne OBE,[2] the Honorary Secretary, John Horwood, and Maynard Bennett, did notable work for the region. They had the full support of the Gloucestershire Planning Department and the Board of Trade. Hundreds of women and girls joined enthusiastically and efficiently in the various industries, and have been of invaluable help to them.

In 1955 the Development Association was able to assert that 'as far as can be seen at the present time, the future of employment in Dean is secure'.[3] The percentage of unemployed was about twelve in every 1,000 (compared with over 300 in every 1,000 in the early 1930s). By attracting new industries the Association had helped to retain the population. The only uncertainties were the future of the Lydney Tinplate Works and the coal mining industry. Nevertheless, representatives of the workers, eg Alderman C. W. Luker, G. T. D. Jenkins, and J. C. Wolridge OBE, watched the situation with increasing concern.[4] Iron ore mining had already ceased.

In 1957, clouds of industrial distress began to appear over Dean. Lydney Tinplate Works, for long the staple industry of the town, closed that year. Rumblings about the future of coal mining were more frequently heard, and the 'Revised Plan for Coal', 1959, warned that it would be unlikely that any collieries would be worked in Dean after 1965. From the mid-1950s the collieries had become increasingly uneconomical, for which some people blamed the National Coal Board, and others the workers. Most of the seams were nearing exhaustion; excess water was an ever present problem; and there were 'washout' areas where coal disappeared or dwindled to only a few inches in thickness. Labour difficulties had arisen: as pits began to close, the younger men went into other industries (even if sometimes this meant travelling 20 miles to Gloucester), leaving the older men to work underground. Five of the six large collieries closed during 1957–62; and the extensive cable works at Lydbrook (see Chapter 4) closed in 1965—a shattering blow to the district. The coalfield was in the twilight of its life . . . and the last colliery, Northern United, closed on Christmas Day 1965.

Previous commendable efforts by the Development Association had absorbed some of the redundant miners and other workers. Renewed efforts were now needed to counter the heavy unemployment. The Member of Parliament for the constituency, Charles H. Loughlin, the trade unions, and representatives of industry (of whom F. Wickstead OBE—Plate 60a—was an outstanding example) met the situation with sympathy and prompt action. Many unemployed were absorbed into the Mitcheldean factory of Rank Xerox Ltd; and in 1966 Reed Corrugated Cases Ltd (boxes and cases), with the district's sincere gratitude and relief, acquired the empty cable work premises at Lydbrook. Assistance came from other factories, individuals, and authorities in Dean's three Rural Districts and in Gloucester. Their efforts, coupled with careful attention to re-training, transference of labour, and appropriate redundancy and retirement arrangements, overcame the crisis. Many people bemoaned the passing of the coalfield, but some would have been justified in applauding it, because it ended the unnatural underground work, thereby bringing men from the dark, dirty, hazardous (and often too hard) jobs to the light, cleanliness and safety of modern factories—though in some instances the wages were lower than hitherto.

A new industrial site at Whimsey in Lower Cinderford, where Painter Bros (metal structures) began operations, and expansion by Listers and a few other works in the town were all welcome. In Lydney and Coleford there were renewed efforts to attract and support new industries. Within a few years an industrial position was reached where employment was reasonably adequate—which situation, removing much of the impetus and challenge, recently led to the lapse of the Development Association, resulting in the cessation of the best example—some might say, the only example—of sustained co-operation between the individuals and Councils of the three Rural Districts. Subsequently, firms have acquired the art of resilience in containing their own difficulties.

Part of the human story behind some of the closures of collieries has been described by Dennis Potter[5] who has also explained the rougher and the tougher side of Forest mining life, and the local coal-mining superstitions and prejudices. Some of the changes of recent years, he avers, have been at the expense of Dean's older working-class culture. In many factories the tough miner or tinplater became the gentle operative. He and his predecessors had worked hard, and played hard (particularly in soccer and rugby—sometimes unavoidably taking the field in pit dirt). Prior to the 1930s he and his family travelled little—restricted perhaps to a visit to Wembley, either to the Exhibition of 1924 or to a subsequent Cup Final, or to the lights of Blackpool, or again to a savings-liquidating week's holiday by the sea at Barry, Penarth or Weston-super-Mare. The needs of his health, and relief to his injuries, had been partly met by the Dilke, Lydney and Gloucester hospitals, and by more distant convalescence homes. Advanced education (particularly for those aspiring to the envied posts of colliery deputy or manager) was provided by the Mining School at Cinderford, which as the West Gloucestershire College of Further Education is still a valuable asset to the Forest, and comple- mentary to the Royal Forest of Dean and Lydney Grammar Schools. The crippled or health-broken miner finds a refuge, friendship and encouragement at the Remploy factory in Parkend (Plate 62b) or at the county's Sheltered Workshops in Cinderford. The one-time miners (some now only identified by blue scars on face or hand—the result of coal injuries), and certainly their children and grandchildren, are now more widely travelled, more enquiring, and have more diverse interests.

Today after five short years the mining era is rarely mentioned, and almost unknown by the young. Some five hundred Free Miners are registered, but hardly a third are really interested in their rights, and of these only a couple of dozen follow their calling. Of the iron mining the only remnants are the scowles, hollows and crevices usually covered with moss, ferns and other plants, and shaded by gnarled yews whose bared roots entwine the rocks; and a few mine heads and adit entrances, sealed for public safety. Underground are the aban- doned caverns and workings described in Chapter 5, a few of them offering adventure to the local Caving Club, and three from which water supplies are extracted. The one-time prosperous coalfield (closed except for the operations of a few Free Miners and occasional opencast mining—a deeply controversial subject) has now recovered from its dying pains. The abandoned shafts are sealed for safety, and most of the spoil heaps have been levelled (eg at Lydbrook, Steam Mills and Speech House Hill) or clothed by nature with birch, hawthorn, bramble and grass, or afforested with Scots and Corsican pines. However, the

Fancy and Lightmoor spoil heaps, looming red and bare, are still being eaten into for ballast. Several fields are affected by subsidence. The colliery buildings have either been removed or converted to use as factories, warehouses, or even centres for youth and adventure. Many of the inevitable drab miners' dwellings have disappeared or have been modernised. Underground, the water-filled abyss, described in Chapter 6, should with the awesome quarries, be forgotten or avoided. Well remembered are the human tragedies, the gallantries, and the comradeship; and the part once played underground by valiant, and usually well-treated, ponies and horses.

Of other industries, gone are the chimney stacks at Lydbrook, Parkend, Lydney, Cinderford and Soudley. Gone, too, are the turn-pike gates, though some of their squat residences remain; the lines of railway wagons (Plate 33) boldly displaying the names of Crawshay, Jarrett, Cannop and the like; the tanners and curriers; the charcoal-burners; the pack animals with their burdens of cordwood; the red faces and clothes of the ore miner and the blacks and greys of the collier.

Man has changed much of what is left: Cinderford gas works is now used as a foundry (a switch of industry from West Dean to East Dean); caravans stand on the site of Cinderford ironworks; Cannop colliery office buildings are used as a field centre (by Bournville College of Further Education); Marions brickworks is now a sawmill; and the Flour Mill colliery turbine building is used as a small refinery for oil. Furthermore, man and nature have in some places improved what at one time was despoiled: in references to industrial places of the past there are contemporary dismal comments such as 'cyclopean sheds' and 'belching chimneys'—these could, for example, have referred to Bishopswood and Flaxley . . . yet today they are places of beauty, with no obvious signs of their industrial past.

Not all has disappeared. A few buildings of the Tufts chemical works survive, and there is pithead gear at Prosper. Ponds of great beauty and interest lie at Soudley (Plate 64a) and Cannop (Plate 64b), formed in the nineteenth century to supply water for ironworks, and smaller ponds for the same purpose remain at Newland and Redbrook and along the Newerne and Cone Streams. All are now accepted as part of the natural landscape, and are not readily attributed to past industries. The many miles of disused tramroads and railways (their earthworks and cinder tracks fast becoming colonised by grass, herb-age, and scrub) invite planned uses such as greenways for walkers, horseriders and cyclists, and as picnic places. Pleasant to record is the survival of some of the older crafts, eg those of wood-turning, cleaving, sawmilling, and charcoal-burning in retorts; also the advent of some newer skills, such as those of refining and working of rare metals, of plywood and paper manufacture, and of electronics and xerography.

Gone are the hated 'truck' system of payment, the distressing 'hodding', the long walks to the distant collieries, and the lights glimmering through the woods heralding the returning tired miners. Gone, too (fortunately) are the hazards of falling roofs and flooded mines. Dwindling on, are the ex-miners' customary 'allowance coal' (now brought from other coalfields) . . . but the miner crippled by accident, pneumoconiosis or silicosis, has few regrets, if any, at the passing of the coalfield—though despite the dirt and the unpleasantness many old miners still make touchingly nostalgic references to the past.

Today the problems besetting the planners for industry are those of consolidation, balance, and improvement of communications; all with the knowledge that there are some 1,500 commuters to Gloucester and elsewhere. There are three distinct centres of industry and population in Dean—at Cinderford, Coleford and Lydney—and others, of significant size, at Mitcheldean, Lydbrook, and Whitecroft.

Cinderford, a town of some importance as a manufacturing centre, has within its immediate environs a population of about 10,000. Mining and ironworks have left their scars, though some spoil heaps have been levelled, and some are being used by the Broadmoor Brick Co Ltd. The small area of opencast coal mining to the north of the town is a temporary enterprise which within a year should leave an improved site. Among Cinderford's flourishing industries are those of R. A. Lister & Co Ltd (Plate 62a), now part of the Hawker Siddeley Group and employing about 500, Engelhard Industries Ltd (refiners and workers of rare metals, in premises vacated by Meredith & Drew) who in 1969 made the crown for the Prince of Wales' investiture, Rosedale Associated Manufacturers Ltd (plastics) employing about 150, Cinderford Engineering Co Ltd (brass founders), G. A. Bilby & Sons (welding, in premises vacated by Teague & Chew), H. V. Barnes & Son Ltd (wood turnery), Runnymede Dispersals Ltd (colour pigments, in the old pithead baths of Eastern United Colliery), and Herbert & Young (ironfounders, in the old gasworks). There are two brickmaking firms (Broadmoor Brick Co Ltd, and Coleford Brick & Tile Co Ltd). Two sawmills operate at Hollywood (the Mills families), and a third at Nailbridge (Smarts); also there are a sawmills and a wood preservation plant at Lightmoor (James Joiner & Sons Ltd). Painter Bros' factory at Whimsey has been acquired by Rank Xerox Ltd. The commendable Sheltered Workshops of the Gloucestershire County Council are fulfilling a most useful purpose. To the south-east of Cinderford are the Newnham Rubber Mills Ltd (at Bullo, making tubings) and G. H. Zeal Ltd in Newnham-on-Severn (clinical thermometers).

Coleford, more compact than Cinderford, has a few industries, and in and nearby the population is about 7,000. As well as the progressive factory of H. W. Carter & Co Ltd, acquired in 1955 by Beecham Foods Ltd (Plate 61b) and now employing about 500, other industries have come to the West Dean RDC site at Tufthorn—in 1965 Formwood Ltd (moulded wood products) employing 160, and using mainly locally grown spruces, and in 1963 Henry Sykes Ltd (pumps) employing about 25. At nearby Sling are the extensive boiler and machine tool works of Fred Watkins (Engineering) Ltd, employing about 150. West of the town are the quarries of Hoveringham Stone Ltd, Rogers Quarries Ltd, and Man-Abell Ltd. To the north is Dean Woodlands Ltd (sawmillers and fence manufacturers); towards Bream, K. Allan & Co Ltd (a small refinery for oils); and to the east, Concrete Utilities Ltd, Wood Distillation Ltd (now charcoal only), and Solvent Reclamation Ltd, where recovery of solvents began in 1965.

Lydney is a service and manufacturing town of increasing importance, with a population of about 6,000 (and another 6,000 within three miles in a string of small settlements). As well as the extensive and progressive Garage and Repair Works of Watts (Factors) Ltd (Plate 58b) there are other industries: along Church Road—Albany Engineering Co Ltd (pumps) employing about 95; and in the premises of the old tinplate works, Watts Tyre & Rubber Co Ltd and (nearby) James R. Crompton & Bros Ltd (makers of paper from manilla hemp and synthetic fibres), employing about 150. Alongside the canal, near the harbour, is the flourishing Pine End plyworks of Factories Direction Ltd (within the William Mallinson Group) employing about 680. The company's main business continues to be to convert West African and other logs, brought to Lydney Harbour (Plate 61a), into high quality exterior grade plywood, mostly made in sheets 8ft × 4ft and in laminations ranging from $\frac{3}{16}$in to 1in; some, however, is scarfed up to 40ft in length when required for boat cladding and other specialist uses. A more recent development is a decorative Veneer Cutting Division now of equal importance to plywood manufacture. Flooring material is also produced. A proportion of waste material is sold to an associate company, Formwood Limited, in Coleford, where it is used in the manufacture of a wide range of mouldings. Another product, densified wood, is used in the aircraft industry for jigs and tools, and for nuclear shielding in atomic power stations. An industry which gave much employment to Lydney was that of producing the Watts Automatic Boiler (Plate 59b), invented jointly by Arthur J. Watts (Plate 59a) and W. H. Franklin. The rights in the boiler were sold in 1960 to Allied Ironfounders Ltd who in 1966 transferred their business to Manchester and now operate as Glynwed Foundries Ltd. Brico Engineering Ltd (pistons) arrived in 1962 and now employ about 400. On the Industrial Trading Estate are many welcome industries—Typrod Ltd, Kayanson (Engineers) Ltd (industrial oil and gas boilers, in premises vacated by Allied Ironfounders Ltd), J. Allen Rubber Co Ltd (now a subsidiary of the London Rubber Co Ltd), Regalfoam Ltd (latex foam products), and Duramin Engineering (Lydney) Ltd, a most important company and pioneers in the road and rail container industry. Near Lydney Junction are Berry Wiggins & Co Ltd (oil refiners).

Three other centres of industry are Lydbrook, Whitecroft and Mitcheldean. Lydbrook, in the north of the Forest, poses problems for the planners not least because of its elongated nature, but it possesses large and valuable industries. Reed Corrugated Cases Ltd (in premises vacated in 1965 by Associated Electrical Industries, successors to Ediswans) make corrugated fibreboard cases and paper containers, employing about 600. There are also Temco Ltd (fine wire manufacturers, a reminder of the skill, energy and perseverance of the late Harold Smith—see Chapter 4 and Plate 24b), S. C. Meredith & Son (Engineers) Ltd (making machinery for cable manufacture on the site of the old tinplate works), Lydwood Ltd (cabinet makers), and Edward Transport (Lydbrook) Ltd.

Whitecroft, in the mid-south of Dean, possesses the long established pin works of the Jarretts, acquired in 1964 by a company in the USA, and renamed Whitecroft-Scovill Ltd, with Michael Jarrett MBE still representing his family as managing director. This progressive enterprise employing about 350, for long one of Dean's most staple and interesting, now has three Divisions. One Division manufactures hard haberdashery, notions and stationery products (included in these general headings are products such as safety pins, hair pins, hair grips, curlers, paper clips, and office pins); also components for the electrical trade. The second Division manufactures gripper metal and plastic fasteners for the clothing trade. The other Division manufactures and assembles aerosol valves. J. Allen Rubber Co Ltd (of Lydney) have storage premises at Whitecroft. It is an important company, being the largest manufacturer of domestic gloves in Britain.

Mitcheldean is an example of a small town possessing an industry of national and international importance—Rank Xerox Ltd. The beginning of the enterprise, first as British Acoustic Films and thereafter as Rank Precision Industries Ltd, both within the Rank Organisation, has been related earlier in this chapter. By 1955 the works were employing about 650, and had a lively apprentice scheme. The premises were extended, and by 1959 the labour force was over one thousand. Photographic equipment was becoming very competitive with the introduction of Japanese manufacture, and in 1959 the company began to plan for diversification and for the manufacture of Xerographic equipment. The first Xerox automatic copying machine (English version) was on the market in 1960. Thereafter there was a vast expansion of the Rank Xerox Ltd plant, and the company now employs over 3,000 people—(the site covering some 60 acres)—an immense boon to the local and national economy. Another industry in Mitcheldean is Litson Joinery Works (of the Little family), and the town is also the headquarters of one of the Read family's road transport enterprises (acquired by British Road Services in 1964), and of the Cottrell family's buses and coaches.

Beyond the above enterprises in the major centres, there are printing (Brights, Wheelers, Fields), and several smaller industries, as well as building contractors (such as those of Giles, Gwynne, Imm, Kear, Marfell and Powell), and a number of small coal levels worked by a few Free Miners. These and the new industries (mostly of a light nature suitable for both sexes), have sustained Dean's inhabitants (previously dependent upon natural resources for their livelihoods) during and following the run down of the traditional industries. The whole story demonstrates the responsiveness of the region to technological changes and its resilience in difficult circumstances—in contrast to the isolationism and conservatism of former centuries.

Within Dean a rapid increase (about 60 per cent) in manufacturing employment was achieved between 1951 and 1966, in spite of the decline of the coal mining—an increase due to both local and national efforts to avoid widespread unemployment. The manufacturing groups strongly represented in 1966 were engineering and metals, timber, paper, and rubber products. Because the problem of redundancies in coal mining had to a large measure by then been solved, the future rate of growth of manufactory employment was not expected to be so spectacular. The population increase during the period 1951–66 was a mere 600, less than half the rate of the national increase, thereby indicating a significant outward migration—during a period when most (and the last) large collieries were closed. Apart from significant increases in Lydney Rural District, the population of the Forest remained generally static in terms of total numbers. The population structure was not greatly different from the norm in North Gloucestershire, but the relative proportions of both the elderly and the children were consistent with a substantial outward migration of young people. The low proportion of professional and employer categories at 12·4 per cent, together with below-average car ownership at 62 per hundred households, and above-average household size at 3·09 persons, can be attributed to the population's earlier dependence on coal mining. The representation of professional and employer categories and car owning households in the fast-growing population of Lydney Rural District was notably higher than the average for the Forest. Lydney was in 1966 the most important centre in terms of jobs (c4,500) followed by Cinderford, Coleford, and Mitcheldean each with c3,000 jobs. In June 1968 the insured population (other than self-employed) in the Cinderford, Coleford, and Lydney areas of the Departments of Employment (which areas approximately cover those of the East Dean, West Dean and Lydney Rural Districts, plus Newnham-on-Severn and Westbury-on-Severn) was:

	INDUSTRY	Males	Females	Total
I	Agriculture, Forestry, Fishing	434	101	535
II	Mining and Quarrying	249	9	258
	TOTAL—EXTRACTIVE INDUSTRIES	683	110	793
III	Food, Drink and Tobacco	452	316	768
IV	Chemicals and Allied Industries	78	9	87
V	Metal Manufacture	367	85	452
VI	Engineering and Electrical Goods	3,153	782	3,935
VII	Shipbuilding and Marine Engineering	—	—	—
VIII	Vehicles	399	35	434
IX	Metal Goods not elsewhere specified	Included in XVI		
X	Textiles	Included in XVI		
XI	Leather, Leather Goods and Fur	—	—	—
XII	Clothing and Footwear	Included in XVI		

		Males	Females	Total
XIII	Bricks, Pottery, Glass, Cement etc	389	19	408
XIV	Timber, Furniture etc	1,006	318	1,324
XV	Paper, Printing and Publishing	460	216	676
XVI	Other Manufacturing Industries	1,218	1,254	2,472
	TOTAL—MANUFACTURING INDUSTRIES	7,522	3,034	10,556
XVII	Construction	857	19	876
XVIII	Gas, Electricity and Water	115	3	118
XIX	Transport and Communication	687	77	764
XX	Distributive Trades	333	556	889
XXI	Insurance, Banking and Finance	44	32	76
XXII	Professional and Scientific Services	454	1,385	1,839
XXIII	Miscellaneous Services	257	400	657
XXIV	Public Administration and Defence	738	182	920
	Ex-Service	—	1	1
	Industry not stated	11	14	25
	TOTAL—SERVICES (CONSTRUCTION NOT INCLUDED)	2,639	2,650	5,289
	GRAND TOTAL—ALL INDUSTRIES	11,701	5,813	17,514

The above estimates were prepared for the purpose of providing an approximate indication of the industrial structure of the region. By June 1969 the total was 18,548, but the breakdown of this figure is not available. The increase is and will be in the manufacturing sector—to a large extent in engineering and metals. Continued growth is expected for Cinderford and Coleford. The greatest concentration of growth is envisaged at Lydney, which would thereby become the major industrial and service centre.[6] It is not known how Dean will be affected by the recommendations which will arise from the study set up to consider the feasibility of Severnside for the reception of population growth after 1981.

Of Dean's woodlands, the problems are chiefly those of marrying timber-growing with amenity and recreation. The silviculture, and the estate management of the Crown lands are in the hands of the Forestry Commission, with the co-operation (in so far as 'vert and venison' are concerned) of the four verderers.[7] The Commission employs about 120, and is represented by the Deputy Surveyor (G. D. Rouse), two district officers (A. Joslin and J. Peal), a chief forester (noted in Chapter 9), seven head foresters, and twelve foresters. Some of the woodlands are run on 'multiple-use' principles, but most are managed silviculturally and commercially with a view to profit. However, it may

not be far in the future when the Forest's value for timber production may be less than that for recreation. During the last decade there
has been a marked improvement in the living standards of the ordinary people in Britain—more cars than ever make possible short or long
excursions to the countryside; and all have led to a great increase in
leisure time, and have created a demand for recreational facilities. The
demands on Dean for such facilities are increasing annually, and are
being catered for by the Forestry Commission, and supervised by their
Forest Warden (M. J. Dunn).

At least half a million day visitors travelling by car and coach visited
Dean in 1970; in addition there were some 5,000 (mainly school
children) who paid educational visits. Longer term visitors included
those who stayed at Forest Park Camp Sites (100,000 visitor nights),
Youth Sites (25,000), three Youth Hostels (7,000), Adventure Training
Centres (3,000), Hotels, and Private Camp Sites. By 1980 the number
of visitors may well be between one and two million: the M5, M50
and the 'Heads of the Valleys Road', and the M4 and the Severn road
bridge have provided easy access to Dean. Already the chief camping
grounds at Christcurch (Plate 63b) and Braceland at peak Bank Holiday periods are used up to 'saturation point'; therefore current proposals are to open another site at Worcester Lodge and an extensive
'wild camping area' adjacent to the Christchurch Camp Site. Five Youth
Camp Sites are set throughout the woodlands. Adventure centres at
Braceland and Biblins are leased to the Gloucestershire County Council; and 'Foyle Lodge', part of the old premises of Cannop Colliery, is
leased to the Bournville College of Further Education. Throughout the
Forest are car parks and picnic sites with toilets, tables, and barbecue
hearths. Near Symonds Yat Rock in the north of the Forest is an outstanding woodland park for 250 cars, and an attractive log cabin
refreshment chalet (Plate 63a), visited annually by upwards of 150,000
people. Ten Nature Trails are laid throughout the woodlands, way-
marked paths have been set out, and a Scenic Motor Drive was inaugurated in 1969, using existing roads. Among other recreational oppor-
tunities available within or neighbouring Dean are canoeing, caving,
orienteering, riding and field studies, and a little fishing and climbing.
The recreational policy is to expand and improve the present facilities
and this, with the complementary need to enhance the amenity and
wild life, has meant changes in what foresters term their 'Working
Plan'. Paramount is the need to minimise as far as possible the impact
of recent unavoidably heavy felling of aging and deteriorating broad-

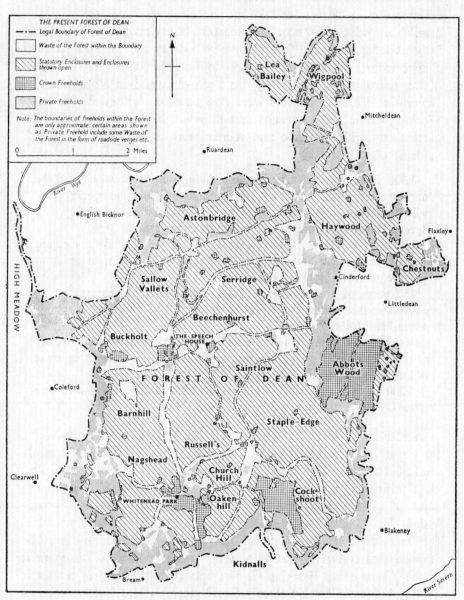

THE PRESENT FOREST OF DEAN
- · - · Legal Boundary of Forest of Dean

Waste of the Forest within the Boundary

Statutory Enclosures and Enclosures thrown open

Crown Freeholds

Private Freeholds

Note: The boundaries of freeholds within the Forest are only approximate; certain areas shown as Private Freehold include some Waste of the Forest in the form of roadside verges etc.

0   1   2 Miles

Fig 26. The present Forest of Dean.

leafed trees (particularly oaks). Furthermore, any long term plan for conservation in Dean must take into account the large area of young conifers introduced for economic reasons. Many people (often without fully understanding the factors involved) decry the Forest's planned change from a broadleafed to a predominantly conifer region (much of the reasoning of the policy has been discussed in *Royal Forest*). Hence, in 1970, 7,000 acres were designated as within an 'Amenity Working Circle', which means that they will be treated or conserved particularly with aesthetic and recreational considerations in mind, made up of:

4,300 acres of broadleafed trees (including scrub) grown beyond the normal rotation age and to be regenerated by the same species. Oak will be the predominant species in the central Cannop Valley and Speech House areas, and mixed woodland elsewhere.

450 acres of conifers, mainly Douglas fir, grown beyond the rotation of maximum mean annual increment to about 80 years, in order to provide groves or blocks of large trees.

650 acres of high landscape value, with light coloured species to emphasise the natural topography. Felling will be phased to a 'Landscape Plan' (*infra*).

400 acres of group felling phased to give an intimate scale variety of tree species and age groups to provide interest for walkers in areas of intense public access.

1,200 acres of open spaces maintained with little or no planted tree cover.

In addition to the 7,000 acres within the 'Amenity Working Circle', there are 2,173 acres of young to middle aged broadleafed (mainly oak) plantations within the 'Commercial Working Circle', wherein no clear felling is proposed for at least 20 years; also there are many acres of mixed plantations wherein the final crop could be broadleafed. The Commission intend to produce a long-term 'Landscape Plan' for Dean (there is already one for the Wye Valley), although it must be stressed that conservation and amenity are by no means disregarded in the 'Commercial Working Circle', because each stand of timber is studied before felling is authorised and many natural features such as streams, escarpments and odd corners are maintained, or reafforested with broadleaves to break up the extensive areas of conifers. The verderers (and, it is to be hoped, such worth-while bodies as the Council for the Preservation of Rural England, the Wyedean Tourist Board, the Gloucestershire Trust for Nature Conservation, and the Ramblers'

63   Multiple use of the Forest[1]: *(above)* The log cabin near Symonds Yat Rock; *(below)* Christchurch Camp

64 Multiple use of the Forest (2): Ponds formed in the nineteenth century to ensure a supply of water to the ironworks: *(above)* Soudley Ponds; *(below)* Cannop Ponds

Association, as well as many individuals) trust that the foregoing intentions will be those which best suit the interests of the majority in Dean.

Thus closes this chronicle of industry, century upon century of activity sheltered beneath a verdant canopy which survives it all, to triumph anew. What was the sum of it? In physical terms, it involved the extraction, processing and marketing of some ten million tons of iron ore, two hundred million of coal, and much stone—to reach which, perhaps half a billion tons of spoil and rock had to be moved. Pack animals, canals, rivers, boats, tramroads, railways, road vehicles all played their part in moving this vast tonnage of minerals. Interspersed throughout the activity were allied and other industries, those of the woodland itself, and several small trades.

What of the participants—the men who toiled in, planned and financed this great and grimy bustle? To the worker, the industries provided a livelihood—often a precarious and meagre one—exchanged for sweat and risk, sometimes for mangled limbs, and occasionally for life itself. The initiators of enterprises ranged from those who ran the 'one-man' or family concerns—the Free Miners and charcoal burners—to the great industrialists, amongst whom were included both natives (the Teagues and Hewletts) and 'foreigners' (the Crawshays, Protheroes, and Partridges); as well as industrial precursors, technicians of courage like David and Robert Mushet, Richard Thomas, Harold Smith and Richard Watkins—a line represented today by John and Arthur Watts, Baden Watkins, Fred Wickstead OBE (all men of vision and great ability) and others. As in the past, there will be great industrial heroes and simple conscientious workers (both men and women), lucky men and unlucky men, visionaries, and so on. All (it is to be hoped) will for long enjoy and share with others the industrial peace, prosperity, and pleasantries which prudent planning and the renowned Forest ensure. Today, the exploited mineral beds are silent, but the oft-battered woodlands live on in sylvan glory, providing to some, a living, but to many more, from far away but 'foreigners' no longer, a place of pleasant relaxation or fascinating exploration.

What else does the future hold? At a time when all values, customs, institutions and practices are being questioned—and often transformed—it would be almost idle to offer more than the merest hint, and that in most general terms. Despite all social and economic change, if man remains the diverse creature he is, he will need the Royal Forest of Dean; but those who live in it, and those others who love it, would be well advised to keep a prudent eye upon its preservation and enhancement, remembering that it has been adapted by countless predecessors to their needs, sometimes without mercy, and that the current diffusion of power and responsibility does not always bring enlightened results, unless guided firmly at times by informed, thoughtful and vocal expressions of public opinion.

References to Chapter 15

1　Nicholls, op cit; Paar, op cit; and Hart, op cit.
2　Payne, Gordon E. *Gloucestershire. A Survey,* 1946; *Report . . . on . . . Population Trends,* 1966.
3　*Forest Newspapers,* 25 Nov 1955.
4　Woods, K. S. *Development of County Towns in the South-West Midlands,* Agriculture Economic Research Institute, 1968, 51–70.
5　Potter, Dennis. *The Changing Forest,* 1962.
6　Collins, N. R. *et al, North Gloucestershire Sub-Regional Study,* 1970; *Outdoor Recreation and the Gloucestershire Countryside,* 1968.
7　Dr Cyril Hart, Viscount Bledisloe, John. H. Watts, and Alderman F. G. Little. See: Hart, C. E. *The Verderers and Forest Laws of Dean,* 1971.

Appendix

DISTRICT MAPS SHOWING INDUSTRIAL SITES

These maps do not relate to any particular century but are included to indicate the various industrial sites throughout many centuries. Some more recent features have been shown to facilitate the location of the sites.

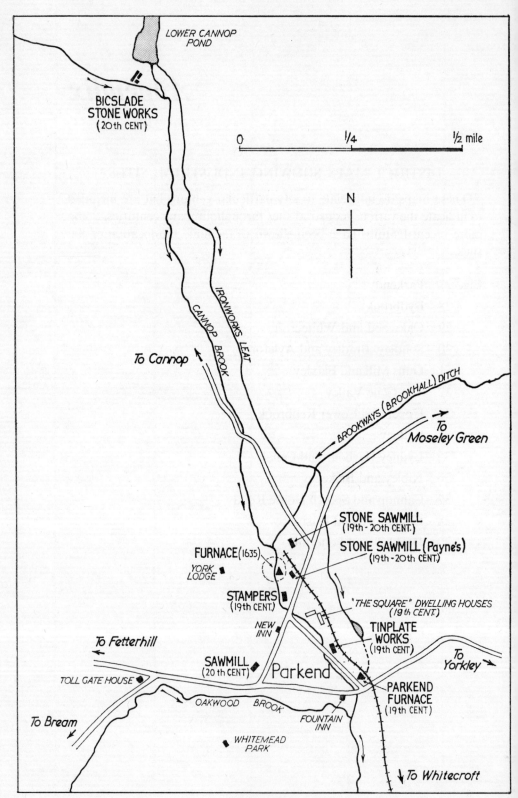

Fig 27. Parkend.

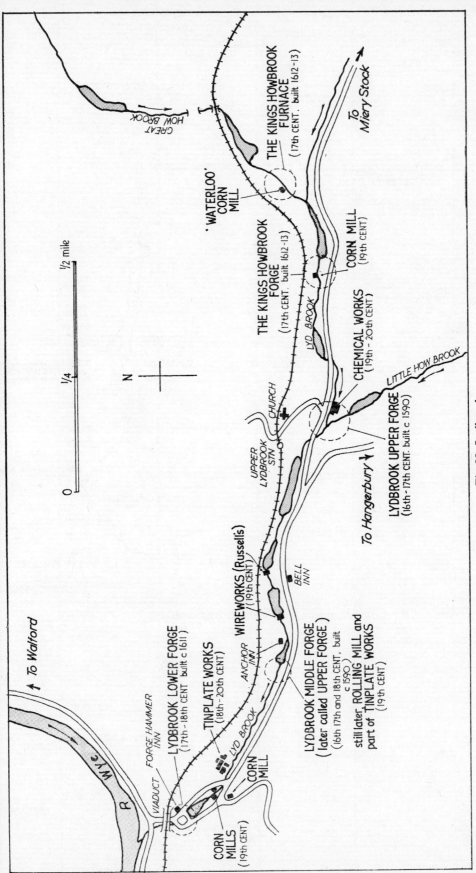

Fig 28. Lydbrook.

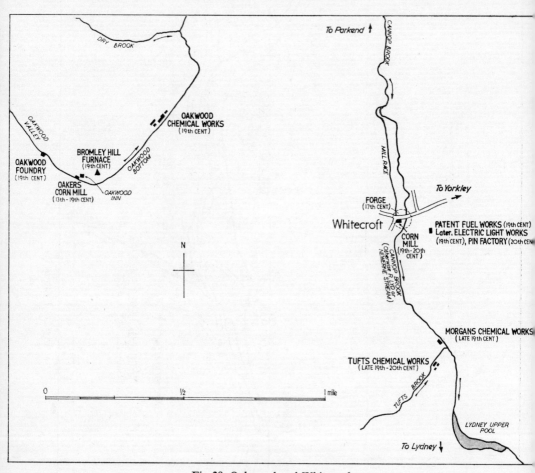

Fig 29. Oakwood and Whitecroft.

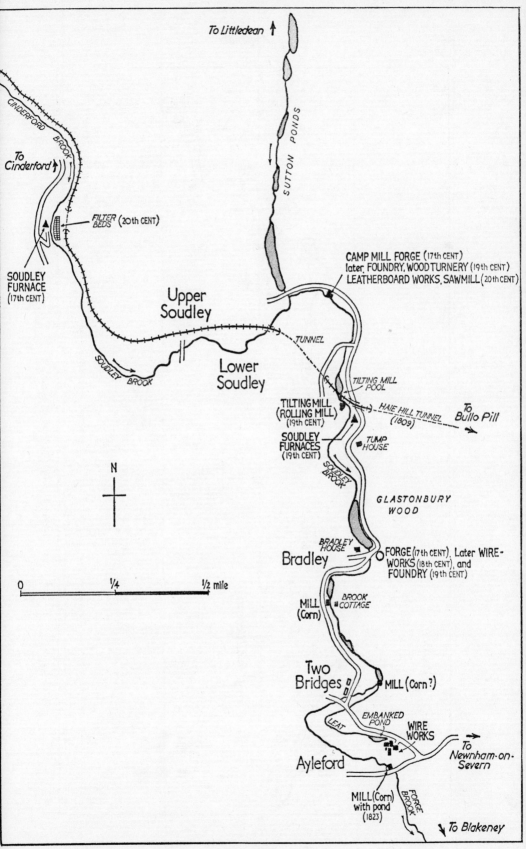

Fig 30. Soudley, Bradley and Ayleford.

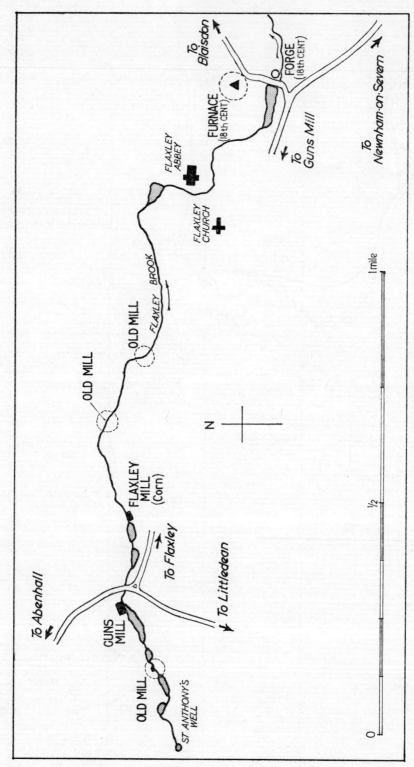

Fig 31. Guns Mill and Flaxley.

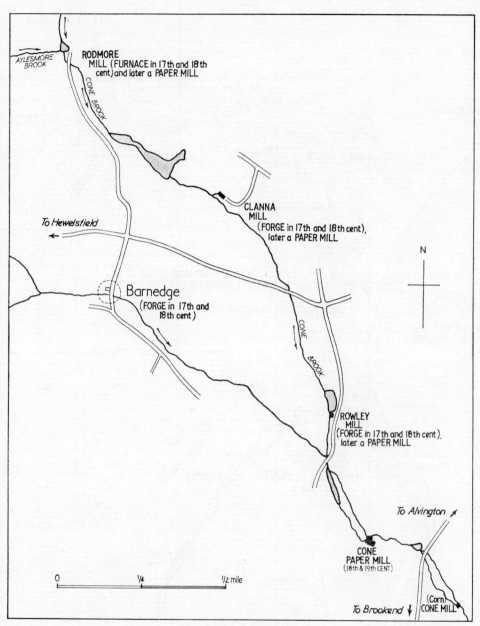

Fig 32. The Cone Valley.

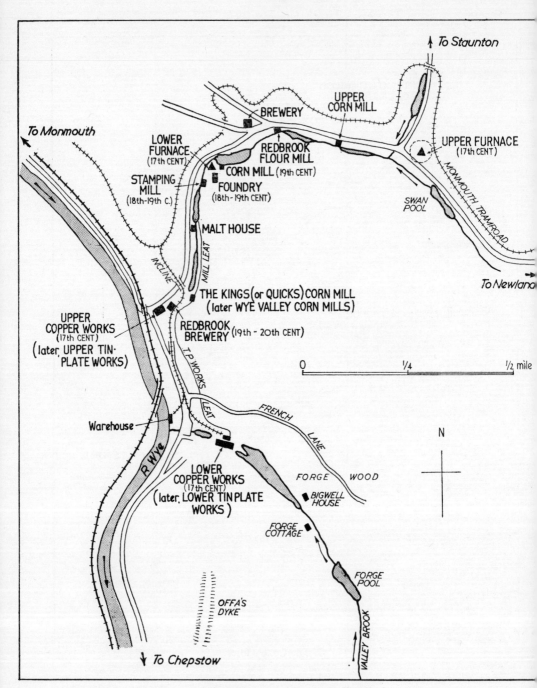

Fig 33. Upper and Lower Redbrook.

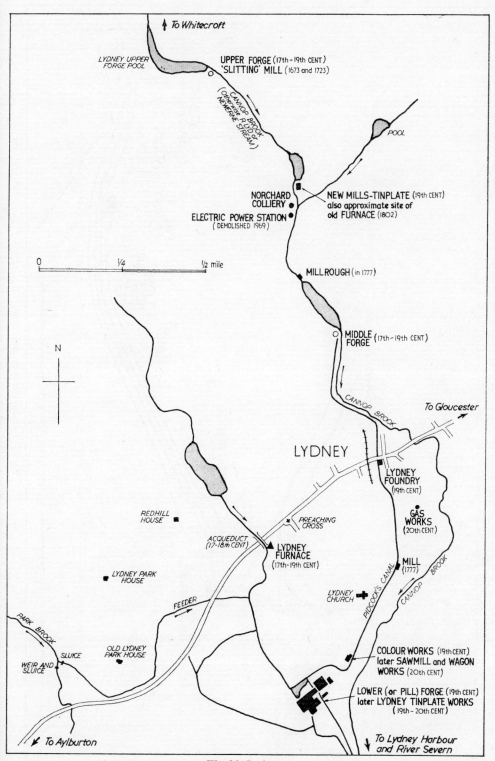

Fig 34. Lydney.

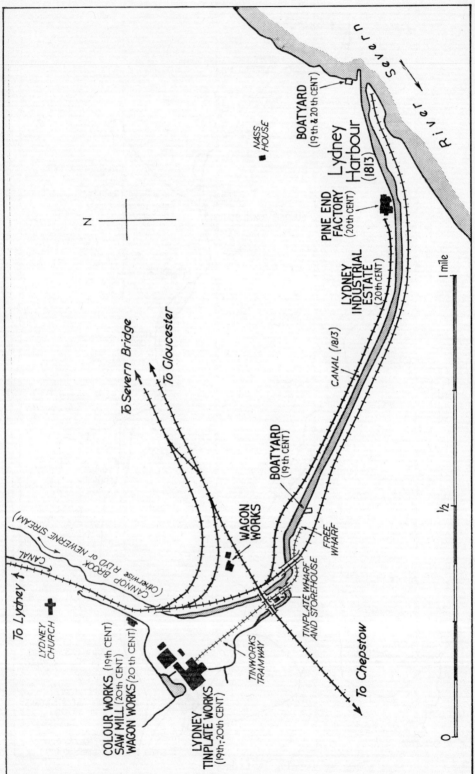

Fig 35. Lydney harbour and canal.

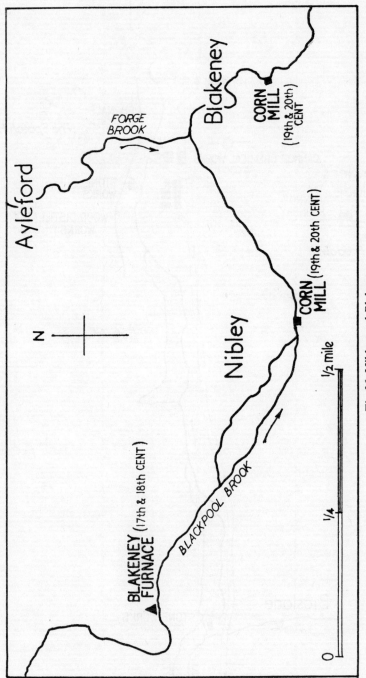

Fig 36. Nibley and Blakeney.

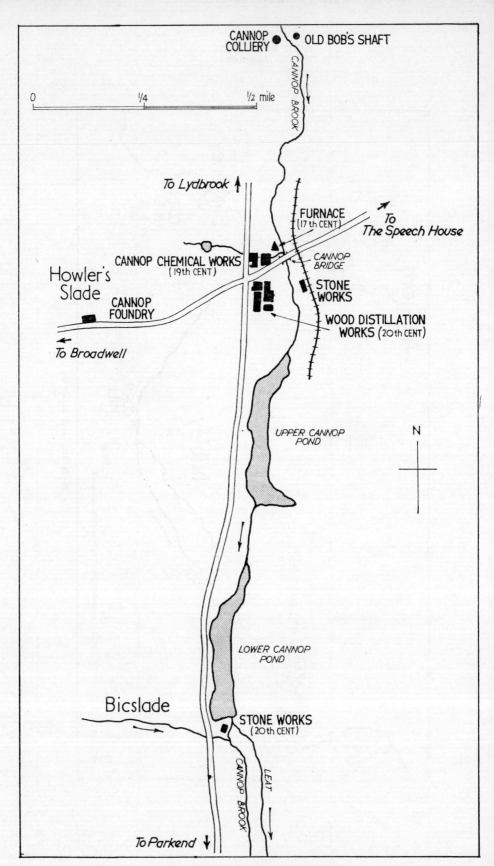

Fig 37. Cannop and Speech House Road.

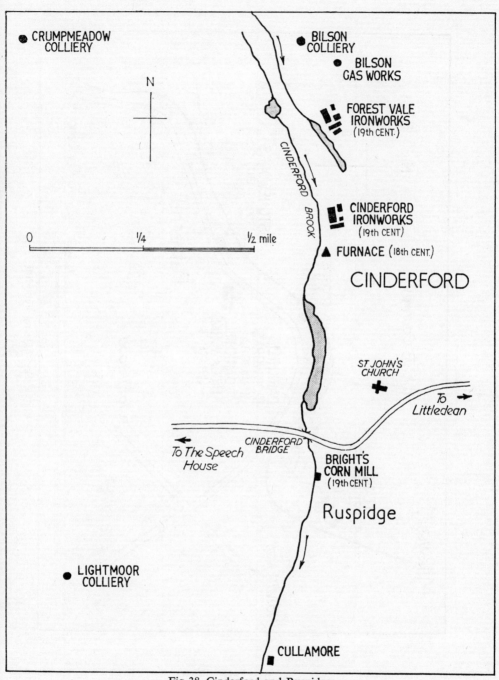

Fig 38. Cinderford and Ruspidge.

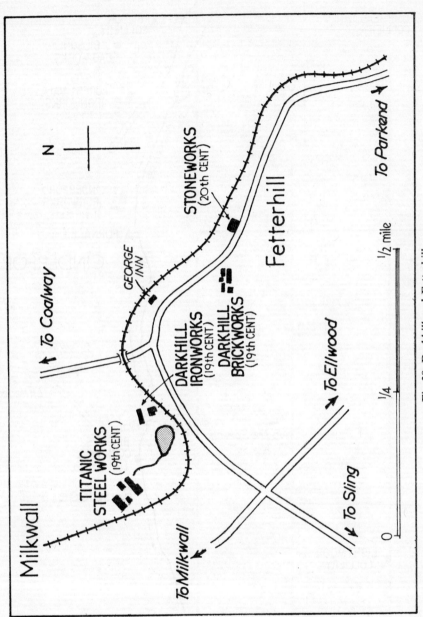

Fig 39. Darkhill and Fetterhill.

Indexes

Index : Subjects

Index of Place Names

Index : Personal and Company Names